REAL ANALYSIS

Fourth Edition

H. L. Royden
Stanford University

P. M. Fitzpatrick
University of Maryland, College Park

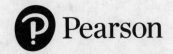

Original edition, entitled REAL ANALYSIS, 4th Edition, by ROYDEN, HALSEY; FITZPATRICK, PATRICK, published by Pearson Education, Inc, publishing as Pearson, Copyright © 2010 by Pearson Education, Inc.

Indian edition published by Pearson India Education Services Pvt. Ltd. Copyright © 2015.

ISBN 978-93-325-5158-9

First Impression, 2015
Fifth Impression, 2016
Sixth Impression, 2017

This edition is manufactured in India and is authorized for sale only in India, Bangladesh, Bhutan, Pakistan, Nepal, Sri Lanka and the Maldives. Circulation of this edition outside of these territories is UNAUTHORIZED.

Published by Pearson India Education Services Pvt.Ltd, CIN: U72200TN2005PTC057128. Formerly known as TutorVista Global Pvt Ltd, licensees of Pearson Education in South Asia

Head Office: 7th Floor, knowledge Boulevard, A-8(A) Sector-62, Noida (U.P) 201309, India

Registered Office: 4th floor, Software Block, Elnet Software City, TS -140, Block 2 & 9
Rajiv Gandhi Salai, Taramani, Chennai, Tamil Nadu 600113.
Fax: 080-30461003, Phone: 080-30461060, www.pearson.co.in,
Email id: companysecretary.india@pearson.com

Printed in India by Tara Art Printers Pvt. Ltd.

I dedicate this book to my wife, Teresita Lega

Contents

Preface

The first three editions of H.L. Royden's *Real Analysis* have contributed to the education of generations of mathematical analysis students. This fourth edition of *Real Analysis* preserves the goal and general structure of its venerable predecessors—to present the measure theory, integration theory, and functional analysis that a modern analyst needs to know.

The book is divided the three parts: Part I treats Lebesgue measure and Lebesgue integration for functions of a single real variable; Part II treats abstract spaces—topological spaces, metric spaces, Banach spaces, and Hilbert spaces; Part III treats integration over general measure spaces, together with the enrichments possessed by the general theory in the presence of topological, algebraic, or dynamical structure.

The material in Parts II and III does not formally depend on Part I. However, a careful treatment of Part I provides the student with the opportunity to encounter new concepts in a familiar setting, which provides a foundation and motivation for the more abstract concepts developed in the second and third parts. Moreover, the Banach spaces created in Part I, the L^p spaces, are one of the most important classes of Banach spaces. The principal reason for establishing the completeness of the L^p spaces and the characterization of their dual spaces is to be able to apply the standard tools of functional analysis in the study of functionals and operators on these spaces. The creation of these tools is the goal of Part II.

NEW TO THE EDITION

- This edition contains 50% more exercises than the previous edition
- Fundamental results, including Egoroff's Theorem and Urysohn's Lemma are now proven in the text.
- The Borel-Cantelli Lemma, Chebychev's Inequality, rapidly Cauchy sequences, and the continuity properties possessed both by measure and the integral are now formally presented in the text along with several other concepts.

There are several changes to each part of the book that are also noteworthy:

Part I

- The concept of uniform integrability and the Vitali Convergence Theorem are now presented and make the centerpiece of the proof of the fundamental theorem of integral calculus for the Lebesgue integral
- A precise analysis of the properties of rapidly Cauchy sequences in the $L^p(E)$ spaces, $1 \leq p \leq \infty$, is now the basis of the proof of the completeness of these spaces
- Weak sequential compactness in the $L^p(E)$ spaces, $1 \leq p \leq \infty$, is now examined in detail and used to prove the existence of minimizers for continuous convex functionals.

Part II

- General structural properties of metric and topological spaces are now separated into two brief chapters in which the principal theorems are proven.
- In the treatment of Banach spaces, beyond the basic results on bounded linear operators, compactness for weak topologies induced by the duality between a Banach space and its dual is now examined in detail.
- There is a new chapter on operators in Hilbert spaces, in which weak sequential compactness is the basis of the proofs of the Hilbert-Schmidt theorem on the eigenvectors of a compact symmetric operator and the characterization by Riesz and Schuader of linear Fredholm operators of index zero acting in a Hilbert space.

Part III

- General measure theory and general integration theory are developed, including the completeness, and the representation of the dual spaces, of the $L^p(X, \mu)$ spaces for, $1 \le p \le \infty$. Weak sequential compactness is explored in these spaces, including the proof of the Dunford-Pettis theorem that characterizes weak sequential compactness in $L^1(X, \mu)$.
- The relationship between topology and measure is examined in order to characterize the dual of $C(X)$, for a compact Hausdorff space X. This leads, via compactness arguments, to (i) a proof of von Neumann's theorem on the existence of unique invariant measures on a compact group and (ii) a proof of the existence, for a mapping on a compact Hausdorf space, of a probability measure with respect to which the mapping is ergodic.

The general theory of measure and integration was born in the early twentieth century. It is now an indispensable ingredient in remarkably diverse areas of mathematics, including probability theory, partial differential equations, functional analysis, harmonic analysis, and dynamical systems. Indeed, it has become a unifying concept. Many different topics can agreeably accompany a treatment of this theory. The companionship between integration and functional analysis and, in particular, between integration and weak convergence, has been fostered here: this is important, for instance, in the analysis of nonlinear partial differential equations (see L.C. Evans' book *Weak Convergence Methods for Nonlinear Partial Differential Equations* [AMS, 1998]).

The bibliography lists a number of books that are not specifically referenced but should be consulted for supplementary material and different viewpoints. In particular, two books on the interesting history of mathematical analysis are listed.

SUGGESTIONS FOR COURSES: FIRST SEMESTER

In Chapter 1, all the background elementary analysis and topology of the real line needed for Part I is established. This initial chapter is meant to be a handy reference. Core material comprises Chapters 2, 3, and 4, the first five sections of Chapter 6, Chapter 7, and the first section of Chapter 8. Following this, selections can be made: Sections 8.2–8.4 are interesting for students who will continue to study duality and compactness for normed linear spaces, while Section 5.3 contains two jewels of classical analysis, the characterization of Lebesgue integrability and of Riemann integrability for bounded functions.

SUGGESTIONS FOR COURSES: SECOND SEMESTER

This course should be based on Part III. Initial core material comprises Section 17.1, Section 18.1–18.4, and Sections 19.1–19.3. The remaining sections in Chapter 17 may be covered at the beginning or as they are needed later: Sections 17.3–17.5 before Chapter 20, and Section 17.2 before Chapter 21. Chapter 20 can then be covered. None of this material depends on Part II. Then several selected topics can be chosen, dipping into Part II as needed.

- Suggestion 1: Prove the Baire Category Theorem and its corollary regarding the partial continuity of the pointwise limit of a sequence of continuous functions (Theorem 7 of Chapter 10), infer from the Riesz-Fischer Theorem that the Nikodym metric space is complete (Theorem 23 of Chapter 18), prove the Vitali-Hahn-Saks Theorem and then prove the Dunford-Pettis Theorem.

- Suggestion 2: Cover Chapter 21 (omitting Section 20.5) on Measure and Topology, with the option of assuming the topological spaces are metrizable, so 20.1 can be skipped.

- Suggestion 3: Prove Riesz's Theorem regarding the closed unit ball of an infinite dimensional normed linear space being noncompact with respect to the topology induced by the norm. Use this as a motivation for regaining sequential compactness with respect to weaker topologies, then use Helley's Theorem to obtain weak sequential compactness properties of the $L^p(X, \mu)$ spaces, $1 < p < \infty$, if $L^q(X, \mu)$ is separable and, if Chapter 21 has already been covered, weak-$*$ sequential compactness results for Radon measures on the Borel σ-algebra of a compact metric space.

SUGGESTIONS FOR COURSES: THIRD SEMESTER

I have used Part II, with some supplemental material, for a course on functional analysis, for students who had taken the first two semesters; the material is tailored, of course, to that chosen for the second semester. Chapter 16 on bounded linear operators on a Hilbert space may be covered right after Chapter 13 on bounded linear operators on a Banach space, since the results regarding weak sequential compactness are obtained directly from the existence of an orthogonal complement for each closed subspace of a Hilbert space. Part II should be interlaced with selections from Part III to provide applications of the abstract space theory to integration. For instance, reflexivity and weak compactness can be considered in general $L^p(X, \mu)$ spaces, using material from Chapter 19. The above suggestion 1 for the second semester course can be taken in the third semester rather than the second, providing a truly striking application of the Baire Category Theorem. The establishment, in Chapter 21, of the representation of the dual of $C(X)$, where X is a compact Hausdorff space, provides another collection of spaces, spaces of signed Radon measures, to which the theorems of Helley, Alaoglu, and Krein-Milman apply. By covering Chapter 22 on Invariant Measures, the student will encounter applications of Alaoglu's Theorem and the Krein-Milman Theorem to prove the existence of Haar measure on a compact group and the existence of measures with respect to which a mapping is ergodic (Theorem 14 of Chapter 22), and an application of Helley's Theorem to establish the existence of invariant measures (the Bogoliubov-Krilov Theorem).

I welcome comments at pmf@math.umd.edu. A list of errata and remarks will be placed on www.math.umd.edu/~pmf/RealAnalysis.

ACKNOWLEDGMENTS

It is a pleasure to acknowledge my indebtedness to teachers, colleagues, and students. A penultimate draft of the entire manuscript was read by Diogo Arsénio, whom I warmly thank for his observations and suggestions, which materially improved that draft. Here in my mathematical home, the University of Maryland, I have written notes for various analysis courses, which have been incorporated into the present edition. A number of students in my graduate analysis classes worked through parts of drafts of this edition, and their comments and suggestions have been most helpful: I thank Avner Halevy, Kevin McGoff, and Himanshu Tiagi. I am pleased to acknowledge a particular debt to Brendan Berg who created the index, proofread the final manuscript, and kindly refined my tex skills. I have benefited from conversations with many friends and colleagues; in particular, with Diogo Arsénio, Michael Boyle, Michael Brin, Craig Evans, Manos Grillakis, Brian Hunt, Jacobo Pejsachowicz, Eric Slud, Robert Warner, and Jim Yorke. Publisher and reviewers: J. Thomas Beale, Duke University; Richard Carmichael, Wake Forest University; Michael Goldberg, Johns Hopkins University; Paul Joyce, University of Idaho; Dmitry Kaliuzhnyi-Verbovetskyi, Drexel University; Giovanni Leoni, Carnegie Mellon University; Bruce Mericle, Mankato State University; Stephen Robinson, Wake Forest University; Martin Schechter, University of California-Irvine; James Stephen White, Jacksonville State University; and Shanshuang Yang, Emory University.

Patrick M. Fitzpatrick
College Park, MD
November, 2009

LEBESGUE INTEGRATION FOR FUNCTIONS OF A SINGLE REAL VARIABLE

Preliminaries on Sets, Mappings, and Relations

Contents

In these preliminaries we describe some notions regarding sets, mappings, and relations that will be used throughout the book. Our purpose is descriptive and the arguments given are directed toward plausibility and understanding rather than rigorous proof based on an axiomatic basis for set theory. There is a system of axioms called the Zermelo-Frankel Axioms for Sets upon which it is possible to formally establish properties of sets and thereby properties of relations and functions. The interested reader may consult the introduction and appendix to John Kelley's book, *General Topology* [Kel75], Paul Halmos's book, *Naive Set Theory* [Hal98], and Thomas Jech's book, *Set Theory* [Jec06].

UNIONS AND INTERSECTIONS OF SETS

For a set A,[1] the membership of the element x in A is denoted by $x \in A$ and the nonmembership of x in A is denoted by $x \notin A$. We often say a member of A belongs to A and call a member of A a *point* in A. Frequently sets are denoted by braces, so that $\{x \mid \text{statement about } x\}$ is the set of all elements x for which the statement about x is true.

Two sets are the same provided they have the same members. Let A and B be sets. We call A a **subset** of B provided each member of A is a member of B; we denote this by $A \subseteq B$ and also say that A is contained in B or B contains A. A subset A of B is called a **proper subset** of B provided $A \neq B$. The **union** of A and B, denoted by $A \cup B$, is the set of all points that belong either to A or to B; that is, $A \cup B = \{x \mid x \in A \text{ or } x \in B\}$. The word *or* is used here in the nonexclusive sense, so that points which belong to both A and B belong to $A \cup B$. The **intersection** of A and B, denoted by $A \cap B$, is the set of all points that belong to both A and B; that is, $A \cap B = \{x \mid x \in A \text{ and } x \in B\}$. The **complement** of A in B, denoted by $B \sim A$, is the set of all points in B that are not in A; that is, $B \sim A = \{x \mid x \in B, x \notin A\}$. If, in a particular discussion, all of the sets are subsets of a reference set X, we often refer to $X \sim A$ simply as the complement of A.

The set that has no members is called the **empty-set** and denoted by $\emptyset$. A set that is not equal to the empty-set is called nonempty. We refer to a set that has a single member as a **singleton set**. Given a set X, the set of all subsets of X is denoted by $\mathcal{P}(X)$ or 2^X; it is called the **power set** of X.

In order to avoid the confusion that might arise when considering sets of sets, we often use the words "collection" and "family" as synonyms for the word "set." Let $\mathcal{F}$ be a collection of sets. We define the union of $\mathcal{F}$, denoted by $\bigcup_{F \in \mathcal{F}} F$, to be the set of points

---

[1] The *Oxford English Dictionary* devotes several hundred pages to the definition of the word "set."

that belong to at least one of the sets in $\mathcal{F}$. We define the intersection of $\mathcal{F}$, denoted by $\bigcap_{F \in \mathcal{F}} F$, to be the set of points that belong to every set in $\mathcal{F}$. The collection of sets $\mathcal{F}$ is said to be **disjoint** provided the intersection of any two sets in $\mathcal{F}$ is empty. For a family $\mathcal{F}$ of sets, the following identities are established by checking set inclusions.

De Morgan's identities

$$X \sim \left[\bigcup_{F \in \mathcal{F}} F \right] = \bigcap_{F \in \mathcal{F}} [X \sim F] \quad \text{and} \quad X \sim \left[\bigcap_{F \in \mathcal{F}} F \right] = \bigcup_{F \in \mathcal{F}} [X \sim F],$$

that is, the complement of the union is the intersection of the complements, and the complement of the intersection is the union of the complements.

For a set Λ, suppose that for each $\lambda \in \Lambda$, there is defined a set E_λ. Let $\mathcal{F}$ be the collection of sets $\{E_\lambda \,|\, \lambda \in \Lambda\}$. We write $\mathcal{F} = \{E_\lambda\}_{\lambda \in \Lambda}$ and refer to this as an **indexing** (or **parametrization**) of $\mathcal{F}$ by the **index set** (or **parameter set**) Λ.

Mappings between sets

Given two sets A and B, by a **mapping** or **function** from A into B we mean a correspondence that assigns to each member of A a member of B. In the case B is the set of real numbers we always use the word "function." Frequently we denote such a mapping by $f: A \rightarrow B$, and for each member x of A, we denote by $f(x)$ the member of B to which x is assigned. For a subset A' of A, we define $f(A') = \{b \,|\, b = f(a)$ for some member a of $A'\}$: $f(A')$ is called the image of A' under f. We call the set A the **domain** of the function f and $f(A)$ the **image** or **range** of f. If $f(A) = B$, the function f is said to be **onto**. If for each member b of $f(A)$ there is exactly one member a of A for which $b = f(a)$, the function f is said to be **one-to-one**. A mapping $f: A \rightarrow B$ that is both one-to-one and onto is said to be **invertible**; we say that this mapping establishes a **one-to-one correspondence** between the sets A and B. Given an invertible mapping $f: A \rightarrow B$, for each point b in B, there is exactly one member a of A for which $f(a) = b$ and it is denoted by $f^{-1}(b)$. This assignment defines the mapping $f^{-1}: B \rightarrow A$, which is called the **inverse** of f. Two sets A and B are said to be **equipotent** provided there is an invertible mapping from A onto B. Two sets which are equipotent are, from the set-theoretic point of view, indistinguishable.

Given two mappings $f: A \rightarrow B$ and $g: C \rightarrow D$ for which $f(A) \subseteq C$ then the composition $g \circ f: A \rightarrow D$ is defined by $[g \circ f](x) = g(f(x))$ for each $x \in A$. It is not difficult to see that the composition of invertible mappings is invertible. For a set D, define the identity mapping $id_D: D \rightarrow D$ is defined by $id_D(x) = x$ for all $x \in D$. A mapping $f: A \rightarrow B$ is invertible if and only if there is a mapping $g: B \rightarrow A$ for which

$$g \circ f = id_A \text{ and } f \circ g = id_B.$$

Even if the mapping $f: A \rightarrow B$ is not invertible, for a set E, we define $f^{-1}(E)$ to be the set $\{a \in A \,|\, f(a) \in E\}$; it is called the **inverse image** of E under f. We have the following useful properties: for any two sets E_1 and E_2,

$$f^{-1}(E_1 \cup E_2) = f^{-1}(E_1) \cup f^{-1}(E_2), \ f^{-1}(E_1 \cap E_2) = f^{-1}(E_1) \cap f^{-1}(E_2)$$

and

$$f^{-1}(E_1 \sim E_2) = f^{-1}(E_1) \sim f^{-1}(E_2).$$

Finally, for a mapping $f: A \to B$ and a subset A' of its domain A, the **restriction** of f to A', denoted by $f|_{A'}$, is the mapping from A' to B which assigns $f(x)$ to each $x \in A'$.

EQUIVALENCE RELATIONS, THE AXIOM OF CHOICE, AND ZORN'S LEMMA

Given two nonempty sets A and B, the **Cartesian product** of A with B, denoted by $A \times B$, is defined to be the collection of all ordered pairs (a, b) where $a \in A$ and $b \in B$ and we consider $(a, b) = (a', b')$ if and only if $a = a'$ and $b = b'$.[2] For a nonempty set X, we call a subset R of $X \times X$ a **relation** on X and write $x R x'$ provided (x, x') belongs to R. The relation R is said to be **reflexive** provided $x R x$, for all $x \in X$; the relation R is said to be **symmetric** provided $x R x'$ if $x' R x$; the relation R is said to be **transitive** provided whenever $x R x'$ and $x' R x''$, then $x R x''$.

Definition *A relation R on a set X is called an **equivalence relation** provided it is reflexive, symmetric, and transitive.*

Given an equivalence relation R on a set X, for each $x \in X$, the set $R_x = \{x' \mid x' \in X, \ x R x'\}$ is called the **equivalence class** of x (with respect to R). The collection of equivalence classes is denoted by X/R. For example, given a set X, the relation of equipotence is an equivalence relation on the collection 2^X of all subsets of X. The equivalence class of a set with respect to the relation equipotence is called the **cardinality** of the set.

Let R be an equivalence relation on a set X. Since R is symmetric and transitive, $R_x = R_{x'}$ if and only if $x R x'$ and therefore the collection of equivalence classes is disjoint. Since the relation R is reflexive, X is the union of the equivalence classes. Therefore X/R is a disjoint collection of nonempty subsets of X whose union is X. Conversely, given a disjoint collection $\mathcal{F}$ of nonempty subsets of X whose union is X, the relation of belonging to the same set in $\mathcal{F}$ is an equivalence relation R on X for which $\mathcal{F} = X/R$.

Given an equivalence relation on a set X, it is often necessary to choose a subset C of X which consists of exactly one member from each equivalence class. Is it obvious that there is such a set? Ernst Zermelo called attention to this question regarding the choice of elements from collections of sets. Suppose, for instance, we define two real numbers to be rationally equivalent provided their difference is a rational number. It is easy to check that this is an equivalence relation on the set of real numbers. But it is not easy to identify a set of real numbers that consists of exactly one member from each rational equivalence class.

Definition *Let $\mathcal{F}$ be a nonempty family of nonempty sets. A **choice function** f on $\mathcal{F}$ is a function f from $\mathcal{F}$ to $\cup_{F \in \mathcal{F}} F$ with the property that for each set F in $\mathcal{F}$, $f(F)$ is a member of F.*

Zermelo's Axiom of Choice *Let $\mathcal{F}$ be a nonempty collection of nonempty sets. Then there is a choice function on $\mathcal{F}$.*

---

[2] In a formal treatment of set theory based on the Zermelo-Frankel Axioms, an ordered pair (a, b) is defined to be the set $\{\{a\}, \{a, b\}\}$ and a function with domain in A and image in B is defined to be a nonempty collection of ordered pairs in $A \times B$ with the property that if the ordered pairs (a, b) and (a, b') belong to the function, then $b = b'$.

Very roughly speaking, a choice function on a family of nonempty sets "chooses" a member from each set in the family. We have adopted an informal, descriptive approach to set theory and accordingly we will freely employ, without further ado, the Axiom of Choice.

Definition *A relation R on a set nonempty X is called a* **partial ordering** *provided it is reflexive, transitive, and, for x, x' in X,*

$$\text{if } x\,R\,x' \text{ and } x'\,R\,x, \text{ then } x = x'.$$

A subset E of X is said to be **totally ordered** *provided for x, x' in E, either x R x' or x' R x. A member x of X is said to be an* **upper bound** *for a subset E of X provided x'Rx for all x' ∈ E, and said to be* **maximal** *provided the only member x' of X for which x R x' is x' = x.*

For a family $\mathcal{F}$ of sets and $A, B \in \mathcal{F}$, define $A\,R\,B$ provided $A \subseteq B$. This relation of **set inclusion** is a partial ordering of $\mathcal{F}$. Observe that a set F in $\mathcal{F}$ is an upper bound for a subfamily $\mathcal{F}'$ of $\mathcal{F}$ provided every set in $\mathcal{F}'$ is a subset of F and a set F in $\mathcal{F}$ is maximal provided it is not a proper subset of any set in $\mathcal{F}$. Similarly, given a family $\mathcal{F}$ of sets and $A, B \in \mathcal{F}$ define $A\,R\,B$ provided $B \subseteq A$. This relation of **set containment** is a partial ordering of $\mathcal{F}$. Observe that a set F in $\mathcal{F}$ is an upper bound for a subfamily $\mathcal{F}'$ of $\mathcal{F}$ provided every set in $\mathcal{F}'$ contains F and a set F in $\mathcal{F}$ is maximal provided it does not properly contain any set in $\mathcal{F}$.

Zorn's Lemma *Let X be a partially ordered set for which every totally ordered subset has an upper bound. Then X has a maximal member.*

We will use Zorn's Lemma to prove some of our most important results, including the Hahn-Banach Theorem, the Tychonoff Product Theorem, and the Krein-Milman Theorem. Zorn's Lemma is equivalent to Zermelo's Axiom of Choice. For a proof of this equivalence and related equivalences, see Kelley [Kel75], pp. 31–36.

We have defined the Cartesian product of two sets. It is useful to define the Cartesian product of a general parametrized collection of sets. For a collecton of sets $\{E_\lambda\}_{\lambda \in \Lambda}$ parametrized by the set Λ, the Cartesian product of $\{E_\lambda\}_{\lambda \in \Lambda}$, which we denote by $\Pi_{\lambda \in \Lambda} E_\lambda$, is defined to be the set of functions f from Λ to $\bigcup_{\lambda \in \Lambda} E_\lambda$ such that for each $\lambda \in \Lambda$, $f(\lambda)$ belongs to E_λ. It is clear that the Axiom of Choice is equivalent to the assertion that the Cartesian product of a nonempty family of nonempty sets is nonempty. Note that the Cartesian product is defined for a parametrized family of sets and that two different parametrizations of the same family will have different Cartesian products. This general definition of Cartesian product is consistent with the definition given for two sets. Indeed, consider two nonempty sets A and B. Define $\Lambda = \{\lambda_1, \lambda_2\}$ where $\lambda_1 \neq \lambda_2$ and then define $E_{\lambda_1} = A$ and $E_{\lambda_2} = B$. The mapping that assigns to the function $f \in \Pi_{\lambda \in \Lambda} E_\lambda$ the ordered pair $(f(\lambda_1), f(\lambda_2))$ is an invertible mapping of the Cartesian product $\Pi_{\lambda \in \Lambda} E_\lambda$ onto the collection of ordered pairs $A \times B$ and therefore these two sets are equipotent. For two sets E and Λ, define $E_\lambda = E$ for all $\lambda \in \Lambda$. Then the Cartesian product $\Pi_{\lambda \in \Lambda} E_\lambda$ is equal to the set of all mappings from Λ to E and is denoted by E^Λ.

CHAPTER 1

The Real Numbers: Sets, Sequences, and Functions

Contents

We assume the reader has a familiarity with the properties of real numbers, sets of real numbers, sequences of real numbers, and real-valued functions of a real variable, which are usually treated in an undergraduate course in analysis. This familiarity will enable the reader to assimilate the present chapter, which is devoted to rapidly but thoroughly establishing those results which will be needed and referred to later. We assume that the set of real numbers, which is denoted by **R**, satisfies three types of axioms. We state these axioms and derive from them properties on the natural numbers, rational numbers, and countable sets. With this as background, we establish properties of open and closed sets of real numbers; convergent, monotone, and Cauchy sequences of real numbers; and continuous real-valued functions of a real variable.

1.1 THE FIELD, POSITIVITY, AND COMPLETENESS AXIOMS

We assume as given the set **R** of real numbers such that for each pair of real numbers a and b, there are defined real numbers $a + b$ and ab called the sum and product, respectively, of a and b for which the following Field Axioms, Positivity Axioms, and Completeness Axiom are satisfied.

The field axioms

Commutativity of Addition: For all real numbers a and b,

$$a + b = b + a.$$

Associativity of Addition: For all real numbers a, b, and c,

$$(a + b) + c = a + (b + c).$$

The Additive Identity: There is a real number, denoted by 0, such that

$$0 + a = a + 0 = a \quad \text{for all real numbers } a.$$

The Additive Inverse: For each real number a, there is a real number b such that

$$a + b = 0.$$

Commutativity of Multiplication: For all real numbers a and b,

$$ab = ba.$$

Associativity of Multiplication: For all real numbers a, b, and c,

$$(ab)c = a(bc).$$

The Multiplicative Identity: There is a real number, denoted by 1, such that

$$1a = a1 = a \quad \text{for all real numbers } a.$$

The Multiplicative Inverse: For each real number $a \neq 0$, there is a real number b such that

$$ab = 1.$$

The Distributive Property: For all real numbers a, b, and c,

$$a(b + c) = ab + ac.$$

The Nontriviality Assumption:

$$1 \neq 0.$$

Any set that satisfies these axioms is called a **field**. It follows from the commutativity of addition that the additive identity, 0, is unique, and we infer from the commutativity of multiplication that the multiplicative unit, 1, also is unique. The additive inverse and multiplicative inverse also are unique. We denote the additive inverse of a by $-a$ and, if $a \neq 0$, its multiplicative inverse by a^{-1} or $1/a$. If we have a field, we can perform all the operations of elementary algebra, including the solution of simultaneous linear equations. We use the various consequences of these axioms without explicit mention.[1]

The positivity axioms

In the real numbers there is a natural notion of order: greater than, less than, and so on. A convenient way to codify these properties is by specifying axioms satisfied by the set of positive numbers. There is a set of real numbers, denoted by $\mathcal{P}$, called the set of **positive numbers.** It has the following two properties:

P1 If a and b are positive, then ab and $a + b$ are also positive.
P2 For a real number a, exactly one of the following three alternatives is true:

$$a \text{ is positive,} \quad -a \text{ is positive,} \quad a = 0.$$

---

[1]A systematic development of the consequences of the Field Axioms may be found in the first chapter of the classic book *A Survey of Modern Algebra* by Garrett Birkhoff and Saunders MacLane [BM97].

The Positivity Axioms lead in a natural way to an ordering of the real numbers: for real numbers a and b, we define $a > b$ to mean that $a - b$ is positive, and $a \geq b$ to mean that $a > b$ or $a = b$. We then define $a < b$ to mean that $b > a$, and $a \leq b$ to mean that $b \geq a$.

Using the Field Axioms and the Positivity Axioms, it is possible to formally establish the familiar properties of inequalities (see Problem 2). Given real numbers a and b for which $a < b$, we define $(a, b) = \{x \mid a < x < b\}$, and say a point in (a, b) lies between a and b. We call a nonempty set I of real numbers an **interval** provided for any two points in I, all the points that lie between these points also belong to I. Of course, the set (a, b) is an interval, as are the following sets:

$$[a, b] = \{x \mid a \leq x \leq b\} \, ; [a, b) = \{x \mid a \leq x < b\} \, ; (a, b] = \{x \mid a < x \leq b\}. \quad (1)$$

The completeness axiom

A nonempty set E of real numbers is said to be **bounded above** provided there is a real number b such that $x \leq b$ for all $x \in E$: the number b is called an **upper bound** for E. Similarly, we define what it means for a set to be **bounded below** and for a number to be a lower bound for a set. A set that is bounded above need not have a largest member. But the next axiom asserts that it does have a smallest upper bound.

The Completeness Axiom *Let* E *be a nonempty set of real numbers that is bounded above. Then among the set of upper bounds for* E *there is a smallest, or least, upper bound.*

For a nonempty set E of real numbers that is bounded above, the **least upper bound** of E, the existence of which is asserted by the Completeness Axiom, will be denoted by l.u.b. S. The least upper bound of E is usually called the **supremum** of E and denoted by sup S. It follows from the Completeness Axiom that every nonempty set E of real numbers that is bounded below has a **greatest lower bound**; it is denoted by g.l.b. E and usually called the **infimum** of E and denoted by inf E. A nonempty set of real numbers is said to be **bounded** provided it is both bounded below and bounded above.

The triangle inequality

We define the **absolute value** of a real number x, $|x|$, to be x if $x \geq 0$ and to be $-x$ if $x < 0$. The following inequality, called the **Triangle Inequality**, is fundamental in mathematical analysis: for any pair of real numbers a and b,

$$|a + b| \leq |a| + |b|.$$

The extended real numbers

It is convenient to introduce the symbols ∞ and $-\infty$ and write $-\infty < x < \infty$ for all real numbers x. We call the set $\mathbf{R} \cup \pm\infty$ the **extended real numbers**. If a nonempty set E of real numbers is not bounded above we define its supremum to be ∞. It is also convenient to define $-\infty$ to be the supremum of the empty-set. Therefore every set of real numbers has a supremum that belongs to the extended real-numbers. Similarly, we can extend the concept of infimum so every set of real numbers has an infimum that belongs to the extended real numbers. We will define limits of sequences of real numbers and it is convenient to allow limits that are extended real numbers. Many properties of sequences of real numbers that converge to real numbers, such as the limit of the sum is the sum of the limits and the limit of the product is the product of the limit, continue to hold for limits that are $\pm\infty$, provided we make the following extension of the meaning of sum and product: $\infty + \infty = \infty$, $-\infty - \infty = -\infty$ and, for each real number x, $x + \infty = \infty$ and $x - \infty = -\infty$; if $x > 0$, $x \cdot \infty = \infty$ and $x \cdot (-\infty) = -\infty$ while if $x < 0$, $x \cdot \infty = -\infty$ and $x \cdot (-\infty) = \infty$. We define $(-\infty, \infty) = \mathbf{R}$. For $a, b \in \mathbf{R}$, we define

$$(a, \infty) = \{x \in \mathbf{R} \mid a < x\}, \ (-\infty, b) = \{x \in \mathbf{R} \mid x < b\}$$

and

$$[a, \infty) = \{x \in \mathbf{R} \mid a \le x\}, \ (-\infty, b] = \{x \in \mathbf{R} \mid x \le b\}.$$

Sets of the above form are unbounded intervals. We leave it as an exercise to infer from the completeness of $\mathbf{R}$ that all unbounded intervals are of the above type and that all bounded intervals are of the form listed in (1) together with intervals of the form (a, b).

PROBLEMS

1. For $a \neq 0$ and $b \neq 0$, show that $(ab)^{-1} = a^{-1}b^{-1}$.

2. Verify the following:
    (i)   For each real number $a \neq 0$, $a^2 > 0$. In particular, $1 > 0$ since $1 \neq 0$ and $1 = 1^2$.
    (ii) For each positive number a, its multiplicative inverse a^{-1} also is positive.
    (iii) If $a > b$, then
    $$ac > bc \text{ if } c > 0 \text{ and } ac < bc \text{ if } c < 0.$$

3. For a nonempty set of real numbers E, show that $\inf E = \sup E$ if and only if E consists of a single point.

4. Let a and b be real numbers.
    (i)   Show that if $ab = 0$, then $a = 0$ or $b = 0$.
    (ii) Verify that $a^2 - b^2 = (a - b)(a + b)$ and conclude from part (i) that if $a^2 = b^2$, then $a = b$ or $a = -b$.
    (iii) Let c be a positive real number. Define $E = \{x \in \mathbf{R} \mid x^2 < c.\}$ Verify that E is nonempty and bounded above. Define $x_0 = \sup E$. Show that $x_0^2 = c$. Use part (ii) to show that there is a unique $x > 0$ for which $x^2 = c$. It is denoted by $\sqrt{c}$.

5. Let a, b, and c be real numbers such that $a \neq 0$ and consider the quadratic equation
    $$ax^2 + bx + c = 0, \ x \in \mathbf{R}.$$
    (i)   Suppose $b^2 - 4ac > 0$. Use the Field Axioms and the preceding problem to complete the square and thereby show that this equation has exactly two solutions given by
    $$x = \frac{-b + \sqrt{b^2 - 4ac}}{2a} \quad \text{and} \quad x = \frac{-b - \sqrt{b^2 - 4ac}}{2a}.$$
    (ii) Now suppose $b^2 - 4ac < 0$. Show that the quadratic equation fails to have any solution.

6. Use the Completeness Axiom to show that every nonempty set of real numbers that is bounded below has an infimum and that

$$\inf E = -\sup \{-x \mid x \in E\}.$$

7. For real numbers a and b, verify the following:
   (i) $|ab| = |a||b|$.
   (ii) $|a + b| \leq |a| + |b|$.
   (iii) For $\epsilon > 0$,
   $$|x - a| < \epsilon \text{ if and only if } a - \epsilon < x < a + \epsilon.$$

1.2   THE NATURAL AND RATIONAL NUMBERS

It is tempting to define the natural numbers to be the numbers $1, 2, 3, \ldots$ and so on. However, it is necessary to be more precise. A convenient way to do this is to first introduce the concept of an *inductive set*.

Definition   *A set E of real numbers is said to be* **inductive** *provided it contains 1 and if the number x belongs to E, the number $x + 1$ also belongs to E.*

The whole set of real numbers $\mathbf{R}$ is inductive. From the inequality $1 > 0$ we infer that the sets $\{x \in \mathbf{R} \mid x \geq 0\}$ and $\{x \in \mathbf{R} \mid x \geq 1\}$ are inductive. The set of **natural numbers**, denoted by $\mathbf{N}$, is defined to be *the intersection of all inductive subsets* of $\mathbf{R}$. The set $\mathbf{N}$ is inductive. To see this, observe that the number 1 belongs to $\mathbf{N}$ since 1 belongs to every inductive set. Furthermore, if the number k belongs to $\mathbf{N}$, then k belongs to every inductive set. Thus, $k + 1$ belongs to every inductive set and therefore $k + 1$ belongs to $\mathbf{N}$.

Principle of Mathematical Induction   *For each natural number n, let $S(n)$ be some mathematical assertion. Suppose $S(1)$ is true. Also suppose that whenever k is a natural number for which $S(k)$ is true, then $S(k + 1)$ is also true. Then $S(n)$ is true for every natural number n.*

Proof   Define $A = \{k \in \mathbf{N} \mid S(k) \text{ is true}\}$. The assumptions mean precisely that A is an inductive set. Thus $\mathbf{N} \subseteq A$. Therefore $S(n)$ is true for every natural number n.   □

Theorem 1   *Every nonempty set of natural numbers has a smallest member.*

Proof   Let E be a nonempty set of natural numbers. Since the set $\{x \in \mathbf{R} \mid x \geq 1\}$ is inductive, the natural numbers are bounded below by 1. Therefore E is bounded below by 1. As a consequence of the Completeness Axiom, E has an infimum; define $c = \inf E$. Since $c + 1$ is not a lower bound for E, there is an $m \in E$ for which $m < c + 1$. We claim that m is the smallest member of E. Otherwise, there is an $n \in E$ for which $n < m$. Since $n \in E$, $c \leq n$. Thus $c \leq n < m < c + 1$ and therefore $m - n < 1$. Therefore the natural number m belongs to the interval $(n, n+1)$. An induction argument shows that for every natural number n, $(n, n+1) \cap \mathbf{N} = \emptyset$ (see Problem 8). This contradiction confirms that m is the smallest member of E.   □

Archimedean Property   *For each pair of positive real numbers a and b, there is a natural number n for which $na > b$.*

Proof Define $c = b/a > 0$. We argue by contradiction. If the theorem is false, then c is an upper bound for the natural numbers. By the Completeness Axiom, the natural numbers have a supremum; define $c_0 = \sup \mathbf{N}$. Then $c_0 - 1$ is not an upper bound for the natural numbers. Choose a natural number n such that $n > c_0 - 1$. Therefore $n + 1 > c_0$. But the natural numbers are inductive so that $n + 1$ is a natural number. Since $n + 1 > c_0$, c_0 is not an upper bound for the natural numbers. This contradiction completes the proof.   □

We frequently use the Archimedean Property of $\mathbf{R}$ reformulated as follows; for each positive real number ϵ, there is a natural number n for which $1/n < \epsilon$.[2]

We define the set of **integers**, denoted by $\mathbf{Z}$, to be the set of numbers consisting of the natural numbers, their negatives, and the number 0. The set of **rational numbers,** denoted by $\mathbf{Q}$, is defined to be the set of quotients of integers, that is, numbers x of the form $x = m/n$, where m and n are integers and $n \neq 0$. A real number is called **irrational** if it is not rational. As we argued in Problem 4, there is a unique positive number x for which $x^2 = 2$; it is denoted by $\sqrt{2}$. This number is not rational. Indeed, suppose p and q are natural numbers for which $(p/q)^2 = 2$. Then $p^2 = 2q^2$. The prime factorization theorem[3] tells us that 2 divides p^2 just twice as often as it divides p. Hence 2 divides p^2 an even number of times. Similarly, 2 divides $2q^2$ an odd number of times. Thus $p^2 \neq 2q^2$ and therefore $\sqrt{2}$ is irrational.

Definition *A set E of real numbers is said to be* **dense** *in $\mathbf{R}$ provided between any two real numbers there lies a member of E.*

Theorem 2 *The rational numbers are dense in $\mathbf{R}$.*

Proof Let a and b be real numbers with $a < b$. First suppose that $a > 0$. By the Archimedean Property of $\mathbf{R}$, there is a natural number q for which $(1/q) < b - a$. Again using the Archimedean Property of $\mathbf{R}$, the set of natural numbers $S = \{n \in \mathbf{N} \mid n/q \geq b\}$ is nonempty. According to Theorem 1, S has a smallest member p. Observe that $1/q < b - a < b$ and hence $p > 1$. Therefore $p - 1$ is a natural number (see Problem 9) and so, by the minimality of the choice of p, $(p - 1)/q < b$. We also have

$$a = b - (b - a) < (p/q) - (1/q) = (p - 1)/q.$$

Therefore the rational number $r = (p - 1)/q$ lies between a and b. If $a < 0$, by the Archimedean property of $\mathbf{R}$, there is a natural number n for which $n > -a$. We infer from the first case considered that there is a rational number r that lies between $n + a$ and $n + b$. Therefore the natural number $r - n$ lies between a and b.   □

PROBLEMS

8. Use an induction argument to show that for each natural number n, the interval $(n, n + 1)$ fails to contain any natural number.

---

[2] Archimedeas explicitly asserted that it was his fellow Greek, Eurathostenes, who identified the property that we have here attributed to Archimedeas.

[3] This theorem asserts that each natural number may be uniquely expressed as the product of prime natural numbers; see [BM97].

9. Use an induction argument to show that if $n > 1$ is a natural number, then $n - 1$ also is a natural number. Then use another induction argument to show that if m and n are natural numbers with $n > m$, then $n - m$ is a natural number.

10. Show that for any integer n, there is exactly one integer in the interval $[n, n + 1)$.

11. Show that any nonempty set of integers that is bounded above has a largest member.

12. Show that the irrational numbers are dense in $\mathbf{R}$.

13. Show that each real number is the supremum of a set of rational numbers and also the supremum of a set of irrational numbers.

14. Show that if $r > 0$, then, for each natural number n, $(1 + r)^n \geq 1 + n \cdot r$.

15. Use induction arguments to prove that for every natural number n,

(i)
$$\sum_{j=1}^{n} j^2 = \frac{n(n+1)(2n+1)}{6}.$$

(ii)
$$1^3 + 2^3 + \ldots + n^3 = (1 + 2 + \ldots + n)^2.$$

(iii)
$$1 + r + \ldots + r^n = \frac{1 - r^{n-1}}{1 - r} \text{ if } r \neq 1$$

1.3   COUNTABLE AND UNCOUNTABLE SETS

In the preliminaries we called two sets A and B equipotent provided there is a one-to-one mapping f of A onto B. We refer to such an f as a one-to-one correspondence between the sets A and B. Equipotence defines an equivalence relation among sets, that is, it is reflexive, symmetric, and transitive (see Problem 20). It is convenient to denote the initial segment of natural numbers $\{k \in \mathbf{N} \mid 1 \leq k \leq n\}$ by $\{1, \ldots, n\}$. The first observation regarding equipotence is that for any natural numbers n and m, the set $\{1, \ldots, n + m\}$ is not equipotent to the set $\{1, \ldots, n\}$. This observation is often called **the pigeonhole principle** and may be proved by an induction argument with respect to n (see Problem 21).

Definition   *A set E is said to be* **finite** *provided either it is empty or there is a natural number n for which E is equipotent to $\{1, \ldots, n\}$. We say that E is* **countably infinite** *provided E is equipotent to the set $\mathbf{N}$ of natural numbers. A set that is either finite or countably infinite is said to be* **countable**. *A set that is not countable is called* **uncountable**.

Observe that if a set is equipotent to a countable set, then it is countable. In the proof of the following theorem we will use the pigeonhole principle and Theorem 1, which tells us that every nonempty set of natural numbers has a smallest, or first, member.

Theorem 3   *A subset of a countable set is countable. In particular, every set of natural numbers is countable.*

Proof   Let B be a countable set and A a nonempty subset of B. First consider the case that B is finite. Let f be a one-to-one correspondence between $\{1, \ldots, n\}$ and B. Define $g(1)$ to be the first natural number $j, 1 \leq j \leq n$, for which $f(j)$ belongs to A. If $A = \{f(g(1))\}$ the proof is complete since $f \circ g$ is a one-to-one correspondence between $\{1\}$ and A. Otherwise, define $g(2)$ to be the first natural number j, $1 \leq j \leq n$, for which $f(j)$ belongs to $A \sim \{f(g(1))\}$. The pigeonhole principle tells us that this inductive selection process terminates after at most N selections, where $N \leq n$. Therefore $f \circ g$ is a one-to-one correspondence between $\{1, \ldots, N\}$ and A. Thus A is finite.

Now consider the case that B is countably infinite. Let f be a one-to-one correspondence between $\mathbf{N}$ and B. Define $g(1)$ to be the first natural number j for which $f(j)$ belongs to A. Arguing as in the first case, we see that if this selection process terminates, then A is finite. Otherwise, this selection process does not terminate and g is properly defined on all of $\mathbf{N}$. It is clear that $f \circ g$ is a one-to-one mapping with domain $\mathbf{N}$ and image contained in A. An induction argument shows that $g(j) \geq j$ for all j. For each $x \in A$, there is some k for which $x = f(k)$. Hence x belongs to the set $\{f(g(1)), \ldots, f(g(k))\}$. Thus the image of $f \circ g$ is A. Therefore A is countably infinite. $\qquad\square$

Corollary 4 *The following sets are countably infinite:*

$$\overbrace{\phantom{\mathbf{N}\times \cdots \times \mathbf{N}}}^{n \text{ times}}$$

(i) *For each natural numbers n, the Cartesian product $\mathbf{N} \times \cdots \times \mathbf{N}$.*
(ii) *The set of rational numbers $\mathbf{Q}$.*

Proof We prove (i) for $n = 2$ and leave the general case as an exercise in induction. Define the mapping g from $\mathbf{N} \times \mathbf{N}$ to $\mathbf{N}$ by $g(m, n) = (m + n)^2 + n$. The mapping g is one-to-one. Indeed, if $g(m, n) = g(m', n')$, then $(m + n)^2 - (m' + n')^2 = n' - n$ and hence

$$|m + n + m' + n'| \cdot |m + n - m' - n'| = |n' - n|.$$

If $n \neq n'$, then the natural number $m + n + m' + n'$ both divides and is greater than the natural number $|n' - n|$, which is impossible. Thus $n = n'$, and hence $m = m'$. Therefore $\mathbf{N} \times \mathbf{N}$ is equipotent to $g(\mathbf{N} \times \mathbf{N})$, a subset of the countable set $\mathbf{N}$. We infer from the preceding theorem that $\mathbf{N} \times \mathbf{N}$ is countable. To verify the countability of $\mathbf{Q}$ we first infer from the prime factorization theorem that each positive rational number x may be written uniquely as $x = p/q$ where p and q are relatively prime natural numbers. Define the mapping g from $\mathbf{Q}$ to $\mathbf{N}$ by $g(0) = 0$, $g(p/q) = (p + q)^2 + q$ if $x = p/q > 0$ and p and q are relatively prime natural numbers and $g(x) = -g(-x)$ if $x < 0$. We leave it as an exercise to show that g is one-to-one. Thus $\mathbf{Q}$ is equipotent to a subset of $\mathbf{N}$ and hence, by the preceding theorem, is countable. We leave it as an exercise to use the pigeonhole principle to show that neither $\mathbf{N} \times \mathbf{N}$ nor $\mathbf{Q}$ is finite. $\qquad\square$

For a countably infinite set X, we say that $\{x_n \mid n \in \mathbf{N}\}$ is an **enumeration** of X provided

$$X = \{x_n \mid n \in \mathbf{N}\} \text{ and } x_n \neq x_m \text{ if } n \neq m.$$

Theorem 5 *A nonempty set is countable if and only if it is the image of a function whose domain is a nonempty countable set.*

Proof Let A be a nonempty countable set and f be mapping of A onto B. We suppose that A is countably infinite and leave the finite case as an exercise. By composing with a one-to-one correspondence between A and $\mathbf{N}$, we may suppose that $A = \mathbf{N}$. Define two points x, x' in A to be equivalent provided $f(x) = f(x')$. This is an equivalence relation, that is, it is reflexive, symmetric, and transitive. Let E be a subset of A consisting of one member of each equivalence class. Then the restriction of f to E is a one-to-one correspondence between E and B. But E is a subset of $\mathbf{N}$ and therefore, by Theorem 3, is countable. The set B is equipotent to E and therefore B is countable. The converse assertion is clear; if B is a nonempty countable set, then it is equipotent either to an initial segment of natural numbers or to the natural numbers. $\qquad\square$

Corollary 6 *The union of a countable collection of countable sets is countable.*

Proof Let Λ be a countable set and for each $\lambda \in \Lambda$, let E_λ be a countable set. We will show that the union $E = \bigcup_{\lambda \in \Lambda} E_\lambda$ is countable. If E is empty, then it is countable. So we assume $E \neq \emptyset$. We consider the case that Λ is countably infinite and leave the finite case as an exercise. Let $\{\lambda_n \mid n \in \mathbf{N}\}$ be an enumeration of Λ. Fix $n \in \mathbf{N}$. If E_{λ_n} is finite and nonempty, choose a natural number $N(n)$ and a one-to-one mapping f_n of $\{1, \ldots, N(n)\}$ onto E_{λ_n}; if E_{λ_n} is countably infinite, choose a a one-to-one mapping f_n of $\mathbf{N}$ onto E_{λ_n}. Define

$$E' = \left\{ (n, k) \in \mathbf{N} \times \mathbf{N} \mid E_{\lambda_n} \text{ is nonempty, and } 1 \le k \le N(n) \text{ if } E_{\lambda_n} \text{ is also finite} \right\}.$$

Define the mapping f of E' to E by $f(n, k) = f_n(k)$. Then f is a mapping of E' onto E. However, E' is a subset of the countable set $\mathbf{N} \times \mathbf{N}$ and hence, by Theorem 3, is countable. Theorem 5 tells us that E also is countable. $\qquad\square$

We call an interval of real numbers degenerate if it is empty or contains a single member.

Theorem 7 *A nondegenerate interval of real numbers is uncountable.*

Proof Let I be a nondegenerate interval of real numbers. Clearly I is not finite. We argue by contradiction to show that I is uncountable. Suppose I is countably infinite. Let $\{x_n \mid n \in \mathbf{N}\}$ be an enumeration of I. Let $[a_1, b_1]$ be a nondegenerate closed, bounded subinterval of I which fails to contain x_1. Then let $[a_2, b_2]$ be a nondegenerate closed, bounded subinterval of $[a_1, b_1]$, which fails to contain x_2. We inductively choose a countable collection $\{[a_n, b_n]\}_{n=1}^{\infty}$ of nondegenerate closed, bounded intervals, which is descending in the sense that, for each n, $[a_{n+1}, b_{n+1}] \subseteq [a_n, b_n]$ and such that for each n, $x_n \notin [a_n, b_n]$. The nonempty set $E = \{a_n \mid n \in \mathbf{N}\}$ is bounded above by b_1. The Completeness Axiom tells us that E has a supremum. Define $x^* = \sup E$. Since x^* is an upper bound for E, $a_n \le x^*$ for all n. On the other hand, since $\{[a_n, b_n]\}_{n=1}^{\infty}$ is descending, for each n, b_n is an upper bound for E. Hence, for each n, $x^* \le b_n$. Therefore x^* belongs to $[a_n, b_n]$ for each n. But x^* belongs to $[a_1, b_1] \subseteq I$ and therefore there is a natural number n_0 for which $x^* = x_{n_0}$. We have a contradiction since $x^* = x_{n_0}$ does not belong to $[a_{n_0}, b_{n_0}]$. Therefore I is uncountable. $\qquad\square$

PROBLEMS

16. Show that the set $\mathbf{Z}$ of integers is countable.

17. Show that a set A is countable if and only if there is a one-to-one mapping of A to $\mathbf{N}$.

18. Use an induction argument to complete the proof of part (i) of Corollary 4.

19. Prove Corollary 6 in the case of a finite family of countable sets.

20. Let both $f: A \to B$ and $g: B \to C$ be one-to-one and onto. Show that the composition $g \circ f: A \to B$ and the inverse $f^{-1}: B \to A$ are also one-to-one and onto.

21. Use an induction argument to establish the pigeonhole principle.

22. Show that $2^{\mathbf{N}}$, the collection of all sets of natural numbers, is uncountable.

23. Show that the Cartesian product of a finite collection of countable sets is countable. Use the preceding problem to show that $\mathbf{N}^{\mathbf{N}}$, the collection of all mappings of $\mathbf{N}$ into $\mathbf{N}$, is not countable.

24. Show that a nondegenerate interval of real numbers fails to be finite.

25. Show that any two nondegenerate intervals of real numbers are equipotent.

26. Is the set $\mathbf{R} \times \mathbf{R}$ equipotent to $\mathbf{R}$?

1.4   OPEN SETS, CLOSED SETS, AND BOREL SETS OF REAL NUMBERS

Definition   *A set $\mathcal{O}$ of real numbers is called* **open** *provided for each $x \in \mathcal{O}$, there is a $r > 0$ for which the interval $(x - r, x + r)$ is contained in $\mathcal{O}$.*

For $a < b$, the interval (a, b) is an open set. Indeed, let x belong to (a, b). Define $r = \min\{b - x, x - a\}$. Observe that $(x - r, x + r)$ is contained in (a, b). Thus (a, b) is an open bounded interval and each bounded open interval is of this form. For $a, b \in \mathbf{R}$, we defined

$$(a, \infty) = \{x \in \mathbf{R} \mid a < x\}, (-\infty, b) = \{x \in \mathbf{R} \mid x < b\} \text{ and } (-\infty, \infty) = \mathbf{R}.$$

Observe that each of these sets is an open interval. Moreover, it is not difficult to see that since each set of real numbers has an infimum and supremum in the set of extended real numbers, each unbounded open interval is of the above form.

Proposition 8   *The set of real numbers $\mathbf{R}$ and the empty-set $\emptyset$ are open; the intersection of any finite collection of open sets is open; and the union of any collection of open sets is open.*

Proof   It is clear that $\mathbf{R}$ and $\emptyset$ are open and the union of any collection of open sets is open. Let $\{\mathcal{O}_k\}_{k=1}^{n}$ be a finite collection of open subsets of $\mathbf{R}$. If the intersection of this collection is empty, then the intersection is the empty-set and therefore is open. Otherwise, let x belong to $\cap_{k=1}^{n} \mathcal{O}_k$. For $1 \leq k \leq n$, choose $r_k > 0$ for which $(x - r_k, x + r_k) \subseteq \mathcal{O}_k$. Define $r = \min\{r_1, \ldots, r_n\}$. Then $r > 0$ and $(x - r, x + r) \subseteq \cap_{k=1}^{n} \mathcal{O}_k$. Therefore $\cap_{k=1}^{n} \mathcal{O}_k$. is open. $\square$

It is not true, however, that the intersection of any collection of open sets is open. For example, for each natural number n, let $\mathcal{O}_n$ be the open interval $(-1/n, 1/n)$. Then, by the Archimedean Property of $\mathbf{R}$, $\cap_{n=1}^{\infty} \mathcal{O}_n = \{0\}$, and $\{0\}$ is not an open set.

Proposition 9 *Every nonempty open set is the disjoint union of a countable collection of open intervals.*

Proof Let $\mathcal{O}$ be a nonempty open subset of $\mathbf{R}$. Let x belong to $\mathcal{O}$. There is a $y > x$ for which $(x, y) \subseteq \mathcal{O}$ and a $z < x$ for which $(z, x) \subseteq \mathcal{O}$. Define the extended real numbrs a_x and b_x by

$$a_x = \inf \left\{ z \mid (z, x) \subseteq \mathcal{O} \right\} \text{ and } b_x = \sup \left\{ y \mid (x, y) \subseteq \mathcal{O} \right\}.$$

Then $I_x = (a_x, b_x)$ is an open interval that contains x. We claim that

$$I_x \subseteq \mathcal{O} \text{ but } a_x \notin \mathcal{O}, b_x \notin \mathcal{O}. \tag{2}$$

Indeed, let w belong to I_x, say $x < w < b_x$. By the definition of b_x, there is a number $y > w$ such that $(x, y) \subseteq \mathcal{O}$, and so $w \in \mathcal{O}$. Moreover, $b_x \notin \mathcal{O}$, for if $b_x \in \mathcal{O}$, then for some $r > 0$ we have $(b_x - r, b_x + r) \subseteq \mathcal{O}$. Thus $(x, b_x + r) \subseteq \mathcal{O}$, contradicting the definition of b_x. Similarly, $a_x \notin \mathcal{O}$. Consider the collection of open intervals $\{I_x\}_{x \in \mathcal{O}}$. Since each x in $\mathcal{O}$ is a member of I_x, and each I_x is contained in $\mathcal{O}$, we have $\mathcal{O} = \bigcup_{x \in \mathcal{O}} I_x$. We infer from (2) that $\{I_x\}_{x \in \mathcal{O}}$ is disjoint. Thus $\mathcal{O}$ is the union of a disjoint collection of open intervals. It remains to show that this collection is countable. By the density of the rationals, Theorem 2, each of these open intervals contains a rational number. This establishes a one-to-one correspondence between the collection of open intervals and a subset of the rational numbers. We infer from Theorem 3 and Corollary 4 that any set of rational numbers is countable. Therefore $\mathcal{O}$ is the union of a countable disjoint collection of open intervals.   □

Definition *For a set E of real numbers, a real number x is called a **point of closure** of E provided every open interval that contains x also contains a point in E. The collection of points of closure of E is called the **closure** of E and denoted by $\overline{E}$.*

It is clear that we always have $E \subseteq \overline{E}$. If E contains all of its points of closure, that is, $E = \overline{E}$, then the set E is said to be **closed**.

Proposition 10 *For a set of real numbers E, its closure $\overline{E}$ is closed. Moreover, $\overline{E}$ is the smallest closed set that contains E in the sense that if F is closed and $E \subseteq F$, then $\overline{E} \subseteq F$.*

Proof The set $\overline{E}$ is closed provided it contains all its points of closure. Let x be a point of closure of $\overline{E}$. Consider an open interval I_x which contains x. There is a point $x' \in \overline{E} \cap I_x$. Since x' is a point of closure of E and the open interval I_x contains x', there is a point $x'' \in E \cap I_x$. Therefore every open interval that x also contains a point of E and hence $x \in \overline{E}$. So the set $\overline{E}$ is closed. It is clear that if $A \subseteq B$, then $\overline{A} \subseteq \overline{B}$, and hence if F is closed and contains E, then $\overline{E} \subseteq \overline{F} = F$.   □

Proposition 11 *A set of real numbers is open if and only if its complement in $\mathbf{R}$ is closed.*

Proof First suppose E is an open subset of $\mathbf{R}$. Let x be a point of closure of $\mathbf{R} \sim E$. Then x cannot belong to E because otherwise there would be an open interval that contains x and is contained in E and thus is disjoint from $\mathbf{R} \sim E$. Therefore x belongs to $\mathbf{R} \sim E$ and hence

$\mathbf{R} \sim E$ is closed. Now suppose $\mathbf{R} \sim E$ is closed. Let x belong to E. Then there must be an open interval that contains x that is contained in E, for otherwise every open interval that contains x contains points in $X \sim E$ and therefore x is a point of closure of $\mathbf{R} \sim E$. Since $\mathbf{R} \sim E$ is closed, x also belongs to $\mathbf{R} \sim E$. This is a contradiction. $\square$

Since $\mathbf{R} \sim [\mathbf{R} \sim E] = E$, it follows from the preceding proposition that *a set is closed if and only if its complement is open*. Therefore, by De Morgan's Identities, Proposition 8 may be reformulated in terms of closed sets as follows.

Proposition 12 *The empty-set $\emptyset$ and $\mathbf{R}$ are closed; the union of any finite collection of closed sets is closed; and the intersection of any collection of closed sets is closed.*

A collection of sets $\{E_\lambda\}_{\lambda \in \Lambda}$ is said to be a **cover** of a set E provided $E \subseteq \bigcup_{\lambda \in \Lambda} E_\lambda$. By a subcover of a cover of E we mean a subcollection of the cover that itself also is a cover of E. If each set E_λ in a cover is open, we call $\{E_\lambda\}_{\lambda \in \Lambda}$ an **open cover** of F. If the cover $\{E_\lambda\}_{\lambda \in \Lambda}$ contains only a finite number of sets, we call it a **finite cover**. This terminology is inconsistent: In "open cover" the adjective "open" refers to the sets in the cover; in "finite cover" the adjective "finite" refers to the collection and does not imply that the sets in the collection are finite sets. Thus the term "open cover" is an abuse of language and should properly be "cover by open sets." Unfortunately, the former terminology is well established in mathematics.

The Heine–Borel Theorem *Let F be a closed and bounded set of real numbers. Then every open cover of F has a finite subcover.*

Proof Let us first consider the case that F is the closed, bounded interval $[a, b]$. Let $\mathcal{F}$ be an open cover of $[a, b]$. Define E to be the set of numbers $x \in [a, b]$ with the property that the interval $[a, x]$ can be covered by a finite number of the sets of $\mathcal{F}$. Since $a \in E$, E is nonempty. Since E is bounded above by b, by the completeness of $\mathbf{R}$, E has a supremum; define $c = \sup E$. Since c belongs to $[a, b]$, there is an $\mathcal{O} \in \mathcal{F}$ that contains c. Since $\mathcal{O}$ is open there is an $\epsilon > 0$, such that the interval $(c - \epsilon, c + \epsilon)$ is contained in $\mathcal{O}$. Now $c - \epsilon$ is not an upper bound for E, and so there must be an $x \in E$ with $x > c - \epsilon$. Since $x \in E$, there is a finite collection $\{\mathcal{O}_1, \ldots, \mathcal{O}_k\}$ of sets in $\mathcal{F}$ that covers $[a, x]$. Consequently, the finite collection $\{\mathcal{O}_1, \ldots, \mathcal{O}_k, \mathcal{O}\}$ covers the interval $[a, c + \epsilon)$. Thus $c = b$, for otherwise $c < b$ and c is not an upper bound for E. Thus $[a, b]$ can be covered by a finite number of sets from $\mathcal{F}$, proving our special case.

Now let F be any closed and bounded set and $\mathcal{F}$ an open cover of F. Since F is bounded, it is contained in some closed, bounded interval $[a, b]$. The preceding proposition tells us that the set $\mathcal{O} = \mathbf{R} \sim F$ is open since F is closed. Let $\mathcal{F}^*$ be the collection of open sets obtained by adding $\mathcal{O}$ to $\mathcal{F}$, that is, $\mathcal{F}^* = \mathcal{F} \cup \mathcal{O}$. Since $\mathcal{F}$ covers F, $\mathcal{F}^*$ covers $[a, b]$. By the case just considered, there is a finite subcollection of $\mathcal{F}^*$ that covers $[a, b]$ and hence F. By removing $\mathcal{O}$ from this finite subcover of F, if $\mathcal{O}$ belongs to the finite subcover, we have a finite collection of sets in $\mathcal{F}$ that covers F. $\square$

We say that a countable collection of sets $\{E_n\}_{n=1}^{\infty}$ is **descending** or **nested** provided $E_{n+1} \subseteq E_n$ for every natural number n. It is said to be **ascending** provided $E_n \subseteq E_{n+1}$ for every natural number n.

The Nested Set Theorem *Let $\{F_n\}_{n=1}^{\infty}$ be a descending countable collection of nonempty closed sets of real numbers for which F_1 bounded. Then*

$$\bigcap_{n=1}^{\infty} F_n \neq \emptyset.$$

Proof We argue by contradiction. Suppose the intersection is empty. Then for each real number x, there is a natural number n for which $x \notin F_n$, that is, $x \in \mathcal{O}_n = \mathbf{R} \sim F_n$. Therefore $\bigcup_{n=1}^{\infty} \mathcal{O}_n = \mathbf{R}$. According to Proposition 4, since each F_n is closed, each $\mathcal{O}_n$ is open. Therefore $\{\mathcal{O}_n\}_{n=1}^{\infty}$ is an open cover of $\mathbf{R}$ and hence also of F_1. The Heine-Borel Theorem tells us that there a natural number N for which $F \subseteq \bigcup_{n=1}^{N} \mathcal{O}_n$. Since $\{F_n\}_{n=1}^{\infty}$ is descending, the collection of complements $\{\mathcal{O}_n\}_{n=1}^{\infty}$ is ascending. Therefore $\bigcup_{n=1}^{N} \mathcal{O}_n = \mathcal{O}_N = \mathbf{R} \sim F_N$. Hence $F_1 \subseteq \mathbf{R} \sim F_N$, which contradicts the assumption that F_N is a nonempty subset of F_1. ☐

Definition *Given a set X, a collection $\mathcal{A}$ of subsets of X is called a σ-algebra (of subsets of X) provided (i) the empty-set, $\emptyset$, belongs to $\mathcal{A}$; (ii) the complement in X of a set in $\mathcal{A}$ also belongs to $\mathcal{A}$; (iii) the union of a countable collection of sets in $\mathcal{A}$ also belongs to $\mathcal{A}$.*

Given a set X, the collection $\{\emptyset, X\}$ is a σ-algebra which has two members and is contained in every σ-algebra of subsets of X. At the other extreme is the collection of sets 2^X which consists of all subsets of X and contains every σ-algebra of subsets of X. For any σ-algebra $\mathcal{A}$, we infer from De Morgan's Identities that $\mathcal{A}$ is closed with respect to the formation of intersections of countable collections of sets that belong to $\mathcal{A}$; moreover, since the empty-set belongs to $\mathcal{A}$, $\mathcal{A}$ is closed with respect to the formation of finite unions and finite intersections of sets that belong to $\mathcal{A}$. We also observe that a σ-algebra is closed with respect to relative complements since if A_1 and A_2 belong to $\mathcal{A}$, so does $A_1 \sim A_2 = A_1 \cap [X \sim A_2]$. The proof of the following proposition follows directly from the definition of σ-algebra.

Proposition 13 *Let $\mathcal{F}$ be a collection of subsets of a set X. Then the intersection $\mathcal{A}$ of all σ-algebras of subsets of X that contain $\mathcal{F}$ is a σ-algebra that contains $\mathcal{F}$. Moreover, it is the smallest σ-algebra of subsets of X that contains $\mathcal{F}$ in the sense that any σ-algebra that contains $\mathcal{F}$ also contains $\mathcal{A}$.*

Let $\{A_n\}_{n=1}^{\infty}$ be a countable collection of sets that belong to a σ-algebra $\mathcal{A}$. Since $\mathcal{A}$ is closed with respect to the formation of countable intersections and unions, the following two sets belong to $\mathcal{A}$:

$$\limsup \{A_n\}_{n=1}^{\infty} = \bigcap_{k=1}^{\infty} \left[\bigcup_{n=k}^{\infty} A_n \right] \text{ and } \liminf \{A_n\}_{n=1}^{\infty} = \bigcup_{k=1}^{\infty} \left[\bigcap_{n=k}^{\infty} A_n \right].$$

The set $\limsup \{A_n\}_{n=1}^{\infty}$ is the set of points that belong to A_n for countably infinitely many indices n while the set $\liminf \{A_n\}_{n=1}^{\infty}$ is the set of points that belong to A_n except for at most finitely many indices n.

Although the union of any collection of open sets is open and the intersection of any finite collection of open sets is open, as we have seen, the intersection of a *countable* collection of open sets need not be open. In our development of Lebesgue measure and integration on the real line, we will see that the smallest σ-algebra of sets of real numbers that contains the open sets is a natural object of study.

Definition   *The collection $\mathcal{B}$ of Borel sets of real numbers is the smallest σ-algebra of sets of real numbers that contains all of the open sets of real numbers.*

Every open set is a Borel set and since a σ-algebra is closed with respect to the formation of complements, we infer from Proposition 4 that every closed set is a Borel set. Therefore, since each singleton set is closed, every countable set is a Borel set. A countable intersection of open sets is called a G_δ set. A countable union of closed sets is called an F_σ set. Since a σ-algebra is closed with respect to the formation of countable unions and countable intersections, each G_δ set and each F_σ set is a Borel set. Moreover, both the lim inf and lim sup of a countable collection of sets of real numbers, each of which is either open or closed, is a Borel set.

PROBLEMS

27. Is the set of rational numbers open or closed?

28. What are the sets of real numbers that are both open and closed?

29. Find two sets A and B such that $A \cap B = \emptyset$ and $\overline{A} \cap \overline{B} \neq \emptyset$.

30. A point x is called an **accumulation point** of a set E provided it is a point of closure of $E \sim \{x\}$.
    (i) Show that the set E' of accumulation points of E is a closed set.
    (ii) Show that $\overline{E} = E \cup E'$.

31. A point x is called an **isolated point** of a set E provided there is an $r > 0$ for which $(x - r, x + r) \cap E = \{x\}$. Show that if a set E consists of isolated points, then it is countable.

32. A point x is called an **interior point** of a set E if there is an $r > 0$ such that the open interval $(x - r, x + r)$ is contained in E. The set of interior points of E is called the **interior** of E denoted by int E. Show that
    (i) E is open if and only if $E = $ int E.
    (ii) E is dense if and only if int$(\mathbf{R} \sim E) = \emptyset$.

33. Show that the Nested Set Theorem is false if F_1 is unbounded.

34. Show that the assertion of the Heine-Borel Theorem is equivalent to the Completeness Axiom for the real numbers. Show that the assertion of the Nested Set Theorem is equivalent to the Completeness Axiom for the real numbers.

35. Show that the collection of Borel sets is the smallest σ-algebra that contains the closed sets.

36. Show that the collection of Borel sets is the smallest σ-algebra that contains intervals of the form $[a, b)$, where $a < b$.

37. Show that each open set is an F_σ set.

1.5 SEQUENCES OF REAL NUMBERS

A **sequence** of real numbers is a real-valued function whose domain is the set of natural numbers. Rather than denoting a sequence with standard functional notation such as $f : \mathbf{N} \to \mathbf{R}$, it is customary to use subscripts, replace $f(n)$ with a_n, and denote a sequence by $\{a_n\}$. A natural number n is called an **index** for the sequence, and the number a_n corresponding to the index n is called the nth **term** of the sequence. Just as we say that a real-valued function is bounded provided its image is a bounded set of real numbers, we say a sequence $\{a_n\}$ is **bounded** provided there is some $c \geq 0$ such that $|a_n| \leq c$ for all n. A sequence is said to be **increasing** provided $a_n \leq a_{n+1}$ for all n, is said to be **decreasing** provided $\{-a_n\}$ is inceasing, and said to be **monotone** provided it is either increasing or decreasing.

Definition *A sequence $\{a_n\}$ is said to **converge** to the number a provided for every $\epsilon > 0$, there is an index N for which*

$$\text{if } n \geq N, \text{ then } |a - a_n| < \epsilon. \tag{3}$$

*We call a the **limit** of the sequence and denote the convergence of $\{a_n\}$ by writing*

$$\{a_n\} \to a \text{ or } \lim_{n \to \infty} a_n = a.$$

We leave the proof of the following proposition as an exercise.

Proposition 14 *Let the sequence of real numbers $\{a_n\}$ converge to the real number a. Then the limit is unique, the sequence is bounded, and, for a real number c,*

$$\text{if } a_n \leq c \text{ for all } n, \text{ then } a \leq c.$$

Theorem 15 (the Monotone Convergence Criterion for Real Sequences) *A monotone sequence of real numbers converges if and only if it is bounded.*

Proof Let $\{a_n\}$ be an increasing sequence. If this sequence converges, then, by the preceding proposition, it is bounded. Now assume that $\{a_n\}$ is bounded. By the Completeness Axiom, the set $S = \{a_n \mid n \in N\}$ has a supremum: define $a = \sup S$. We claim that $\{a_n\} \to a$. Indeed, let $\epsilon > 0$. Since s is an upper bound for S, $a_n \leq a$ for all n. Since $a - \epsilon$ is not an upper bound for S, there is an index N for which $a_N > a - \epsilon$. Since the sequence is increasing, $a_n > a - \epsilon$ for all $n \geq N$. Thus if $n \geq N$, then $|a - a_n| < \epsilon$. Therefore $\{a_n\} \to a$. The proof for the case when the sequence is decreasing is the same. $\qquad \square$

For a sequence $\{a_n\}$ and a strictly increasing sequence of natural numbers $\{n_k\}$, we call the sequence $\{a_{n_k}\}$ whose kth term is a_{n_k} a **subsequence** of $\{a_n\}$.

Theorem 16 (the Bolzano-Weierstrass Theorem) *Every bounded sequence of real numbers has a convergent subsequence.*

Proof Let $\{a_n\}$ be a bounded sequence of real numbers Choose $M \geq 0$ such that $|a_n| \leq M$ for all n. Let n be a natural number. Define $E_n = \overline{\{a_j \mid j \geq n\}}$. Then $E_n \subseteq [-M, M]$ and E_n is closed since it is the closure of a set. Therefore $\{E_n\}$ is a descending sequence of nonempty closed bounded subsets of $\mathbf{R}$. The Nested Set Theorem tells us that $\bigcap_{n=1}^{\infty} E_n \neq \emptyset$; choose $a \in \bigcap_{n=1}^{\infty} E_n$. For each natural number k, a is a point of closure of $\{a_j \mid j \geq k\}$. Hence, for infinitely many indices $j \geq n$, a_j belongs to $(a - 1/k, a + 1/k)$. We may therefore inductively choose a strictly increasing sequence of natural numbers $\{n_k\}$ such that $|a-a_{n_k}|<1/k$ for all k. By the Archimedean Property of **R**, the subsequence $\{a_{n_k}\}$ converges to a. $\square$

Definition *A sequence of real numbers* $\{a_n\}$ *is said to be* **Cauchy** *provided for each* $\epsilon > 0$, *there is an index N for which*

$$if \, n, m \geq N, \, then \, |a_m - a_n| < \epsilon. \tag{4}$$

Theorem 17 (the Cauchy Convergence Criterion for Real Sequences) *A sequence of real numbers converges if and only if it is Cauchy.*

Proof First suppose that $\{a_n\} \to a$. Observe that for all natural numbers n and m,

$$|a_n - a_m| = |(a_n - a) + (a - a_m)| \leq |a_n - a| + |a_m - a|. \tag{5}$$

Let $\epsilon > 0$. Since $\{a_n\} \to a$, we may choose a natural number N such that if $n \geq N$, then $|a_n - a| < \epsilon/2$. We infer from (5) that if $n, m \geq N$, then $|a_n - a_m| < \epsilon$. Therefore the sequence $\{a_n\}$ is Cauchy. To prove the converse, let $\{a_n\}$ be a Cauchy sequence. We claim that it is bounded. Indeed, for $\epsilon = 1$, choose N such that if $n, m \geq N$, then $|a_n - a_m| < 1$. Thus

$$|a_n| = |(a_n - a_N) + a_N| \leq |a_n - a_N| + |a_N| \leq 1 + |a_N| \text{ for all } n \geq N.$$

Define $M = 1 + \max\{|a_1|, \ldots, |a_N|\}$. Then $|a_n| \leq M$ for all n. Thus $\{a_n\}$ is bounded. The Bolzano-Weierstrass Theorem tells us there is a subsequence $\{a_{n_k}\}$ which converges to a. We claim that the whole sequence converges to a. Indeed, let $\epsilon > 0$. Since $\{a_n\}$ is Cauchy we may choose a natural number N such that

$$if \, n, m \geq N, \, then \, |a_n - a_m| < \epsilon/2.$$

On the other hand, since $\{a_{n_k}\} \to a$ we may choose a natural number n_k such that $|a - a_{n_k}| < \epsilon/2$ and $n_k \geq N$. Therefore

$$|a_n - a| = |(a_n - a_{n_k}) + (a_{n_k} - a)| \leq |a_n - a_{n_k}| + |a - a_{n_k}| < \epsilon \text{ for all } n \geq N.   \square$$

Theorem 18 (Linearity and Montonicity of Convergence of Real Sequences) *Let* $\{a_n\}$ *and* $\{b_n\}$ *be convergent sequences of real numbers. Then for each pair of real numbers* α *and* β, *the sequence* $\{\alpha \cdot a_n + \beta \cdot b_n\}$ *is convergent and*

$$\lim_{n \to \infty} [\alpha \cdot a_n + \beta \cdot b_n] = \alpha \cdot \lim_{n \to \infty} a_n + \beta \cdot \lim_{n \to \infty} b_n. \tag{6}$$

Moreover,

$$if \, a_n \leq b_n \text{ for all } n, \text{ then } \lim_{n \to \infty} a_n \leq \lim_{n \to \infty} b_n. \tag{7}$$

Proof Define

$$\lim_{n \to \infty} a_n = a \text{ and } \lim_{n \to \infty} b_n = b.$$

Observe that

$$|[\alpha \cdot a_n + \beta \cdot b_n] - [\alpha \cdot a + \beta \cdot b]| \leq |\alpha| \cdot |a_n - a| + |\beta| \cdot |b_n - b| \text{ for all } n. \tag{8}$$

Let $\epsilon > 0$. Choose a natural number N such that

$$|a_n - a| < \epsilon/[2 + 2|\alpha|] \text{ and } |b_n - b| < \epsilon/[2 + 2|\beta|] \text{ for all } n \geq N.$$

We infer from (8) that

$$|[\alpha \cdot a_n + \beta \cdot b_n] - [\alpha \cdot a + \beta \cdot b]| < \epsilon \text{ for all } n \geq N.$$

Therefore (6) holds. To verify (7), set $c_n = b_n - a_n$ for all n and $c = b - a$, Then $c_n \geq 0$ for all n and, by linearity of convergence, $\{c_n\} \to c$. We must show $c \geq 0$. Let $\epsilon > 0$. There is an N such that

$$-\epsilon < c - c_n < \epsilon \text{ for all } n \geq N.$$

In particular, $0 \leq c_N < c + \epsilon$. Since $c > -\epsilon$ for every positive number ϵ, $c \geq 0$.   □

If a sequence $\{a_n\}$ has the property that for each real number c, there is an index N such that if $n \geq N$, then $a_n \geq c$ we say that $\{a_n\}$ **converges to infinity**, call ∞ the limit of $\{a_n\}$ and write $\lim_{n \to \infty} a_n = \infty$. Similar definitions are made at $-\infty$. With this extended concept of convergence we may assert that any monotone sequence $\{a_n\}$ of real numbers, bounded or unbounded, converges to an extended real number and therefore $\lim_{n \to \infty} a_n$ is properly defined.

The extended concept of supremum and infimum of a set and of convergence for any monotone sequence of real numbers allows us to make the following definition.

Definition   *Let $\{a_n\}$ be a sequence of real numbers. The limit superior of $\{a_n\}$, denoted by* $\limsup\{a_n\}$, *is defined by*

$$\limsup\{a_n\} = \lim_{n \to \infty} [\sup \{a_k \mid k \geq n\}].$$

The limit inferior of $\{a_n\}$, denoted by $\liminf\{a_n\}$, is defined by

$$\liminf\{a_n\} = \lim_{n \to \infty} [\inf \{a_k \mid k \geq n\}].$$

We leave the proof of the following proposition as an exercise.

Proposition 19   *Let $\{a_n\}$ and $\{b_n\}$ be sequences of real numbers.*

(i) $\limsup\{a_n\} = \ell \in \mathbf{R}$ *if and only if for each $\epsilon > 0$, there are infinitely many indices n for which $a_n > \ell - \epsilon$ and only finitely many indices n for which $a_n > \ell + \epsilon$.*

(ii) $\limsup\{a_n\} = \infty$ *if and only if $\{a_n\}$ is not bounded above.*

(iii)

$$\limsup\{a_n\} = -\liminf\{-a_n\}.$$

(iv) *A sequence of real numbers $\{a_n\}$ converges to an extended real number a if and only if*

$$\liminf\{a_n\} = \limsup\{a_n\} = a.$$

(v) *If $a_n \leq b_n$ for all n, then*

$$\limsup\{a_n\} \leq \liminf\{b_n\}.$$

For each sequence $\{a_k\}$ of real numbers, there corresponds a sequence of **partial sums** $\{s_n\}$ defined by $s_n = \sum_{k=1}^{n} a_k$ for each index n. We say that the series $\sum_{k=1}^{\infty} a_k$ is **summable** to the real number s provided $\{s_n\} \to s$ and write $s = \sum_{k=1}^{\infty} a_k$.

We leave the proof of the following proposition as an exercise.

Proposition 20 *Let $\{a_n\}$ be a sequence of real numbers.*

(i) *The series $\sum_{k=1}^{\infty} a_k$ is summable if and only if for each $\epsilon > 0$, there is an index N for which*

$$\left| \sum_{k=n}^{n+m} a_k \right| < \epsilon \text{ for } n \geq N \text{ and any natural number } m.$$

(ii) *If the series $\sum_{k=1}^{\infty} |a_k|$ is summable, then $\sum_{k=1}^{\infty} a_k$ also is summable.*

(iii) *If each term a_k is nonnegative, then the series $\sum_{k=1}^{\infty} a_k$ is summable if and only if the sequence of partial sums is bounded.*

PROBLEMS

38. We call an extended real number a **cluster point** of a sequence $\{a_n\}$ if a subsequence converges to this extended real number. Show that $\liminf\{a_n\}$ is the smallest cluster point of $\{a_n\}$ and $\limsup\{a_n\}$ is the largest cluster point of $\{a_n\}$.

39. Prove Proposition 19.

40. Show that a sequence $\{a_n\}$ is convergent to an extended real number if and only if there is exactly one extended real number that is a cluster point of the sequence.

41. Show that $\liminf a_n \leq \limsup a_n$.

42. Prove that if, for all n, $a_n > 0$ and $b_n \geq 0$, then

$$\limsup [a_n \cdot b_n] \leq (\limsup a_n) \cdot (\limsup b_n),$$

provided the product on the right is not of the form $0 \cdot \infty$.

43. Show that every real sequence has a monotone subsequence. Use this to provide another proof of the Bolzano-Weierstrass Theorem.

44. Let p be a natural number greater than 1, and x a real number, $0 < x < 1$. Show that there is a sequence $\{a_n\}$ of integers with $0 \leq a_n < p$ for each n such that

$$x = \sum_{n=1}^{\infty} \frac{a_n}{p^n}$$

and that this sequence is unique except when x is of the form q/p^n, in which case there are exactly two such sequences. Show that, conversely, if $\{a_n\}$ is any sequence of integers with $0 \leq a_n < p$, the series

$$\sum_{n=1}^{\infty} \frac{a_n}{p^n}$$

converges to a real number x with $0 \leq x \leq 1$. If $p = 10$, this sequence is called the *decimal expansion* of x. For $p = 2$ it is called the *binary* expansion; and for $p = 3$, the *ternary* expansion.

45. Prove Proposition 20.

46. Show that the assertion of the Bolzano-Weierstrass Theorem is equivalent to the Completeness Axiom for the real numbers. Show that the assertion of the Monotone Convergence Theorem is equivalent to the Completeness Axiom for the real numbers.

1.6 CONTINUOUS REAL-VALUED FUNCTIONS OF A REAL VARIABLE

Let f be a real-valued function defined on a set E of real numbers. We say that f is **continuous at the point** x in E provided that for each $\epsilon > 0$, there is a $\delta > 0$ for which

$$\text{if } x' \in E \text{ and } |x' - x| < \delta, \text{ then } |f(x') - f(x)| < \epsilon.$$

The function f is said to be **continuous** (on E) provided it is continuous at each point in its domain E. The function f is said to be **Lipschitz** provided there is a $c \geq 0$ for which

$$|f(x') - f(x)| \leq c \cdot |x' - x| \text{ for all } x', x \in E.$$

It is clear that a Lipschitz functon is continuous. Indeed, for a number $x \in E$ and any $\epsilon > 0$, $\delta = \epsilon/c$ responds to the ϵ challenge regarding the criterion for the continuity of f at x. Not all continuous functions are Lipschitz. For example, if $f(x) = \sqrt{x}$ for $0 \leq x \leq 1$, then f is continuous on $[0, 1]$ but is not Lipschitz.

We leave as an exercise the proof of the following characterization of continuity at a point in terms of sequential convergence.

Proposition 21 *A real-valued function f defined on a set E of real numbers is continuous at the point $x_* \in E$ if and only if whenever a sequence $\{x_n\}$ in E converges to x_*, its image sequence $\{f(x_n)\}$ converges to $f(x_*)$.*

We have the following characterization of continuity of a function on all of its domain.

Proposition 22 *Let f be a real-valued function defined on a set E of real numbers. Then f is continuous on E if and only if for each open set $\mathcal{O}$,*

$$f^{-1}(\mathcal{O}) = E \cap \mathcal{U} \text{ where } \mathcal{U} \text{ is an open set.} \tag{9}$$

Proof First assume the inverse image under f of any open set is the intersection of the domain with an open set. Let x belong to E. To show that f is continuous at x, let $\epsilon > 0$. The interval $I = (f(x) - \epsilon, f(x) + \epsilon)$ is an open set. Therefore there is an open set $\mathcal{U}$ such that

$$f^{-1}(I) = \{x' \in E \mid f(x) - \epsilon < f(x') < f(x) + \epsilon\} = E \cap \mathcal{U}.$$

In particular, $f(E \cap \mathcal{U}) \subseteq I$ and x belongs to $E \cap \mathcal{U}$. Since $\mathcal{U}$ is open there is a $\delta > 0$ such that $(x - \delta, x + \delta) \subseteq \mathcal{U}$. Thus if $x' \in E$ and $|x' - x| < \delta$, then $|f(x') - f(x)| < \epsilon$. Hence f is continuous at x.

Suppose now that f is continuous. Let $\mathcal{O}$ be an open set and x belong to $f^{-1}(\mathcal{O})$. Then $f(x)$ belongs to the open set $\mathcal{O}$ so that there is an $\epsilon > 0$, such that $(f(x) - \epsilon, f(x) + \epsilon) \subseteq \mathcal{O}$. Since f is continuous at x, there is a $\delta > 0$ such that if x' belongs to E and $|x' - x| < \delta$, then $|f(x') - f(x)| < \epsilon$. Define $I_x = (x - \delta, x + \delta)$. Then $f(E \cap I_x) \subseteq \mathcal{O}$. Define

$$\mathcal{U} = \bigcup_{x \in f^{-1}(\mathcal{O})} I_x.$$

Since $\mathcal{U}$ is the union of open sets it is open. It has been constructed so that (9) holds.   □

The Extreme Value Theorem   *A continuous real-valued function on a nonempty closed, bounded set of real numbers takes a minimum and maximum value.*

Proof   Let f be a continuous real-valued function on the nonempty closed bounded set E of real numbers. We first show that f is bounded on E, that is, there is a real number M such that

$$|f(x)| \leq M \text{ for all } x \in E. \tag{10}$$

Let x belong to E. Let $\delta > 0$ respond to the $\epsilon = 1$ challenge regarding the criterion for continuity of f at x. Define $I_x = (x - \delta, x + \delta)$. Therefore if x' belongs to $E \cap I_x$, then $|f(x') - f(x)| < 1$ and so $|f(x')| \leq |f(x)| + 1$. The collection $\{I_x\}_{x \in E}$ is an open cover of E. The Heine-Borel Theorem tells us that there are a finite number of points $\{x_1, \ldots, x_n\}$ in E such that $\{I_{x_k}\}_{k=1}^n$ also covers E. Define $M = 1 + \max\{|f(x_1)|, \ldots, |f(x_n)|\}$. We claim that (10) holds for this choice of E. Indeed, let x belong to E. There is an index k such that x belongs to I_{x_k} and therefore $|f(x)| \leq 1 + |f(x_k)| \leq M$. To see that f takes a maximum value on E, define $m = \sup f(E)$. If f failed to take the value m on E, then the function $x \mapsto 1/(f(x) - m), x \in E$ is a continuous function on E which is unbounded. This contradicts what we have just proved. Therefore f takes a maximum value of E. Since $-f$ is continuous, $-f$ takes a maximum value, that is, f takes a minimum value on E.   □

The Intermediate Value Theorem   *Let f be a continuous real-valued function on the closed, bounded interval $[a, b]$ for which $f(a) < c < f(b)$. Then there is a point x_0 in (a, b) at which $f(x_0) = c$.*

Proof   We will define by induction a descending countable collection $\{[a_n, b_n]\}_{n=1}^\infty$ of closed intervals whose intersection consists of a single point $x_0 \in (a, b)$ at which $f(x_0) = c$. Define $a_1 = a$ and $b_1 = b$. Consider the midpoint m_1 of $[a_1, b_1]$. If $c < f(m_1)$, define $a_2 = a_1$ and $b_2 = m_1$. If $f(m_1) \geq c$, define $a_2 = m_1$ and $b_2 = b_1$. Therefore $f(a_2) \leq c \leq f(b_2)$ and $b_2 - a_2 = [b_1 - a_1]/2$. We inductively continue this bisection process to obtain a descending collection $\{[a_n, b_n]\}_{n=1}^\infty$ of closed intervals such that

$$f(a_n) \leq c \leq f(b_n) \text{ and } b_n - a_n = [b - a]/2^{n-1} \text{ for all } n. \tag{11}$$

According to the Nested Set Theorem, $\bigcap_{n=1}^\infty [a_n, b_n]$ is nonempty. Let x_0 belong to $\bigcap_{n=1}^\infty [a_n, b_n]$. Observe that

$$|a_n - x_0| \leq b_n - a_n = [b - a]/2^{n-1} \text{ for all } n.$$

Therefore $\{a_n\} \to x_0$. By the continuity of f at x_0, $\{f(a_n)\} \to f(x_0)$. Since $f(a_n) \leq c$ for all n, and the set $(-\infty, c]$ is closed, $f(x_0) \leq c$. By a similar argument, $f(x_0) \geq c$. Hence $f(x_0) = c$.   □

Definition   *A real-valued function f defined on a set E of real numbers is said to be* **uniformly continuous** *provided for each $\epsilon > 0$, there is a $\delta > 0$ such that for all x, x' in E,*

$$\text{if } |x - x'| < \delta, \text{ then } |f(x) - f(x')| < \epsilon.$$

Theorem 23 *A continuous real-valued function on a closed, bounded set of real numbers is uniformly continuous.*

Proof Let f be a continuous real-valued function on a closed bounded set E of real numbers. Let $\epsilon > 0$. For each $x \in E$, there is a $\delta_x > 0$ such that if $x' \in E$ and $|x' - x| < \delta_x$, then $|f(x') - f(x)| < \epsilon/2$. Define I_x to be the open interval $(x - \delta_x/2, \, x + \delta_x/2)$. Then $\{I_x\}_{x \in E}$ is an open cover of E. According to the Heine-Borel Theorem, there is a finite subcollection $\{I_{x_1}, \ldots, I_{x_n}\}$ which covers E. Define

$$\delta = \frac{1}{2} \min\{\delta_{x_1}, \ldots, \delta_{x_n}\}.$$

We claim that this $\delta > 0$ responds to the $\epsilon > 0$ challenge regarding the criterion for f to be uniformly continuous on E. Indeed, let x and x' belong to E with $|x - x'| < \delta$. Since $\{I_{x_1}, \ldots, I_{x_n}\}$ covers E, there is an index k for which $|x - x_k| < \delta_{x_k}/2$. Since $|x - x'| < \delta \le \delta_{x_k}/2$,

$$|x' - x_k| \le |x' - x| + |x - x_k| < \delta_{x_k}/2 + \delta_{x_k}/2 = \delta_{x_k}.$$

By the definition of δ_{x_k}, since $|x - x_k| < \delta_{x_k}$ and $|x' - x_k| < \delta_{x_k}$ we have $|f(x) - f(x_k)| < \epsilon/2$ and $|f(x') - f(x_k)| < \epsilon/2$. Therefore

$$|f(x) - f(x')| \le |f(x) - f(x_k)| + |f(x') - f(x_k)| < \epsilon/2 + \epsilon/2 = \epsilon. \qquad \square$$

Definition *A real-valued function f defined on a set E of real numbers is said to be* **increasing** *provided $f(x) \le f(x')$ whenever x, x' belong to E and $x \le x'$, and* **decreasing** *provided $-f$ is increasing. It is called* **monotone** *if it is either increasing or decreasing.*

Let f be a monotone real-valued function defined on an open interval I that contains the point x_0. We infer from the Monotone Convergence Theorem for Sequence for Real Sequences that if $\{x_n\}$ is a sequence in $I \cap (x_0, \infty)$ which converges to x_0, then the sequence $\{f(x_n)\}$ converges to a real number and the limit is independent of the choice of sequence $\{x_n\}$. We denote the limit by $f(x_0^+)$. Similarly, we define $f(x_0^-)$. Then clearly f is continuous at x_0 if and only if $f(x_0^-) = f(x_0) = f(x_0^+)$. If f fails to be continuous at x_0, then the only point of the image of f that lies between $f(x_0^+)$ and $f(x_0^-)$ is $f(x_0)$ and f is said to have a **jump discontinuity** at x_0. Thus, by the Intermediate Value Theorem, a monotone function on an open interval is continuous if and only if its image is an interval (see Problem 55).

PROBLEMS

47. Let E be a closed set of real numbers and f a real-valued function that is defined and continuous on E. Show that there is a function g defined and continuous on all of $\mathbf{R}$ such that $f(x) = g(x)$ for each $x \in E$. (Hint: Take g to be linear on each of the intervals of which $\mathbf{R} \sim E$ is composed.)

48. Define the real-valued function f on $\mathbf{R}$ by setting

$$f(x) = \begin{cases} x & \text{if } x \text{ irrational} \\ p \sin \frac{1}{q} & \text{if } x = \frac{p}{q} \text{ in lowest terms.} \end{cases}$$

At what points is f continuous?

49. Let f and g be continuous real-valued functions with a common domain E.
    (i) Show that the sum, $f + g$, and product, fg, are also continuous functions.
    (ii) If h is a continuous function with image contained in E, show that the composition $f \circ h$ is continuous.
    (iii) Let $\max\{f, g\}$ be the function defined by $\max\{f, g\}(x) = \max\{f(x), g(x)\}$, for $x \in E$. Show that $\max\{f, g\}$ is continuous.
    (iv) Show that $|f|$ is continuous.

50. Show that a Lipschitz function is uniformly continuous but there are uniformly continuous functions that are not Lipschitz.

51. A continuous function φ on $[a, b]$ is called **piecewise linear** provided there is a partition $a = x_0 < x_1 < \cdots < x_n = b$ of $[a, b]$ for which φ is linear on each interval $[x_i, x_{i+1}]$. Let f be a continuous function on $[a, b]$ and ϵ a positive number. Show that there is a piecewise linear function φ on $[a, b]$ with $|f(x) - \varphi(x)| < \epsilon$ for all $x \in [a, b]$.

52. Show that a nonempty set E of real numbers is closed and bounded if and only if every continuous real-valued function on E takes a maximum value.

53. Show that a set E of real numbers is closed and bounded if and only if every open cover of E has a finite subcover.

54. Show that a nonempty set E of real numbers is an interval if and only if every continuous real-valued function on E has an interval as its image.

55. Show that a monotone function on an open interval is continuous if and only if its image is an interval.

56. Let f be a real-valued function defined on $\mathbf{R}$. Show that the set of points at which f is continuous is a G_δ set.

57. Let $\{f_n\}$ be a sequence of continuous functions defined on $\mathbf{R}$. Show that the set of points x at which the sequence $\{f_n(x)\}$ converges to a real number is the intersection of a countable collection of F_σ sets.

58. Let f be a continuous real-valued function on $\mathbf{R}$. Show that the inverse image with respect to f of an open set is open, of a closed set is closed, and of a Borel set is Borel.

59. A sequence $\{f_n\}$ of real-valued functions defined on a set E is said to converge uniformly on E to a function f if given $\epsilon > 0$, there is an N such that for all $x \in E$ and all $n \geq N$, we have $|f_n(x) - f(x)| < \epsilon$. Let $\{f_n\}$ be a sequence of continuous functions defined on a set E. Prove that if $\{f_n\}$ converges uniformly to f on E, then f is continuous on E.

60. Prove Proposition 21. Use this proposition and the Bolzano-Weierstrass Theorem to provide another proof of the Extreme Value Theorem.

CHAPTER 2

Lebesgue Measure

Contents

2.1 INTRODUCTION

The Riemann integral of a bounded function over a closed, bounded interval is defined using approximations of the function that are associated with partitions of its domain into finite collections of subintervals. The generalization of the Riemann integral to the Lebesgue integral will be achieved by using approximations of the function that are associated with decompositions of its domain into finite collections of sets which we call Lebesgue measurable. Each interval is Lebesgue measurable. The richness of the collection of Lebesgue measurable sets provides better upper and lower approximations of a function, and therefore of its integral, than are possible by just employing intervals. This leads to a larger class of functions that are Lebesgue integrable over very general domains and an integral that has better properties. For instance, under quite general circumstances we will prove that if a sequence of functions converges pointwise to a limiting function, then the integral of the limit function is the limit of the integrals of the approximating functions. In this chapter we establish the basis for the forthcoming study of Lebesgue measurable functions and the Lebesgue integral: the basis is the concept of measurable set and the Lebesgue measure of such a set.

The length $\ell(I)$ of an interval I is defined to be the difference of the endpoints of I if I is bounded, and ∞ if I is unbounded. Length is an example of a *set function*, that is, a function that associates an extended real number to each set in a collection of sets. In the case of length, the domain is the collection of all intervals. In this chapter we extend the set function length to a large collection of sets of real numbers. For instance, the "length" of an open set will be the sum of the lengths of the countable number of open intervals of which it is composed. However, the collection of sets consisting of intervals and open sets is still too limited for our purposes. We construct a collection of sets called **Lebesgue measurable sets**, and a set function of this collection called **Lebesgue measure** which is denoted by m.

The collection of Lebesgue measurable sets is a σ-algebra[1] which contains all open sets and all closed sets. The set function m possesses the following three properties.

The measure of an interval is its length   Each nonempty interval I is Lebesgue measurable and
$$m(I) = \ell(I).$$

Measure is translation invariant   If E is Lebesgue measurable and y is any number, then the translate of E by y, $E + y = \{x + y \mid x \in E\}$, also is Lebesgue measurable and

$$m(E + y) = m(E).$$

Measure is countably additivity over countable disjoint unions of sets[2]   If $\{E_k\}_{k=1}^{\infty}$ is a countable disjoint collection of Lebesgue measurable sets, then

$$m\left(\bigcup_{k=1}^{\infty} E_k\right) = \sum_{k=1}^{\infty} m(E_k).$$

It is not possible to construct a set function that possesses the above three properties and is defined for all sets of real numbers (see page 48). In fact, there is not even a set function defined for all sets of real numbers that possesses the first two properties and is finitely additive (see Theorem 18). We respond to this limitation by constructing a set function on a very rich class of sets that does possess the above three properties. The construction has two stages.

We first construct a set function called **outer–measure**, which we denote by m^*. It is defined for any set, and thus, in particular, for any interval. The outer measure of an interval is its length. Outer measure is translation invariant. However, outer measure is not finitely additive. But it is countably subadditive in the sense that if $\{E_k\}_{k=1}^{\infty}$ is any countable collection of sets, disjoint or not, then

$$m^*\left(\bigcup_{k=1}^{\infty} E_k\right) \le \sum_{k=1}^{\infty} m^*(E_k).$$

The second stage in the construction is to determine what it means for a set to be **Lebesgue measurable** and show that the collection of Lebesgue measurable sets is a σ-algebra containing the open and closed sets. We then restrict the set function m^* to the collection of Lebesgue measurable sets, denote it by m, and prove m is countably additive. We call m **Lebesgue measure**.

---

[1] A collection of subsets of **R** is called a σ-algebra provided it contains **R** and is closed with respect to the formation of complements and countable unions; by De Morgan's Identities, such a collection is also closed with respect to the formation of countable intersections.

[2] For a collection of sets to be disjoint we mean what is sometimes called pairwise disjoint, that is, that each pair of sets in the collection has empty intersection.

PROBLEMS

In the first three problems, let m be a set function defined for all sets in a σ-algebra $\mathcal{A}$ with values in $[0, \infty]$. Assume m is countably additive over countable disjoint collections of sets in $\mathcal{A}$

1. Prove that if A and B are two sets in $\mathcal{A}$ with $A \subseteq B$, then $m(A) \leq m(B)$. This property is called *monotonicity*.

2. Prove that if there is a set A in the collection $\mathcal{A}$ for which $m(A) < \infty$, then $m(\emptyset) = 0$.

3. Let $\{E_k\}_{k=1}^{\infty}$ be a countable collection of sets in $\mathcal{A}$. Prove that $m(\bigcup_{k=1}^{\infty} E_k) \leq \sum_{k=1}^{\infty} m(E_k)$.

4. A set function c, defined on all subsets of **R**, is defined as follows. Define $c(E)$ to be ∞ if E has infinitely many members and $c(E)$ to be equal to the number of elements in E if E is finite; define $c(\emptyset) = 0$. Show that c is a countably additive and translation invariant set function. This set function is called the **counting measure**.

2.2 LEBESGUE OUTER MEASURE

Let I be a nonempty interval of real numbers. We define its length, $\ell(I)$, to be ∞ if I is unbounded and otherwise define its length to be the difference of its endpoints. For a set A of real numbers, consider the countable collections $\{I_k\}_{k=1}^{\infty}$ of nonempty open, bounded intervals that cover A, that is, collections for which $A \subseteq \bigcup_{k=1}^{\infty} I_k$. For each such collection, consider the sum of the lengths of the intervals in the collection. Since the lengths are positive numbers, each sum is uniquely defined independently of the order of the terms. We define the **outer measure**[3] of A, $m^*(A)$, to be the infimum of all such sums, that is

$$m^*(A) = \inf \left\{ \sum_{k=1}^{\infty} \ell(I_k) \ \middle| \ A \subseteq \bigcup_{k=1}^{\infty} I_k \right\}.$$

It follows immediately from the definition of outer measure that $m^*(\emptyset) = 0$. Moreover, since any cover of a set B is also a cover of any subset of B, outer measure is **monotone** in the sense that

$$\text{if } A \subseteq B, \text{ then } m^*(A) \leq m^*(B).$$

Example A countable set has outer measure zero. Indeed, let C be a countable set enumerated as $C = \{c_k\}_{k=1}^{\infty}$. Let $\epsilon > 0$. For each natural number k, define $I_k = (c_k - \epsilon/2^{k+1}, c_k + \epsilon/2^{k+1})$. The countable collection of open intervals $\{I_k\}_{k=1}^{\infty}$ covers C. Therefore

$$0 \leq m^*(C) \leq \sum_{k=1}^{\infty} \ell(I_k) = \sum_{k=1}^{\infty} \epsilon/2^k = \epsilon.$$

This inequality holds for each $\epsilon > 0$. Hence $m^*(E) = 0$.

Proposition 1 *The outer measure of an interval is its length.*

---

[3]There is a general concept of outer measure, which will be considered in Part III. The set function m^* is a particular example of this general concept, which is properly identified as Lebesgue outer measure on the real line. In Part I, we refer to m^* simply as outer measure.

Proof We begin with the case of a closed, bounded interval $[a, b]$. Let $\epsilon > 0$. Since the open interval $(a - \epsilon, b + \epsilon)$ contains $[a, b]$ we have $m^*([a, b]) \leq \ell((a - \epsilon, b + \epsilon)) = b - a + 2\epsilon$. This holds for any $\epsilon > 0$. Therefore $m^*([a, b]) \leq b - a$. It remains to show that $m^*([a, b]) \geq b - a$. But this is equivalent to showing that if $\{I_k\}_{k=1}^{\infty}$ is any countable collection of open, bounded intervals covering $[a, b]$, then

$$\sum_{k=1}^{\infty} \ell(I_k) \geq b - a. \tag{1}$$

By the Heine-Borel Theorem,[4] any collection of open intervals covering $[a, b]$ has a finite subcollection that also covers $[a, b]$. Choose a natural number n for which $\{I_k\}_{k=1}^{n}$ covers $[a, b]$. We will show that

$$\sum_{k=1}^{n} \ell(I_k) \geq b - a, \tag{2}$$

and therefore (1) holds. Since a belongs to $\bigcup_{k=1}^{n} I_k$, there must be one of the I_k's that contains a. Select such an interval and denote it by (a_1, b_1). We have $a_1 < a < b_1$. If $b_1 \geq b$, the inequality (2) is established since

$$\sum_{k=1}^{n} \ell(I_k) \geq b_1 - a_1 > b - a.$$

Otherwise, $b_1 \in [a, b)$, and since $b_1 \notin (a_1, b_1)$, there is an interval in the collection $\{I_k\}_{k=1}^{n}$, which we label (a_2, b_2), distinct from (a_1, b_1), for which $b_1 \in (a_2, b_2)$; that is, $a_2 < b_1 < b_2$. If $b_2 \geq b$, the inequality (2) is established since

$$\sum_{k=1}^{n} \ell(I_k) \geq (b_1 - a_1) + (b_2 - a_2) = b_2 - (a_2 - b_1) - a_1 > b_2 - a_1 > b - a.$$

We continue this selection process until it terminates, as it must since there are only n intervals in the collection $\{I_k\}_{k=1}^{n}$. Thus we obtain a subcollection $\{(a_k, b_k)\}_{k=1}^{N}$ of $\{I_k\}_{k=1}^{n}$ for which

$$a_1 < a,$$

while

$$a_{k+1} < b_k \text{ for } 1 \leq k \leq N - 1,$$

and, since the selection process terminated,

$$b_N > b.$$

Thus

$$\sum_{k=1}^{n} \ell(I_k) \geq \sum_{k=1}^{N} \ell((a_i, b_i))$$

$$= (b_N - a_N) + (b_{N-1} - a_{N-1}) + \cdots + (b_1 - a_1)$$

$$= b_N - (a_N - b_{N-1}) - \ldots - (a_2 - b_1) - a_1$$

$$> b_N - a_1 > b - a.$$

---

[4]See page 18.

Thus the inequality (2) holds.

If I is any bounded interval, then given $\epsilon > 0$, there are two closed, bounded intervals J_1 and J_2 such that

$$J_1 \subseteq I \subseteq J_2$$

while

$$\ell(I) - \epsilon < \ell(J_1) \text{ and } \ell(J_2) < \ell(I) + \epsilon.$$

By the equality of outer measure and length for closed, bounded intervals and the monotonicity of outer measure,

$$\ell(I) - \epsilon < \ell(J_1) = m^*(J_1) \le m^*(I) \le m^*(J_2) = \ell(J_2) < \ell(I) + \epsilon.$$

This holds for each $\epsilon > 0$. Therefore $\ell(I) = m^*(I)$.

If I is an unbounded interval, then for each natural number n, there is an interval $J \subseteq I$ with $\ell(J) = n$. Hence $m^*(I) \ge m^*(J) = \ell(J) = n$. This holds for each natural number n. Therefore $m^*(I) = \infty$. $\qquad\square$

Proposition 2 *Outer measure is translation invariant, that is, for any set A and number y,*

$$m^*(A + y) = m^*(A).$$

Proof Observe that if $\{I_k\}_{k=1}^{\infty}$ is any countable collection of sets, then $\{I_k\}_{k=1}^{\infty}$ covers A if and only if $\{I_k + y\}_{k=1}^{\infty}$ covers $A + y$. Moreover, if each I_k is an open interval, then each $I_k + y$ is an open interval of the same length and so

$$\sum_{k=1}^{\infty} \ell(I_k) = \sum_{k=1}^{\infty} \ell(I_k + y).$$

The conclusion follows from these two observations. $\qquad\square$

Proposition 3 *Outer measure is countably subadditive, that is, if $\{E_k\}_{k=1}^{\infty}$ is any countable collection of sets, disjoint or not, then*

$$m^*\left(\bigcup_{k=1}^{\infty} E_k\right) \le \sum_{k=1}^{\infty} m^*(E_k).$$

Proof If one of the E_k's has infinite outer measure, the inequality holds trivially. We therefore suppose each of the E_k's has finite outer measure. Let $\epsilon > 0$. For each natural number k, there is a countable collection $\{I_{k,i}\}_{i=1}^{\infty}$ of open, bounded intervals for which

$$E_k \subseteq \bigcup_{i=1}^{\infty} I_{k,i} \text{ and } \sum_{i=1}^{\infty} \ell(I_{k,i}) < m^*(E_k) + \epsilon/2^k.$$

Now $\{I_{k,i}\}_{1 \le k,i \le \infty}$ is a countable collection of open, bounded intervals that covers $\bigcup_{k=1}^{\infty} E_k$: the collection is countable since it is a countable collection of countable collections. Thus, by the definition of outer measure,

$$m^*\left(\bigcup_{k=1}^{\infty} E_k\right) \leq \sum_{1 \leq k, i < \infty} \ell(I_{k,i}) = \sum_{k=1}^{\infty} \left[\sum_{i=1}^{\infty} \ell(I_{k,i})\right]$$

$$< \sum_{k=1}^{\infty} \left[m^*(E_k) + \epsilon/2^k\right]$$

$$= \left[\sum_{k=1}^{\infty} m^*(E_k)\right] + \epsilon.$$

Since this holds for each $\epsilon > 0$, it also holds for $\epsilon = 0$. The proof is complete. $\qquad \square$

If $\{E_k\}_{k=1}^n$ is any finite collection of sets, disjoint or not, then

$$m^*\left(\bigcup_{k=1}^{n} E_k\right) \leq \sum_{k=1}^{n} m^*(E_k).$$

This **finite subadditivity** property follows from countable subadditivity by taking $E_k = \emptyset$ for $k > n$.

PROBLEMS

5. By using properties of outer measure, prove that the interval $[0, 1]$ is not countable.

6. Let A be the set of irrational numbers in the interval $[0, 1]$. Prove that $m^*(A) = 1$.

7. A set of real numbers is said to be a G_δ set provided it is the intersection of a countable collection of open sets. Show that for any bounded set E, there is a G_δ set G for which

$$E \subseteq G \text{ and } m^*(G) = m^*(E).$$

8. Let B be the set of rational numbers in the interval $[0, 1]$, and let $\{I_k\}_{k=1}^n$ be a finite collection of open intervals that covers B. Prove that $\sum_{k=1}^n m^*(I_k) \geq 1$.

9. Prove that if $m^*(A) = 0$, then $m^*(A \cup B) = m^*(B)$.

10. Let A and B be bounded sets for which there is an $\alpha > 0$ such that $|a - b| \geq \alpha$ for all $a \in A$, $b \in B$. Prove that $m^*(A \cup B) = m^*(A) + m^*(B)$.

2.3 THE σ-ALGEBRA OF LEBESGUE MEASURABLE SETS

Outer measure has four virtues: (i) it is defined for all sets of real numbers, (ii) the outer measure of an interval is its length, (iii) outer measure is countably subadditive, and (iv) outer measure is translation invariant. But outer measure fails to be countably additive. In fact, it is not even finitely additive (see Theorem 18): there are disjoint sets A and B for which

$$m^*(A \cup B) < m^*(A) + m^*(B). \tag{3}$$

To ameliorate this fundamental defect we identify a σ-algebra of sets, called the Lebesgue measurable sets, which contains all intervals and all open sets and has the property that the restriction of the set function outer measure to the collection of Lebesgue measurable sets is countably additive. There are a number of ways to define what it means for a set to be measurable.[5] We follow an approach due to Constantine Carathéodory.

Definition *A set E is said to be **measurable** provided for any set A,[6]*

$$m^*(A) = m^*(A \cap E) + m^*(A \cap E^C).$$

We immediately see one advantage possessed by measurable sets, namely, that the strict inequality (3) cannot occur if one of the sets is measurable. Indeed, if, say, A is measurable and B is any set disjoint from A, then

$$m^*(A \cup B) = m^*([A \cup B] \cap A)) + m^*([A \cup B)] \cap A^C) = m^*(A) + m^*(B).$$

Since, by Proposition 3, outer measure is finitely subadditive and $A = [A \cap E] \cup [A \cap E^C]$, we always have

$$m^*(A) \le m^*(A \cap E) + m^*(A \cap E^C).$$

Therefore E is measurable if and only if for each set A we have

$$m^*(A) \ge m^*(A \cap E) + m^*(A \cap E^C). \tag{4}$$

This inequality trivially holds if $m^*(A) = \infty$. Thus it suffices to establish (4) for sets A that have finite outer measure.

Observe that the definition of measurability is symmetric in E and E^C, and therefore a set is measurable if and only if its complement is measurable. Clearly the empty-set Ø and the set **R** of all real numbers are measurable.

Proposition 4 *Any set of outer measure zero is measurable. In particular, any countable set is measurable.*

Proof Let the set E have outer measure zero. Let A be any set. Since

$$A \cap E \subseteq E \text{ and } A \cap E^C \subseteq A,$$

by the monotonicity of outer measure,

$$m^*(A \cap E) \le m^*(E) = 0 \text{ and } m^*(A \cap E^C) \le m^*(A).$$

Thus,

$$m^*(A) \ge m^*(A \cap E^C) = 0 + m^*(A \cap E^C) = m^*(A \cap E) + m^*(A \cap E^C),$$

and therefore E is measurable.   □

---

[5]We should fully identify what we here call a measurable set as a Lebesgue measurable subset of the real line. A more general concept of measurable set will be studied in Part III. However, there will be no confusion in the first part of this book in simply using the adjective measurable.

[6]Recall that for a set E, by E^C we denote the set $\{x \in \mathbf{R} \mid x \notin E\}$, the **complement** of E in **R**. We also denote E^C by $\mathbf{R} \sim E$. More generally, for two sets A and B, we let $A \sim B$ denote $\{a \in A \mid x \notin B\}$ and call it the **relative complement** of B in A.

Proposition 5 *The union of a finite collection of measurable sets is measurable.*

Proof As a first step in the proof, we show that the union of two measurable sets E_1 and E_2 is measurable. Let A be any set. First using the measurability of E_1, then the measurability of E_2, we have

$$m^*(A) = m^*(A \cap E_1) + m^*(A \cap E_1^C)$$

$$= m^*(A \cap E_1) + m^*([A \cap E_1^C] \cap E_2) + m^*([A \cap E_1^C] \cap E_2^C).$$

There are the following set identities:

$$[A \cap E_1^C] \cap E_2^C = A \cap [E_1 \cup E_2]^C$$

and

$$[A \cap E_1] \cup [A \cap E_1^C \cap E_2] = A \cap [E_1 \cup E_2].$$

We infer from these identities and the finite subadditivity of outer measure that

$$m^*(A) = m^*(A \cap E_1) + m^*([A \cap E_1^C] \cap E_2) + m^*([A \cap E_1^C] \cap E_2^C)$$

$$= m^*(A \cap E_1) + m^*([A \cap E_1^C] \cap E_2) + m^*(A \cap [E_1 \cup E_2]^C)$$

$$\geq m^*(A \cap [E_1 \cup E_2]) + m^*(A \cap [E_1 \cup E_2]^C).$$

Thus $E_1 \cup E_2$ is measurable.

Now let $\{E_k\}_{k=1}^n$ be any finite collection of measurable sets. We prove the measurability of the union $\bigcup_{k=1}^n E_k$, for general n, by induction. This is trivial for $n = 1$. Suppose it is true for $n - 1$. Thus, since

$$\bigcup_{k=1}^n E_k = \left[\bigcup_{k=1}^{n-1} E_k \right] \cup E_n,$$

and we have established the measurability of the union of two measurable sets, the set $\bigcup_{k=1}^n E_k$ is measurable. $\qquad \square$

Proposition 6 *Let A be any set and $\{E_k\}_{k=1}^n$ a finite disjoint collection of measurable sets. Then*

$$m^* \left(A \cap \left[\bigcup_{k=1}^n E_k \right] \right) = \sum_{k=1}^n m^*(A \cap E_k).$$

In particular,

$$m^* \left(\bigcup_{k=1}^n E_k \right) = \sum_{k=1}^n m^*(E_k).$$

Proof The proof proceeds by induction on n. It is clearly true for $n = 1$. Assume it is true for $n - 1$. Since the collection $\{E_k\}_{k=1}^n$ is disjoint,

$$A \cap \left[\bigcup_{k=1}^n E_k \right] \cap E_n = A \cap E_n$$

and

$$A \cap \left[\bigcup_{k=1}^{n} E_k \right] \cap E_n^C = A \cap \left[\bigcup_{k=1}^{n-1} E_k \right].$$

Hence, by the measurability of E_n and the induction assumption,

$$m^* \left(A \cap \left[\bigcup_{k=1}^{n} E_k \right] \right) = m^*(A \cap E_n) + m^* \left(A \cap \left[\bigcup_{k=1}^{n-1} E_k \right] \right)$$

$$= m^*(A \cap E_n) + \sum_{k=1}^{n-1} m^*(A \cap E_k)$$

$$= \sum_{k=1}^{n} m^*(A \cap E_k).$$ □

A collection of subsets of **R** is called an **algebra** provided it contains **R** and is closed with respect to the formation of complements and finite unions; by De Morgan's Identities, such a collection is also closed with respect to the formation of finite intersections. We infer from Proposition 5, together with the measurability of the complement of a measurable set, that the collection of measurable sets is an algebra. It is useful to observe that the union of a countable collection of measurable sets is also the union of a countable disjoint collection of measurable sets. Indeed, let $\{A_k\}_{k=1}^{\infty}$ be a countable collection of measurable sets. Define $A_1' = A_1$ and for each $k \geq 2$, define

$$A_k' = A_k \sim \bigcup_{i=1}^{k-1} A_i.$$

Since the collection of measurable sets is an algebra, $\{A_k'\}_{k=1}^{\infty}$ is a disjoint collection of measurable sets whose union is the same as that of $\{A_k\}_{k=1}^{\infty}$.

Proposition 7 *The union of a countable collection of measurable sets is measurable.*

Proof Let E be the union of a countable collection of measurable sets. As we observed above, there is a countable disjoint collection of measurable sets $\{E_k\}_{k=1}^{\infty}$ for which $E = \bigcup_{k=1}^{\infty} E_k$. Let A be any set. Let n be a natural number. Define $F_n = \bigcup_{k=1}^{n} E_k$. Since F_n is measurable and $F_n^C \supseteq E^C$,

$$m^*(A) = m^*(A \cap F_n) + m^*(A \cap F_n^C) \geq m^*(A \cap F_n) + m^*(A \cap E^C).$$

By Proposition 6,

$$m^*(A \cap F_n) = \sum_{k=1}^{n} m^*(A \cap E_k).$$

Thus

$$m^*(A) \geq \sum_{k=1}^{n} m^*(A \cap E_k) + m^*(A \cap E^C).$$

The left-hand side of this inequality is independent of n. Therefore

$$m^*(A) \geq \sum_{k=1}^{\infty} m^*(A \cap E_k) + m^*\left(A \cap E^C\right).$$

Hence, by the countable subadditivity of outer measure,

$$m^*(A) \geq m^*(A \cap E) + m^*\left(A \cap E^C\right).$$

Thus E is measurable.   □

A collection of subsets of **R** is called an σ-**algebra** provided it contains **R** and is closed with respect to the formation of complements and countable unions; by De Morgan's Identities, such a collection is also closed with respect to the formation of countable intersections. The preceding proposition tells us that the collection of measurable sets is a σ-algebra.

Proposition 8 *Every interval is measurable.*

Proof As we observed above, the measurable sets are a σ-algebra. Therefore to show that every interval is measurable it suffices to show that every interval of the form (a, ∞) is measurable (see Problem 11). Consider such an interval. Let A be any set. We assume a does not belong to A. Otherwise, replace A by $A \sim \{a\}$, leaving the outer measure unchanged. We must show that

$$m^*(A_1) + m^*(A_2) \leq m^*(A), \tag{5}$$

where

$$A_1 = A \cap (-\infty, a) \text{ and } A_2 = A \cap (a, \infty).$$

By the definition of $m^*(A)$ as an infimum, to verify (5) it is necessary and sufficient to show that for any countable collection $\{I_k\}_{k=1}^{\infty}$ of open, bounded intervals that covers A,

$$m^*(A_1) + m^*(A_2) \leq \sum_{k=1}^{\infty} \ell(I_k). \tag{6}$$

Indeed, for such a covering, for each index k, define

$$I_k' = I_k \cap (-\infty, a) \text{ and } I_k'' = I_k \cap (a, \infty)$$

Then I_k' and I_k'' are intervals and

$$\ell(I_k) = \ell(I_k') + \ell(I_k'').$$

Since $\{I_k'\}_{k=1}^{\infty}$ and $\{I_k''\}_{k=1}^{\infty}$ are countable collections of open, bounded intervals that cover A_1 and A_2, respectively, by the definition of outer measure,

$$m^*(A_1) \leq \sum_{k=1}^{\infty} \ell(I_k') \text{ and } m^*(A_2) \leq \sum_{k=1}^{\infty} \ell(I_k'').$$

Therefore

$$m^*(A_1) + m^*(A_1) \le \sum_{k=1}^{\infty} \ell(I'_k) + \sum_{k=1}^{\infty} \ell(I''_k).$$

$$= \sum_{k=1}^{\infty} [\ell(I'_k) + \ell(I''_k)]$$

$$= \sum_{k=1}^{\infty} \ell(I_k).$$

Thus (6) holds and the proof is complete.   □

Every open set is the disjoint union of a countable collection of open intervals.[7] We therefore infer from the two preceding propositions that every open set is measurable. Every closed set is the complement of an open set and therefore every closed set is measurable. Recall that a set of real numbers is said to be a G_δ set provided it is the intersection of a countable collection of open sets and said to be an F_σ set provided it is the union of a countable collection of closed sets. We infer from Proposition 7 that every G_δ set and every F_σ set is measurable.

The intersection of all the σ-algebras of subsets of **R** that contain the open sets is a σ-algebra called the Borel σ-algebra; members of this collection are called **Borel sets**. The Borel σ-algebra is contained in every σ-algebra that contains all open sets. Therefore, since the measurable sets are a σ-algebra containing all open sets, every Borel set is measurable. We have established the following theorem.

Theorem 9 *The collection $\mathcal{M}$ of measurable sets is a σ-algebra that contains the σ-algebra $\mathcal{B}$ of Borel sets. Each interval, each open set, each closed set, each G_δ set, and each F_σ set is measurable.*

Proposition 10 *The translate of a measurable set is measurable.*

Proof Let E be a measurable set. Let A be any set and y be a real number. By the measurability of E and the translation invariance of outer measure,

$$m^*(A) = m^*(A - y) = m^*([A - y] \cap E) + m^*\left([A - y] \cap E^C\right)$$

$$= m^*(A \cap [E + y]) + m^*\left(A \cap [E + y]^C\right).$$

Therefore $E + y$ is measurable.   □

PROBLEMS

11. Prove that if a σ-algebra of subsets of **R** contains intervals of the form (a, ∞), then it contains all intervals.

12. Show that every interval is a Borel set.

---

[7]See page 17.

13. Show that (i) the translate of an F_σ set is also F_σ, (ii) the translate of a G_δ set is also G_δ, and (iii) the translate of a set of measure zero also has measure zero.

14. Show that if a set E has positive outer measure, then there is a bounded subset of E that also has positive outer measure.

15. Show that if E has finite measure and $\epsilon > 0$, then E is the disjoint union of a finite number of measurable sets, each of which has measure at most ϵ.

2.4 OUTER AND INNER APPROXIMATION OF LEBESGUE MEASURABLE SETS

We now present two characterizations of measurability of a set, one based on inner approximation by closed sets and the other on outer approximation by open sets, which provide alternate angles of vision on measurability. These characterizations will be essential tools for our forthcoming study of approximation properties of measurable and integrable functions.

Measurable sets possess the following **excision property**: If A is a measurable set of finite outer measure that is contained in B, then

$$m^*(B \sim A) = m^*(B) - m^*(A). \tag{7}$$

Indeed, by the measurability of A,

$$m^*(B) = m^*(B \cap A) + m^*(B \cap A^C) = m^*(A) + m^*(B \sim A),$$

and hence, since $m^*(A) < \infty$, we have (7).

Theorem 11 *Let E be any set of real numbers. Then each of the following four assertions is equivalent to the measurability of E.*

(Outer Approximation by Open Sets and G_δ Sets)

   (i) For each $\epsilon > 0$, there is an open set $\mathcal{O}$ containing E for which $m^*(\mathcal{O} \sim E) < \epsilon$.

   (ii) There is a G_δ set G containing E for which $m^*(G \sim E) = 0$.

(Inner Approximation by Closed Sets and F_σ Sets)

   (iii) For each $\epsilon > 0$, there is a closed set F contained in E for which $m^*(E \sim F) < \epsilon$.

   (iv) There is an F_σ set F contained in E for which $m^*(E \sim F) = 0$.

Proof We establish the equivalence of the measurability of E with each of the two outer approximation properties (i) and (ii). The remainder of the proof follows from De Morgan's Identities together with the observations that a set is measurable if and only if its complement is measurable, is open if and only if its complement is closed, and is F_σ if and only if its complement is G_δ.

Assume E is measurable. Let $\epsilon > 0$. First consider the case that $m^*(E) < \infty$. By the definition of outer measure, there is a countable collection of open intervals $\{I_k\}_{k=1}^\infty$ which covers E and for which

$$\sum_{k=1}^\infty \ell(I_k) < m^*(E) + \epsilon.$$

Define $\mathcal{O} = \bigcup_{k=1}^\infty I_k$. Then $\mathcal{O}$ is an open set containing E. By the definition of the outer measure of $\mathcal{O}$,

$$m^*(\mathcal{O}) \le \sum_{k=1}^\infty \ell(I_k) < m^*(E) + \epsilon,$$

so that

$$m^*(\mathcal{O}) - m^*(E) < \epsilon.$$

However, E is measurable and has finite outer measure. Therefore, by the excision property of measurable sets noted above,

$$m^*(\mathcal{O} \sim E) = m^*(\mathcal{O}) - m^*(E) < \epsilon.$$

Now consider the case that $m^*(E) = \infty$. Then E may be expressed as the disjoint union of a countable collection $\{E_k\}_{k=1}^{\infty}$ of measurable sets, each of which has finite outer measure. By the finite measure case, for each index k, there is an open set $\mathcal{O}_k$ containing E_k for which $m^*(\mathcal{O}_k \sim E_k) < \epsilon/2^k$. The set $\mathcal{O} = \bigcup_{k=1}^{\infty} \mathcal{O}_k$ is open, it contains E and

$$\mathcal{O} \sim E = \bigcup_{k=1}^{\infty} \mathcal{O}_k \sim E \subseteq \bigcup_{k=1}^{\infty} [\mathcal{O}_k \sim E_k].$$

Therefore

$$m^*(\mathcal{O} \sim E)) \leq \sum_{k=1}^{\infty} m^*(\mathcal{O}_k \sim E_k) < \sum_{k=1}^{\infty} \epsilon/2^k = \epsilon.$$

Thus property (i) holds for E.

Now assume property (i) holds for E. For each natural number k, choose an open set $\mathcal{O}$ that contains E and for which $m^*(\mathcal{O}_k \sim E) < 1/k$. Define $G = \bigcap_{k=1}^{\infty} \mathcal{O}_k$. Then G is a G_δ set that contains E. Moreover, since for each k, $G \sim E \subseteq \mathcal{O}_k \sim E$, by the monotonicity of outer measure,

$$m^*(G \sim E) \leq m^*(\mathcal{O}_k \sim E) < 1/k.$$

Therefore $m^*(G \sim E) = 0$ and so (ii) holds. Now assume property (ii) holds for E. Since a set of measure zero is measurable, as is a G_δ set, and the measurable sets are an algebra, the set

$$E = G \cap [G \sim E]^C$$

is measurable. $\square$

The following property of measurable sets of finite outer measure asserts that such sets are "nearly" equal to the disjoint union of a finite number of open intervals.

Theorem 12 *Let E be a measurable set of finite outer measure. Then for each $\epsilon > 0$, there is a finite disjoint collection of open intervals $\{I_k\}_{k=1}^{n}$ for which if $\mathcal{O} = \bigcup_{k=1}^{n} I_k$, then*[8]

$$m^*(E \sim \mathcal{O}) + m^*(\mathcal{O} \sim E) < \epsilon.$$

Proof According to assertion (i) of Theorem 11, there is an open set $\mathcal{U}$ such that

$$E \subseteq \mathcal{U} \text{ and } m^*(\mathcal{U} \sim E) < \epsilon/2. \tag{8}$$

---

[8]For two sets A and B, the **symmetric difference** of A and B, which is denoted by $A \Delta B$, is defined to be the set $[A \sim B] \cup [B \sim A]$. With this notation the conclusion is that $m^*(E \Delta \mathcal{O}) < \epsilon$.

Since E is measurable and has finite outer measure, we infer from the excision property of outer measure that $\mathcal{U}$ also has finite outer measure. Every open set of real numbers is the disjoint union of a countable collection of open intervals.[9] Let $\mathcal{U}$ be the union of the countable disjoint collection of open intervals $\{I_k\}_{k=1}^{\infty}$. Each interval is measurable and its outer measure is its length. Therefore, by Proposition 6 and the monotonicity of outer measure, for each natural number n,

$$\sum_{k=1}^{n} \ell(I_k) = m^*\left(\bigcup_{k=1}^{n} I_k\right) \leq m^*(\mathcal{U}) < \infty.$$

The right-hand side of this inequality is independent of n. Therefore

$$\sum_{k=1}^{\infty} \ell(I_k) < \infty.$$

Choose a natural number n for which

$$\sum_{k=n+1}^{\infty} \ell(I_k) < \epsilon/2.$$

Define $\mathcal{O} = \bigcup_{k=1}^{n} I_k$. Since $\mathcal{O} \sim E \subseteq \mathcal{U} \sim E$, by the monotonicity of outer measure and (8),

$$m^*(\mathcal{O} \sim E) \leq m^*(\mathcal{U} \sim E) < \epsilon/2.$$

On the other hand, since $E \subseteq \mathcal{U}$,

$$E \sim \mathcal{O} \subseteq \mathcal{U} \sim \mathcal{O} = \bigcup_{k=n+1}^{\infty} I_k,$$

so that by the definition of outer measure,

$$m^*(E \sim \mathcal{O}) \leq \sum_{k=n+1}^{\infty} \ell(I_k) < \epsilon/2.$$

Thus

$$m^*(\mathcal{O} \sim E) + m^*(E \sim \mathcal{O}) < \epsilon. \qquad \square$$

Remark *A comment regarding assertion (i) in Theorem 11 is in order. By the definition of outer measure, for any bounded set E, regardless of whether or not it is measurable, and any $\epsilon > 0$, there is an open set $\mathcal{O}$ such that $E \subseteq \mathcal{O}$ and $m^*(\mathcal{O}) < m^*(E) + \epsilon$ and therefore $m^*(\mathcal{O}) - m^*(E) < \epsilon$. This does not imply that $m^*(\mathcal{O} \sim E) < \epsilon$, because the excision property*

$$m^*(\mathcal{O} \sim E) = m^*(\mathcal{O}) - m^*(E)$$

is false unless E is measurable (see Problem 19).

---

[9]See page 17.

PROBLEMS

16. Complete the proof of Theorem 11 by showing that measurability is equivalent to (iii) and also equivalent to (iv).

17. Show that a set E is measurable if and only if for each $\epsilon > 0$, there is a closed set F and open set $\mathcal{O}$ for which $F \subseteq E \subseteq \mathcal{O}$ and $m^*(\mathcal{O} \sim F) < \epsilon$.

18. Let E have finite outer measure. Show that there is an F_σ set F and a G_δ set G such that

$$F \subseteq E \subseteq G \text{ and } m^*(F) = m^*(E) = m^*(G).$$

19. Let E have finite outer measure. Show that if E is not measurable, then there is an open set $\mathcal{O}$ containing E that has finite outer measure and for which

$$m^*(\mathcal{O} \sim E) > m^*(\mathcal{O}) - m^*(E).$$

20. (Lebesgue) Let E have finite outer measure. Show that E is measurable if and only if for each open, bounded interval (a, b),

$$b - a = m^*((a, b) \cap E) + m^*((a, b) \sim E).$$

21. Use property (ii) of Theorem 11 as the primitive definition of a measurable set and prove that the union of two measurable sets is measurable. Then do the same for property (iv).

22. For any set A, define $m^{**}(A) \in [0, \infty]$ by

$$m^{**}(A) = \inf \left\{ m^*(\mathcal{O}) \mid \mathcal{O} \supseteq A, \mathcal{O} \text{ open.} \right\}$$

How is this set function m^{**} related to outer measure m^*?

23. For any set A, define $m^{***}(A) \in [0, \infty]$ by

$$m^{***}(A) = \sup \left\{ m^*(F) \mid F \subseteq A, F \text{ closed.} \right\}$$

How is this set function m^{***} related to outer measure m^*?

2.5 COUNTABLE ADDITIVITY, CONTINUITY, AND THE BOREL-CANTELLI LEMMA

Definition *The restriction of the set function outer measure to the class of measurable sets is called* **Lebesgue measure**. *It is denoted by m, so that if E is a measurable set, its Lebesgue measure, $m(E)$, is defined by*

$$m(E) = m^*(E).$$

The following proposition is of fundamental importance.

Proposition 13 *Lebesgue measure is countably additive, that is, if $\{E_k\}_{k=1}^{\infty}$ is a countable disjoint collection of measurable sets, then its union $\bigcup_{k=1}^{\infty} E_k$ also is measurable and*

$$m\left(\bigcup_{k=1}^{\infty} E_k \right) = \sum_{k=1}^{\infty} m(E_k).$$

Proof Proposition 7 tells us that $\bigcup_{k=1}^{\infty} E_k$ is measurable. According to Proposition 3, outer measure is countably subadditive. Thus

$$m\left(\bigcup_{k=1}^{\infty} E_k\right) \leq \sum_{k=1}^{\infty} m(E_k). \tag{9}$$

It remains to prove this inequality in the opposite directon. According to Proposition 6, for each natural number n,

$$m\left(\bigcup_{k=1}^{n} E_k\right) = \sum_{k=1}^{n} m(E_k).$$

Since $\bigcup_{k=1}^{\infty} E_k$ contains $\bigcup_{k=1}^{n} E_k$, by the monotonicity of outer measure and the preceding equality,

$$m\left(\bigcup_{k=1}^{\infty} E_k\right) \geq \sum_{k=1}^{n} m(E_k) \text{ for each } n.$$

The left-hand side of this inequality is independent of n. Therefore

$$m\left(\bigcup_{k=1}^{\infty} E_k\right) \geq \sum_{k=1}^{\infty} m(E_k). \tag{10}$$

From the inequalities (9) and (10) it follows that these are equalities. □

According to Proposition 1, the outer measure of an interval is its length while according to Proposition 2, outer measure is translation invariant. Therefore the preceding proposition completes the proof of the following theorem, which has been the principal goal of this chapter.

Theorem 14 *The set function Lebesgue measure, defined on the σ-algebra of Lebesgue measurable sets, assigns length to any interval, is translation invariant, and is countable additive.*

A countable collection of sets $\{E_k\}_{k=1}^{\infty}$ is said to be **ascending** provided for each k, $E_k \subseteq E_{k+1}$, and said to be **descending** provided for each k, $E_{k+1} \subseteq E_k$.

Theorem 15 (the Continuity of Measure) *Lebesgue measure possesses the following continuity properties:*

(i) *If $\{A_k\}_{k=1}^{\infty}$ is an ascending collection of measurable sets, then*

$$m\left(\bigcup_{k=1}^{\infty} A_k\right) = \lim_{k \to \infty} m(A_k). \tag{11}$$

(ii) *If $\{B_k\}_{k=1}^{\infty}$ is a descending collection of measurable sets and $m(B_1) < \infty$, then*

$$m\left(\bigcap_{k=1}^{\infty} B_k\right) = \lim_{k \to \infty} m(B_k). \tag{12}$$

Proof We first prove (i). If there is an index k_0 for which $m(A_{k_0}) = \infty$, then, by the monotonicity of measure, $m\left(\bigcup_{k=1}^{\infty} A_k\right) = \infty$ and $m(A_k) = \infty$ for all $k \geq k_0$. Therefore (11) holds since each side equals ∞. It remains to consider the case that $m(A_k) < \infty$ for all k. Define $A_0 = \emptyset$ and then define $C_k = A_k \sim A_{k-1}$ for each $k \geq 1$. By construction, since the sequence $\{A_k\}_{k=1}^{\infty}$ is ascending,

$$\{C_k\}_{k=1}^{\infty} \text{ is disjoint and } \bigcup_{k=1}^{\infty} A_k = \bigcup_{k=1}^{\infty} C_k.$$

By the countable additivity of m,

$$m\left(\bigcup_{k=1}^{\infty} A_k\right) = m\left(\bigcup_{k=1}^{\infty} C_k\right) = \sum_{k=1}^{\infty} m(A_k \sim A_{k-1}). \tag{13}$$

Since $\{A_k\}_{k=1}^{\infty}$ is ascending, we infer from the excision property of measure that

$$\begin{aligned} \sum_{k=1}^{\infty} m(A_k \sim A_{k-1}) &= \sum_{k=1}^{\infty} [m(A_k) - m(A_{k-1})] \\ &= \lim_{n \to \infty} \sum_{k=1}^{n} [m(A_k) - m(A_{k-1})] \\ &= \lim_{n \to \infty} [m(A_n) - m(A_0)]. \end{aligned} \tag{14}$$

Since $m(A_0) = m(\emptyset) = 0$, (11) follows from (13) and (14).

To prove (ii) we define $D_k = B_1 \sim B_k$ for each k. Since the sequence $\{B_k\}_{k=1}^{\infty}$ is descending, the sequence $\{D_k\}_{k=1}^{\infty}$ is ascending. By part (i),

$$m\left(\bigcup_{k=1}^{\infty} D_k\right) = \lim_{k \to \infty} m(D_k).$$

According to De Morgan's Identities,

$$\bigcup_{k=1}^{\infty} D_k = \bigcup_{k=1}^{\infty} [B_1 \sim B_k] = B_1 \sim \bigcap_{k=1}^{\infty} B_k.$$

On the other hand, by the excision property of measure, for each k, since $m(B_k) < \infty$, $m(D_k) = m(B_1) - m(B_k)$. Therefore

$$m\left(B_1 \sim \bigcap_{k=1}^{\infty} B_k\right) = \lim_{n \to \infty} [m(B_1) - m(B_n)].$$

Once more using excision we obtain the equality (12). □

For a measurable set E, we say that a property holds **almost everywhere on** E, or it holds for almost all $x \in E$, provided there is a subset E_0 of E for which $m(E_0) = 0$ and the property holds for all $x \in E \sim E_0$.

The Borel-Cantelli Lemma *Let $\{E_k\}_{k=1}^{\infty}$ be a countable collection of measurable sets for which $\sum_{k=1}^{\infty} m(E_k) < \infty$. Then almost all $x \in \mathbf{R}$ belong to at most finitely many of the E_k's.*

Proof For each n, by the countable subadditivity of m,

$$m\left(\bigcup_{k=n}^{\infty} E_k\right) \leq \sum_{k=n}^{\infty} m(E_k) < \infty.$$

Hence, by the continuity of measure,

$$m\left(\bigcap_{n=1}^{\infty}\left[\bigcup_{k=n}^{\infty} E_k\right]\right) = \lim_{n \to \infty} m(\bigcup_{k=n}^{\infty} E_k) \leq \lim_{n \to \infty} \sum_{k=n}^{\infty} m(E_k) = 0.$$

Therefore almost all $x \in \mathbf{R}$ fail to belong to $\bigcap_{n=1}^{\infty}\left[\bigcup_{k=n}^{\infty} E_k\right]$ and therefore belong to at most finitely many E_k's. $\square$

The set function Lebesgue measure inherits the properties possessed by Lebesgue outer measure. For future reference we name some of these properties.

(Finite Additivity) For any finite disjoint collection $\{E_k\}_{k=1}^{n}$ of measurable sets,

$$m\left(\bigcup_{k=1}^{n} E_k\right) = \sum_{k=1}^{n} m(E_k).$$

(Monotonicity) If A and B are measurable sets and $A \subseteq B$, then

$$m(A) \leq m(B).$$

(Excision) If, moreover, $A \subseteq B$ and $m(A) < \infty$, then

$$m(B \sim A) = m(B) - m(A),$$

so that if $m(A) = 0$, then

$$m(B \sim A) = m(B).$$

(Countable Monotonicity) For any countable collection $\{E_k\}_{k=1}^{\infty}$ of measurable sets that covers a measurable set E,

$$m(E) \leq \sum_{k=1}^{\infty} m(E_k).$$

Countable monotonicity is an amalgamation of the monotonicity and countable subadditivity properties of measure that is often invoked.

Remark *In our forthcoming study of Lebesgue integration it will be apparent that it is the countable additivity of Lebesgue measure that provides the Lebesgue integral with its decisive advantage over the Riemann integral.*

PROBLEMS

24. Show that if E_1 and E_2 are measurable, then

$$m(E_1 \cup E_2) + m(E_1 \cap E_2) = m(E_1) + m(E_2).$$

25. Show that the assumption that $m(B_1) < \infty$ is necessary in part (ii) of the theorem regarding continuity of measure.

26. Let $\{E_k\}_{k=1}^{\infty}$ be a countable disjoint collection of measurable sets. Prove that for any set A,

$$m^*\left(A \cap \bigcup_{k=1}^{\infty} E_k\right) = \sum_{k=1}^{\infty} m^*(A \cap E_k).$$

27. Let $\mathcal{M}'$ be any σ-algebra of subsets of $\mathbf{R}$ and m' a set function on $\mathcal{M}'$ which takes values in $[0, \infty]$, is countably additive, and such that $m'(\emptyset) = 0$.

    (i) Show that m' is finitely additive, monotone, countably monotone, and possesses the excision property.

    (ii) Show that m' possesses the same continuity properties as Lebesgue measure.

28. Show that continuity of measure together with finite additivity of measure implies countable additivity of measure.

2.6 NONMEASURABLE SETS

We have defined what it means for a set to be measurable and studied properties of the collection of measurable sets. It is only natural to ask if, in fact, there are any sets that fail to be measurable. The answer is not at all obvious.

We know that if a set E has outer measure zero, then it is measurable, and since any subset of E also has outer measure zero, every subset of E is measurable. This is the best that can be said regarding the inheritance of measurability through the relation of set inclusion: we now show that if E is any set of real numbers with positive outer measure, then there are subsets of E that fail to be measurable.

Lemma 16 *Let E be a bounded measurable set of real numbers. Suppose there is a bounded, countably infinite set of real numbers Λ for which the collection of translates of E, $\{\lambda + E\}_{\lambda \in \Lambda}$, is disjoint. Then $m(E) = 0$.*

Proof The translate of a measurable set is measurable. Thus, by the countable additivity of measure over countable disjoint unions of measurable sets,

$$m\left[\bigcup_{\lambda \in \Lambda}(\lambda + E)\right] = \sum_{\lambda \in \Lambda} m(\lambda + E). \tag{15}$$

Since both E and Λ are bounded sets, the set $\bigcup_{\lambda \in \Lambda}(\lambda + E)$ also is bounded and therefore has finite measure. Thus the left-hand side of (15) is finite. However, since measure is translation invariant, $m(\lambda + E) = m(E) > 0$ for each $\lambda \in \Lambda$. Thus, since the set Λ is countably infinite and the right-hand sum in (15) is finite, we must have $m(E) = 0$. $\qquad\square$

For any nonempty set E of real numbers, we define two points in E to be **rationally equivalent** provided their difference belongs to $\mathbf{Q}$, the set of rational numbers. It is easy to see that this is an equivalence relation, that is, it is reflexive, symmetric, and transitive. We call it the rational equivalence relation on E. For this relation, there is the disjoint decomposition of E into the collection of equivalence classes. By a **choice set** for the rational equivalence relation on E we mean a set $\mathcal{C}_E$ consisting of exactly one member of each equivalence class. We infer from the Axiom of Choice[10] that there are such choice sets. A choice set $\mathcal{C}_E$ is characterized by the following two properties:

  (i) the difference of two points in $\mathcal{C}_E$ is not rational;
  (ii) for each point x in E, there is a point c in $\mathcal{C}_E$ for which $x = c + q$, with q rational.

This first characteristic property of $\mathcal{C}_E$ may be conveniently reformulated as follows:

$$\text{For any set } \Lambda \subseteq \mathbf{Q}, \ \{\lambda + \mathcal{C}_E\}_{\lambda \in \Lambda} \text{ is disjoint.} \tag{16}$$

Theorem 17 (**Vitali**) *Any set E of real numbers with positive outer measure contains a subset that fails to be measurable.*

Proof By the countable subadditivity of outer measure, we may suppose E is bounded. Let $\mathcal{C}_E$ be any choice set for the rational equivalence relation on E. We claim that $\mathcal{C}_E$ is not measurable. To verify this claim, we assume it is measurable and derive a contradiction.

Let Λ_0 be any bounded, countably infinite set of rational numbers. Since $\mathcal{C}_E$ is measurable, and, by (16), the collection of translates of $\mathcal{C}_E$ by members of Λ_0 is disjoint, it follows from Lemma 16 that $m(\mathcal{C}_E) = 0$. Hence, again using the translation invariance and the countable additivity of measure over countable disjoint unions of measurable sets,

$$m \left[\bigcup_{\lambda \in \Lambda_0} (\lambda + \mathcal{C}_E) \right] = \sum_{\lambda \in \Lambda_0} m(\lambda + \mathcal{C}_E) = 0.$$

To obtain a contradiction we make a special choice of Λ_0. Because E is bounded it is contained in some interval $[-b, b]$. We choose

$$\Lambda_0 = [-2b, \ 2b] \cap \mathbf{Q}.$$

Then Λ_0 is bounded, and is countably infinite since the rationals are countable and dense.[11] We claim that

$$E \subseteq \bigcup_{\lambda \in [-2b, \ 2b] \cap \mathbf{Q}} (\lambda + \mathcal{C}_E). \tag{17}$$

Indeed, by the second characteristic property of $\mathcal{C}_E$, if x belongs to E, there is a number c in the choice set $\mathcal{C}_E$ for which $x = c + q$ with q rational. But x and c belong to $[-b, b]$, so that q belongs to $[-2b, 2b]$. Thus the inclusion (17) holds. This is a contradiction because E, a set of positive outer measure, is not a subset of a set of measure zero. The assumption that $\mathcal{C}_E$ is measurable has led to a contradiction and thus it must fail to be measurable.   □

---

[10]See page 5.
[11]See pages 12 and 14.

Theorem 18 *There are disjoint sets of real numbers A and B for which*

$$m^*(A \cup B) < m^*(A) + m^*(B).$$

Proof We prove this by contradiction. Assume $m^*(A \cup B) = m^*(A) + m^*(B)$ for every disjoint pair of sets A and B. Then, by the very definition of measurable set, every set must be measurable. This contradicts the preceding theorem. $\qquad\square$

PROBLEMS

29. (i)   Show that rational equivalence defines an equivalence relation on any set.

   (ii) Explicitly find a choice set for the rational equivalence relation on $\mathbf{Q}$.

   (iii) Define two numbers to be irrationally equivalent provided their difference is irrational. Is this an equivalence relation on $\mathbf{R}$? Is this an equivalence relation on $\mathbf{Q}$?

30. Show that any choice set for the rational equivalence relation on a set of positive outer measure must be uncountably infinite.

31. Justify the assertion in the proof of Vitali's Theorem that it suffices to consider the case that E is bounded.

32. Does Lemma 16 remain true if Λ is allowed to be finite or to be uncountably infinite? Does it remain true if Λ is allowed to be unbounded?

33. Let E be a nonmeasurable set of finite outer measure. Show that there is a G_δ set G that contains E for which

$$m^*(E) = m^*(G), \text{ while } m^*(G \sim E) > 0.$$

2.7 THE CANTOR SET AND THE CANTOR-LEBESGUE FUNCTION

We have shown that a countable set has measure zero and a Borel set is Lebesgue measurable. These two assertions prompt the following two questions.

Question 1 If a set has measure zero, is it also countable?

Question 2 If a set is measurable, is it also Borel?

   The answer to each of these questions is negative. In this section we construct a set called the Cantor set and a function called the Cantor-Lebesgue function. By studying these we answer the above two questions and later provide answers to other questions regarding finer properties of functions.

   Consider the closed, bounded interval $I = [0, 1]$. The first step in the construction of the Cantor set is to subdivide I into three intervals of equal length 1/3 and remove the interior of the middle interval, that is, we remove the interval $(1/3, 2/3)$ from the interval $[0, 1]$ to obtain the closed set C_1, which is the union of two disjoint closed intervals, each of length 1/3 :

$$C_1 = [0, 1/3] \cup [2/3, 1].$$

We now repeat this "open middle one-third removal" on each of the two intervals in C_1 to obtain a closed set C_2, which is the union of 2^2 closed intervals, each of length $1/3^2$:

$$C_2 = [0, 1/9] \cup [2/9, 1/3] \cup [2/3, 7/9] \cup [8/9, 1].$$

We now repeat this "open middle one-third removal" on each of the four intervals in C_2 to obtain a closed set C_3, which is the union of 2^3 closed intervals, each of length $1/3^3$. We continue this removal operation countably many times to obtain the countable collection of sets $\{C_k\}_{k=1}^{\infty}$. We define the Cantor set $\mathbf{C}$ by

$$\mathbf{C} = \bigcap_{k=1}^{\infty} C_k.$$

The collection $\{C_k\}_{k=1}^{\infty}$ possesses the following two properties:

(i) $\{C_k\}_{k=1}^{\infty}$ is a descending sequence of closed sets;

(ii) For each k, C_k is the disjoint union of 2^k closed intervals, each of length $1/3^k$.

Proposition 19 *The Cantor set* $\mathbf{C}$ *is a closed, uncountable set of measure zero.*

Proof The intersection of any collection of closed sets is closed. Therefore $\mathbf{C}$ is closed. Each closed set is measurable so that each C_k and $\mathbf{C}$ itself is measurable.

Now each C_k is the disjoint union of 2^k intervals, each of length $1/3^k$, so that by the finite additivity of Lebesgue measure,

$$m(C_k) = (2/3)^k.$$

By the monotonicity of measure, since $m(\mathbf{C}) \leq m(C_k) = (2/3)^k$, for all k, $m(\mathbf{C}) = 0$. It remains to show that $\mathbf{C}$ is uncountable. To do so we argue by contradiction. Suppose $\mathbf{C}$ is countable. Let $\{c_k\}_{k=1}^{\infty}$ be an enumeration of $\mathbf{C}$. One of the two disjoint Cantor intervals whose union is C_1 fails to contain the point c_1; denote it by F_1. One of the two disjoint Cantor intervals in C_2 whose union is F_1 fails to contain the point c_2; denote it by F_2. Continuing in this way, we construct a countable collection of sets $\{F_k\}_{k=1}^{\infty}$, which, for each k, possesses the following three properties: (i) F_k is closed and $F_{k+1} \subseteq F_k$; (ii) $F_k \subseteq C_k$; and (iii) $c_k \notin F_k$. From (i) and the Nested Set Theorem[12] we conclude that the intersection $\bigcap_{k=1}^{\infty} F_k$ is nonempty. Let the point x belong to this intersection. By property (ii),

$$\bigcap_{k=1}^{\infty} F_k \subseteq \bigcap_{k=1}^{\infty} C_k = \mathbf{C},$$

and therefore the point x belongs to $\mathbf{C}$. However, $\{c_k\}_{k=1}^{\infty}$ is an enumeration of $\mathbf{C}$ so that $x = c_n$ for some index n. Thus $c_n = x \in \bigcap_{k=1}^{\infty} F_k \subseteq F_n$. This contradicts property (iii). Hence $\mathbf{C}$ must be uncountable. $\qquad\square$

A real-valued function f that is defined on a set of real numbers is said to be **increasing** provided $f(u) \leq f(v)$ whenever $u \leq v$ and said to be **strictly increasing**, provided $f(u) < f(v)$ whenever $u < v$.

We now define the Cantor-Lebesgue function, a continuous, increasing function φ defined on $[0, 1]$ which has the remarkable property that, despite the fact that $\varphi(1) > \varphi(0)$, its derivative exists and is zero on a set of measure 1. For each k, let $\mathcal{O}_k$ be the union of the $2^k - 1$ intervals which have been removed during the first k stages of the Cantor deletion process. Thus $C_k = [0, 1] \sim \mathcal{O}_k$. Define $\mathcal{O} = \bigcup_{k=1}^{\infty} \mathcal{O}_k$. Then, by De Morgan's Identities, $\mathbf{C} = [0, 1] \sim \mathcal{O}$. We begin by defining φ on $\mathcal{O}$ and then we define it on $\mathbf{C}$.

---

[12]See page 19.

Fix a natural number k. Define φ on $\mathcal{O}_k$ to be the increasing function on $\mathcal{O}_k$ which is constant on each of its $2^k - 1$ open intervals and takes the $2^k - 1$ values

$$\{1/2^k, \; 2/2^k, \; 3/2^k, \; \ldots, \; [2^k - 1]/2^k\}.$$

Thus, on the single interval removed at the first stage of the deletion process, the prescription for φ is

$$\varphi(x) = 1/2 \text{ if } x \in (1/3, 2/3).$$

On the three intervals that are removed in the first two stages, the prescription for φ is

$$\varphi(x) = \begin{cases} 1/4 & \text{if } x \in (1/9, \; 2/9) \\ 2/4 & \text{if } x \in (3/9, \; 6/9) = (1/3, 2/3) \\ 3/4 & \text{if } x \in (7/9, \; 8/9) \end{cases}$$

We extend φ to all of $[0, 1]$ by defining it on $\mathbf{C}$ as follows:

$$\varphi(0) = 0 \text{ and } \varphi(x) = \sup \{\varphi(t) \mid t \in \mathcal{O} \cap [0, \; x)\} \text{ if } x \in \mathbf{C} \sim \{0\}.$$

Proposition 20 *The Cantor-Lebesgue function φ is an increasing continuous function that maps $[0, 1]$ onto $[0, 1]$. Its derivative exists on the open set $\mathcal{O}$, the complement in $[0, 1]$ of the Cantor set,*

$$\varphi' = 0 \text{ on } \mathcal{O} \text{ while } m(\mathcal{O}) = 1.$$

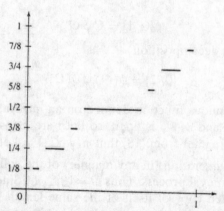

The graph of the Cantor-Lebesgue function on $\mathcal{O}_3 = [0, 1] \sim C_3$

Proof Since φ is increasing on $\mathcal{O}$, its extension above to $[0, 1]$ also is increasing. As for continuity, φ certainly is continuous at each point in $\mathcal{O}$ since for each such point belongs to an open interval on which it is constant. Now consider a point $x_0 \in \mathbf{C}$ with $x_0 \neq 0, 1$. Since the point x_0 belongs to $\mathbf{C}$ it is not a member of the $2^k - 1$ intervals removed in the first k stages of the removal process, whose union we denote by $\mathcal{O}_k$. Therefore, if k is sufficiently large, x_0 lies between two consecutive intervals in $\mathcal{O}_k$: choose a_k in the lower of these and b_k in the upper one. The function φ was defined to increase by $1/2^k$ across two consecutive intervals in $\mathcal{O}_k$. Therefore

$$a_k < x_0 < b_k \text{ and } \varphi(b_k) - \varphi(a_k) = 1/2^k.$$

Since k may be arbitrarily large, the function φ fails to have a jump discontinuity at x_0. For an increasing function, a jump discontinuity is the only possible type of discontinuity. Therefore φ is continuous at x_0. If x_0 is an endpoint of $[0, 1]$, a similar argument establishes continuity at x_0.

Since φ is constant on each of the intervals removed at any stage of the removal process, its derivative exists and equals 0 at each point in $\mathcal{O}$. Since $\mathbf{C}$ has measure zero, its complement in $[0, 1]$, $\mathcal{O}$, has measure 1. Finally, since $\varphi(0) = 0$, $\varphi(1) = 1$ and φ is increasing and continuous, we infer from the Intermediate Value Theorem that φ maps $[0, 1]$ onto $[0, 1]$.   □

Proposition 21 *Let φ be the Cantor-Lebesgue function and define the function ψ on $[0, 1]$ by*

$$\psi(x) = \varphi(x) + x \text{ for all } x \in [0, 1].$$

Then ψ is a strictly increasing continuous function that maps $[0, 1]$ onto $[0, 2]$,

   (i) maps the Cantor set C onto a measurable set of positive measure and

   (ii) maps a measurable set, a subset of the Cantor set, onto a nonmeasurable set.

Proof The function ψ is continuous since it is the sum of two continuous functions and is strictly increasing since it is the sum of an increasing and a strictly increasing function. Moreover, since $\psi(0) = 0$ and $\psi(1) = 2$, $\psi([0, 1]) = [0, 2]$. For $\mathcal{O} = [0, 1] \sim C$, we have the disjoint decomposition

$$[0, 1] = \mathbf{C} \cup \mathcal{O}$$

which ψ lifts to the disjoint decomposition

$$[0, 2] = \psi(\mathcal{O}) \cup \psi(\mathbf{C}). \tag{18}$$

A strictly increasing continuous function defined on an interval has a continuous inverse. Therefore $\psi(C)$ is closed and $\psi(\mathcal{O})$ is open, so both are measurable. We will show that $m(\psi(\mathcal{O})) = 1$ and therefore infer from (18) that $m(\psi(\mathbf{C})) = 1$ and thereby prove (i).

Let $\{I_k\}_{k=1}^{\infty}$ be an enumeration (in any manner) of the collection of intervals that are removed in the Cantor removal process. Thus $\mathcal{O} = \bigcup_{k=1}^{\infty} I_k$. Since φ is constant on each I_k, ψ maps I_k onto a translated copy of itself of the same length. Since ψ is one-to-one, the collection $\{\psi(I_k)\}_{k=1}^{\infty}$ is disjoint. By the countable additivity of measure,

$$m(\psi(\mathcal{O})) = \sum_{k=1}^{\infty} \ell(\psi(I_k)) = \sum_{k=1}^{\infty} \ell(I_k) = m(\mathcal{O}).$$

But $m(\mathbf{C}) = 0$ so that $m(\mathcal{O}) = 1$. Therefore $m(\psi(\mathcal{O})) = 1$ and hence, by (18), $m(\psi(\mathbf{C})) = 1$. We have established (i).

To verify (ii) we note that Vitali's Theorem tells us that $\psi(\mathbf{C})$ contains a set W, which is nonmeasurable. The set $\psi^{-1}(W)$ is measurable and has measure zero since it is a subset of the Cantor set. The set $\psi^{-1}(W)$ is a measurable subset of the Cantor set, which is mapped by ψ onto a nonmeasurable set.   □

Proposition 22 *There is a measurable set, a subset of the Cantor set, that is not a Borel set.*

Proof The strictly increasing continuous function ψ defined on $[0, 1]$ that is described in the preceding proposition maps a measurable set A onto a nonmeasurable set. A strictly increasing continuous function defined on an interval maps Borel sets onto Borel sets (see Problem 47). Therefore the set A is not Borel since otherwise its image under ψ would be Borel and therefore would be measurable. $\qquad\square$

PROBLEMS

34. Show that there is a continuous, strictly increasing function on the interval $[0, 1]$ that maps a set of positive measure onto a set of measure zero.

35. Let f be an increasing function on the open interval I. For $x_0 \in I$ show that f is continuous at x_0 if and only if there are sequences $\{a_n\}$ and $\{b_n\}$ in I such that for each n, $a_n < x_0 < b_n$, and $\lim_{n \to \infty}[f(b_n) - f(a_n)] = 0$.

36. Show that if f is any increasing function on $[0, 1]$ that agrees with the Cantor-Lebesgue function φ on the complement of the Cantor set, then $f = \varphi$ on all of $[0, 1]$.

37. Let f be a continuous function defined on E. Is it true that $f^{-1}(A)$ is always measurable if A is measurable?

38. Let the function $f : [a, b] \to \mathbf{R}$ be Lipschitz, that is, there is a constant $c \geq 0$ such that for all $u, v \in [a, b]$, $|f(u) - f(v)| \leq c|u - v|$. Show that f maps a set of measure zero onto a set of measure zero. Show that f maps an F_σ set onto an F_σ set. Conclude that f maps a measurable set to a measurable set.

39. Let F be the subset of $[0, 1]$ constructed in the same manner as the Cantor set except that each of the intervals removed at the nth deletion stage has length $\alpha 3^{-n}$ with $0 < \alpha < 1$. Show that F is a closed set, $[0, 1] \sim F$ dense in $[0, 1]$, and $m(F) = 1 - \alpha$. Such a set F is called a generalized Cantor set.

40. Show that there is an open set of real numbers that, contrary to intuition, has a boundary of positive measure. (Hint: Consider the complement of the generalized Cantor set of the preceding problem.)

41. A nonempty subset X of $\mathbf{R}$ is called perfect provided it is closed and each neighborhood of any point in X contains infinitely many points of X. Show that the Cantor set is perfect. (Hint: The endpoints of all of the subintervals occurring in the Cantor construction belong to **C**.)

42. Prove that every perfect subset X of $\mathbf{R}$ is uncountable. (Hint: If X is countable, construct a descending sequence of bounded, closed subsets of X whose intersection is empty.)

43. Use the preceding two problems to provide another proof of the uncountability of the Cantor set.

44. A subset A of $\mathbf{R}$ is said to be **nowhere dense** in $\mathbf{R}$ provided that for every open set $\mathcal{O}$ has an open subset that is disjoint from A. Show that the Cantor set is nowhere dense in $\mathbf{R}$.

45. Show that a strictly increasing function that is defined on an interval has a continuous inverse.

46. Let f be a continuous function and B be a Borel set. Show that $f^{-1}(B)$ is a Borel set. (Hint: The collection of sets E for which $f^{-1}(E)$ is Borel is a σ-algebra containing the open sets.)

47. Use the preceding two problems to show that a continuous strictly increasing function that is defined on an interval maps Borel sets to Borel sets.

CHAPTER 3

Lebesgue Measurable Functions

Contents

We devote this chapter to the study of measurable functions in order to lay the foundation for the study of the Lebesgue integral, which we begin in the next chapter. All continuous functions on a measurable domain are measurable, as are all monotone and step functions on a closed, bounded interval. Linear combinations of measurable functions are measurable. The pointwise limit of a sequence of measurable functions is measurable. We establish results regarding the approximation of measurable functions by simple functions and by continuous functions.

3.1 SUMS, PRODUCTS, AND COMPOSITIONS

All the functions considered in this chapter take values in the extended real numbers, that is, the set $\mathbf{R} \cup \{\pm\infty\}$. Recall that a property is said to hold **almost everywhere** (abbreviated a.e.) on a measurable set E provided it holds on $E \sim E_0$, where E_0 is a subset of E for which $m(E_0) = 0$.

Given two functions h and g defined on E, for notational brevity we often write "$h \leq g$ on E" to mean that $h(x) \leq g(x)$ for all $x \in E$. We say that a sequence of functions $\{f_n\}$ on E is increasing provided $f_n \leq f_{n+1}$ on E for each index n.

Proposition 1 *Let the function f have a measurable domain E. Then the following statements are equivalent:*

(i) *For each real number c, the set $\{x \in E \mid f(x) > c\}$ is measurable.*

(ii) *For each real number c, the set $\{x \in E \mid f(x) \geq c\}$ is measurable.*

(iii) *For each real number c, the set $\{x \in E \mid f(x) < c\}$ is measurable.*

(iv) *For each real number c, the set $\{x \in E \mid f(x) \leq c\}$ is measurable.*

Each of these properties implies that for each extended real number c,

$$\text{the set } \{x \in E \mid f(x) = c\} \text{ is measurable.}$$

Proof Since the sets in (i) and (iv) are complementary in E, as are the sets in (ii) and (iii), and the complement in E of a measurable subset of E is measurable, (i) and (iv) are equivalent, as are (ii) and (iii).

Now (i) implies (ii), since

$$\{x\in E \mid f(x)\geq c\} = \bigcap_{k=1}^{\infty}\{x\in E \mid f(x) > c - 1/k\},$$

and the intersection of a countable collection of measurable sets is measurable. Similarly, (ii) implies (i), since

$$\{x\in E \mid f(x) > c\} = \bigcup_{k=1}^{\infty}\{x\in E \mid f(x) \geq c + 1/k\},$$

and the union of a countable collection of measurable sets is measurable.

Thus statements (i)–(iv) are equivalent. Now assume one, and hence all, of them hold. If c is a real number, $\{x \in E \mid f(x) = c\} = \{x \in E \mid f(x)) \geq c\} \cap \{x \in E \mid f(x) \leq c\}$, so $f^{-1}(c)$ is measurable since it is the intersection of two measurable sets. On the other hand, if c is infinite, say $c = \infty$,

$$\{x\in E \mid f(x) = \infty\} = \bigcap_{k=1}^{\infty}\{x\in E \mid f(x) > k\}$$

so $f^{-1}(\infty)$ is measurable since it is the intersection of a countable collection of measurable sets. $\qquad\square$

Definition *An extended real-valued function f defined on E is said to be* **Lebesgue measurable**, *or simply* **measurable**, *provided its domain E is measurable and it satisfies one of the four statements of Proposition 1.*

Proposition 2 *Let the function f be defined on a measurable set E. Then f is measurable if and only if for each open set $\mathcal{O}$, the inverse image of $\mathcal{O}$ under f, $f^{-1}(\mathcal{O}) = \{x \in E \mid f(x) \in \mathcal{O}\}$, is measurable.*

Proof If the inverse image of each open set is measurable, then since each interval (c, ∞) is open, the function f is measurable. Conversely, suppose f is measurable. Let $\mathcal{O}$ be open. Then[1] we can express $\mathcal{O}$ as the union of a countable collection of open, bounded intervals $\{I_k\}_{k=1}^{\infty}$ where each I_k may be expressed as $B_k \cap A_k$, where $B_k = (-\infty, b_k)$ and $A_k = (a_k, \infty)$. Since f is a measurable function, each $f^{-1}(B_k)$ and $f^{-1}(A_k)$ are measurable sets. On the other hand, the measurable sets are a σ-algebra and therefore $f^{-1}(\mathcal{O})$ is measurable since

$$f^{-1}(\mathcal{O}) = f^{-1}\left[\bigcup_{k=1}^{\infty} B_k \cap A_k\right] = \bigcup_{k=1}^{\infty} f^{-1}(B_k) \cap f^{-1}(A_k).$$

$\qquad\square$

The following proposition tells us that the most familiar functions from elementary analysis, the continuous functions, are measurable.

Proposition 3 *A real-valued function that is continuous on its measurable domain is measurable.*

---

[1] See page 17.

Proof Let the function f be continuous on the measurable set E. Let $\mathcal{O}$ be open. Since f is continuous, $f^{-1}(\mathcal{O}) = E \cap \mathcal{U}$, where $\mathcal{U}$ is open.[2] Thus $f^{-1}(\mathcal{O})$, being the intersection of two measurable sets, is measurable. It follows from the preceding proposition that f is measurable. □

A real-valued function that is either increasing or decreasing is said to be monotone. We leave the proof of the next proposition as an exercise (see Problem 24).

Proposition 4 *A monotone function that is defined on an interval is measurable.*

Proposition 5 *Let f be an extended real-valued function on E.*

(i) *If f is measurable on E and $f = g$ a.e. on E, then g is measurable on E.*

(ii) *For a measurable subset D of E, f is measurable on E if and only if the restrictions of f to D and $E \sim D$ are measurable.*

Proof First assume f is measurable. Define $A = \{x \in E \mid f(x) \neq g(x)\}$. Observe that

$$\{x \in E \mid g(x) > c\} = \{x \in A \mid g(x) > c\} \cup \left[\{x \in E \mid f(x) > c\} \cap [E \sim A]\right]$$

Since $f = g$ a.e. on E, $m(A) = 0$. Thus $\{x \in A \mid g(x) > c\}$ is measurable since it is a subset of a set of measure zero. The set $\{x \in E \mid f(x) > c\}$ is measurable since f is measurable on E. Since both E and A are measurable and the measurable sets are an algebra, the set $\{x \in E \mid g(x) > c\}$ is measurable. To verify (ii), just observe that for any c,

$$\{x \in E \mid f(x) > c\} = \{x \in D \mid f(x) > c\} \cup \{x \in E \sim D \mid f(x) > c\}$$

and once more use the fact that the measurable sets are an algebra. □

The sum $f + g$ of two measurable extended real-valued functions f and g is not properly defined at points at which f and g take infinite values of opposite sign. Assume f and g are finite a.e. on E. Define E_0 to be the set of points in E at which both f and g are finite. If the restriction of $f + g$ to E_0 is measurable, then, by the preceding proposition, any extension of $f + g$, as an extended real-valued function, to all of E also is measurable. This is the sense in which we consider it unambiguous to state that the sum of two measurable functions that are finite a.e. is measurable. Similar remarks apply to products. The following proposition tells us that standard algebraic operations performed on measurable functions that are finite a.e. again lead to measurable functions

Theorem 6 *Let f and g be measurable functions on E that are finite a.e. on E.*

(Linearity) *For any α and β,*

$$\alpha f + \beta g \text{ is measurable on } E.$$

(Products)

$$fg \text{ is measurable on } E.$$

---

[2]See page 25.

Proof By the above remarks, we may assume f and g are finite on all of E. If $\alpha = 0$, then the function αf also is measurable. If $\alpha \neq 0$, observe that for a number c,

$$\{x \in E \mid \alpha f(x) > c\} = \{x \in E \mid f(x) > c/\alpha\} \text{ if } \alpha > 0$$

and

$$\{x \in E \mid \alpha f(x) > c\} = \{x \in E \mid f(x) < c/\alpha\} \text{ if } \alpha < 0.$$

Thus the measurability of f implies the measurability of αf. Therefore to establish linearity it suffices to consider the case that $\alpha = \beta = 1$.

For $x \in E$, if $f(x) + g(x) < c$, then $f(x) < c - g(x)$ and so, by the density of the set of rational numbers $\mathbf{Q}$ in $\mathbf{R}$, there is a rational number q for which

$$f(x) < q < c - g(x).$$

Hence

$$\{x \in E \mid f(x) + g(x) < c\} = \bigcup_{q \in \mathbf{Q}} \{x \in E \mid g(x) < c - q\} \cap \{x \in E \mid f(x) < q\}.$$

The rational numbers are countable. Thus $\{x \in E \mid f(x) + g(x) < c\}$ is measurable, since it is the union of a countable collection of measurable sets. Hence $f + g$ is measurable.

To prove that the product of measurable functions is measurable, first observe that

$$fg = \frac{1}{2}[(f + g)^2 - f^2 - g^2].$$

Thus, since we have established linearity, to show that the product of two measurable functions is measurable it suffices to show that the square of a measurable function is measurable. For $c \geq 0$,

$$\{x \in E \mid f^2(x) > c\} = \{x \in E \mid f(x) > \sqrt{c}\} \cup \{x \in E \mid f(x) < -\sqrt{c}\}$$

while for $c < 0$,

$$\{x \in E \mid f^2(x) > c\} = E.$$

Thus f^2 is measurable. $\qquad\square$

Many of the properties of functions considered in elementary analysis, including continuity and differentiability, are preserved under the operation of composition of functions. However, the composition of measurable functions may not be measurable.

Example There are two measurable real-valued functions, each defined on all of $\mathbf{R}$, whose composition fails to be measurable. By Lemma 21 of Chapter 2, there is a continuous, strictly increasing function ψ defined on $[0, 1]$ and a measurable subset A of $[0, 1]$ for which $\psi(A)$ is nonmeasurable. Extend ψ to a continuous, strictly increasing function that maps $\mathbf{R}$ onto $\mathbf{R}$. The function ψ^{-1} is continuous and therefore is measurable. On the other hand, A is a measurable set and so its characteristic function χ_A is a measurable function. We claim that the composition $f = \chi_A \circ \psi^{-1}$ is not measurable. Indeed, if I is any open interval containing 1 but not 0, then its inverse image under f is the nonmeasurable set $\psi(A)$.

Despite the setback imposed by this example, there is the following useful proposition regarding the preservation of measurability under composition (also see Problem 11).

Proposition 7 *Let g be a measurable real-valued function defined on E and f a continuous real-valued function defined on all of $\mathbf{R}$. Then the composition $f \circ g$ is a measurable function on E.*

Proof According to Proposition 2, a function is measurable if and only if the inverse image of each open set is measurable. Let $\mathcal{O}$ be open. Then

$$(f \circ g)^{-1}(\mathcal{O}) = g^{-1}(f^{-1}(\mathcal{O})).$$

Since f is continuous and defined on an open set, the set $\mathcal{U} = f^{-1}(\mathcal{O})$ is open.[3] We infer from the measurability of the function g that $g^{-1}(\mathcal{U})$ is measurable. Thus the inverse image $(f \circ g)^{-1}(\mathcal{O})$ is measurable and so the composite function $f \circ g$ is measurable.   □

An immediate important consequence of the above composition result is that if f is measurable with domain E, then $|f|$ is measurable, and indeed

$|f|^p$ is measurable with the same domain E for each $p > 0$.

For a finite family $\{f_k\}_{k=1}^n$ of functions with common domain E, the function

$$\max\{f_1, \ldots, f_n\}$$

is defined on E by

$$\max\{f_1, \ldots, f_n\}(x) = \max\{f_1(x), \ldots, f_n(x)\} \text{ for } x \in E.$$

The function $\min\{f_1, \ldots, f_n\}$ is defined the same way.

Proposition 8 *For a finite family $\{f_k\}_{k=1}^n$ of measurable functions with common domain E, the functions $\max\{f_1, \ldots, f_n\}$ and $\min\{f_1, \ldots, f_n\}$ also are measurable.*

Proof For any c, we have

$$\{x \in E \mid \max\{f_1, \ldots, f_n\}(x) > c\} = \bigcup_{k=1}^n \{x \in E \mid f_k(x) > c\}$$

so this set is measurable since it is the finite union of measurable sets. Thus the function $\max\{f_1, \ldots, f_n\}$ is measurable. A similar argument shows that the function $\min\{f_1, \ldots, f_n\}$ also is measurable.   □

---

[3] See page 25.

For a function f defined on E, we have the associated functions $|f|$, f^+, and f^- defined on E by

$$|f|(x) = \max\{f(x), -f(x)\}, \quad f^+(x) = \max\{f(x), 0\}, \quad f^-(x) = \max\{-f(x), 0\}.$$

If f is measurable on E, then, by the preceding proposition, so are the functions $|f|$, f^+, and f^-. This will be important when we study integration since the expression of f as the difference of two nonnegative functions,

$$f = f^+ - f^- \text{ on } E,$$

plays an important part in defining the Lebesgue integral.

PROBLEMS

1. Suppose f and g are continuous functions on $[a, b]$. Show that if $f = g$ a.e. on $[a, b]$, then, in fact, $f = g$ on $[a, b]$. Is a similar assertion true if $[a, b]$ is replaced by a general measurable set E?

2. Let D and E be measurable sets and f a function with domain $D \cup E$. We proved that f is measurable on $D \cup E$ if and only if its restrictions to D and E are measurable. Is the same true if "measurable" is replaced by "continuous"?

3. Suppose a function f has a measurable domain and is continuous except at a finite number of points. Is f necessarily measurable?

4. Suppose f is a real-valued function on $\mathbf{R}$ such that $f^{-1}(c)$ is measurable for each number c. Is f necessarily measurable?

5. Suppose the function f is defined on a measurable set E and has the property that $\{x \in E \mid f(x) > c\}$ is measurable for each rational number c. Is f necessarily measurable?

6. Let f be a function with measurable domain D. Show that f is measurable if and only if the function g defined on $\mathbf{R}$ by $g(x) = f(x)$ for $x \in D$ and $g(x) = 0$ for $x \notin D$ is measurable.

7. Let the function f be defined on a measurable set E. Show that f is measurable if and only if for each Borel set A, $f^{-1}(A)$ is measurable. (Hint: The collection of sets A that have the property that $f^{-1}(A)$ is measurable is a σ-algebra.)

8. (Borel measurability) A function f is said to be **Borel measurable** provided its domain E is a Borel set and for each c, the set $\{x \in E \mid f(x) > c\}$ is a Borel set. Verify that Proposition 1 and Theorem 6 remain valid if we replace "(Lebesgue) measurable set" by "'Borel set." Show that: (i) every Borel measurable function is Lebesgue measurable; (ii) if f is Borel measurable and B is a Borel set, then $f^{-1}(B)$ is a Borel set; (iii) if f and g are Borel measurable, so is $f \circ g$; and (iv) if f is Borel measurable and g is Lebesgue measurable, then $f \circ g$ is Lebesgue measurable.

9. Let $\{f_n\}$ be a sequence of measurable functions defined on a measurable set E. Define E_0 to be the set of points x in E at which $\{f_n(x)\}$ converges. Is the set E_0 measurable?

10. Suppose f and g are real-valued functions defined on all of $\mathbf{R}$, f is measurable, and g is continuous. Is the composition $f \circ g$ necessarily measurable?

11. Let f be a measurable function and g be a one-to-one function from $\mathbf{R}$ onto $\mathbf{R}$ which has a Lipschitz inverse. Show that the composition $f \circ g$ is measurable. (Hint: Examine Problem 38 in Chapter 2.)

3.2 SEQUENTIAL POINTWISE LIMITS AND SIMPLE APPROXIMATION

For a sequence $\{f_n\}$ of functions with common domain E and a function f on E, there are several distinct ways in which it is necessary to consider what it means to state that

"the sequence $\{f_n\}$ converges to f."

In this chapter we consider the concepts of pointwise convergence and uniform convergence, which are familiar from elementary analysis. In later chapters we consider many other modes of convergence for a sequence of functions.

Definition *For a sequence $\{f_n\}$ of functions with common domain E, a function f on E and a subset A of E, we say that*

(i) *The sequence $\{f_n\}$ converges to f pointwise on A provided*

$$\lim_{n \to \infty} f_n(x) = f(x) \text{ for all } x \in A.$$

(ii) *The sequence $\{f_n\}$ converges to f pointwise a.e. on A provided it converges to f pointwise on $A \sim B$, where $m(B) = 0$.*

(iii) *The sequence $\{f_n\}$ converges to f uniformly on A provided for each $\epsilon > 0$, there is an index N for which*

$$|f - f_n| < \epsilon \text{ on } A \text{ for all } n \geq N.$$

When considering sequences of functions $\{f_n\}$ and their convergence to a function f, we often implicitly assume that all of the functions have a common domain. We write "$\{f_n\} \to f$ pointwise on A" to indicate the sequence $\{f_n\}$ converges to f pointwise on A and use similar notation for uniform convergence.

The pointwise limit of continuous functions may not be continuous. The pointwise limit of Riemann integrable functions may not be Riemann integrable. The following proposition is the first indication that the measureable functions have much better stability properties.

Proposition 9 *Let $\{f_n\}$ be a sequence of measurable functions on E that converges pointwise a.e. on E to the function f. Then f is measurable.*

Proof Let E_0 be a subset of E for which $m(E_0) = 0$ and $\{f_n\}$ converges to f pointwise on $E \sim E_0$. Since $m(E_0) = 0$, it follows from Proposition 5 that f is measurable if and only if its restriction to $E \sim E_0$ is measurable. Therefore, by possibly replacing E by $E \sim E_0$, we may assume the sequence converges pointwise on all of E.

Fix a number c. We must show that $\{x \in E \mid f(x) < c\}$ is measurable. Observe that for a point $x \in E$, since $\lim_{n \to \infty} f_n(x) = f(x)$,

$$f(x) < c$$

if and only if

there are natural numbers n and k for which $f_j(x) < c - 1/n$ for all $j \geq k$.

But for any natural numbers n and j, since the function f_j is measurable, the set $\{x \in E \mid f_j(x) < c - 1/n\}$ is measurable. Therefore, for any k, the intersection of the countably collection of measureable sets

$$\bigcap_{j=k}^{\infty} \{x \in E \mid f_j(x) < c - 1/n\}$$

also is measurable. Consequently, since the union of a countable collection of measurable sets is measurable,

$$\{x \in E \mid f(x) < c\} = \bigcup_{1 \le k, n < \infty} \left[\bigcap_{j=k}^{\infty} \{x \in E \mid f_j(x) < c - 1/n\} \right]$$

is measurable.   □

If A is any set, the **characteristic function** of A, χ_A, is the function on **R** defined by

$$\chi_A(x) = \begin{cases} 1 & \text{if } x \in A \\ 0 & \text{if } x \notin A. \end{cases}$$

It is clear that the function χ_A is measurable if and only if the set A is measurable. Thus the existence of a nonmeasurable set implies the existence of a nonmeasurable function. Linear combinations of characteristic functions of measurable sets play a role in Lebesgue integration similar to that played by step functions in Riemann integration, and so we name these functions.

Definition   *A real-valued function φ defined on a measurable set E is called* **simple** *provided it is measurable and takes only a finite number of values.*

We emphasize that a simple function only takes real values. Linear combinations and products of simple functions are simple since each of them takes on only a finite number of values. If φ is simple, has domain E and takes the distinct values $c_1, \ldots, c_n$, then

$$\varphi = \sum_{k=1}^{n} c_k \cdot \chi_{E_k} \text{ on } E, \text{ where } E_k = \{x \in E \mid \varphi(x) = c_k\}.$$

This particular expression of φ as a linear combination of characteristic functions is called the **canonical representation of the simple function** φ.

The Simple Approximation Lemma   *Let f be a measurable real-valued function on E. Assume f is bounded on E, that is, there is an $M \ge 0$ for which $|f| \le M$ on E. Then for each $\epsilon > 0$, there are simple functions φ_ϵ and ψ_ϵ defined on E which have the following approximation properties:*

$$\varphi_\epsilon \le f \le \psi_\epsilon \text{ and } 0 \le \psi_\epsilon - \varphi_\epsilon < \epsilon \text{ on } E.$$

Proof Let (c, d) be an open, bounded interval that contains the image of E, $f(E)$, and

$$c = y_0 < y_1 < \ldots < y_{n-1} < y_n = d$$

be a partition of the closed, bounded interval $[c, d]$ such that $y_k - y_{k-1} < \epsilon$ for $1 \le k \le n$. Defne

$$I_k = [y_{k-1}, y_k) \text{ and } E_k = f^{-1}(I_k) \text{ for } 1 \le k \le n.$$

Since each I_k is an interval and the function f is measurable, each set E_k is measurable. Define the simple functions φ_ϵ and ψ_ϵ on E by

$$\varphi_\epsilon = \sum_{k=1}^{n} y_{k-1} \cdot \chi_{E_k} \text{ and } \psi_\epsilon = \sum_{k=1}^{n} y_k \cdot \chi_{E_k}.$$

Let x belong to E. Since $f(E) \subseteq (c, d)$, there is a unique k, $1 \le k \le n$, for which $y_{k-1} \le f(x) < y_k$ and therefore

$$\varphi_\epsilon(x) = y_{k-1} \le f(x) < y_k = \psi_\epsilon(x).$$

But $y_k - y_{k-1} < \epsilon$, and therefore φ_ϵ and ψ_ϵ have the required approximation properties. $\square$

To the several characterizations of measurable functions that we already established, we add the following one.

The Simple Approximation Theorem *An extended real-valued function f on a measurable set E is measurable if and only if there is a sequence $\{\varphi_n\}$ of simple functions on E which converges pointwise on E to f and has the property that*

$$|\varphi_n| \le |f| \text{ on } E \text{ for all } n.$$

If f is nonnegative, we may choose $\{\varphi_n\}$ to be increasing.

Proof Since each simple function is measurable, Proposition 9 tells us that a function is measurable if it is the pointwise limit of a sequence of simple functions. It remains to prove the converse.

Assume f is measurable. We also assume $f \ge 0$ on E. The general case follows by expressing f as the difference of nonnegative measurable functions (see Problem 23). Let n be a natural number. Define $E_n = \{x \in E \mid f(x) \le n.\}$ Then E_n is a measurable set and the restriction of f to E_n is a nonnegative bounded measurable function. By the Simple Approximation Lemma, applied to the restriction of f to E_n and with the choice of $\epsilon = 1/n$, we may select simple functions φ_n and ψ_n defined on E_n which have the following approximation properties:

$$0 \le \varphi_n \le f \le \psi_n \text{ on } E_n \text{ and } 0 \le \psi_n - \varphi_n < 1/n \text{ on } E_n.$$

Observe that

$$0 \le \varphi_n \le f \text{ and } 0 \le f - \varphi_n \le \psi_n - \varphi_n < 1/n \text{ on } E_n. \tag{1}$$

Extend φ_n to all of E by setting $\varphi_n(x) = n$ if $f(x) > n$. The function φ_n is a simple function defined on E and $0 \le \varphi_n \le f$ on E. We claim that the sequence $\{\psi_n\}$ converges to f pointwise on E. Let x belong to E.

Case 1: Assume $f(x)$ is finite. Choose a natural number N for which $f(x) < N$. Then

$$0 \le f(x) - \varphi_n(x) < 1/n \text{ for } n \ge N,$$

and therefore $\lim_{n \to \infty} \psi_n(x) = f(x)$.

Case 2: Assume $f(x) = \infty$. Then $\varphi_n(x) = n$ for all n, so that $\lim_{n \to \infty} \varphi_n(x) = f(x)$.

By replacing each φ_n with $\max\{\varphi_1, \ldots, \varphi_n\}$ we have $\{\varphi_n\}$ increasing. □

PROBLEMS

12. Let f be a bounded measurable function on E. Show that there are sequences of simple functions on E, $\{\varphi_n\}$ and $\{\psi_n\}$, such that $\{\varphi_n\}$ is increasing and $\{\psi_n\}$ is decreasing and each of these sequences converges to f uniformly on E.

13. A real-valued measurable function is said to be *semisimple* provided it takes only a countable number of values. Let f be any measurable function on E. Show that there is a sequence of semisimple functions $\{f_n\}$ on E that converges to f uniformly on E.

14. Let f be a measurable function on E that is finite a.e. on E and $m(E) < \infty$. For each $\epsilon > 0$, show that there is a measurable set F contained in E such that f is bounded on F and $m(E \sim F) < \epsilon$.

15. Let f be a measurable function on E that is finite a.e. on E and $m(E) < \infty$. Show that for each $\epsilon > 0$, there is a measurable set F contained in E and a sequence $\{\varphi_n\}$ of simple functions on E such that $\{\varphi_n\} \to f$ uniformly on F and $m(E \sim F) < \epsilon$. (Hint: See the preceding problem.)

16. Let I be a closed, bounded interval and E a measurable subset of I. Let $\epsilon > 0$. Show that there is a step function h on I and a measurable subset F of I for which

$$h = \chi_E \text{ on } F \text{ and } m(I \sim F) < \epsilon.$$

(Hint: Use Theorem 12 of Chapter 2.)

17. Let I be a closed, bounded interval and ψ a simple function defined on I. Let $\epsilon > 0$. Show that there is a step function h on I and a measurable subset F of I for which

$$h = \psi \text{ on } F \text{ and } m(I \sim F) < \epsilon.$$

(Hint: Use the fact that a simple function is a linear combination of characteristic functions and the preceding problem.)

18. Let I be a closed, bounded interval and f a bounded measurable function defined on I. Let $\epsilon > 0$. Show that there is a step function h on I and a measurable subset F of I for which

$$|h - f| < \epsilon \text{ on } F \text{ and } m(I \sim F) < \epsilon.$$

19. Show that the sum and product of two simple functions are simple as are the max and the min.

20. Let A and B be any sets. Show that

$$\chi_{A \cap B} = \chi_A \cdot \chi_B$$
$$\chi_{A \cup B} = \chi_A + \chi_B - \chi_A \cdot \chi_B$$
$$\chi_{A^C} = 1 - \chi_A.$$

21. For a sequence $\{f_n\}$ of measurable functions with common domain E, show that each of the following functions is measurable:

$$\inf \{f_n\}, \sup \{f_n\}, \liminf \{f_n\} \text{ and } \limsup \{f_n\}.$$

22. (Dini's Theorem) Let $\{f_n\}$ be an increasing sequence of continuous functions on $[a, b]$ which converges pointwise on $[a, b]$ to the continuous function f on $[a, b]$. Show that the convergence is uniform on $[a, b]$. (Hint: Let $\epsilon > 0$. For each natural number n, define $E_n = \{x \in [a, b] \mid f(x) - f_n(x) < \epsilon\}$. (Show that $\{E_n\}$ is an open cover of $[a, b]$ and use the Heine-Borel Theorem.)

23. Express a measurable function as the difference of nonnegative measurable functions and thereby prove the general Simple Approximation Theorem based on the special case of a nonnegative measurable function.

24. Let I be an interval and $f: I \to \mathbf{R}$ be increasing. Show that f is measurable by first showing that, for each natural number n, the strictly increasing function $x \mapsto f(x) + x/n$ is measurable, and then taking pointwise limits.

3.3   LITTLEWOOD'S THREE PRINCIPLES, EGOROFF'S THEOREM, AND LUSIN'S THEOREM

Speaking of the theory of functions of a real variable, J. E. Littlewood says,[4] "The extent of knowledge required is nothing like so great as is sometimes supposed. There are three principles, roughly expressible in the following terms: Every [measurable] set is nearly a finite union of intervals; every [measurable] function is nearly continuous; every pointwise convergent sequence of [measurable] functions is nearly uniformly convergent. Most of the results of [the theory] are fairly intuitive applications of these ideas, and the student armed with them should be equal to most occasions when real variable theory is called for. If one of the principles would be the obvious means to settle the problem if it were 'quite' true, it is natural to ask if the 'nearly' is near enough, and for a problem that is actually solvable it generally is."

Theorem 12 of Chapter 2 is one precise formulation of Littlewood's first principle: It tells us that given a measurable set E of finite measure, then for each $\epsilon > 0$, there is a finite disjoint collection of open intervals whose union $\mathcal{U}$ is "nearly equal to" E in the sense that $m(E \sim \mathcal{U}) + m(\mathcal{U} \sim E) < \epsilon$.

A precise realization of the last of Littlewood's principle is the following surprising theorem.

Egoroff's Theorem   *Assume E has finite measure. Let $\{f_n\}$ be a sequence of measurable functions on E that converges pointwise on E to the real-valued function f. Then for each $\epsilon > 0$, there is a closed set F contained in E for which*

$$\{f_n\} \to f \text{ uniformly on } F \text{ and } m(E \sim F) < \epsilon.$$

---

[4]Littlewood [Lit41], page 23.

To prove Egoroff's Theorem it is convenient to first establish the following lemma.

Lemma 10 *Under the assumptions of Egoroff's Theorem, for each $\eta > 0$ and $\delta > 0$, there is a measurable subset A of E and an index N for which*

$$|f_n - f| < \eta \text{ on } A \text{ for all } n \geq N \text{ and } m(E \sim A) < \delta.$$

Proof For each k, the function $|f - f_k|$ is properly defined, since f is real-valued, and it is measurable, so that the set $\{x \in E \,|\, |f(x) - f_k(x)| < \eta\}$ is measurable. The intersection of a countable collection of measurable sets is measurable. Therefore

$$E_n = \{x \in E \,|\, |f(x) - f_k(x)| < \eta \text{ for all } k \geq n\}$$

is a measurable set. Then $\{E_n\}_{n=1}^{\infty}$ is an ascending collection of measurable sets, and $E = \bigcup_{n=1}^{\infty} E_n$, since $\{f_n\}$ converges pointwise to f on E. We infer from the continuity of measure that

$$m(E) = \lim_{n \to \infty} m(E_n).$$

Since $m(E) < \infty$, we may choose an index N for which $m(E_N) > m(E) - \epsilon$. Define $A = E_n$ and observe that, by the excision property of measure, $m(E \sim A) = m(E) - m(E_N) < \epsilon$. $\square$

Proof of Egoroff's Theorem For each natural number n, let A_n be a measurable subset of E and $N(n)$ an index which satisfy the conclusion of the preceding lemma with $\delta = \epsilon/2^{n+1}$ and $\eta = 1/n$, that is,

$$m(E \sim A_n) < \epsilon/2^{n+1} \tag{2}$$

and

$$|f_k - f| < 1/n \text{ on } A_n \text{ for all } k \geq N(n). \tag{3}$$

Define

$$A = \bigcap_{n=1}^{\infty} A_n.$$

By De Morgan's Identities, the countably subadditivity of measure and (2),

$$m(E \sim A) = m\left(\bigcup_{n=1}^{\infty} [E \sim A_n]\right) \leq \sum_{n=1}^{\infty} m(E \sim A_n) < \sum_{n=1}^{\infty} \epsilon/2^{n+1} = \epsilon/2.$$

We claim that $\{f_n\}$ converges to f uniformly on A. Indeed, let $\epsilon > 0$. Choose an index n_0 such that $1/n_0 < \epsilon$. Then, by (3),

$$|f_k - f| < 1/n_0 \text{ on } A_{n_0} \text{ for } k \geq N(n_0).$$

However, $A \subseteq A_{n_0}$ and $1/n_0 < \epsilon$ and therefore

$$|f_k - f| < \epsilon \text{ on } A \text{ for } k \geq N(n_0).$$

Thus $\{f_n\}$ converges to f uniformly on A and $m(E \sim A) < \epsilon/2$.

Finally, by Theorem 11 of Chapter 2, we may choose a closed set F contained in A for which $m(A \sim F) < \epsilon/2$. Thus $m(E \sim F) < \epsilon$ and $\{f_n\} \to f$ uniformly on F. $\square$

It is clear that Egoroff's Theorem also holds if the convergence is pointwise a.e. and the limit function is finite a.e.

We now present a precise version of Littlewood's second principle in the case the measurable function is simple and then use this special case to prove the general case of the principle, Lusin's Theorem.

Proposition 11 *Let f be a simple function defined on E. Then for each $\epsilon > 0$, there is a continuous function g on $\mathbf{R}$ and a closed set F contained in E for which*

$$f = g \text{ on } F \text{ and } m(E \sim F) < \epsilon.$$

Proof Let $a_1, a_2, \ldots, a_n$ be the finite number of distinct values taken by f, and let them be taken on the sets $E_1, E_2, \ldots, E_n$, respectively. The collection $\{E_k\}_{k=1}^n$ is disjoint since the a_k's are distinct. According to Theorem 11 of Chapter 2, we may choose closed sets $F_1, F_2, \ldots, F_n$ such that for each index k, $1 \le k \le n$,

$$F_k \subseteq E_k \text{ and } m(E_k \sim F_k) < \epsilon/n.$$

Then $F = \bigcup_{k=1}^n F_k$, being the union of a finite collection of closed sets, is closed. Since $\{E_k\}_{k=1}^n$ is disjoint,

$$m(E \sim F) = m\left(\bigcup_{k=1}^n [E_k \sim F_k] \right) = \sum_{k=1}^n m(E_k \sim F_k) < \epsilon.$$

Define g on F to take the value a_k on F_k for $1 \le k \le n$. Since the collection $\{F_k\}_{k=1}^n$ is disjoint, g is properly defined. Moreover, g is continuous on F since for a point $x \in F_i$, there is an open interval containing x which is disjoint from the closed set $\bigcup_{k \ne i} F_k$ and hence on the intersection of this interval with F the function g is constant. But g can be extended from a continuous function on the closed set F to a continuous function on all of $\mathbf{R}$ (see Problem 25). The continuous function g on $\mathbf{R}$ has the required approximation properties. $\square$

Lusin's Theorem *Let f be a real-valued measurable function on E. Then for each $\epsilon > 0$, there is a continuous function g on $\mathbf{R}$ and a closed set F contained in E for which*

$$f = g \text{ on } F \text{ and } m(E \sim F) < \epsilon.$$

Proof We consider the case that $m(E) < \infty$ and leave the extension to $m(E) = \infty$ as an exercise. According to the Simple Approximation Theorem, there is a sequence $\{f_n\}$ of simple functions defined on E that converges to f pointwise on E. Let n be a natural number. By the preceding proposition, with f replaced by f_n and ϵ replaced by $\epsilon/2^{n+1}$, we may choose a continuous function g_n on $\mathbf{R}$ and a closed set F_n contained in E for which

$$f_n = g_n \text{ on } F_n \text{ and } m(E \sim F_n) < \epsilon/2^{n+1}.$$

According to Egoroff's Theorem, there is a closed set F_0 contained in E such that $\{f_n\}$ converges to f uniformly on F_0 and $m(E \sim F_0) < \epsilon/2$. Define $F = \bigcap_{n=0}^\infty F_n$. Observe that, by De Morgan's Identities and the countable subadditivity of measure,

$$m(E \sim F) = m\left([E \sim F_0] \cup \bigcup_{n=1}^{\infty} [E \sim F_n]\right) \le \epsilon/2 + \sum_{n=1}^{\infty} \epsilon/2^{n+1} = \epsilon.$$

The set F is closed since it is the intersection of closed sets. Each f_n is continuous on F since $F \subseteq F_n$ and $f_n = g_n$ on F_n. Finally, $\{f_n\}$ converges to f uniformly on F since $F \subseteq F_0$. However, the uniform limit of continuous functions is continuous, so the restriction of f to F is continuous on F. Finally, there is a continuous function g defined on all of $\mathbf{R}$ whose restriction to F equals f (see Problem 25). This function g has the required approximation properties. □

PROBLEMS

25. Suppose f is a function that is continuous on a closed set F of real numbers. Show that f has a continuous extension to all of $\mathbf{R}$. This is a special case of the forthcoming Tietze Extension Theorem. (Hint: Express $\mathbf{R} \sim F$ as the union of a countable disjoint collection of open intervals and define f to be linear on the closure of each of these intervals.)

26. For the function f and the set F in the statement of Lusin's Theorem, show that the restriction of f to F is a continuous function. Must there be any points at which f, considered as a function on E, is continuous?

27. Show that the conclusion of Egoroff's Theorem can fail if we drop the assumption that the domain has finite measure.

28. Show that Egoroff's Theorem continues to hold if the convergence is pointwise a.e. and f is finite a.e.

29. Prove the extension of Lusin's Theorem to the case that E has infinite measure.

30. Prove the extension of Lusin's Theorem to the case that f is not necessarily real-valued, but may be finite a.e.

31. Let $\{f_n\}$ be a sequence of measurable functions on E that converges to the real-valued f pointwise on E. Show that $E = \bigcup_{k=1}^{\infty} E_k$, where for each index k, E_k is measurable, and $\{f_n\}$ converges uniformly to f on each E_k if $k > 1$, and $m(E_1) = 0$.

CHAPTER 4

Lebesgue Integration

Contents

We now turn to our main object of interest in Part I, the Lebesgue integral. We define this integral in four stages. We first define the integral for simple functions over a set of finite measure. Then for bounded measurable functions f over a set of finite measure, in terms of integrals of upper and lower approximations of f by simple functions. We define the integral of a general nonnegative measurable function f over E to be the supremum of the integrals of lower approximations of f by bounded measurable functions that vanish outside a set of finite measure; the integral of such a function is nonnegative, but may be infinite. Finally, a general measurable function is said to be integrable over E provided $\int_E |f| < \infty$. We prove that linear combinations of integrable functions are integrable and that, on the class of integrable functions, the Lebesgue integral is a monotone, linear functional. A principal virtue of the Lebesgue integral, beyond the extent of the class of integrable functions, is the availability of quite general criteria which guarantee that if a sequence of integrable functions $\{f_n\}$ converge pointwise almost everywhere on E to f, then

$$\lim_{n \to \infty} \int_E f_n = \int_E [\lim_{n \to \infty} f_n] \equiv \int_E f.$$

We refer to that as passage of the limit under the integral sign. Based on Egoroff's Theorem, a consequence of the countable additivity of Lebesgue measure, we prove four theorems that provide criteria for justification of this passage: the Bounded Convergence Theorem, the Monotone Convergence Theorem, the Lebesgue Dominated Convergence Theorem, and the Vitali Convergence Theorem.

4.1 THE RIEMANN INTEGRAL

We recall a few definitions pertaining to the Riemann integral. Let f be a bounded real-valued function defined on the closed, bounded interval $[a, b]$. Let $P = \{x_0, x_1, \ldots, x_n\}$ be a partition of $[a, b]$, that is,

$$a = x_0 < x_1 < \ldots < x_n = b.$$

Define the **lower and upper Darboux sums** for f with respect to P, respectively, by

$$L(f, P) = \sum_{i=1}^{n} m_i \cdot (x_i - x_{i-1})$$

and

$$U(f, P) = \sum_{i=1}^{n} M_i \cdot (x_i - x_{i-1}),$$

where,[1] for $1 \le i \le n$,

$$m_i = \inf \left\{ f(x) \mid x_{i-1} < x < x_i \right\} \text{ and } M_i = \sup \left\{ f(x) \mid x_{i-1} < x < x_i \right\}.$$

We then define the **lower and upper Riemann integrals** of f over $[a, b]$, respectively, by

$$(R) \underline{\int_{a}^{b}} f = \sup \left\{ L(f, P) \mid P \text{ a partition of } [a, b] \right\}$$

and

$$(R) \overline{\int_{a}^{b}} f = \inf \left\{ U(f, P) \mid P \text{ a partition of } [a, b] \right\}.$$

Since f is assumed to be bounded and the interval $[a, b]$ has finite length, the lower and upper Riemann integrals are finite. The upper integral is always at least as large as the lower integral, and if the two are equal we say that f is **Riemann integrable** over $[a, b]$[2] and call this common value the Riemann integral of f over $[a, b]$. We denote it by

$$(R) \int_{a}^{b} f$$

to temporarily distinguish it from the Lebesgue integral, which we consider in the next section.

A real-valued function ψ defined on $[a, b]$ is called a **step function** provided there is a partition $P = \{x_0, x_1, \ldots, x_n\}$ of $[a, b]$ and numbers $c_1, \ldots, c_n$ such that for $1 \le i \le n$,

$$\psi(x) = c_i \text{ if } x_{i-1} < x < x_i.$$

Observe that

$$L(\psi, P) = \sum_{i=1}^{n} c_i(x_i - x_{i-1}) = U(\psi, P).$$

---

[1] If we define

$$m_i = \inf \left\{ f(x) \mid x_{i-1} \le x \le x_i \right\} \text{ and } M_i = \sup \left\{ f(x) \mid x_{i-1} \le x \le x_i \right\},$$

so the infima and suprema are taken over closed subintervals, we arrive at the same value of the upper and lower Riemann integral.

[2] An elegant theorem of Henri Lebesgue, Theorem 8 of Chapter 5, tells us that a necessary and sufficient condition for a bounded function f to be Riemann integrable over $[a, b]$ is that the set of points in $[a, b]$ at which f fails to be continuous has Lebesgue measure zero.

From this and the definition of the upper and lower Riemann integrals, we infer that a step function ψ is Riemann integrable and

$$(R)\int_a^b \psi = \sum_{i=1}^n c_i(x_i - x_{i-1}).$$

Therefore, we may reformulate the definition of the lower and upper Riemann integrals as follows:

$$(R)\underline{\int_a^b} f = \sup\left\{(R)\int_a^b \varphi \,\Big|\, \varphi \text{ a step function and } \varphi \le f \text{ on } [a, b]\right\},$$

and

$$(R)\overline{\int_a^b} f = \inf\left\{(R)\int_a^b \psi \,\Big|\, \psi \text{ a step function and } \psi \ge f \text{ on } [a, b]\right\}.$$

Example (**Dirichlet's Function**) Define f on $[0, 1]$ by setting $f(x) = 1$ if x is rational and 0 if x is irrational. Let P be any partition of $[0, 1]$. By the density of the rationals and the irrationals,[3]

$$L(f, P) = 0 \text{ and } U(f, P) = 1.$$

Thus

$$(R)\underline{\int_0^1} f = 0 < 1 = (R)\overline{\int_0^1} f,$$

so f is not Riemann integrable. The set of rational numbers in $[0,1]$ is countable.[4] Let $\{q_k\}_{k=1}^\infty$ be an enumeration of the rational numbers in $[0, 1]$. For a natural number n, define f_n on $[0, 1]$ by setting $f_n(x) = 1$, if $x = q_k$ for some q_k with $1 \le k \le n$, and $f(x) = 0$ otherwise. Then each f_n is a step function, so it is Riemann integrable. Thus, $\{f_n\}$ is an increasing sequence of Riemann integrable functions on $[0, 1]$,

$$|f_n| \le 1 \text{ on } [0, 1] \text{ for all } n$$

and

$$\{f_n\} \to f \text{ pointwise on } [0, 1].$$

However, the limit function f fails to be Riemann integrable on $[0, 1]$.

PROBLEMS

1. Show that, in the above Dirichlet function example, $\{f_n\}$ fails to converge to f uniformly on $[0, 1]$.

2. A partition P' of $[a, b]$ is called a refinement of a partition P provided each partition point of P is also a partition point of P'. For a bounded function f on $[a, b]$, show that under refinement lower Darboux sums increase and upper Darboux sums decrease.

---

[3]See page 12.
[4]See page 14.

3. Use the preceding problem to show that for a bounded function on a closed, bounded interval, each lower Darboux sum is no greater than each upper Darboux sum. From this conclude that the lower Riemann integral is no greater than the upper Riemann integral.

4. Suppose the bounded function f on $[a, b]$ is Riemann integrable over $[a, b]$. Show that there is a sequence $\{P_n\}$ of partitions of $[a, b]$ for which $\lim_{n \to \infty} [U(f, P_n) - L(f, P_n)] = 0$.

5. Let f be a bounded function on $[a, b]$. Suppose there is a sequence $\{P_n\}$ of partitions of $[a, b]$ for which $\lim_{n \to \infty} [U(f, P_n) - L(f, P_n)] = 0$. Show that f is Riemann integrable over $[a, b]$.

6. Use the preceding problem to show that since a continuous function f on a closed, bounded interval $[a, b]$ is uniformly continuous on $[a, b]$, it is Riemann integrable over $[a, b]$.

7. Let f be an increasing real-valued function on $[0, 1]$. For a natural number n, define P_n to be the partition of $[0, 1]$ into n subintervals of length $1/n$. Show that $U(f, P_n) - L(f, P_n) \le 1/n[f(1) - f(0)]$. Use Problem 5 to show that f is Riemann integrable over $[0, 1]$.

8. Let $\{f_n\}$ be a sequence of bounded functions that converges uniformly to f on the closed, bounded interval $[a, b]$. If each f_n is Riemann integrable over $[a, b]$, show that f also is Riemann integrable over $[a, b]$. Is it true that

$$\lim_{n \to \infty} \int_a^b f_n = \int_a^b f?$$

4.2   THE LEBESGUE INTEGRAL OF A BOUNDED MEASURABLE FUNCTION OVER A SET OF FINITE MEASURE

The Dirichlet function, which was examined in the preceding section, exhibits one of the principal shortcomings of the Riemann integral: a uniformly bounded sequence of Riemann integrable functions on a closed, bounded interval can converge pointwise to a function that is not Riemann integrable. We will see that the Lebesgue integral does not suffer from this shortcoming.

Henceforth we only consider the Lebesgue integral, unless explicitly mentioned otherwise, and so we use the pure integral symbol to denote the Lebesgue integral. The forthcoming Theorem 3 tells us that any bounded function that is Riemann integrable over $[a, b]$ is also Lebesgue integrable over $[a, b]$ and the two integrals are equal.

Recall that a measurable real-valued function ψ defined on a set E is said to be simple provided it takes only a finite number of real values. If ψ takes the distinct values $a_1, \ldots, a_n$ on E, then, by the measurability of ψ, its level sets $\psi^{-1}(a_i)$ are measurable and we have the canonical representation of ψ on E as

$$\psi = \sum_{i=1}^n a_i \cdot \chi_{E_i} \text{ on } E, \text{ where each } E_i = \psi^{-1}(a_i) = \{x \in E \mid \psi(x) = a_i\}. \tag{1}$$

The canonical representation is characterized by the E_i's being disjoint and the a_i's being distinct.

Definition *For a simple function ψ defined on a set of finite measure E, we define the integral of ψ over E by*

$$\int_E \psi = \sum_{i=1}^n a_i \cdot m(E_i),$$

where ψ has the canonical representation given by (1).

Lemma 1 *Let $\{E_i\}_{i=1}^n$ be a finite disjoint collection of measurable subsets of a set of finite measure E. For $1 \le i \le n$, let a_i be a real number.*

$$\text{If } \varphi = \sum_{i=1}^n a_i \cdot \chi_{E_i} \text{ on } E, \text{ then } \int_E \varphi = \sum_{i=1}^n a_i \cdot m(E_i).$$

Proof The collection $\{E_i\}_{i=1}^n$ is disjoint but the above may not be the canonical representation since the a_i's may not be distinct. We must account for possible repetitions. Let $\{\lambda_1, \ldots, \lambda_m\}$ be the distinct values taken by φ. For $1 \le j \le m$, set $A_j = \{x \in E \mid \varphi(x) = \lambda_j\}$. By definition of the integral in terms of canonical representations,

$$\int_E \varphi = \sum_{j=1}^m \lambda_j \cdot m(A_j).$$

For $1 \le j \le m$, let I_j be the set of indices i in $\{1, \ldots, n\}$ for which $a_i = \lambda_j$. Then $\{1, \ldots, n\} = \bigcup_{j=1}^m I_j$, and the union is disjoint. Moreover, by finite additivity of measure,

$$m(A_j) = \sum_{i \in I_j} m(E_i) \text{ for all } 1 \le j \le m.$$

Therefore

$$\sum_{i=1}^n a_i \cdot m(E_i) = \sum_{j=1}^m \left[\sum_{i \in I_j} a_i \cdot m(E_i) \right] = \sum_{j=1}^m \lambda_j \left[\sum_{i \in I_j} m(E_i) \right]$$

$$= \sum_{j=1}^m \lambda_j \cdot m(A_j) = \int_E \varphi. \qquad \square$$

One of our goals is to establish linearity and monotonicity properties for the general Lebesgue integral. The following is the first result in this direction.

Proposition 2 (**Linearity and Monotonicity of Integration**) *Let φ and ψ be simple functions defined on a set of finite measure E. Then for any α and β,*

$$\int_E (\alpha \varphi + \beta \psi) = \alpha \int_E \varphi + \beta \int_E \psi.$$

Moreover,

$$\text{if } \varphi \le \psi \text{ on } E, \text{ then } \int_E \varphi \le \int_E \psi.$$

Proof Since both φ and ψ take only a finite number of values on E, we may choose a finite disjoint collection $\{E_i\}_{i=1}^n$ of measurable subsets of E, the union of which is E, such that φ and ψ are constant on each E_i. For each i, $1 \le i \le n$, let a_i and b_i, respectively, be the values taken by φ and ψ on E_i. By the preceding lemma,

$$\int_E \varphi = \sum_{i=1}^n a_i \cdot m(E_i) \text{ and } \int_E \psi = \sum_{i=1}^n b_i \cdot m(E_i)$$

However, the simple function $\alpha\varphi + \beta\psi$ takes the constant value $\alpha a_i + \beta b_i$ on E_i. Thus, again by the preceding lemma,

$$\int_E (\alpha\varphi + \beta\psi) = \sum_{i=1}^{n} (\alpha a_i + \beta b_i) \cdot m(E_i)$$

$$= \alpha \sum_{i=1}^{n} a_i \cdot m(E_i) + \beta \sum_{i=1}^{n} b_i \cdot m(E_i) = \alpha \int_E \varphi + \beta \int_E \psi.$$

To prove monotonicity, assume $\varphi \le \psi$ on E. Define $\eta = \psi - \varphi$ on E. By linearity,

$$\int_E \psi - \int_E \varphi = \int_E (\psi - \varphi) = \int_E \eta \ge 0,$$

since the nonnegative simple function η has a nonnegative integral. $\square$

The linearity of integration over sets of finite measure of simple functions shows that the restriction in the statement of Lemma 1 that the collection $\{E_i\}_{i=1}^{n}$ be disjoint is unnecessary.

A step function takes only a finite number of values and each interval is measurable. Thus a step function is simple. Since the measure of a singleton set is zero and the measure of an interval is its length, we infer from the linearity of Lebesgue integration for simple functions defined on sets of finite measure that the Riemann integral over a closed, bounded interval of a step function agrees with the Lebesgue integral.

Let f be a bounded real-valued function defined on a set of finite measure E. By analogy with the Riemann integral, we define the **lower and upper Lebesgue integral**, respectively, of f over E to be

$$\sup \left\{ \int_E \varphi \;\middle|\; \varphi \text{ simple and } \varphi \le f \text{ on } E, \right\}$$

and

$$\inf \left\{ \int_E \psi \;\middle|\; \psi \text{ simple and } f \le \psi \text{ on } E. \right\}$$

Since f is assumed to be bounded, by the monotonicity property of the integral for simple functions, the lower and upper integrals are finite and the upper integral is always at least as large as the lower integral.

Definition *A bounded function f on a domain E of finite measure is said to be* **Lebesgue integrable** *over E provided its upper and lower Lebesgue integrals over E are equal. The common value of the upper and lower integrals is called the* **Lebesgue integral**, *or simply the integral, of f over E and is denoted by $\int_E f$.*

Theorem 3 *Let f be a bounded function defined on the closed, bounded interval $[a, b]$. If f is Riemann integrable over $[a, b]$, then it is Lebesgue integrable over $[a, b]$ and the two integrals are equal.*

Proof The assertion that f is Riemann integrable means that, setting $I = [a, b]$,

$$\sup \left\{ (R) \int_I \varphi \, \middle| \, \varphi \text{ a step function}, \varphi \le f \right\} = \inf \left\{ (R) \int_I \psi \, \middle| \, \psi \text{ a step function}, f \le \psi \right\}$$

To prove that f is Lebesgue integrable we must show that

$$\sup \left\{ \int_I \varphi \, \middle| \, \varphi \text{ simple}, \varphi \le f \right\} = \inf \left\{ \int_I \psi \, \middle| \, \psi \text{ simple}, f \le \psi \right\}.$$

However, each step function is a simple function and, as we have already observed, for a step function, the Riemann integral and the Lebesgue integral are the same. Therefore the first equality implies the second and also the equality of the Riemann and Lebesgue integrals. □

We are now fully justified in using the symbol $\int_E f$, without any preliminary (R), to denote the integral of a bounded function that is Lebesgue integrable over a set of finite measure. In the case of an interval $E = [a, b]$, we sometimes use the familiar notation $\int_a^b f$ to denote $\int_{[a, b]} f$ and sometimes it is useful to use the classic Leibniz notation $\int_a^b f(x) \, dx$.

Example The set E of rational numbers in $[0, 1]$ is a measurable set of measure zero. The Dirichlet function f is the restriction to $[0, 1]$ of the characteristic function of E, χ_E. Thus f is integrable over $[0, 1]$ and

$$\int_{[0, 1]} f = \int_{[0, 1]} 1 \cdot \chi_E = 1 \cdot m(E) = 0.$$

We have shown that f is not Riemann integrable over $[0, 1]$. ·

Theorem 4 *Let f be a bounded measurable function on a set of finite measure E. Then f is integrable over E.*

Proof Let n be a natural number. By the Simple Approximation Lemma, with $\epsilon = 1/n$, there are two simple functions φ_n and ψ_n defined on E for which

$$\varphi_n \le f \le \psi_n \text{ on } E,$$

and

$$0 \le \psi_n - \varphi_n \le 1/n \text{ on } E.$$

By the monotonicity and linearity of the integral for simple functions,

$$0 \le \int_E \psi_n - \int_E \varphi_n = \int_E [\psi_n - \varphi_n] \le 1/n \cdot m(E).$$

However,

$$0 \le \inf \left\{ \int_E \psi \ \middle| \ \psi \text{ simple}, \psi \ge f \right\} - \sup \left\{ \int_E \varphi \ \middle| \ \varphi \text{ simple}, \varphi \le f \right\}$$

$$\le \int_E \psi_n - \int_E \varphi_n \le 1/n \cdot m(E).$$

This inequality holds for every natural number n and $m(E)$ is finite. Therefore the upper and lower Lebesgue integrals are equal and thus the function f is integrable over E. □

It turns out that the converse of the preceding theorem is true; a bounded function on a set of finite measure is Lebesgue integrable if and only if it is measurable: we prove this later (see the forthcoming Theorem 7 of Chapter 5). This shows, in particular, that not every bounded function defined on a set of finite measure is Lebesgue integrable. In fact, for any measurable set E of finite positive measure, the restriction to E of the characteristic function of each nonmeasurable subset of E fails to be Lebesgue integrable over E.

Theorem 5 (**Linearity and Monotonicity of Integration**) *Let f and g be bounded measurable functions on a set of finite measure E. Then for any α and β,*

$$\int_E (\alpha f + \beta g) = \alpha \int_E f + \beta \int_E g. \tag{2}$$

Moreover,

$$\text{if } f \le g \text{ on } E, \text{ then } \int_E f \le \int_E g. \tag{3}$$

Proof A linear combination of measurable bounded functions is measurable and bounded. Thus, by Theorem 4, $\alpha f + \beta g$ is integrable over E. We first prove linearity for $\beta = 0$. If ψ is a simple function so is $\alpha \psi$, and conversely (if $\alpha \ne 0$). We established linearity of integration for simple functions. Let $\alpha > 0$. Since the Lebesgue integral is equal to the upper Lebesgue integral,

$$\int_E \alpha f = \inf_{\psi \ge \alpha f} \int_E \psi = \alpha \inf_{[\psi/\alpha] \ge f} \int_E [\psi/\alpha] = \alpha \int_E f.$$

For $\alpha < 0$, since the Lebesgue integral is equal both to the upper Lebesgue integral and the lower Lebesgue integral,

$$\int_E \alpha f = \inf_{\varphi \ge \alpha f} \int_E \varphi = \alpha \sup_{[\varphi/\alpha] \le f} \int_E [\varphi/\alpha] = \alpha \int_E f.$$

It remains to establish linearity in the case that $\alpha = \beta = 1$. Let ψ_1 and ψ_2 be simple functions for which $f \le \psi_1$ and $g \le \psi_2$ on E. Then $\psi_1 + \psi_2$ is a simple function and $f + g \le \psi_1 + \psi_2$ on E. Hence, since $\int_E (f + g)$ is equal to the upper Lebesgue integral of $f + g$ over E, by the linearity of integration for simple functions,

$$\int_E (f + g) \le \int_E (\psi_1 + \psi_2) = \int_E \psi_1 + \int_E \psi_2.$$

The greatest lower bound for the sums of integrals on the right-hand side, as ψ_1 and ψ_2 vary among simple functions for which $f \le \psi_1$ and $g \le \psi_2$, equals $\int_E f + \int_E g$. These inequalities tell us that $\int_E (f + g)$ is a lower bound for these same sums. Therefore,

$$\int_E (f + g) \le \int_E f + \int_E g.$$

It remains to prove this inequality in the opposite direction. Let φ_1 and φ_2 be simple functions for which $\varphi_1 \le f$ and $\varphi_2 \le g$ on E. Then $\varphi_1 + \varphi_2 \le f + g$ on E and $\varphi_1 + \varphi_2$ is simple. Hence, since $\int_E (f + g)$ is equal to the lower Lebesgue integral of $f + g$ over E, by the linearity of integration for simple functions,

$$\int_E (f + g) \ge \int_E (\varphi_1 + \varphi_2) = \int_E \varphi_1 + \int_E \varphi_2.$$

The least upper bound bound for the sums of integrals on the right-hand side, as φ_1 and φ_2 vary among simple functions for which $\varphi_1 \le f$ and $\varphi_2 \le g$, equals $\int_E f + \int_E g$. These inequalities tell us that $\int_E (f + g)$ is an upper bound for these same sums. Therefore,

$$\int_E (f + g) \ge \int_E f + \int_E g.$$

This completes the proof of linearity of integration.

To prove monotonicity, assume $f \le g$ on E. Define $h = g - f$ on E. By linearity,

$$\int_E g - \int_E f = \int_E (g - f) = \int_E h.$$

The function h is nonnegative and therefore $\psi \le h$ on E, where $\psi \equiv 0$ on E. Since the integral of h equals its lower integral, $\int_E h \ge \int_E \psi = 0$. Therefore, $\int_E f \le \int_E g$.   □

Corollary 6 *Let f be a bounded measurable function on a set of finite measure E. Suppose A and B are disjoint measurable subsets of E. Then*

$$\int_{A \cup B} f = \int_A f + \int_B f. \tag{4}$$

Proof Both $f \cdot \chi_A$ and $f \cdot \chi_B$ are bounded measurable functions on E. Since A and B are disjoint,

$$f \cdot \chi_{A \cup B} = f \cdot \chi_A + f \cdot \chi_B.$$

Furthermore, for any measurable subset E_1 of E (see Problem 10),

$$\int_{E_1} f = \int_E f \cdot \chi_{E_1}.$$

Therefore, by the linearity of integration,

$$\int_{A \cup B} f = \int_E f \cdot \chi_{A \cup B} = \int_E f \cdot \chi_A + \int_E f \cdot \chi_B = \int_A f + \int_B f.$$ □

Corollary 7 *Let f be a bounded measurable function on a set of finite measure E. Then*

$$\left| \int_E f \right| \le \int_E |f|. \tag{5}$$

Proof The function $|f|$ is measurable and bounded. Now

$$-|f| \le f \le |f| \text{ on } E.$$

By the linearity and monotonicity of integration,

$$-\int_E |f| \le \int_E f \le \int_E |f|,$$

that is, (5) holds.   □

Proposition 8 *Let $\{f_n\}$ be a sequence of bounded measurable functions on a set of finite measure E.*

If $\{f_n\} \to f$ uniformly on E, then $\lim\limits_{n \to \infty} \int_E f_n = \int_E f.$

Proof Since the convergence is uniform and each f_n is bounded, the limit function f is bounded. The function f is measurable since it is the pointwise limit of a sequence of measurable functions. Let $\epsilon > 0$. Choose an index N for which

$$|f - f_n| < \epsilon/m(E) \text{ on } E \text{ for all } n \ge N. \tag{6}$$

By the linearity and monotonicity of integration and the preceding corollary, for each $n \ge N$,

$$\left| \int_E f - \int_E f_n \right| = \left| \int_E [f - f_n] \right| \le \int_E |f - f_n| \le [\epsilon/m(E)] \cdot m(E) = \epsilon.$$

Therefore $\lim_{n \to \infty} \int_E f_n = \int_E f$.   □

This proposition is rather weak since frequently a sequence will be presented that converges pointwise but not uniformly. It is important to understand when it is possible to infer from

$$\{f_n\} \to f \text{ pointwise a.e. on } E$$

that

$$\lim_{n \to \infty} \left[\int_E f_n \right] = \int_E \left[\lim_{n \to \infty} f \right] = \int_E f.$$

We refer to this equality as **passage of the limit under the integral sign**.[5] Before proving our first important result regarding this passage, we present an instructive example.

---

[5]This phrase is taken from I. P. Natanson's *Theory of Functions of a Real Variable* [Nat55].

Example For each natural number n, define f_n on $[0, 1]$ to have the value 0 if $x \geq 2/n$, have $f(1/n) = n$, $f(0) = 0$ and to be linear on the intervals $[0, 1/n]$ and $[1/n, 2/n]$. Observe that $\int_0^1 f_n = 1$ for each n. Define $f \equiv 0$ on $[0, 1]$. Then

$$\{f_n\} \to f \text{ pointwise on } [0, 1], \text{ but } \lim_{n \to \infty} \int_0^1 f_n \neq \int_0^1 f.$$

Thus, pointwise convergence alone is not sufficient to justify passage of the limit under the integral sign.

The Bounded Convergence Theorem *Let $\{f_n\}$ be a sequence of measurable functions on a set of finite measure E. Suppose $\{f_n\}$ is uniformly pointwise bounded on E, that is, there is a number $M \geq 0$ for which*

$$|f_n| \leq M \text{ on } E \text{ for all } n.$$

If $\{f_n\} \to f$ pointwise on E, then $\displaystyle\lim_{n \to \infty} \int_E f_n = \int_E f.$

Proof The proof of this theorem furnishes a nice illustration of Littlewood's Third Principle. If the convergence is uniform, we have the easy proof of the preceding proposition. However, Egoroff's Theorem tells us, roughly, that pointwise convergence is "nearly" uniform.

The pointwise limit of a sequence of measurable functions is measurable. Therefore f is measurable. Clearly $|f| \leq M$ on E. Let A be any measurable subset of E and n a natural number. By the linearity and additivity over domains of the integral,

$$\int_E f_n - \int_E f = \int_E [f_n - f] = \int_A [f_n - f] + \int_{E \sim A} f_n + \int_{E \sim A} (-f).$$

Therefore, by Corollary 7 and the monotonicity of integration,

$$\left| \int_E f_n - \int_E f \right| \leq \int_A |f_n - f| + 2M \cdot m(E \sim A). \tag{7}$$

To prove convergence of the integrals, let $\epsilon > 0$. Since $m(E) < \infty$ and f is real-valued, Egoroff's Theorem tells us that there is a measurable subset A of E for which $\{f_n\} \to f$ uniformly on A and $m(E \sim A) < \epsilon/4M$. By uniform convergence, there is an index N for which

$$|f_n - f| < \frac{\epsilon}{2 \cdot m(E)} \text{ on } A \text{ for all } n \geq N.$$

Therefore, for $n \geq N$, we infer from (7) and the monotonicity of integration that

$$\left| \int_E f_n - \int_E f \right| \leq \frac{\epsilon}{2 \cdot m(E)} \cdot m(A) + 2M \cdot m(E \sim A) < \epsilon.$$

Hence the sequence of integrals $\{\int_E f_n\}$ converges to $\int_E f$. $\square$

Remark *Prior to the proof of the Bounded Convergence Theorem, no use was made of the countable additivity of Lebesgue measure on the real line. Only finite additivity was used, and it was used just once, in the proof of Lemma 1. But for the proof of the Bounded Convergence Theorem we used Egoroff's Theorem. The proof of Egoroff's Theorem needed the continuity of Lebesgue measure, a consequence of countable additivity of Lebesgue measure.*

PROBLEMS

9. Let E have measure zero. Show that if f is a bounded function on E, then f is measurable and $\int_E f = 0$.

10. Let f be a bounded measurable function on a set of finite measure E. For a measurable subset A of E, show that $\int_A f = \int_E f \cdot \chi_A$.

11. Does the Bounded Convergence Theorem hold for the Riemann integral?

12. Let f be a bounded measurable function on a set of finite measure E. Assume g is bounded and $f = g$ a.e. on E. Show that $\int_E f = \int_E g$.

13. Does the Bounded Convergence Theorem hold if $m(E) < \infty$ but we drop the assumption that the sequence $\{|f_n|\}$ is uniformly bounded on E?

14. Show that Proposition 8 is a special case of the Bounded Convergence Theorem.

15. Verify the assertions in the last Remark of this section.

16. Let f be a nonnegative bounded measurable function on a set of finite measure E. Assume $\int_E f = 0$. Show that $f = 0$ a.e. on E.

4.3 THE LEBESGUE INTEGRAL OF A MEASURABLE NONNEGATIVE FUNCTION

A measurable function f on E is said to vanish outside a set of finite measure provided there is a subset E_0 of E for which $m(E_0) < \infty$ and $f \equiv 0$ on $E \sim E_0$. It is convenient to say that a function that vanishes outside a set of finite measure has finite support and define its support to be $\{x \in E \mid f(x) \neq 0\}$.[6] In the preceding section, we defined the integral of a bounded measurable function f over a set of finite measure E. However, even if $m(E) = \infty$, if f is bounded and measurable on E but has finite support, we can define its integral over E by

$$\int_E f = \int_{E_0} f,$$

where E_0 has finite measure and $f \equiv 0$ on $E \sim E_0$. This integral is properly defined, that is, it is independent of the choice of set of finite measure E_0 outside of which f vanishes. This is a consequence of the additivity over domains property of integration for bounded measurable functions over a set of finite measure.

Definition *For f a nonnegative measurable function on E, we define the integral of f over E by*[7]

$$\int_E f = \sup \left\{ \int_E h \;\middle|\; h \text{ bounded, measurable, of finite support and } 0 \leq h \leq f \text{ on } E \right\}. \quad (8)$$

---

[6]But care is needed here. In the study of continuous real-valued functions on a topological space, the support of a function is defined to be the closure of the set of points at which the function is nonzero.

[7]This is a definition of the integral of a nonnegative extended real-valued measurable function; it is not a definition of what it means for such a function to be integrable. The integral is defined regardless of whether the function is bounded or the domain has finite measure. Of course, the integral is nonnegative since it is defined to be the supremum of a set of nonnegative numbers. But the integral may be equal to ∞, as it is, for instance, for a nonnegative measurable function that takes a positive constant value of a subset of E of infinite measure or the value ∞ on a subset of E of positive measure.

Chebychev's Inequality *Let f be a nonnegative measurable function on E. Then for any* $\lambda > 0$,

$$m\{x \in E \mid f(x) \geq \lambda\} \leq \frac{1}{\lambda} \cdot \int_E f. \tag{9}$$

Proof Define $E_\lambda = \{x \in E \mid f(x) \geq \lambda\}$. First suppose $m(E_\lambda) = \infty$. Let n be a natural number. Define $E_{\lambda, n} = E_\lambda \cap [-n, n]$ and $\psi_n = \lambda \cdot \chi_{E_{\lambda, n}}$. Then ψ_n is a bounded measurable function of finite support,

$$\lambda \cdot m(E_{\lambda, n}) = \int_E \psi_n \text{ and } 0 \leq \psi_n \leq f \text{ on } E \text{ for all } n.$$

We infer from the continuity of measure that

$$\infty = \lambda \cdot m(E_\lambda) = \lambda \cdot \lim_{n \to \infty} m(E_{\lambda, n}) = \lim_{n \to \infty} \int_E \psi_n \leq \int_E f.$$

Thus inequality (9) holds since both sides equal ∞. Now consider the case $m(E_\lambda) < \infty$. Define $h = \lambda \cdot \chi_{E_\lambda}$. Then h is a bounded measurable function of finite support and $0 \leq h \leq f$ on E. By the definition of the integral of f over E,

$$\lambda \cdot m(E_\lambda) = \int_E h \leq \int_E f.$$

Divide both sides of this inequality by λ to obtain Chebychev's Inequality.   □

Proposition 9 *Let f be a nonnegative measurable function on E. Then*

$$\int_E f = 0 \text{ if and only if } f = 0 \text{ a.e. on } E. \tag{10}$$

Proof First assume $\int_E f = 0$. Then, by Chebychev's Inequality, for each natural number n, $m\{x \in X \mid f(x) \geq 1/n\} = 0$. By the countable additivity of Lebesgue measure, $m\{x \in X \mid f(x) > 0\} = 0$. Conversely, suppose $f = 0$ a.e. on E. Let φ be a simple function and h a bounded measurable function of finite support for which $0 \leq \varphi \leq h \leq f$ on E. Then $\varphi = 0$ a.e. on E and hence $\int_E \varphi = 0$. Since this holds for all such φ, we infer that $\int_E h = 0$. Since this holds for all such h, we infer that $\int_E f = 0$.   □

Theorem 10 (Linearity and Monotonicity of Integration) *Let f and g be nonnegative measurable functions on E. Then for any* $\alpha > 0$ *and* $\beta > 0$,

$$\int_E (\alpha f + \beta g) = \alpha \int_E f + \beta \int_E g. \tag{11}$$

Moreover,

$$if f \leq g \text{ on } E, \text{ then } \int_E f \leq \int_E g. \tag{12}$$

Proof For $\alpha > 0$, $0 \le h \le f$ on E if and only if $0 \le \alpha h \le \alpha f$ on E. Therefore, by the linearity of the integral of bounded functions of finite support, $\int_E \alpha f = \alpha \int_E f$. Thus, to prove linearity we need only consider the case $\alpha = \beta = 1$. Let h and g be bounded measurable functions of finite support for which $0 \le h \le f$ and $0 \le k \le g$ on E. We have $0 \le h + k \le f + g$ on E, and $h + k$ also is a bounded measurable function of finite support. Thus, by the linearity of integration for bounded measurable functions of finite support,

$$\int_E h + \int_E k = \int_E (h + k) \le \int_E (f + g).$$

The least upper bound for the sums of integrals on the left-hand side, as h and k vary among bounded measurable functions of finite support for which $h \le f$ and $k \le g$, equals $\int_E f + \int_E g$. These inequalities tell us that $\int_E (f + g)$ is an upper bound for these same sums. Therefore,

$$\int_E f + \int_E g \le \int_E (f + g).$$

It remains to prove this inequality in the opposite direction, that is,

$$\int_E (f + g) \le \int_E f + \int_E g.$$

By the definition of $\int_E (f + g)$ as the supremum of $\int_E \ell$ as ℓ ranges over all bounded measurable functions of finite support for which $0 \le \ell \le f + g$ on E, to verify this inequality it is necessary and sufficient to show that for any such function ℓ,

$$\int_E \ell \le \int_E f + \int_E g. \tag{13}$$

For such a function ℓ, define the functions h and k on E by

$$h = \min\{f, \ell\} \text{ and } k = \ell - h \text{ on } E.$$

Let x belong to E. If $\ell(x) \le f(x)$, then $k(x) = 0 \le g(x)$; if $\ell(x) > f(x)$, then $h(x) = \ell(x) - f(x) \le g(x)$. Therefore, $h \le g$ on E. Both h and k are bounded measurable functions of finite support. We have

$$0 \le h \le f, 0 \le k \le g \text{ and } \ell = h + k \text{ on } E.$$

Hence, again using the linearity of integration for bounded measurable functions of finite support and the definitions of $\int_E f$ and $\int_E g$, we have

$$\int_E \ell = \int_E h + \int_E k \le \int_E f + \int_E g.$$

Thus (13) holds and the proof of linearity is complete.

In view of the definition of $\int_E f$ as a supremum, to prove the monotonicity inequality (12) it is necessary and sufficient to show that if h is a bounded measurable function of finite support for which $0 \le h \le f$ on E, then

$$\int_E h \le \int_E g. \tag{14}$$

Let h be such a function. Then $h \le g$ on E. Therefore, by the definition of $\int_E g$ as a supremum, $\int_E h \le \int_E g$. This completes the proof of monotonicity. $\qquad\square$

Theorem 11 (Additivity Over Domains of Integration) *Let f be a nonnegative measurable function on E. If A and B are disjoint measurable subsets of E, then*

$$\int_{A \cup B} f = \int_A f + \int_B f.$$

In particular, if E_0 is a subset of E of measure zero, then

$$\int_E f = \int_{E \sim E_0} f. \tag{15}$$

Proof Additivity over domains of integration follows from linearity as it did for bounded functions on sets of finite measure. The excision formula (15) follows from additivity over domains and the observation that, by Proposition 9, the integral of a nonnegative function over a set of measure zero is zero. $\qquad\square$

The following lemma will enable us to establish several criteria to justify passage of the limit under the integral sign.

Fatou's Lemma *Let $\{f_n\}$ be a sequence of nonnegative measurable functions on E.*

If $\{f_n\} \to f$ pointwise a.e. on E, then $\displaystyle\int_E f \le \liminf \int_E f_n.$ $\tag{16}$

Proof In view of (15), by possibly excising from E a set of measure zero, we assume the pointwise convergence is on all of E. The function f is nonnegative and measurable since it is the pointwise limit of a sequence of such functions. To verify the inequality in (16) it is necessary and sufficient to show that if h is any bounded measurable function of finite support for which $0 \le h \le f$ on E, then

$$\int_E h \le \liminf \int_E f_n. \tag{17}$$

Let h be such a function. Choose $M \ge 0$ for which $|h| \le M$ on E. Define $E_0 = \{x \in E \mid h(x) \ne 0\}$. Then $m(E_0) < \infty$. Let n be a natural number. Define a function h_n on E by

$$h_n = \min\{h, f_n\} \text{ on } E.$$

Observe that the function h_n is measurable, that

$$0 \le h_n \le M \text{ on } E_0 \text{ and } h_n \equiv 0 \text{ on } E \sim E_0.$$

Furthermore, for each x in E, since $h(x) \le f(x)$ and $\{f_n(x)\} \to f(x)$, $\{h_n(x)\} \to h(x)$. We infer from the Bounded Convergence Theorem applied to the uniformly bounded sequence of restrictions of h_n to the set of finite measure E_0, and the vanishing of each h_n on $E \sim E_0$, that

$$\lim_{n \to \infty} \int_E h_n = \lim_{n \to \infty} \int_{E_0} h_n = \int_{E_0} h = \int_E h.$$

However, for each n, $h_n \leq f_n$ on E and therefore, by the definition of the integral of f_n over E, $\int_E h_n \leq \int_E f_n$. Thus,

$$\int_E h = \lim_{n \to \infty} \int_E h_n \leq \liminf \int_E f_n. \qquad \square$$

The inequality in Fatou's Lemma may be strict.

Example Let $E = (0, 1]$ and for a natural number n, define $f_n = n \cdot \chi_{(0, 1/n)}$. Then $\{f_n\}$ converges pointwise on E to $f \equiv 0$ on E. However,

$$\int_E f = 0 < 1 = \lim_{n \to \infty} \int_E f_n.$$

As another example of strict inequality in Fatou's Lemma, let $E = \mathbf{R}$ and for a natural number n, define $g_n = \chi_{(n, n+1)}$. Then $\{g_n\}$ converges pointwise on E to $g \equiv 0$ on E. However,

$$\int_E g = 0 < 1 = \lim_{n \to \infty} \int_E g_n.$$

However, the inequality in Fatou's Lemma is an equality if the sequence $\{f_n\}$ is increasing.

The Monotone Convergence Theorem   *Let $\{f_n\}$ be an increasing sequence of nonnegative measurable functions on E.*

If $\{f_n\} \to f$ pointwise a.e. on E, then $\displaystyle \lim_{n \to \infty} \int_E f_n = \int_E f.$

Proof According to Fatou's Lemma,

$$\int_E f \leq \liminf \int_E f_n.$$

However, for each index n, $f_n \leq f$ a.e. on E, and so, by the monotonicity of integration for nonnegative measurable functions and (15), $\int_E f_n \leq \int_E f$. Therefore

$$\limsup \int_E f_n \leq \int_E f.$$

Hence

$$\int_E f = \lim_{n \to \infty} \int_E f_n. \qquad \square$$

Corollary 12   *Let $\{u_n\}$ be a sequence of nonnegative measurable functions on E.*

If $f = \displaystyle\sum_{n=1}^{\infty} u_n$ pointwise a.e. on E, then $\displaystyle \int_E f = \sum_{n=1}^{\infty} \int_E u_n.$

Proof Apply the Monotone Convergence Theorem with $f_n = \sum_{k=1}^{n} u_k$, for each index n, and then use the linearity of integration for nonnegative measurable functions. $\square$

Definition *A nonnegative measurable function f on a measurable set E is said to be **integrable** over E provided*

$$\int_E f < \infty.$$

Proposition 13 *Let the nonnegative function f be integrable over E. Then f is finite a.e. on E.*

Proof Let n be a natural number. Chebychev's Inequality and the monotonicity of measure tell us that

$$m\left\{x \in E \mid f(x) = \infty\right\} \leq m\left\{x \in E \mid f(x) \geq n\right\} \leq \frac{1}{n}\int_E f.$$

But $\int_E f$ is finite and therefore $m\{x \in E \mid f(x) = \infty\} = 0$.   □

Beppo Levi's Lemma *Let $\{f_n\}$ be an increasing sequence of nonnegative measurable functions on E. If the sequence of integrals $\{\int_E f_n\}$ is bounded, then $\{f_n\}$ converges pointwise on E to a measurable function f that is finite a.e. on E and*

$$\lim_{n \to \infty} \int_E f_n = \int_E f < \infty.$$

Proof Every monotone sequence of extended real numbers converges to an extended real number.[8] Since $\{f_n\}$ is an increasing sequence of extended real-valued functions on E, we may define the extended real-valued nonnegative function f pointwise on E by

$$f(x) = \lim_{n \to \infty} f_n(x) \text{ for all } x \in E.$$

According to the Monotone Convergence Theorem, $\{\int_E f_n\} \to \int_E f$. Therefore, since the sequence of real numbers $\{\int_E f_n\}$ is bounded, its limit is finite and so $\int_E f < \infty$. We infer from the preceding proposition that f is finite a.e. on E.   □

PROBLEMS

17. Let E be a set of measure zero and define $f \equiv \infty$ on E. Show that $\int_E f = 0$.

18. Show that the integral of a bounded measurable function of finite support is properly defined.

19. For a number α, define $f(x) = x^\alpha$ for $0 < x \leq 1$, and $f(0) = 0$. Compute $\int_0^1 f$.

20. Let $\{f_n\}$ be a sequence of nonnegative measurable functions that converges to f pointwise on E. Let $M \geq 0$ be such that $\int_E f_n \leq M$ for all n. Show that $\int_E f \leq M$. Verify that this property is equivalent to the statement of Fatou's Lemma.

21. Let the function f be nonnegative and integrable over E and $\epsilon > 0$. Show there is a simple function η on E that has finite support, $0 \leq \eta \leq f$ on E and $\int_E |f - \eta| < \epsilon$. If E is a closed, bounded interval, show there is a step function h on E that has finite support and $\int_E |f - h| < \epsilon$.

22. Let $\{f_n\}$ be a sequence of nonnegative measurable functions on **R** that converges pointwise on **R** to f and f be integrable over **R**. Show that

$$\text{if } \int_{\mathbf{R}} f = \lim_{n \to \infty} \int_{\mathbf{R}} f_n, \text{ then } \int_E f = \lim_{n \to \infty} \int_E f_n \text{ for any measurable set } E.$$

---

[8]See page 23.

23. Let $\{a_n\}$ be a sequence of nonnegative real numbers. Define the function f on $E = [1, \infty)$ by setting $f(x) = a_n$ if $n \le x < n + 1$. Show that $\int_E f = \sum_{n=1}^{\infty} a_n$.

24. Let f be a nonnegative measurable function on E.
   (i) Show there is an increasing sequence $\{\varphi_n\}$ of nonnegative simple functions on E, each of finite support, which converges pointwise on E to f.
   (ii) Show that $\int_E f = \sup \{\int_E \varphi \mid \varphi$ simple, of finite support and $0 \le \varphi \le, f$ on $E\}$.

25. Let $\{f_n\}$ be a sequence of nonnegative measurable functions on E that converges pointwise on E to f. Suppose $f_n \le f$ on E for each n. Show that

$$\lim_{n \to \infty} \int_E f_n = \int_E f.$$

26. Show that the Monotone Convergence Theorem may not hold for decreasing sequences of functions.

27. Prove the following generalization of Fatou's Lemma: If $\{f_n\}$ is a sequence of nonnegative measurable functions on E, then

$$\int_E \liminf f_n \le \liminf \int_E f_n.$$

4.4 THE GENERAL LEBESGUE INTEGRAL

For an extended real-valued function f on E, we have defined the positive part f^+ and the negative part f^- of f, respectively, by

$$f^+(x) = \max\{f(x), 0\} \text{ and } f^-(x) = \max\{-f(x), 0\} \text{ for all } x \in E.$$

Then f^+ and f^- are nonnegative functions on E,

$$f = f^+ - f^- \text{ on } E$$

and

$$|f| = f^+ + f^- \text{ on } E.$$

Observe that f is measurable if and only if both f^+ and f^- are measurable.

Proposition 14 Let f be a measurable function on E. Then f^+ and f^- are integrable over E if and only if $|f|$ is integrable over E.

Proof Assume f^+ and f^- are integrable nonnegative functions. By the linearity of integration for nonnegative functions, $|f| = f^+ + f^-$ is integrable over E. Conversely, suppose $|f|$ is integrable over E. Since $0 \le f^+ \le |f|$ and $0 \le f^- \le |f|$ on E, we infer from the monotonicity of integration for nonnegative functions that both f^+ and f^- are integrable over E. $\qquad \square$

Definition A measurable function f on E is said to be **integrable** over E provided $|f|$ is integrable over E. When this is so we define the integral of f over E by

$$\int_E f = \int_E f^+ - \int_E f^-.$$

Of course, for a nonnegative function f, since $f = f^+$ and $f^- \equiv 0$ on E, this definition of integral coincides with the one just considered. By the linearity of integration for bounded measurable functions of finite support, the above definition of integral also agrees with the definition of integral for this class of functions.

Proposition 15 *Let f be integrable over E. Then f is finite a.e. on E and*

$$\int_E f = \int_{E \sim E_0} f \text{ if } E_0 \subseteq E \text{ and } m(E_0) = 0. \tag{18}$$

Proof Proposition 13, tells us that $|f|$ is finite a.e. on E. Thus f is finite a.e. on E. Moreover, (18) follows by applying (15) to the positive and negative parts of f. $\square$

The following criterion for integrability is the Lebesgue integral correspondent of the comparison test for the convergence of series of real numbers.

Proposition 16 (the Integral Comparison Test) *Let f be a measurable function on E. Suppose there is a nonnegative function g that is integrable over E and dominates f in the sense that*

$$|f| \leq g \text{ on } E.$$

Then f is integrable over E and

$$\left| \int_E f \right| \leq \int_E |f|.$$

Proof By the monotonicity of integration for nonnegative functions, $|f|$, and hence f, is integrable. By the triangle inequality for real numbers and the linearity of integration for nonnegative functions,

$$\left| \int_E f \right| = \left| \int_E f^+ - \int_E f^- \right| \leq \int_E f^+ + \int_E f^- = \int_E |f|.$$ $\square$

We have arrived at our final stage of generality for the Lebesgue integral for functions of a single real variable. Before proving the linearity property for integration, we need to address, with respect to integration, a point already addressed with respect to measurability. The point is that for two functions f and g which are integrable over E, the sum $f + g$ is not properly defined at points in E where f and g take infinite values of opposite sign. However, by Proposition 15, if we define A to be the set of points in E at which both f and g are finite, then $m(E \sim A) = 0$. Once we show that $f + g$ is integrable over A, we define

$$\int_E (f + g) = \int_A (f + g).$$

We infer from (18) that $\int_E (f + g)$ is equal to the integral over E of any extension of $(f+g)|_A$ to an extended real-valued function on all of E.

Theorem 17 (Linearity and Monotonicity of Integration) *Let the functions f and g be integrable over E. Then for any α and β, the function αf + βg is integrable over E and*

$$\int_E (\alpha f + \beta g) = \alpha \int_E f + \beta \int_E g.$$

Moreover,

$$\text{if } f \leq g \text{ on } E, \text{ then } \int_E f \leq \int_E g.$$

Proof If $\alpha > 0$, then $[\alpha f]^+ = \alpha f^+$ and $[\alpha f]^- = \alpha f^-$, while if $\alpha < 0$, $[\alpha f]^+ = -\alpha f^-$ and $[\alpha f]^- = -\alpha f^+$. Therefore $\int_E \alpha f = \alpha \int_E f$, since we established this for nonnegative functions f and $\alpha > 0$. So it suffices to establish linearity in the case $\alpha = \beta = 1$. By the linearity of integration for nonnegative functions, $|f| + |g|$ is integrable over E. Since $|f + g| \leq |f| + |g|$ on E, by the integral comparison test, $f + g$ also is integrable over E. Proposition 15 tells us that f and g are finite a.e. on E. According to the same proposition, by possibly excising from E a set of measure zero, we may assume that f and g are finite on E. To verify linearity is to show that

$$\int_E [f+g]^+ - \int_E [f+g]^- = \left[\int_E f^+ - \int_E f^- \right] + \left[\int_E g^+ - \int_E g^- \right]. \tag{19}$$

But

$$(f+g)^+ - (f+g)^- = f + g = (f^+ - f^-) + (g^+ - g^-) \text{ on } E,$$

and therefore, since each of these six functions takes real values on E,

$$(f+g)^+ + f^- + g^- = (f+g)^- + f^+ + g^+ \text{ on } E.$$

We infer from linearity of integration for nonnegative functions that

$$\int_E (f+g)^+ + \int_E f^- + \int_E g^- = \int_E (f+g)^- + \int_E f^+ + \int_E g^+.$$

Since f, g and $f + g$ are integrable over E, each of these six integrals is finite. Rearrange these integrals to obtain (19). This completes the proof of linearity.

To establish monotonicity we again argue as above that we may assume g and f are finite on E. Define $h = g - f$ on E. Then h is a properly defined nonnegative measurable function on E. By linearity of integration for integrable functions and monotonicity of integration for nonnegative functions,

$$\int_E g - \int_E f = \int_E (g - f) = \int_E h \geq 0. \qquad \square$$

Corollary 18 (Additivity Over Domains of Integration) *Let f be integrable over E. Assume A and B are disjoint measurable subsets of E. Then*

$$\int_{A \cup B} f = \int_A f + \int_B f. \tag{20}$$

Proof Observe that $|f \cdot \chi_A| \leq |f|$ and $|f \cdot \chi_B| \leq |f|$ on E. By the integral comparison test, the measurable functions $f \cdot \chi_A$ and $f \cdot \chi_B$ are integrable over E. Since A and B are disjoint

$$f \cdot \chi_{A \cup B} = f \cdot \chi_A + f \cdot \chi_B \text{ on } E. \tag{21}$$

But for any measurable subset C of E (see Problem 28),

$$\int_C f = \int_E f \cdot \chi_C.$$

Thus (20) follows from (21) and the linearity of integration. □

The following generalization of the Bounded Convergence Theorem provides another justification for passage of the limit under the integral sign.

The Lebesgue Dominated Convergence Theorem *Let $\{f_n\}$ be a sequence of measurable functions on E. Suppose there is a function g that is integrable over E and dominates $\{f_n\}$ on E in the sense that $|f_n| \leq g$ on E for all n.*

If $\{f_n\} \to f$ pointwise a.e. on E, then f is integrable over E and $\lim_{n \to \infty} \int_E f_n = \int_E f$.

Proof Since $|f_n| \leq g$ on E and $|f| \leq g$ a.e. on E and g is integrable over E, by the integral comparison test, f and each f_n also are integrable over E. We infer from Proposition 15 that, by possibly excising from E a countable collection of sets of measure zero and using the countable additivity of Lebesgue measure, we may assume that f and each f_n is finite on E. The function $g - f$ and for each n, the function $g - f_n$, are properly defined, nonnegative and measurable. Moreover, the sequence $\{g - f_n\}$ converges pointwise a.e. on E to $g - f$. Fatou's Lemma tells us that

$$\int_E (g - f) \leq \liminf \int_E (g - f_n).$$

Thus, by the linearity of integration for integrable functions,

$$\int_E g - \int_E f = \int_E (g - f) \leq \liminf \int_E (g - f_n) = \int_E g - \limsup \int_E f_n,$$

that is,

$$\limsup \int_E f_n \leq \int_E f.$$

Similarly, considering the sequence $\{g + f_n\}$, we obtain

$$\int_E f \leq \liminf \int_E f_n.$$

The proof is complete. □

The following generalization of the Lebesgue Dominated Convergence Theorem, the proof of which we leave as an exercise (see Problem 32), is often useful (see Problem 33).

Theorem 19 (**General Lebesgue Dominated Convergence Theorem**) *Let* $\{f_n\}$ *be a sequence of measurable functions on E that converges pointwise a.e. on E to f. Suppose there is a sequence* $\{g_n\}$ *of nonnegative measurable functions on E that converges pointwise a.e. on E to g and dominates* $\{f_n\}$ *on E in the sense that*

$$|f_n| \le g_n \text{ on } E \text{ for all } n.$$

If $\displaystyle\lim_{n\to\infty} \int_E g_n = \int_E g < \infty$, *then* $\displaystyle\lim_{n\to\infty} \int_E f_n = \int_E f$.

Remark *In Fatou's Lemma and the Lebesgue Dominated Convergence Theorem, the assumption of pointwise convergence a.e. on E rather than on all of E is not a decoration pinned on to honor generality. It is necessary for future applications of these results. We provide one illustration of this necessity. Suppose f is an increasing function on all of* **R**. *A forthcoming theorem of Lebesgue (Lebesgue's Theorem of Chapter 6) tells us that*

$$\lim_{n\to\infty} \frac{f(x+1/n) - f(x)}{1/n} = f'(x) \text{ for almost all } x. \qquad (22)$$

From this and Fatou's Lemma we will show that for any closed, bounded interval $[a, b]$,

$$\int_a^b f'(x)\, dx \le f(b) - f(a).$$

In general, given a nondegenerate closed, bounded interval $[a, b]$ *and a subset A of* $[a, b]$ *that has measure zero, there is an increasing function f on* $[a, b]$ *for which the limit in (22) fails to exist at each point in A (see Problem 10 of Chapter 6).*

PROBLEMS

28. Let f be integrable over E and C a measurable subset of E. Show that $\int_C f = \int_E f \cdot \chi_C$.

29. For a measurable function f on $[1, \infty)$ which is bounded on bounded sets, define $a_n = \int_n^{n+1} f$ for each natural number n. Is it true that f is integrable over $[1, \infty)$ if and only if the series $\sum_{n=1}^\infty a_n$ converges? Is it true that f is integrable over $[1, \infty)$ if and only if the series $\sum_{n=1}^\infty a_n$ converges absolutely?

30. Let g be a nonnegative integrable function over E and suppose $\{f_n\}$ is a sequence of measurable functions on E such that for each n, $|f_n| \le g$ a.e. on E. Show that

$$\int_E \liminf f_n \le \liminf \int_E f_n \le \limsup \int_E f_n \le \int_E \limsup f_n.$$

31. Let f be a measurable function on E which can be expressed as $f = g + h$ on E, where g is finite and integrable over E and h is nonnegative on E. Define $\int_E f = \int_E g + \int_E h$. Show that this is properly defined in the sense that it is independent of the particular choice of finite integrable function g and nonnegative function h whose sum is f.

32. Prove the General Lebesgue Dominated Convergence Theorem by following the proof of the Lebesgue Dominated Convergence Theorem, but replacing the sequences $\{g - f_n\}$ and $\{g + f_n'\}$ respectively, by $\{g_n - f_n\}$ and $\{g_n + f_n\}$.

33. Let $\{f_n\}$ be a sequence of integrable functions on E for which $f_n \to f$ a.e. on E and f is integrable over E. Show that $\int_E |f - f_n| \to 0$ if and only if $\lim_{n \to \infty} \int_E |f_n| = \int_E |f|$. (Hint: Use the General Lebesgue Dominated Convergence Theorem.)

34. Let f be a nonnegative measurable function on $\mathbf{R}$. Show that

$$\lim_{n \to \infty} \int_{-n}^{n} f = \int_{\mathbf{R}} f.$$

35. Let f be a real-valued function of two variables (x, y) that is defined on the square $Q = \{(x, y) \mid 0 \le x \le 1, 0 \le y \le 1\}$ and is a measurable function of x for each fixed value of y. Suppose for each fixed value of x, $\lim_{y \to 0} f(x, y) = f(x)$ and that for all y, we have $|f(x, y)| \le g(x)$, where g is integrable over $[0, 1]$. Show that

$$\lim_{y \to 0} \int_0^1 f(x, y)dx = \int_0^1 f(x)dx.$$

Also show that if the function $f(x, y)$ is continuous in y for each x, then

$$h(y) = \int_0^1 f(x, y)dx$$

is a continuous function of y.

36. Let f be a real-valued function of two variables (x, y) that is defined on the square $Q = \{(x, y) \mid 0 \le x \le 1, 0 \le y \le 1\}$ and is a measurable function of x for each fixed value of y. For each $(x, y) \in Q$ let the partial derivative $\partial f / \partial y$ exist. Suppose there is a function g that is integrable over $[0, 1]$ and such that

$$\left| \frac{\partial f}{\partial y}(x, y) \right| \le g(x) \text{ for all } (x, y) \in Q.$$

Prove that

$$\frac{d}{dy}\left[\int_0^1 f(x, y)\, dx \right] = \int_0^1 \frac{\partial f}{\partial y}(x, y)\, dx \text{ for all } y \in [0, 1].$$

4.5   COUNTABLE ADDITIVITY AND CONTINUITY OF INTEGRATION

The linearity and monotonicity properties of the Lebesgue integral, which we established in the preceding section, are extensions of familiar properties of the Riemann integral. In this brief section we establish two properties of the Lebesgue integral which have no counterpart for the Riemann integral. The following countable additivity property for Lebesgue integration is a companion of the countable additivity property for Lebesgue measure.

Theorem 20 (the Countable Additivity of Integration) *Let f be integrable over E and $\{E_n\}_{n=1}^{\infty}$ a disjoint countable collection of measurable subsets of E whose union is E. Then*

$$\int_E f = \sum_{n=1}^{\infty} \int_{E_n} f. \tag{23}$$

Proof Let n be a natural number. Define $f_n = f \cdot \chi_n$ where χ_n is the characteristic function of the measurable set $\bigcup_{k=1}^{n} E_k$. Then f_n is a measurable function on E and

$$|f_n| \leq |f| \text{ on } E.$$

Observe that $\{f_n\} \to f$ pointwise on E. Thus, by the Lebesgue Dominated Convergence Theorem,

$$\int_E f = \lim_{n \to \infty} \int_E f_n.$$

On the other hand, since $\{E_n\}_{n=1}^{\infty}$ is disjoint, it follows from the additivity over domains property of the integral that for each n,

$$\int_E f_n = \sum_{k=1}^{n} \int_{E_k} f.$$

Thus

$$\int_E f = \lim_{n \to \infty} \int_E f_n = \lim_{n \to \infty} \left[\sum_{k=1}^{n} \int_{E_k} f \right] = \sum_{n=1}^{\infty} \int_{E_n} f. \qquad \square$$

We leave it to the reader to use the countable additivity of integration to prove the following result regarding the continuity of integration: use as a pattern the proof of continuity of measure based on countable additivity of measure.

Theorem 21 (the Continuity of Integration) *Let f be integrable over E.*

(i) *If $\{E_n\}_{n=1}^{\infty}$ is an ascending countable collection of measurable subsets of E, then*

$$\int_{\bigcup_{n=1}^{\infty} E_n} f = \lim_{n \to \infty} \int_{E_n} f \qquad (24)$$

(ii) *If $\{E_n\}_{n=1}^{\infty}$ is a descending countable collection of measurable subsets of E, then*

$$\int_{\bigcap_{n=1}^{\infty} E_n} f = \lim_{n \to \infty} \int_{E_n} f. \qquad (25)$$

PROBLEMS

37. Let f be a integrable function on E. Show that for each $\epsilon > 0$, there is a natural number N for which if $n \geq N$, then $\left| \int_{E_n} f \right| < \epsilon$ where $E_n = \{x \in E \mid |x| \geq n\}$.

38. For each of the two functions f on $[1, \infty)$ defined below, show that $\lim_{n \to \infty} \int_1^n f$ exists while f is not integrable over $[1, \infty)$. Does this contradict the continuity of integration?
    (i) Define $f(x) = (-1)^n/n$, for $n \leq x < n+1$.
    (ii) Define $f(x) = (\sin x)/x$ for $1 \leq x < \infty$.

39. Prove the theorem regarding the continuity of integration.

4.6   UNIFORM INTEGRABILITY: THE VITALI CONVERGENCE THEOREM

We conclude this first chapter on Lebesgue integration by establishing, for functions that are integrable over a set of finite measure, a criterion for justifying passage of the limit under the integral sign which is suggested by the following lemma and proposition.

Lemma 22   *Let E be a set of finite measure and δ > 0. Then E is the disjoint union of a finite collection of sets, each of which has measure less than δ.*

Proof   By the continuity of measure,

$$\lim_{n \to \infty} m(E \sim [-n,\, n]) = m(\emptyset) = 0.$$

Choose a natural number n_0 for which $m(E \sim [-n_0,\, n_0]) < \delta$. By choosing a fine enough partition of $[-n_0,\, n_0]$, express $E \cap [-n_0,\, n_0]$ as the disjoint union of a finite collection of sets, each of which has measure less than δ. $\square$

Proposition 23   *Let f be a measurable function on E. If f is integrable over E, then for each ε > 0, there is a δ > 0 for which*

$$\text{if } A \subseteq E \text{ is measurable and } m(A) < \delta, \text{ then } \int_A |f| < \epsilon. \tag{26}$$

Conversely, in the case $m(E) < \infty$, if for each ε > 0, there is a δ > 0 for which (26) holds, then f is integrable over E.

Proof   The theorem follows by establishing it separately for the positive and negative parts of f. We therefore suppose $f \geq 0$ on E. First assume f is integrable over E. Let $\epsilon > 0$. By the definition of the integral of a nonnegative integrable function, there is a measurable bounded function f_ϵ of finite support for which

$$0 \leq f_\epsilon \leq f \text{ on } E \text{ and } 0 \leq \int_E f - \int_E f_\epsilon < \epsilon/2.$$

Since $f - f_\epsilon \geq 0$ on E, if $A \subseteq E$ is measurable, then, by the linearity and additivity over domains of the integral,

$$\int_A f - \int_A f_\epsilon = \int_A [f - f_\epsilon] \leq \int_E [f - f_\epsilon] = \int_E f - \int_E f_\epsilon < \epsilon/2.$$

But f_ϵ is bounded. Choose $M > 0$ for which $0 \leq f_\epsilon < M$ on E_0. Therefore, if $A \subseteq E$ is measurable, then

$$\int_A f < \int_A f_\epsilon + \epsilon/2 \leq M \cdot m(A) + \epsilon/2.$$

Define $\delta = \epsilon/2M$. Then (26) holds for this choice of δ. Conversely, suppose $m(E) < \infty$ and for each $\epsilon > 0$, there is a δ > 0 for which (26) holds. Let $\delta_0 > 0$ respond to the $\epsilon = 1$ challenge. Since $m(E) < \infty$, according to the preceding lemma, we may express E as the disjoint union of a finite collection of measurable subsets $\{E_k\}_{k=1}^N$, each of which has measure less than δ. Therefore

$$\sum_{k=1}^{N} \int_{E_k} f < N.$$

By the additivity over domains of integration it follows that if h is a nonnegative measurable function of finite support and $0 \le h \le f$ on E, then $\int_E h < N$. Therefore f is integrable. $\square$

Definition *A family $\mathcal{F}$ of measurable functions on E is said to be* **uniformly integrable** *over[9] E provided for each $\epsilon > 0$, there is a $\delta > 0$ such that for each $f \in \mathcal{F}$,*

$$\text{if } A \subseteq E \text{ is measurable and } m(A) < \delta, \text{ then } \int_A |f| < \epsilon. \tag{27}$$

Example Let g be a nonnegative integrable function over E. Define

$$\mathcal{F} = \{ f \mid f \text{ is measurable on } E \text{ and } |f| \le g \text{ on } E \}.$$

Then $\mathcal{F}$ is uniformly integrable. This follows from Proposition 23, with f replaced by g, and the observation that for any measurable subset A of E, by the monotonicity of integration, if f belongs to $\mathcal{F}$, then

$$\int_A |f| \le \int_A g.$$

Proposition 24 *Let $\{f_k\}_{k=1}^n$ be a finite collection of functions, each of which is integrable over E. Then $\{f_k\}_{k=1}^n$ is uniformly integrable.*

Proof Let $\epsilon > 0$. For $1 \le k \le n$, by Proposition 23, there is a $\delta_k > 0$ for which

$$\text{if } A \subseteq E \text{ is measurable and } m(A) < \delta_k, \text{ then } \int_A |f_k| < \epsilon. \tag{28}$$

Define $\delta = \min\{\delta_1, \ldots, \delta_n\}$. This δ responds to the ϵ challenge regarding the criterion for the collection $\{f_k\}_{k=1}^n$ to be uniformly integrable. $\square$

Proposition 25 *Assume E has finite measure. Let the sequence of functions $\{f_n\}$ be uniformly integrable over E. If $\{f_n\} \to f$ pointwise a.e. on E, then f is integrable over E.*

Proof Let $\delta_0 > 0$ respond to the $\epsilon = 1$ challenge in the uniform integrability criteria for the sequence $\{f_n\}$. Since $m(E) < \infty$, by Lemma 22, we may express E as the disjoint union of a finite collection of measurable subsets $\{E_k\}_{k=1}^N$ such that $m(E_k) < \delta_0$ for $1 \le k \le N$. For any n, by the monotonicity and additivity over domains property of the integral,

$$\int_E |f_n| = \sum_{k=1}^{N} \int_{E_k} |f_n| < N.$$

---

[9]What is here called "uniformly integrable" is sometimes called "equiintegrable."

We infer from Fatou's Lemma that

$$\int_E |f| \leq \liminf \int_E |f_n| \leq N.$$

Thus $|f|$ is integrable over E. □

The Vitali Convergence Theorem   *Let E be of finite measure. Suppose the sequence of functions $\{f_n\}$ is uniformly integrable over E.*

If $\{f_n\} \to f$ pointwise a.e. on E, then f is integrable over E and $\lim_{n\to\infty} \int_E f_n = \int_E f$.

Proof Propositions 25 tells us that f is integrable over E and hence, by Proposition 15, is finite a.e. on E. Therefore, using Proposition 15 once more, by possibly excising from E a set of measure zero, we suppose the convergence is pointwise on all of E and f is real-valued. We infer from the integral comparison test and the linearity, monotonicity, and additivity over domains property of integration that, for any measurable subset A of E and any natural number n,

$$\left| \int_E f_n - \int_E f \right| = \left| \int_E (f_n - f) \right|$$

$$\leq \int_E |f_n - f|$$

$$= \int_{E \sim A} |f_n - f| + \int_A |f_n - f| \tag{29}$$

$$\leq \int_{E \sim A} |f_n - f| + \int_A |f_n| + \int_A |f|.$$

Let $\epsilon > 0$. By the uniform integrability of $\{f_n\}$, there is a $\delta > 0$ such that $\int_A |f_n| < \epsilon/3$ for any measurable subset of E for which $m(A) < \delta$. Therefore, by Fatou's Lemma, we also have $\int_A |f| \leq \epsilon/3$ for any measurable subset of A for which $m(A) < \delta$. Since f is real-valued and E has finite measure, Egoroff's Theorem tells us that there is a measurable subset E_0 of E for which $m(E_0) < \delta$ and $\{f_n\} \to f$ uniformly on $E \sim E_0$. Choose a natural number N such that $|f_n - f| < \epsilon/[3 \cdot m(E)]$ on $E \sim E_0$ for all $n \geq N$. Take $A = E_0$ in the integral inequality (29). If $n \geq N$, then

$$\left| \int_E f_n - \int_E f \right| \leq \int_{E \sim E_0} |f_n - f| + \int_{E_0} |f_n| + \int_{E_0} |f_n|$$

$$< \epsilon/[3 \cdot m(E)] \cdot m(E \sim E_0) + \epsilon/3 + \epsilon/3 \leq \epsilon.$$

This completes the proof. □

The following theorem shows that the concept of uniform integrability is an essential ingredient in the justification, for a sequence $\{h_n\}$ of nonnegative functions on a set of finite measure that converges pointwise to $h \equiv 0$, of passage of the limit under the integral sign.

Theorem 26 *Let E be of finite measure. Suppose $\{h_n\}$ is a sequence of nonnegative integrable functions that converges pointwise a.e. on E to $h \equiv 0$. Then*

$$\lim_{n \to \infty} \int_E h_n = 0 \text{ if and only if } \{h_n\} \text{ is uniformly integrable over E.}$$

Proof If $\{h_n\}$ is uniformly integrable, then, by the Vitali Convergence Theorem, $\lim_{n \to \infty} \int_E h_n = 0$. Conversely, suppose $\lim_{n \to \infty} \int_E h_n = 0$. Let $\epsilon > 0$. We may choose a natural number N for which $\int_E h_n < \epsilon$ if $n \geq N$. Therefore, since each $h_n \geq 0$ on E,

$$\text{if } A \subseteq E \text{ is measurable and } n \geq N, \text{ then } \int_A h_n < \epsilon. \tag{30}$$

According to Propositions 23 and 24, the finite collection $\{h_n\}_{n=1}^{N-1}$ is uniformly integrable over E. Let δ respond to the ϵ challenge regarding the criterion for the uniform integrability of $\{h_n\}_{n=1}^{N-1}$. We infer from (30) that δ also responds to the ϵ challenge regarding the criterion for the uniform integrability of $\{h_n\}_{n=1}^{\infty}$. $\qquad \square$

PROBLEMS

40. Let f be integrable over $\mathbf{R}$. Show that the function F defined by

$$F(x) = \int_{-\infty}^{x} f \text{ for all } x \in \mathbf{R}$$

is properly defined and continuous. Is it necessarily Lipschitz?

41. Show that Proposition 25 is false if $E = \mathbf{R}$.

42. Show that Theorem 26 is false without the assumption that the h_n's are nonnegative.

43. Let the sequences of functions $\{h_n\}$ and $\{g_n\}$ be uniformly integrable over E. Show that for any α and β, the sequence of linear combinations $\{\alpha f_n + \beta g_n\}$ also is uniformly integrable over E.

44. Let f be integrable over $\mathbf{R}$ and $\epsilon > 0$. Establish the following three approximation properties.
    (i)   There is a simple function η on $\mathbf{R}$ which has finite support and $\int_{\mathbf{R}} |f - \eta| < \epsilon$ (Hint: First verify this if f is nonnegative.]
    (ii) There is a step function s on $\mathbf{R}$ which vanishes outside a closed, bounded interval and $\int_{\mathbf{R}} |f - s| < \epsilon$. (Hint: Apply part (i) and Problem 18 of Chapter 3.)
    (iii) There is a continuous function g on $\mathbf{R}$ which vanishes outside a bounded set and $\int_{\mathbf{R}} |f - g| < \epsilon$.

45. Let f be integrable over E. Define $\hat{f}$ to be the extension of f to all of $\mathbf{R}$ obtained by setting $\hat{f} \equiv 0$ outside of E. Show that $\hat{f}$ is integrable over $\mathbf{R}$ and $\int_E f = \int_{\mathbf{R}} \hat{f}$. Use this and part (i) and (iii) of the preceding problem to show that for $\epsilon > 0$, there is a simple function η on E and a continuous function g on E for which $\int_E |f - \eta| < \epsilon$ and $\int_E |f - g| < \epsilon$.

46. (Riemann-Lebesgue) Let f be integrable over $(-\infty, \infty)$. Show that

$$\lim_{n \to \infty} \int_{-\infty}^{\infty} f(x) \cos nx \, dx = 0.$$

(Hint: First show this for f is a step function that vanishes outside a closed, bounded interval and then use the approximation property (ii) of Problem 44.)

47. Let f be integrable over $(-\infty, \infty)$.
    (i) Show that for each t,

$$\int_{-\infty}^{\infty} f(x) \, dx = \int_{-\infty}^{\infty} f(x+t) \, dx.$$

    (ii) Let g be a bounded measurable function on $\mathbf{R}$. Show that

$$\lim_{t \to 0} \int_{-\infty}^{\infty} g(x) \cdot [f(x) - f(x+t)] = 0.$$

(Hint: First show this, using uniform continuity of f on $\mathbf{R}$, if f is continuous and vanishes outside a bounded set. Then use the approximation property (iii) of Problem 44.)

48. Let f be integrable over E and g be a bounded measurable function on E. Show that $f \cdot g$ is integrable over E.

49. Let f be integrable over $\mathbf{R}$. Show that the following four assertions are equivalent:
    (i) $f = 0$ a.e on $\mathbf{R}$.
    (ii) $\int_{\mathbf{R}} fg = 0$ for every bounded measurable function g on $\mathbf{R}$.
    (iii) $\int_A f = 0$ for every measurable set A.
    (iv) $\int_{\mathcal{O}} f = 0$ for every open set $\mathcal{O}$.

50. Let $\mathcal{F}$ be a family of functions, each of which is integrable over E. Show that $\mathcal{F}$ is uniformly integrable over E if and only if for each $\epsilon > 0$, there is a $\delta > 0$ such that for each $f \in \mathcal{F}$,

$$\text{if } A \subseteq E \text{ is measurable and } m(A) < \delta, \text{ then } \left| \int_A f \right| < \epsilon.$$

51. Let $\mathcal{F}$ be a family of functions, each of which is integrable over E. Show that $\mathcal{F}$ is uniformly integrable over E if and only if for each $\epsilon > 0$, there is a $\delta > 0$ such that for all $f \in \mathcal{F}$,

$$\text{if } \mathcal{U} \text{ is open and } m(E \cap \mathcal{U}) < \delta, \text{ then } \int_{E \cap \mathcal{U}} |f| < \epsilon.$$

52. (a) Let $\mathcal{F}$ be the family of functions f on $[0, 1]$, each of which is integrable over $[0, 1]$ and has $\int_0^1 |f| \le 1$. Is $\mathcal{F}$ uniformly integrable over $[0, 1]$?
    (b) Let $\mathcal{F}$ be the family of functions f on $[0, 1]$, each of which is continuous on $[0, 1]$ and has $|f| \le 1$ on $[0, 1]$. Is $\mathcal{F}$ uniformly integrable over $[0, 1]$?
    (c) Let $\mathcal{F}$ be the family of functions f on $[0, 1]$, each of which is integrable over $[0, 1]$ and has $\int_a^b |f| \le b - a$ for all $[a, b] \subseteq [0, 1]$. Is $\mathcal{F}$ uniformly integrable over $[0, 1]$?

CHAPTER 5

Lebesgue Integration: Further Topics

Contents

In this brief chapter, we first consider a generalization of the Vitali Convergence Theorem to sequences of integrable functions on a set of infinite measure; for a pointwise convergent sequence of integrable functions, tightness must be added to uniform integrablity in order to justify passage of the limit under the integral sign. We then consider a mode of sequential convergence for sequences of measurable functions called convergence in measure and examine its relationship to pointwise convergence and convergence of integrals. Finally, we prove that a bounded function is Lebesgue integrable over a set of finite measure if and only if it is measurable, and that a bounded function is Riemann integrable over a closed, bounded interval if and only if it is continuous at almost all points in its domain.

5.1 UNIFORM INTEGRABILITY AND TIGHTNESS: A GENERAL VITALI CONVERGENCE THEOREM

The Vitali Convergence Theorem of the preceding chapter tells us that if $m(E) < \infty$, $\{f_n\}$ is uniformly integrable over E and converges pointwise almost everywhere on E to f, then f is integrable over E and passage of the limit under the integral sign is justified, that is,

$$\lim_{n \to \infty} \left[\int_E f_n \right] = \int_E \lim_{n \to \infty} f_n = \int_E f. \tag{1}$$

This theorem requires that E have finite measure. Indeed, for each natural number n, define $f_n = \chi_{[n, n+1]}$ and $f \equiv 0$ on $\mathbf{R}$. Then $\{f_n\}$ is uniformly integrable over $\mathbf{R}$ and converges pointwise on $\mathbf{R}$ to f. However,

$$\lim_{n \to \infty} \left[\int_E f_n \right] = 1 \neq 0 = \int_E \lim_{n \to \infty} f_n = \int_E f.$$

The following property of functions that are integrable over sets of infinite measure suggests an additional property which should accompany uniform integrability in order to justify passage of the limit under the integral sign for sequences of functions on a domain of infinite measure.

Proposition 1 *Let f be integrable over E. Then for each $\epsilon > 0$, there is a set of finite measure E_0 for which*

$$\int_{E \sim E_0} |f| < \epsilon.$$

Proof Let $\epsilon > 0$. The nonnegative function $|f|$ is integrable over E. By the definition of the integral of a nonnegative function, there is a bounded measurable function g on E, which vanishes outside a subset E_0 of E of finite measure, for which $0 \leq g \leq |f|$ and $\int_E |f| - \int_E g < \epsilon$. Therefore, by the linearity and additivity over domains properties of integration,

$$\int_{E \sim E_0} |f| = \int_{E \sim E_0} [|f| - g] \leq \int_E [|f| - g] < \epsilon. \qquad \square$$

Definition *A family $\mathcal{F}$ of measurable functions on E is said to be **tight** over E provided for each $\epsilon > 0$, there is a a subset E_0 of E of finite measure for which*

$$\int_{E \sim E_0} |f| < \epsilon \text{ for all } f \in \mathcal{F}.$$

We infer from Proposition 23 of the preceding chapter that if $\mathcal{F}$ is a family of functions on E that is uniformly integrable and tight over E, then each function in $\mathcal{F}$ is integrable over E.

The Vitali Convergence Theorem *Let $\{f_n\}$ be a sequence of functions on E that is uniformly integrable and tight over E. Suppose $\{f_n\} \to f$ pointwise a.e. on E. Then f is integrable over E and*

$$\lim_{n \to \infty} \int_E f_n = \int_E f.$$

Proof Let $\epsilon > 0$. By the tightness over E of the sequence $\{f_n\}$, there is a measurable subset E_0 of E which has finite measure and

$$\int_{E \sim E_0} |f_n| < \epsilon/4 \text{ for all } n.$$

We infer from Fatou's Lemma that $\int_{E \sim E_0} |f| \leq \epsilon/4$. Therefore f is integrable over $E \sim E_0$. Moreover, by the linearity and monotonicity of integration,

$$\left| \int_{E \sim E_0} [f_n - f] \right| \leq \int_{E \sim E_0} |f_n| + \int_{E \sim E_0} |f| < \epsilon/2 \text{ for all } n. \tag{2}$$

But E_0 has finite measure and $\{f_n\}$ is uniformly integrable over E_0. Therefore, by the Vitali Convergence Theorem for functions on domains of finite measure, f is integrable over E_0 and we may choose an index N for which

$$\left| \int_{E_0} [f_n - f] \right| < \epsilon/2 \text{ for all } n \geq N. \tag{3}$$

Therefore f is integrable over E and, by (2) and (3),

$$\left| \int_E [f_n - f] \right| < \epsilon \text{ for all } n \geq N.$$

The proof is complete. ☐

We leave the proof of the following corollary as an exercise.

Corollary 2 *Let $\{h_n\}$ be a sequence of nonnegative integrable functions on E. Suppose $\{h_n(x)\} \to 0$ for almost all x in E. Then*

$$\lim_{n \to \infty} \int_E h_n = 0 \text{ if and only if } \{h_n\} \text{ is uniformly integrable and tight over } E.$$

PROBLEMS

1. Prove Corollary 2.

2. Let $\{f_k\}_{k=1}^n$ be a finite family of functions, each of which is integrable over E. Show that $\{f_k\}_{k=1}^n$ is uniformly integrable and tight over E.

3. Let the sequences of functions $\{h_n\}$ and $\{g_n\}$ be uniformly integrable and tight over E. Show that for any α and β, $\{\alpha f_n + \beta g_n\}$ also is uniformly integrable and tight over E.

4. Let $\{f_n\}$ be a sequence of measurable functions on E. Show that $\{f_n\}$ is uniformly integrable and tight over E if and only if for each $\epsilon > 0$, there is a measurable subset E_0 of E that has finite measure and a $\delta > 0$ such that for each measurable subset A of E and index n,

$$\text{if } m(A \cap E_0) < \delta, \text{ then } \int_A |f_n| < \epsilon.$$

5. Let $\{f_n\}$ be a sequence of integrable functions on $\mathbf{R}$. Show that $\{f_n\}$ is uniformly integrable and tight over $\mathbf{R}$ if and only if for each $\epsilon > 0$, there are positive numbers r and δ such that for each open subset $\mathcal{O}$ of $\mathbf{R}$ and index n,

$$\text{if } m(\mathcal{O} \cap (-r, r)) < \delta, \text{ then } \int_{\mathcal{O}} |f_n| < \epsilon.$$

5.2 CONVERGENCE IN MEASURE

We have considered sequences of functions that converge uniformly, that converge pointwise, and that converge pointwise almost everywhere. To this list we add one more mode of convergence that has useful relationships both to pointwise convergence almost everywhere and to forthcoming criteria for justifying the passage of the limit under the integral sign.

Definition *Let $\{f_n\}$ be a sequence of measurable functions on E and f a measurable function on E for which f and each f_n is finite a.e. on E. The sequence $\{f_n\}$ is said to **converge in measure** on E to f provided for each $\eta > 0$,*

$$\lim_{n \to \infty} m \{x \in E \mid |f_n(x) - f(x)| > \eta\} = 0.$$

When we write $\{f_n\} \to f$ in measure on E we are implicitly assuming that f and each f_n is measurable, and finite a.e. on E. Observe that if $\{f_n\} \to f$ uniformly on E, and f is a real-valued measurable function on E, then $\{f_n\} \to f$ in measure on E since for $\eta > 0$, the set $\{x \in E \,|\, |f_n(x) - f(x)| > \eta\}$ is empty for n sufficiently large. However, we also have the following much stronger result.

Proposition 3   *Assume E has finite measure. Let $\{f_n\}$ be a sequence of measurable functions on E that converges pointwise a.e. on E to f and f is finite a.e. on E. Then $\{f_n\} \to f$ in measure on E.*

Proof   First observe that f is measurable since it is the pointwise limit almost everywhere of a sequence of measurable functions. Let $\eta > 0$. To prove convergence in measure we let $\epsilon > 0$ and seek an index N such that

$$m\left\{x \in E \;\middle|\; |f_n(x) - f(x)| > \eta\right\} < \epsilon \text{ for all } n \geq N. \tag{4}$$

Egoroff's Theorem tells us that there is a measurable subset F of E with $m(E \sim F) < \epsilon$ such that $\{f_n\} \to f$ uniformly on F. Thus there is an index N such that

$$|f_n - f| < \eta \text{ on } F \text{ for all } n \geq N.$$

Thus, for $n \geq N$, $\{x \in E \,|\, |f_n(x) - f(x)| > \eta\} \subseteq E \sim F$ and so (4) holds for this choice of N. $\square$

The above proposition is false if E has infinite measure. The following example shows that the converse of this proposition also is false.

Example   Consider the sequence of subintervals of $[0, 1]$, $\{I_n\}_{n=1}^{\infty}$, which has initial terms listed as

$$[0, 1], [0, 1/2], [1/2, 1], [0, 1/3], [1/3, 2/3], [2/3, 1],$$
$$[0, 1/4], [1/4, 1/2], [1/2, 3/4], [3/4, 1] \dots$$

For each index n, define f_n to be the restriction to $[0, 1]$ of the characteristic function of I_n. Let f be the function that is identically zero on $[0, 1]$. We claim that $\{f_n\} \to f$ in measure. Indeed, observe that $\lim_{n \to \infty} \ell(I_n) = 0$ since for each natural number m,

$$\text{if } n > 1 + \cdots + m = \frac{m(m+1)}{2}, \text{ then } \ell(I_n) < 1/m.$$

Thus, for $0 < \eta < 1$, since $\{x \in E \,|\, |f_n(x) - f(x)| > \eta\} \subseteq I_n$,

$$0 \leq \lim_{n \to \infty} m\left\{x \in E \;\middle|\; |f_n(x) - f(x)| > \eta\right\} \leq \lim_{n \to \infty} \ell(I_n) = 0.$$

However, it is clear that there is no point x in $[0, 1]$ at which $\{f_n(x)\}$ converges to $f(x)$ since for each point x in $[0, 1]$, $f_n(x) = 1$ for infinitely many indices n, while $f(x) = 0$.

Theorem 4 *(Riesz)* *If $\{f_n\} \to f$ in measure on E, then there is a subsequence $\{f_{n_k}\}$ that converges pointwise a.e. on E to f.*

Proof By the definition of convergence in measure, there is a strictly increasing sequence of natural numbers $\{n_k\}$ for which

$$m\{x \in E \mid |f_j(x) - f(x)| > 1/k\} < 1/2^k \text{ for all } j \geq n_k.$$

For each index k, define

$$E_k = \{x \in E \mid |f_{n_k} - f(x)| > 1/k\}.$$

Then $m(E_k) < 1/2^k$ and therefore $\sum_{k=1}^{\infty} m(E_k) < \infty$. The Borel-Cantelli Lemma tells us that for almost all $x \in E$, there is an index $K(x)$ such that $x \notin E_k$ if $k \geq K(x)$, that is,

$$|f_{n_k}(x) - f(x)| \leq 1/k \text{ for all } k \geq K(x).$$

Therefore

$$\lim_{k \to \infty} f_{n_k}(x) = f(x). \qquad \square$$

Corollary 5 *Let $\{f_n\}$ be a sequence of nonnegative integrable functions on E. Then*

$$\lim_{n \to \infty} \int_E f_n = 0 \tag{5}$$

if and only if

$\{f_n\} \to 0$ *in measure on E and $\{f_n\}$ is uniformly integrable and tight over E.* (6)

Proof First assume (5). Corollary 2 tells us that $\{f_n\}$ is uniformly integrable and tight over E. To show that $\{f_n\} \to 0$ in measure on E, let $\eta > 0$. By Chebychev's Inequality, for each index n,

$$m\{x \in E \mid f_n > \eta\} \leq \frac{1}{\eta} \cdot \int_E f_n.$$

Thus,

$$0 \leq \lim_{n \to \infty} m\{x \in E \mid f_n > \eta\} \leq \frac{1}{\eta} \cdot \lim_{n \to \infty} \int_E f_n = 0.$$

Hence $\{f_n\} \to 0$ in measure on E.

To prove the converse, we argue by contradiction. Assume (6) holds but (5) fails to hold. Then there is some $\epsilon_0 > 0$ and a subsequence $\{f_{n_k}\}$ for which

$$\int_E f_{n_k} \geq \epsilon_0 \text{ for all } k.$$

However, by Theorem 4, a subsequence of $\{f_{n_k}\}$ converges to $f \equiv 0$ pointwise almost everywhere on E and this subsequence is uniformly integrable and tight so that, by the Vitali Convergence Theorem, we arrive at a contradiction to the existence of the above ϵ_0. This completes the proof. $\qquad \square$

PROBLEMS

6. Let $\{f_n\} \to f$ in measure on E and g be a measurable function on E that is finite a.e. on E. Show that $\{f_n\} \to g$ in measure on E if and only if $f = g$ a.e. on E.

7. Let E have finite measure, $\{f_n\} \to f$ in measure on E and g be a measurable function on E that is finite a.e. on E. Prove that $\{f_n \cdot g\} \to f \cdot g$ in measure, and use this to show that $\{f_n^2\} \to f^2$ in measure. Infer from this that if $\{g_n\} \to g$ in measure, then $\{f_n \cdot g_n\} \to f \cdot g$ in measure.

8. Show that Fatou's Lemma, the Monotone Convergence Theorem, the Lebesgue Dominated Convergence Theorem, and the Vitali Convergence Theorem remain valid if "pointwise convergence *a.e.*" is replaced by "convergence in measure."

9. Show that Proposition 3 does not necessarily hold for sets E of infinite measure.

10. Show that linear combinations of sequences that converge in measure on a set of finite measure also converge in measure.

11. Assume E has finite measure. Let $\{f_n\}$ be a sequence of measurable functions on E and f a measurable on E for which f and each f_n is finite a.e. on E. Prove that $\{f_n\} \to f$ in measure on E if and only if every subsequence of $\{f_n\}$ has in turn a further subsequence that converges to f pointwise a.e. on E.

12. Show that a sequence $\{a_j\}$ of real numbers converges to a real number if $|a_{j+1} - a_j| \leq 1/2^j$ for all j by showing that the sequence $\{a_j\}$ must be Cauchy.

13. A sequence $\{f_n\}$ of measurable functions on E is said to be **Cauchy in measure** provided given $\eta > 0$ and $\epsilon > 0$ there is an index N such that for all $m, n \geq N$,

$$m\left\{x \in E \mid |f_n(x) - f_m(x)| \geq \eta\right\} < \epsilon.$$

Show that if $\{f_n\}$ is Cauchy in measure, then there is a measurable function f on E to which the sequence $\{f_n\}$ converges in measure. (Hint: Choose a strictly increasing sequence of natural numbers $\{n_j\}$ such that for each index j, if $E_j = \{x \in E \mid |f_{n_{j+1}}(x) - f_{n_j}(x)| > 1/2^j\}$, then $m(E_j) < 1/2^j$. Now use the Borel-Cantelli Lemma and the preceding problem.)

14. Assume $m(E) < \infty$. For two measurable functions g and h on E, define

$$\rho(g, h) = \int_E \frac{|g - h|}{1 + |g - h|}.$$

Show that $\{f_n\} \to f$ in measure on E if and only if $\lim_{n \to \infty} \rho(f_n, f) = 0$.

5.3   CHARACTERIZATIONS OF RIEMANN AND LEBESGUE INTEGRABILITY

Lemma 6   *Let $\{\varphi_n\}$ and $\{\psi_n\}$ be sequences of functions, each of which is integrable over E, such that $\{\varphi_n\}$ is increasing while $\{\psi_n\}$ is decreasing on E. Let the function f on E have the property that*

$$\varphi_n \leq f \leq \psi_n \text{ on } E \text{ for all } n.$$

If

$$\lim_{n \to \infty} \int_E [\psi_n - \varphi_n] = 0,$$

then

$$\{\varphi_n\} \to f \text{ pointwise a.e. on } E, \{\psi_n\} \to f \text{ pointwise a.e. on } E, f \text{ is integrable over } E,$$

$$\lim_{n \to \infty} \int_E \varphi_n = \int_E f \text{ and } \lim_{n \to \infty} \int_E \psi_n = \int_E f$$

Proof For x in E, define

$$\varphi^*(x) = \lim_{n \to \infty} \varphi_n(x) \text{ and } \psi^*(x) = \lim_{n \to \infty} \psi_n(x).$$

The functions are φ^* and ψ^* properly defined since monotone sequences of extended real-valued numbers converge to an extended real number and they are measurable since each is the pointwise limit of a sequence of measurable functions. We have the inequalities

$$\varphi_n \le \varphi^* \le f \le \psi^* \le \psi_n \text{ on } E \text{ for all } n. \tag{7}$$

By the monotonicity and linearity of the integral of nonnegative measurable functions,

$$0 \le \int_E (\psi^* - \varphi^*) \le \int_E (\psi_n - \varphi_n) \text{ for all } n,$$

so that

$$0 \le \int_E (\psi^* - \varphi^*) \le \lim_{n \to \infty} \int_E (\psi_n - \varphi_n) = 0.$$

Since $\psi^* - \varphi^*$ is a nonnegative measurable function and $\int_E (\psi^* - \varphi^*) = 0$, Proposition 9 of Chapter 4 tells us that $\psi^* = \varphi^*$ a.e. on E. But $\varphi^* \le f \le \psi^*$ on E. Therefore

$$\{\varphi_n\} \to f \text{ and } \{\psi_n\} \to f \text{ pointwise a.e. on } E.$$

Therefore f is measurable. Observe that since $0 \le f - \varphi_1 \le \psi_1 - \varphi_1$ on E and ψ_1 and φ_1 are integrable over E, we infer from the integral comparison test that f is integrable over E. We infer from inequality (7) that for all n,

$$0 \le \int_E \psi_n - \int_E f = \int_E (\psi_n - f) \le \int_E (\psi_n - \varphi_n)$$

and

$$0 \le \int_E f - \int_E \varphi_n = \int_E (f - \varphi_n) \le \int_E (\psi_n - \varphi_n)$$

and therefore

$$\lim_{n \to \infty} \int_E \varphi_n = \int_E f = \lim_{n \to \infty} \int_E \psi_n. \qquad \square$$

Theorem 7 *Let f be a bounded function on a set of finite measure E. Then f is Lebesgue integrable over E if and only if it is measurable.*

Proof We have already shown that a bounded measurable function on a set of finite measure is Lebesgue integrable (see page 74). It remains to prove the converse. Suppose f is integrable. From the equality of the upper and lower Lebesgue integrals we conclude that there are sequences of simple functions $\{\varphi_n\}$ and $\{\psi_n\}$ for which

$$\varphi_n \le f \le \psi_n \text{ on } E \text{ for all } n,$$

and

$$\lim_{n \to \infty} \int_E [\psi_n - \varphi_n] = 0.$$

Since the maximum and minimum of a pair of simple functions are again simple, using the monotonicity of integration and by possibly replacing φ_n by $\max_{1 \le i \le n} \varphi_i$ and ψ_n by $\min_{1 \le i \le n} \psi_i$, we may suppose $\{\varphi_n\}$ is increasing and $\{\psi_n\}$ is decreasing. By the preceding lemma, $\{\varphi_n\} \to f$ pointwise almost everywhere on E. Therefore f is measurable since it is the pointwise limit almost everywhere of a sequence of measurable functions. $\qquad\square$

At the very beginning of our consideration of integration, we showed that if a bounded function on the closed, bounded interval $[a, b]$ is Riemann integrable over $[a, b]$, then it is Lebesgue integrable over $[a, b]$ and the integrals are equal. We may therefore infer from the preceding theorem that if a bounded function on $[a, b]$ is Riemann integrable, then it is measurable. The following theorem is much more precise.

Theorem 8 (**Lebesgue**) *Let f be a bounded function on the closed, bounded interval $[a, b]$. Then f is Riemann integrable over $[a, b]$ if and only if the set of points in $[a, b]$ at which f fails to be continuous has measure zero.*

Proof We first suppose f is Riemann integrable. We infer from the equality of the upper and lower Riemann integrals over $[a, b]$ that there are sequences of partitions $\{P_n\}$ and $\{P'_n\}$ of $[a, b]$ for which

$$\lim_{n \to \infty} [U(f, P_n) - L(f, P'_n)] = 0,$$

where $U(f, P_n)$ and $L(f, P'_n)$ upper and lower Darboux sums. Since, under refinement, lower Darboux sums increase and upper Darboux sums decrease, by possibly replacing each P_n by a common refinement of $P_1, \ldots, P_n, P'_1, \ldots, P'_n$, we may assume each P_{n+1} is a refinement of P_n and $P_n = P'_n$. For each index n, define φ_n to be the lower step function associated with f with respect to P_n, that is, which agrees with f at the partition points of P_n and which on each open interval determined by P_n has constant value equal to the infimum of f on that interval. We define the upper step function ψ_n in a similar manner. By definition of the Darboux sums,

$$L(f, P_n) = \int_a^b \varphi_n \text{ and } U(f, P_n) = \int_a^b \psi_n \text{ for all } n.$$

Then $\{\varphi_n\}$ and $\{\psi_n\}$ are sequences of integrable functions such that for each index n, $\varphi_n \le f \le \psi_n$ on E. Moreover, the sequence $\{\varphi_n\}$ is increasing and $\{\psi_n\}$ is decreasing, because each P_{n+1} is a refinement of P_n. Finally,

$$\lim_{n \to \infty} \int_a^b [\psi_n - \varphi_n] = \lim_{n \to \infty} [U(f, P_n) - L(f, P_n)] = 0.$$

We infer from the preceding lemma that

$$\{\varphi_n\} \to f \text{ and } \{\psi_n\} \to f \text{ pointwise a.e on } [a, b].$$

The set E of points x at which either $\{\psi_n(x)\}$ or $\{\varphi_n(x)\}$ fail to converge to $f(x)$ has measure 0. Let E_0 be the union of E and the set of all the partition points in the P_n's. As the union of a set of measure zero and a countable set, $m(E_0) = 0$. We claim that f is continuous at each point in $E \sim E_0$. Indeed, let x_0 belong to $E \sim E_0$. To show that f is continuous at x_0, let $\epsilon > 0$. Since $\{\psi_n(x_0)\}$ and $\{\varphi_n(x_0)\}$ converge to $f(x_0)$, we may choose a natural number n_0 for which

$$f(x_0) - \epsilon < \varphi_{n_0}(x_0) \leq f(x_0) \leq \psi_{n_0}(x_0) < f(x_0) + \epsilon. \tag{8}$$

Since x_0 is not a partition point of P_{n_0}, we may choose $\delta > 0$ such that the open interval $(x_0 - \delta, x_0 + \delta)$ is contained in the open interval I_{n_0} determined by P_{n_0} which contains x_0. This containment implies that

$$\text{if } |x - x_0| < \delta, \text{ then } \varphi_{n_0}(x_0) \leq \varphi_{n_0}(x) \leq f(x) \leq \psi_{n_0}(x) \leq \psi_{n_0}(x).$$

From this inequality and inequality (8) we infer that

$$\text{if } |x - x_0| < \delta, \text{ then } |f(x) - f(x_0)| < \epsilon.$$

Thus f is continuous at x_0.

It remains to prove the converse. Assume f is continuous at almost all points in $[a, b]$. Let $\{P_n\}$ be any sequence of partitions of $[a, b]$ for which[1]

$$\lim_{n \to \infty} \text{gap } P_n = 0.$$

We claim that

$$\lim_{n \to \infty} [U(f, P_n) - L(f, P_n)] = 0. \tag{9}$$

If this is verified, then from the following estimate for the lower and upper Riemann integrals,

$$0 \leq \overline{\int_a^b} f - \underline{\int_a^b} f \leq [U(f, P_n) - L(f, P_n)] \text{ for all } n,$$

we conclude that f is integrable over $[a, b]$. For each n, let φ_n and ψ_n be the lower and upper step functions associated with f over the partition P_n. To prove (9) is to prove that

$$\lim_{n \to \infty} \int_a^b [\psi_n - \varphi_n] = 0. \tag{10}$$

The Riemann integral of a step function equals its Lebesgue integral. Moreover, since the function f is bounded on the bounded set $[a, b]$, the sequences $\{\varphi_n\}$ and $\{\psi_n\}$ are uniformly bounded on $[a, b]$. Hence, by the Bounded Convergence Theorem, to verify (10) it suffices to show that $\{\varphi_n\} \to f$ and $\{\psi_n\} \to f$ pointwise on the set of points in (a, b) at which f is continuous and which are not partition points of any partition P_n. Let x_0 be such a point. We show that

$$\lim_{n \to \infty} \varphi_n(x_0) = f(x_0) \text{ and } \lim_{n \to \infty} \psi_n(x_0) = f(x_0). \tag{11}$$

---

[1]The gap of a partition P is defined to be the maximum distance between consecutive points of the partition.

Let $\epsilon > 0$. Let $\delta > 0$ be such that

$$f(x_0) - \epsilon/2 < f(x) < f(x_0) + \epsilon/2 \text{ if } |x - x_0| < \delta. \tag{12}$$

Choose an index N for which $\text{gap } P_n < \delta$ if $n \geq N$. If $n \geq N$ and I_n is the open partition interval determined by P_n, which contains x_0, then $I_n \subseteq (x_0 - \delta, x_0 + \delta)$. We infer from (12) that

$$f(x_0) - \epsilon/2 \leq \varphi_n(x_0) < f(x_0) < \psi_n(x_0) \leq f(x_0) + \epsilon/2$$

and therefore

$$0 \leq \psi_n(x_0) - f(x_0) < \epsilon \text{ and } 0 \leq f(x_0) - \varphi_n(x_0) < \epsilon \text{ for all } n \geq N.$$

Thus (11) holds and the proof is complete.   □

PROBLEMS

15. Let f and g be bounded functions that are Riemann integrable over $[a, b]$. Show that the product fg also is Riemann integrable over $[a, b]$.

16. Let f be a bounded function on $[a, b]$ whose set of discontinuities has measure zero. Show that f is measurable. Then show that the same holds without the assumption of boundedness.

17. Let f be a function on $[0, 1]$ that is continuous on $(0, 1]$. Show that it is possible for the sequence $\{\int_{[1/n, 1]} f\}$ to converge and yet f is not Lebesgue integrable over $[0, 1]$. Can this happen if f is nonnegative?

CHAPTER 6

Differentiation and Integration

Contents

The fundamental theorems of integral and differential calculus, with respect to the Riemann integral, are the workhorses of calculus. In this chapter we formulate these two theorems for the Lebesgue integral. For a function f on the closed, bounded interval $[a, b]$, when is

$$\int_a^b f' = f(b) - f(a)? \tag{i}$$

Assume f is continuous. Extend f to take the value $f(b)$ on $(b, b + 1]$, and for $0 < h \leq 1$, define the divided difference function $\text{Diff}_h f$ and average value function $\text{Av}_h f$ on $[a, b]$ by

$$\text{Diff}_h f(x) = \frac{f(x+h) - f(x)}{h} \quad \text{and} \quad \text{Av}_h f(x) = \frac{1}{h} \int_x^{x+h} f(t)\, dt \text{ for all } x \text{ in } [a, b].$$

A change of variables and cancellation provides the discrete formulation of (i) for the Riemann integral:

$$\int_a^b \text{Diff}_h f = \text{Av}_h f(b) - \text{Av}_h f(a).$$

The limit of the right-hand side as $h \to 0^+$ equals $f(b) - f(a)$. We prove a striking theorem of Henri Lebesgue which tells us that a monotone function on (a, b) has a finite derivative almost everywhere. We then define what it means for a function to be absolutely continuous and prove that if f is absolutely continuous, then f is the difference of monotone functions and the collection of divided differences, $\{\text{Diff}_h f\}_{0 < h \leq 1}$, is uniformly integrable. Therefore, by the Vitali Convergence Theorem, (i) follows for f absolutely continuous by taking the limit as $h \to 0^+$ in its discrete formulation. If f is monotone and (i) holds, we prove that f must be absolutely continuous. From the integral form of the fundamental theorem, (i), we obtain the differential form, namely, if f is Lebesgue integrable over $[a, b]$, then

$$\frac{d}{dx}\left[\int_a^x f\right] = f(x) \text{ for almost all } x \text{ in } [a, b]. \tag{ii}$$

6.1   CONTINUITY OF MONOTONE FUNCTIONS

Recall that a function is defined to be monotone if it is either increasing or decreasing. Monotone functions play a decisive role in resolving the question posed in the preamble. There are two reasons for this. First, a theorem of Lebesgue (page 112) asserts that a monotone function on an open interval is differentiable almost everywhere. Second, a theorem of Jordan (page 117) tells us that a very general family of functions on a closed, bounded interval, those of bounded variation, which includes Lipschitz functions, may be expressed as the difference of monotone functions and therefore they also are differentiable almost everywhere on the interior of their domain. In this brief preliminary section we consider continuity properties of monotone functions.

Theorem 1 *Let f be a monotone function on the open interval (a, b). Then f is continuous except possibly at a countable number of points in (a, b).*

Proof Assume f is increasing. Furthermore, assume (a, b) is bounded and f is increasing on the closed interval $[a, b]$. Otherwise, express (a, b) as the union of an ascending sequence of open, bounded intervals, the closures of which are contained in (a, b), and take the union of the discontinuities in each of this countable collection of intervals. For each $x_0 \in (a, b)$, f has a limit from the left and from the right at x_0. Define

$$f(x_0^-) = \lim_{x \to x_0^-} f(x) = \sup \{ f(x) \mid a < x < x_0 \},$$

$$f(x_0^+) = \lim_{x \to x_0^+} f(x) = \inf \{ f(x) \mid x_0 < x < b \}.$$

Since f is increasing, $f(x_0^-) \leq f(x_0^+)$. The function f fails to be continuous at x_0 if and only if $f(x_0^-) < f(x_0^+)$, in which case we define the open "jump" interval $J(x_0)$ by

$$J(x_0) = \{ y \mid f(x_0^-) < y < f(x_0^+) \}.$$

Each jump interval is contained in the bounded interval $[f(a), f(b)]$ and the collection of jump intervals is disjoint. Therefore, for each natural number n, there are only a finite number of jump intervals of length greater than $1/n$. Thus the set of points of discontinuity of f is the union of a countable collection of finite sets and therefore is countable.   □

Proposition 2 *Let C be a countable subset of the open interval (a, b). Then there is an increasing function on (a, b) that is continuous only at points in $(a, b) \sim C$.*

Proof If C is finite the proof is clear. Assume C is countably infinite. Let $\{q_n\}_{n=1}^{\infty}$ be an enumeration of C. Define the function f on (a, b) by setting[1]

$$f(x) = \sum_{\{n \mid q_n \leq x\}} \frac{1}{2^n} \quad \text{for all } a < x < b.$$

---

[1] We use the convention that a sum over the empty-set is zero.

Since a geometric series with a ratio less than 1 converges, f is properly defined. Moreover,

$$\text{if } a < u < v < b, \text{ then } f(v) - f(u) = \sum_{\{n \mid u < q_n \leq v\}} \frac{1}{2^n}. \tag{1}$$

Thus f is increasing. Let $x_0 = q_k$ belong to C. Then, by (1),

$$f(x_0) - f(x) \geq \frac{1}{2^k} \text{ for all } x < x_0.$$

Therefore f fails to be continuous at x_0. Now let x_0 belong to $(a, b) \sim C$. Let n be a natural number. There is an open interval I containing x_0 for which q_n does not belong to I for $1 \leq k \leq n$. We infer from (1) that $|f(x) - f(x_0)| < 1/2^n$ for all $x \in I$. Therefore f is continuous at x_0. $\qquad \square$

PROBLEMS

1. Let C be a countable subset of the nondegenerate closed, bounded interval $[a, b]$. Show that there is an increasing function on $[a, b]$ that is continuous only at points in $[a, b] \sim C$.

2. Show that there is a strictly increasing function on $[0, 1]$ that is continuous only at the irrational numbers in $[0, 1]$.

3. Let f be a monotone function on a subset E of $\mathbf{R}$. Show that f is continuous except possibly at a countable number of points in E.

4. Let E be a subset of $\mathbf{R}$ and C a countable subset of E. Is there a monotone function on E that is continuous only at points in $E \sim C$?

6.2   DIFFERENTIABILITY OF MONOTONE FUNCTIONS: LEBESGUE'S THEOREM

A closed, bounded interval $[c, d]$ is said to be nondegenerate provided $c < d$.

Definition *A collection $\mathcal{F}$ of closed, bounded, nondegenerate intervals is said to cover a set E in the sense of Vitali provided for each point x in E and $\epsilon > 0$, there is an interval I in $\mathcal{F}$ that contains x and has $\ell(I) < \epsilon$.*

The Vitali Covering Lemma *Let E be a set of finite outer measure and $\mathcal{F}$ a collection of closed, bounded intervals that covers E in the sense of Vitali. Then for each $\epsilon > 0$, there is a finite disjoint subcollection $\{I_k\}_{k=1}^n$ of $\mathcal{F}$ for which*

$$m^* \left[E \sim \bigcup_{k=1}^n I_k \right] < \epsilon. \tag{2}$$

Proof Since $m^*(E) < \infty$, there is an open set $\mathcal{O}$ containing E for which $m(\mathcal{O}) < \infty$. Because $\mathcal{F}$ is a Vitali covering of E, we may assume that each interval in $\mathcal{F}$ is contained in $\mathcal{O}$. By the countable additivity and monotonicity of measure,

$$\text{if } \{I_k\}_{k=1}^\infty \subseteq \mathcal{F} \text{ is disjoint, then } \sum_{k=1}^\infty \ell(I_k) \leq m(\mathcal{O}) < \infty. \tag{3}$$

Moreover, since each I_k is closed and $\mathcal{F}$ is a Vitali covering of E,

$$\text{if } \{I_k\}_{k=1}^n \subseteq \mathcal{F}, \text{ then } E \sim \bigcup_{k=1}^{\infty} I_k \subseteq \bigcup_{I \in \mathcal{F}_n} I \text{ where } \mathcal{F}_n = \left\{ I \in \mathcal{F} \;\middle|\; I \cap \bigcup_{k=1}^n I_k = \emptyset \right\}. \quad (4)$$

If there is a finite disjoint subcollection of $\mathcal{F}$ that covers E, the proof is complete. Otherwise, we inductively choose a disjoint countable subcollection $\{I_k\}_{k=1}^{\infty}$ of $\mathcal{F}$ which has the following property:

$$E \sim \bigcup_{k=1}^n I_k \subseteq \bigcup_{k=n+1}^{\infty} 5 * I_k \text{ for all } n, \quad (5)$$

where, for a closed, bounded interval I, $5 * I$ denotes the closed interval that has the same midpoint as I and 5 times its length. To begin this selection, let I_1 be any interval in $\mathcal{F}$. Suppose n is a natural number and the finite disjoint subcollection $\{I_k\}_{k=1}^n$ of $\mathcal{F}$ has been chosen. Since $E \sim \bigcup_{k=1}^n I_k \neq \emptyset$, the collection $\mathcal{F}_n$ defined in (4) is nonempty. Moreover, the supremum, s_n, of the lengths of the intervals in $\mathcal{F}_n$ is finite since $m(\mathcal{O})$ is an upper bound for these lengths. Choose I_{n+1} to be an interval in $\mathcal{F}_n$ for which $\ell(I_{n+1}) > s_n/2$. This inductively defines $\{I_k\}_{k=1}^{\infty}$, a countable disjoint subcollection of $\mathcal{F}$ such that for each n,

$$\ell(I_{n+1}) > \ell(I)/2 \text{ if } I \in \mathcal{F} \text{ and } I \cap \bigcup_{k=1}^n I_k = \emptyset. \quad (6)$$

We infer from (3) that $\{\ell(I_k)\} \to 0$. Fix a natural number n. To verify the inclusion (5), let x belong to $E \sim \bigcup_{k=1}^n I_k$. We infer from (4) that there is an $I \in \mathcal{F}$ which contains x and is disjoint from $\bigcup_{k=1}^n I_k$. Now I must have nonempty intersection with some I_k, for otherwise, by (6), $\ell(I_k) > \ell(I)/2$ for all k, which contradicts the convergence of $\{\ell(I_k)\}$ to 0. Let N be the first natural number for which $I \cap I_N \neq \emptyset$. Then $N > n$. Since $I \cap \bigcup_{k=1}^{N-1} I_k = \emptyset$, we infer from (6) that $\ell(I_N) > \ell(I)/2$. Since x belongs to I and $I \cap I_N \neq \emptyset$, the distance from x to the midpoint of I_N is at most $\ell(I) + 1/2 \cdot \ell(I_N)$ and hence, since $\ell(I) < 2 \cdot \ell(I_N)$, the distance from x to the midpoint of I_N is less than $5/2 \cdot \ell(I_N)$. This means that x belongs to $5 * I_N$. Thus,

$$x \in 5 * I_N \subseteq \bigcup_{k=n+1}^{\infty} 5 * I_k.$$

We have established the inclusion (5).

Let $\epsilon > 0$. We infer from (3) that here is a natural number n for which $\sum_{k=n+1}^{\infty} \ell(I_k) < \epsilon/5$. This choice of n, together with the inclusion (5) and the monotonicity and countable additivity of measure, establishes (2). $\qquad \square$

For a real-valued function f and an interior point x of its domain, the **upper derivative** of f at x, $\overline{D}f(x)$ and the **lower derivative** of f at x, $\underline{D}f(x)$ are defined as follows:

$$\overline{D}f(x) = \lim_{h \to 0} \left[\sup_{0 < |t| \leq h} \frac{f(x+t) - f(x)}{t} \right];$$

$$\underline{D}f(x) = \lim_{h \to 0} \left[\inf_{0 < |t| \leq h} \frac{f(x+t) - f(x)}{t} \right].$$

We have $\overline{D}f(x) \geq \underline{D}f(x)$. If $\overline{D}f(x)$ equals $\underline{D}f(x)$ and is finite, we say that f is **differentiable** at x and define $f'(x)$ to be the common value of the upper and lower derivatives.

The Mean Value Theorem of calculus tells us that if a function f is continuous on the closed, bounded interval $[c, d]$ and differentiable on its interior (c, d) with $f' \geq \alpha$ on (c, d), then

$$\alpha \cdot (d - c) \leq [f(d) - f(c)].$$

The proof of the following generalization of this inequality, inequality (7), is a nice illustration of the fruitful interplay between the Vitali Covering Lemma and monotonicity properties of functions.

Lemma 3 *Let f be an increasing function on the closed, bounded interval $[a, b]$. Then, for each $\alpha > 0$,*

$$m^*\{x \in (a, b) \mid \overline{D}f(x) \geq \alpha\} \leq \frac{1}{\alpha} \cdot [f(b) - f(a)] \tag{7}$$

and

$$m^*\{x \in (a, b) \mid \overline{D}f(x) = \infty\} = 0. \tag{8}$$

Proof Let $\alpha > 0$. Define $E_\alpha = \{x \in (a, b) \mid \overline{D}f(x) \geq \alpha\}$. Choose $\alpha' \in (0, \alpha)$. Let $\mathcal{F}$ be the collection of closed, bounded intervals $[c, d]$ contained in (a, b) for which $f(d) - f(c) \geq \alpha'(d - c)$. Since $\overline{D}f \geq \alpha$ on E_α, $\mathcal{F}$ is a Vitali covering of E_α. The Vitali Covering Lemma tells us that there is a finite disjoint subcollection $\{[c_k, d_k]\}_{k=1}^n$ of $\mathcal{F}$ for which

$$m^*\left[E_\alpha \sim \bigcup_{k=1}^n [c_k, d_k]\right] < \epsilon.$$

Since $E_\alpha \subseteq \bigcup_{k=1}^n [c_k, d_k] \cup \{E_\alpha \sim \bigcup_{k=1}^n [c_k, d_k]\}$, by the finite subadditivity of outer measure, the preceding inequality and the choice of the intervals $[c_k, d_k]$,

$$m^*(E_\alpha) < \sum_{k=1}^n (d_k - c_k) + \epsilon \leq \frac{1}{\alpha'} \cdot \sum_{k=1}^n [f(d_k) - f(c_k)] + \epsilon. \tag{9}$$

However, the function f is increasing on $[a, b]$ and $\{[c_k, d_k]\}_{k=1}^n$ is a disjoint collection of subintervals of $[a, b]$. Therefore

$$\sum_{k=1}^n [f(d_k) - f(c_k)] \leq f(b) - f(a).$$

Thus for each $\epsilon > 0$, and each $\alpha' \in (0, \alpha)$,

$$m^*(E_\alpha) \leq \frac{1}{\alpha'} \cdot [f(b) - f(a)] + \epsilon.$$

This proves (7). For each natural number n, $\{x \in (a, b) \mid \overline{D}f(x) = \infty\} \subseteq E_n$ and therefore

$$m^*\{x \in (a, b) \mid \overline{D}f(x) = \infty\} \leq m^*(E_n) \leq \frac{1}{n} \cdot (f(b) - f(a)).$$

This proves (8). $\qquad\square$

Lebesgue's Theorem *If the function f is monotone on the open interval (a, b), then it is differentiable almost everywhere on (a, b).*

Proof Assume f is increasing. Furthermore, assume (a, b) is bounded. Otherwise, express (a, b) as the union of an ascending sequence of open, bounded intervals and use the continuity of Lebesgue measure. The set of points x in (a, b) at which $\overline{D}f(x) > \underline{D}f(x)$ is the union of the sets

$$E_{\alpha,\beta} = \{x \in (a, b) \mid \overline{D}f(x) > \alpha > \beta > \underline{D}f(x)\}$$

where α and β are rational numbers. Hence, since this is a countable collection, by the countable subadditivity of outer measure, it suffices to prove that each $E_{\alpha,\beta}$ has outer measure zero. Fix rationals α, β with $\alpha > \beta$ and set $E = E_{\alpha,\beta}$. Let $\epsilon > 0$. Choose an open set $\mathcal{O}$ for which

$$E \subseteq \mathcal{O} \subseteq (a, b) \text{ and } m(\mathcal{O}) < m^*(E) + \epsilon. \tag{10}$$

Let $\mathcal{F}$ be the collection of closed, bounded intervals $[c, d]$ contained in $\mathcal{O}$ for which $f(d) - f(c) < \beta(d - c)$. Since $\underline{D}f < \beta$ on E, $\mathcal{F}$ is a Vitali covering of E. The Vitali Covering Lemma tells us that there is a finite disjoint subcollection $\{[c_k, d_k]\}_{k=1}^n$ of $\mathcal{F}$ for which

$$m^*\left[E \sim \bigcup_{k=1}^n [c_k, d_k]\right] < \epsilon. \tag{11}$$

By the choice of the intervals $[c_k, d_k]$, the inclusion of the union of the disjoint collection intervals $\{[c_k, d_k]\}_{k=1}^n$ in $\mathcal{O}$ and (10),

$$\sum_{k=1}^n [f(d_k) - f(c_k)] < \beta \left[\sum_{k=1}^n (d_k - c_k)\right] \leq \beta \cdot m(\mathcal{O}) \leq \beta \cdot [m^*(E) + \epsilon]. \tag{12}$$

For $1 \leq k \leq n$, we infer from the preceding lemma, applied to the restriction of f to $[c_k, d_k]$, that

$$m^*(E \cap (c_k, d_k)) \leq \frac{1}{\alpha}[f(d_k) - f(c_k)].$$

Therefore, by (11),

$$m^*(E) \leq \sum_{k=1}^n m^*(E \cap (c_k, d_k)) + \epsilon \leq \frac{1}{\alpha}\left[\sum_{k=1}^n [f(d_k) - f(c_k)]\right] + \epsilon. \tag{13}$$

We infer from (12) and (13) that

$$m^*(E) \leq \frac{\beta}{\alpha} \cdot m^*(E) + \frac{1}{\alpha} \cdot \epsilon + \epsilon \text{ for all } \epsilon > 0.$$

Therefore, since $0 \leq m^*(E) < \infty$ and $\beta/\alpha < 1$, $m^*(E) = 0$. $\qquad \square$

Lebesgue's Theorem is the best possible in the sense that if E is a set of measure zero contained in the open interval (a, b), there is an increasing function on (a, b) that fails to be differentiable at each point in E (see Problem 10).

Remark *Frigyes Riesz and Béla Sz.-Nagy[2] remark that Lebesgue's Theorem is "one of the most striking and most important in real variable theory." Indeed, in 1872 Karl Weierstrass presented mathematics with a continuous function on an open interval which failed to be differentiable at any point.[3] Further pathology was revealed and there followed a period of uncertainty regarding the spread of pathology in mathematical analysis. Lebesgue's Theorem, which was published in 1904, and its consequences, which we pursue in Section 5, helped restore confidence in the harmony of mathematics analysis.*

Let f be integrable over the closed, bounded interval $[a, b]$. Extend f to take the value $f(b)$ on $(b, b+1]$. For $0 < h \le 1$, define the **divided difference function** $\text{Diff}_h f$ and **average value function** $\text{Av}_h f$ of $[a, b]$ by

$$\text{Diff}_h f(x) = \frac{f(x+h) - f(x)}{h} \text{ and } \text{Av}_h f(x) = \frac{1}{h} \cdot \int_x^{x+h} f \text{ for all } x \in [a, b].$$

By a change of variables in the integral and cancellation, for all $a \le u < v \le b$,

$$\int_u^v \text{Diff}_h f = \text{Av}_h f(v) - \text{Av}_h f(u). \tag{14}$$

Corollary 4 *Let f be an increasing function on the closed, bounded interval $[a, b]$. Then f' is integrable over $[a, b]$ and*

$$\int_b^a f' \le f(b) - f(a). \tag{15}$$

Proof Since f is increasing on $[a, b+1]$, it is measurable (see Problem 22) and therefore the divided difference functions are also measurable. Lebesgue's Theorem tells us that f is differentiable almost everywhere on (a, b). Therefore $\{\text{Diff}_{1/n} f\}$ is a sequence of nonnegative measurable functions that converges pointwise almost everywhere on $[a, b]$ to f'. According to Fatou's Lemma,

$$\int_a^b f' \le \liminf_{n \to \infty} \left[\int_a^b \text{Diff}_{1/n} f \right] \tag{16}$$

By the change of variable formula (14), for each natural number n, since f is increasing,

$$\int_a^b \text{Diff}_{1/n} f = \frac{1}{1/n} \cdot \int_b^{b+1/n} f - \frac{1}{1/n} \cdot \int_a^{a+1/n} f = f(b) - \frac{1}{1/n} \cdot \int_a^{a+1/n} \le f(b) - f(a).$$

Thus

$$\limsup_{n \to \infty} \left[\int_a^b \text{Diff}_{1/n} f \right] \le f(b) - f(a). \tag{17}$$

The inequality (15) follows from the inequalities (16) and (17). □

---

[2]See page 5 of their book *Functional Analysis* [RSN90].

[3]A simpler example of such a function, due to Bartel van der Waerden, is examined in Chapter 8 of Patrick Fitzpatrick's *Advanced Calculus* [Fit09].

Remark *The integral in* (15) *is independent of the values taken by f at the endpoints. On the other hand, the right-hand side of this equality holds for the extension of any increasing extension of f on the open, bounded interval* (a, b) *to its closure* $[a, b]$. *Therefore a tighter form of equality* (15) *is*

$$\int_a^b f' \leq \sup_{x \in (a, b)} f(x) - \inf_{x \in (a, b)} f(x). \tag{18}$$

The right-hand side of this inequality equals $f(b) - f(a)$ *if and only if f is continuous at the endpoints. However, even if f is increasing and continuous on* $[a, b]$, *inequality* (15) *may be strict. It is strict for the Cantor-Lebesgue function* φ *on* $[0, 1]$ *since* $\varphi(1) - \varphi(0) = 1$ *while* φ' *vanishes almost everywhere on* $(0, 1)$. *We show that for an increasing function f on* $[a, b]$, (15) *is an equality if and only if the function is absolutely continuous on* $[a, b]$ *(see the forthcoming Corollary 12).*

Remark *For a continuous function f on a closed, bounded interval* $[a, b]$ *that is differentiable on the open interval* (a, b), *in the absence of a monotonicity assumption on f we cannot infer that its derivative* f' *is integrable over* $[a, b]$. *We leave it as an exercise to show that for f defined on* $[0, 1]$ *by*

$$f(x) = \begin{cases} x^2 \sin(1/x^2) & \text{for } 0 < x \leq 1 \\ 0 & \text{for } x = 0, \end{cases}$$

f' *is not integrable over* $[0, 1]$.

PROBLEMS

5. Show that the Vitali Covering Lemma does not extend to the case in which the covering collection has degenerate closed intervals.

6. Show that the Vitali Covering Lemma does extend to the case in which the covering collection consists of nondegenerate general intervals.

7. Let f be continuous on $\mathbf{R}$. Is there an open interval on which f is monotone?

8. Let I and J be closed, bounded intervals and $\gamma > 0$ be such that $\ell(I) > \gamma \cdot \ell(J)$. Assume $I \cap J \neq \emptyset$. Show that if $\gamma \geq 1/2$, then $J \subseteq 5 * I$, where $5 * I$ denotes the interval with the same center as I and five times its length. Is the same true if $0 < \gamma < 1/2$?

9. Show that a set E of real numbers has measure zero if and only if there is a countable collection of open intervals $\{I_k\}_{k=1}^{\infty}$ for which each point in E belongs to infinitely many of the I_k's and $\sum_{k=1}^{\infty} \ell(I_k) < \infty$.

10. (Riesz-Nagy) Let E be a set of measure zero contained in the open interval (a, b). According to the preceding problem, there is a countable collection of open intervals contained in (a, b), $\{(c_k, d_k)\}_{k=1}^{\infty}$, for which each point in E belongs to infinitely many intervals in the collection and $\sum_{k=1}^{\infty} (d_k - c_k) < \infty$. Define

$$f(x) = \sum_{k=1}^{\infty} \ell((c_k, d_k) \cap (-\infty, x)) \text{ for all } x \text{ in } (a, b).$$

Show that f is increasing and fails to be differentiable at each point in E.

11. For real numbers $\alpha < \beta$ and $\gamma > 0$, show that if g is integrable over $[\alpha + \gamma, \beta + \gamma]$, then

$$\int_\alpha^\beta g(t + \gamma)\, dt = \int_{\alpha+\gamma}^{\beta+\gamma} g(t)\, dt.$$

Prove this change of variables formula by successively considering simple functions, bounded measurable functions, nonnegative integrable functions, and general integrable functions. Use it to prove (14).

12. Compute the upper and lower derivatives of the characteristic function of the rationals.

13. Let E be a set of finite outer measure and $\mathcal{F}$ a collection of closed, bounded intervals that cover E in the sense of Vitali. Show that there is a countable disjoint collection $\{I_k\}_{k=1}^\infty$ of intervals in $\mathcal{F}$ for which

$$m^* \left[E \sim \bigcup_{k=1}^\infty I_k \right] = 0.$$

14. Use the Vitali Covering Lemma to show that the union of any collection (countable or uncountable) of closed, bounded nondegenerate intervals is measurable.

15. Define f on $\mathbf{R}$ by

$$f(x) = \begin{cases} x \, \sin(1/x) & \text{if } x \neq 0 \\ 0 & \text{if } x = 0. \end{cases}$$

Find the upper and lower derivatives of f at $x = 0$.

16. Let g be integrable over $[a, b]$. Define the antiderivative of g to be the function f defined on $[a, b]$ by

$$f(x) = \int_a^x g \text{ for all } x \in [a, b].$$

Show that f is differentiable almost everywhere on (a, b).

17. Let f be an increasing bounded function on the open, bounded interval (a, b). Verify (15).

18. Show that if f is defined on (a, b) and $c \in (a, b)$ is a local minimizer for f, then $\underline{D}f(c) \leq 0 \leq \overline{D}f(c)$.

19. Let f be continuous on $[a, b]$ with $\overline{D}f \geq 0$ on (a, b). Show that f is increasing on $[a, b]$. (Hint: First show this for a function g for which $\overline{D}g \geq \epsilon > 0$ on (a, b). Apply this to the function $g(x) = f(x) + \epsilon x$.)

20. Let f and g be real-valued functions on (a, b). Show that

$$\underline{D}f + \underline{D}g \leq \underline{D}(f + g) \leq \overline{D}(f + g) \leq \overline{D}f + \overline{D}g \text{ on } (a, b).$$

21. Let f be defined on $[a, b]$ and g a continuous function on $[\alpha, \beta]$ that is differentiable at $\gamma \in (\alpha, \beta)$ with $g(\gamma) = c \in (a, b)$. Verify the following.

   (i) If $g'(\gamma) > 0$, then $\overline{D}(f \circ g)(\gamma) = \overline{D}f(c) \cdot g'(\gamma)$.

   (ii) If $g'(\gamma) = 0$ and the upper and lower derivatives of f at c are finite, then $\overline{D}(f \circ g)(\gamma) = 0$.

22. Show that a strictly increasing function that is defined on an interval is measurable and then use this to show that a monotone function that is defined on an interval is measurable.

23. Show that a continuous function f on $[a, b]$ is Lipschitz if its upper and lower derivatives are bounded on (a, b).

24. Show that for f defined in the last remark of this section, f' is not integrable over $[0, 1]$.

6.3 FUNCTIONS OF BOUNDED VARIATION: JORDAN'S THEOREM

Lebesgue's Theorem tells us that a monotone function on an open interval is differentiable almost everywhere. Therefore the *difference* of two increasing functions on an open interval also is differentiable almost everywhere. We now provide a characterization of the class of functions on a closed, bounded interval that may be expressed as the difference of increasing functions, which shows that this class is surprisingly large: it includes, for instance, all Lipschitz functions.

Let f be a real-valued function defined on the closed, bounded interval $[a, b]$ and $P = \{x_0, \ldots, x_k\}$ be a partition of $[a, b]$. Define the variation of f with respect to P by

$$V(f, P) = \sum_{i=1}^{k} |f(x_i) - f(x_{i-1})|,$$

and the **total variation** of f on $[a, b]$ by

$$TV(f) = \sup \left\{ V(f, P) \mid P \text{ a partition of } [a, b] \right\}.$$

For a subinterval $[c, d]$ of $[a, b]$, $TV(f_{[c, d]})$ denotes the total variation of the restriction of f to $[c, d]$.

Definition *A real-valued function f on the closed, bounded interval $[a, b]$ is said to be of* **bounded variation** *on $[a, b]$ provided*

$$TV(f) < \infty.$$

Example Let f be an increasing function on $[a, b]$. Then f is of bounded variation on $[a, b]$ and

$$TV(f) = f(b) - f(a).$$

Indeed, for any partition $P = \{x_0, \ldots, x_k\}$ of $[a, b]$,

$$V(f, P) = \sum_{i=1}^{k} |f(x_i) - f(x_{i-1})| = \sum_{i=1}^{k} [f(x_i) - f(x_{i-1})] = f(b) - f(a).$$

Example Let f be a Lipschitz function on $[a, b]$. Then f is of bounded variation of $[a, b]$, and $TV(f) \leq c \cdot (b - a)$, where

$$|f(u) - f(v)| \leq c|u - v| \text{ for all } u, v \text{ in } [a, b].$$

Indeed, for a partition $P = \{x_0, \ldots, x_k\}$ of $[a, b]$,

$$V(f, P) = \sum_{i=1}^{k} |f(x_i) - f(x_{i-1})| \leq c \cdot \sum_{i=1}^{k} [x_i - x_{i-1}] = c \cdot [b - a].$$

Thus, $c \cdot [b - a]$ is an upper bound of the set of all variations of f with respect to a partition of $[a, b]$ and hence $TV(f) \leq c \cdot [b - a]$.

Example Define the function f on $[0, 1]$ by

$$f(x) = \begin{cases} x \cos(\pi/2x) & \text{if } 0 < x \leq 1 \\ 0 & \text{if } x = 0. \end{cases}$$

Then f is continuous on $[0, 1]$. But f is not of bounded variation on $[0, 1]$. Indeed, for a natural number n, consider the partition $P_n = \{0, 1/2n, 1/[2n-1], \ldots, 1/3, 1/2, 1\}$ of $[0, 1]$. Then

$$V(f, P_n) = 1 + 1/2 + \ldots + 1/n.$$

Hence f is not of bounded variation on $[0, 1]$, since the harmonic series diverges.

Observe that if c belongs to (a, b), P is a partition of $[a, b]$, and P' is the refinement of P obtained by adjoining c to P, then, by the triangle inequality, $V(f, P) \leq V(f, P')$. Thus, in the definition of the total variation of a function on $[a, b]$, the supremum can be taken over partitions of $[a, b]$ that contain the point c. Now a partition P of $[a, b]$ that contains the point c induces, and is induced by, partitions P_1 and P_2 of $[a, c]$ and $[c, b]$, respectively, and for such partitions

$$V(f_{[a, b]}, P) = V(f_{[a, c]}, P_1) + V(f_{[c, b]}, P_2). \tag{19}$$

Take the supremum among such partitions to conclude that

$$TV(f_{[a, b]}) = TV(f_{[a, c]}) + TV(f_{[c, b]}). \tag{20}$$

We infer from this that if f is of bounded variation on $[a, b]$, then

$$TV(f_{[a, v]}) - TV(f_{[a, u]}) = TV(f_{[u, v]}) \geq 0 \text{ for all } a \leq u < v \leq b. \tag{21}$$

Therefore the function $x \mapsto TV(f_{[a, x]})$, which we call the **total variation function** for f, is a real-valued increasing function on $[a, b]$. Moreover, for $a \leq u < v \leq b$, if we take the crudest partition $P = \{u, v\}$ of $[u, v]$, we have

$$f(u) - f(v) \leq |f(v) - f(u)| = V(f_{[u, v]}, P) \leq TV(f_{[u, v]}) = TV(f_{[a, v]}) - TV(f_{[a, u]}).$$

Thus

$$f(v) + TV(f_{[a, v]}) \geq f(u) + TV(f_{[a, u]}) \text{ for all } a \leq u < v \leq b. \tag{22}$$

We have established the following lemma.

Lemma 5 *Let the function f be of bounded variation on the closed, bounded interval $[a, b]$. Then f has the following explicit expression as the difference of two increasing functions on $[a, b]$:*

$$f(x) = [f(x) + TV(f_{[a, x]})] - TV(f_{[a, x]}) \text{ for all } x \in [a, b]. \tag{23}$$

Jordan's Theorem *A function f is of bounded variation on the closed, bounded interval $[a, b]$ if and only if it is the difference of two increasing functions on $[a, b]$.*

Proof Let f be of bounded variation on $[a, b]$. The preceding lemma provides an explicit representation of f as the difference of increasing functions. To prove the converse, let $f = g - h$ on $[a, b]$, where g and h are increasing functions on $[a, b]$. For any partition $P = \{x_0, \dots, x_k\}$ of $[a, b]$,

$$V(f, P) = \sum_{i=1}^{k} |f(x_i) - f(x_{i-1})|$$

$$= \sum_{i=1}^{k} |[g(x_i) - g(x_{i-1})] + [h(x_{i-1}) - h(x_i)]|$$

$$\leq \sum_{i=1}^{k} |g(x_i) - g(x_{i-1})| + \sum_{i=1}^{k} |h(x_{i-1}) - h(x_i)|$$

$$= \sum_{i=1}^{k} [g(x_i) - g(x_{i-1})] + \sum_{i=1}^{k} [h(x_i) - h(x_{i-1})]$$

$$= [g(b) - g(a)] + [h(b) - h(a)].$$

Thus, the set of variations of f with respect to partitions of $[a, b]$ is bounded above by $[g(b) - g(a)] + [h(b) - h(a)]$ and therefore f is of bounded variation of $[a, b]$. $\qquad\square$

We call the expression of a function of bounded variation f as the difference of increasing functions a **Jordan decomposition** of f.

Corollary 6 *If the function f is of bounded variation on the closed, bounded interval $[a, b]$, then it is differentiable almost everywhere on the open interval (a, b) and f' is integrable over $[a, b]$.*

Proof According to Jordan's Theorem, f is the difference of two increasing functions on $[a, b]$. Thus Lebesgue's Theorem tells us that f is the difference of two functions which are differentiable almost everywhere on (a, b). Therefore f is differentiable almost everywhere on (a, b). The integrability of f' follows from Corollary 4. $\qquad\square$

PROBLEMS

25. Suppose f is continuous on $[0, 1]$. Must there be a nondegenerate closed subinterval $[a, b]$ of $[0, 1]$ for which the restriction of f to $[a, b]$ is of bounded variation?

26. Let f be the Dirichlet function, the characteristic function of the rationals in $[0, 1]$. Is f of bounded variation on $[0, 1]$?

27. Define $f(x) = \sin x$ on $[0, 2\pi]$. Find two increasing functions h and g for which $f = h - g$ on $[0, 2\pi]$.

28. Let f be a step function on $[a, b]$. Find a formula for its total variation.

29. (a) Define

$$f(x) = \begin{cases} x^2 \cos(1/x^2) & \text{if } x \neq 0, x \in [-1, 1] \\ 0 & \text{if } x = 0. \end{cases}$$

Is f of bounded variation on $[-1, 1]$?

(b) Define

$$g(x) = \begin{cases} x^2 \cos(1/x) & \text{if } x \neq 0, x \in [-1, 1] \\ 0 & \text{if } x = 0. \end{cases}$$

Is g of bounded variation on $[-1, 1]$?

30. Show that the linear combination of two functions of bounded variation is also of bounded variation. Is the product of two such functions also of bounded variation?

31. Let P be a partition of $[a, b]$ that is a refinement of the partition P'. For a real-valued function f on $[a, b]$, show that $V(f, P') \leq V(f, P)$.

32. Assume f is of bounded variation on $[a, b]$. Show that there is a sequence of partitions $\{P_n\}$ of $[a, b]$ for which the sequence $\{TV(f, P_n)\}$ is increasing and converges to $TV(f)$.

33. Let $\{f_n\}$ be a sequence of real-valued functions on $[a, b]$ that converges pointwise on $[a, b]$ to the real-valued function f. Show that

$$TV(f) \leq \liminf TV(f_n).$$

34. Let f and g be of bounded variation on $[a, b]$. Show that

$$TV(f + g) \leq TV(f) + TV(g) \text{ and } TV(\alpha f) = |\alpha| TV(f).$$

35. For α and β positive numbers, define the function f on $[0, 1]$ by

$$f(x) = \begin{cases} x^\alpha \sin(1/x^\beta) & \text{for } 0 < x \leq 1 \\ 0 & \text{for } x = 0. \end{cases}$$

Show that if $\alpha > \beta$, then f is of bounded variation on $[0, 1]$, by showing that f' is integrable over $[0, 1]$. Then show that if $\alpha \leq \beta$, then f is not of bounded variation on $[0, 1]$.

36. Let f fail to be of bounded variation on $[0, 1]$. Show that there is a point x_0 in $[0, 1]$ such that f fails to be of bounded variation on each nondegenerate closed subinterval of $[0, 1]$ that contains x_0.

6.4 ABSOLUTELY CONTINUOUS FUNCTIONS

Definition *A real-valued function f on a closed, bounded interval $[a, b]$ is said to be* **absolutely continuous** *on $[a, b]$ provided for each $\epsilon > 0$, there is a $\delta > 0$ such that for every finite disjoint collection $\{(a_k, b_k)\}_{k=1}^n$ of open intervals in (a, b),*

$$\text{if } \sum_{k=1}^n [b_k - a_k] < \delta, \text{ then } \sum_{k=1}^n |f(b_k) - f(a_k)| < \epsilon.$$

The criterion for absolute continuity in the case the finite collection of intervals consists of a single interval is the criterion for the uniform continuity of f on $[a, b]$. Thus absolutely continuous functions are continuous. The converse is false, even for increasing functions.

Example   The Cantor-Lebesgue function φ is increasing and continuous on $[0, 1]$, but it is not absolutely continuous (see also Problems 40 and 48). Indeed, to see that φ is not absolutely continuous, let n be a natural number. At the n-th stage of the construction of the Cantor set, a disjoint collection $\{[c_k, d_k]\}_{1 \le k \le 2^n}$ of 2^n subintervals of $[0, 1]$ have been constructed that cover the Cantor set, each of which has length $(1/3)^n$. The Cantor-Lebesgue function is constant on each of the intervals that comprise the complement in $[0, 1]$ of this collection of intervals. Therefore, since φ is increasing and $\varphi(1) - \varphi(0) = 1$,

$$\sum_{1 \le k \le 2^n} [d_k - c_k] = (2/3)^n \text{ while } \sum_{1 \le k \le 2^n} [\varphi(d_k) - \varphi(c_k)] = 1.$$

There is no response to the $\epsilon = 1$ challenge regarding the criterion for φ to be absolutely continuous.

Clearly linear combinations of absolutely continuous functions are absolutely continuous. However, the composition of absolutely continuous functions may fail to be absolutely continuous (see Problems 43, 44, and 45).

Proposition 7   *If the function f is Lipschitz on a closed, bounded interval $[a, b]$, then it is absolutely continuous on $[a, b]$.*

Proof   Let $c > 0$ be a Lipschitz constant for f on $[a, b]$, that is,

$$|f(u) - f(v)| \le c|u - v| \text{ for all } u, v \in [a, b].$$

Then, regarding the criterion for the absolute continuity of f, it is clear that $\delta = \epsilon/c$ responds to any $\epsilon > 0$ challenge.   □

There are absolutely continuous functions that fail to be Lipschitz: the function f on $[0, 1]$, defined by $f(x) = \sqrt{x}$ for $0 \le x \le 1$, is absolutely continuous but not Lipschitz (see Problem 37).

Theorem 8   *Let the function f be absolutely continuous on the closed, bounded interval $[a, b]$. Then f is the difference of increasing absolutely continuous functions and, in particular, is of bounded variation.*

Proof   We first prove that f is of bounded variation. Indeed, let δ respond to the $\epsilon = 1$ challenge regarding the criterion for the absolute continuity of f. Let P be a partition of $[a, b]$ into N closed intervals $\{[c_k, d_k]\}_{k=1}^N$, each of length less than δ. Then, by the definition of δ in relation to the absolute continuity of f, it is clear that $TV(f_{[c_k, d_k]}) \le 1$, for $1 \le k \le n$. The additivity formula (19) extends to finite sums. Hence

$$TV(f) = \sum_{k=1}^N TV(f_{[c_k, d_k]}) \le N.$$

Therefore f is of bounded variation. In view of (23) and the absolute continuity of sums of absolutely continuous functions, to show that f is the difference of increasing absolutely continuous functions it suffices to show that the total variation function for f is absolutely continuous. Let $\epsilon > 0$. Choose δ as a response to the $\epsilon/2$ challenge regarding the criterion for the absolute continuity of f on $[a, b]$. Let $\{(c_k, d_k)\}_{k=1}^{n}$ be a disjoint collection of open subintervals of (a, b) for which $\sum_{k=1}^{n}[d_k - c_k] < \delta$. For $1 \leq k \leq n$, let P_k be a partition of $[c_k, d_k]$. By the choice of δ in relation to the absolute continuity of f on $[a, b]$,

$$\sum_{k=1}^{n} TV(f_{[c_k, d_k]}, P_k) < \epsilon/2.$$

Take the supremum as, for $1 \leq k \leq n$, P_k vary among partitions of $[c_k, d_k]$, to obtain

$$\sum_{k=1}^{n} TV(f_{[c_k, d_k]}) \leq \epsilon/2 < \epsilon.$$

We infer from (21) that, for $1 \leq k \leq n$, $TV(f_{[c_k, d_k]}) = TV(f_{[a, d_k]}) - TV(f_{[a, c_k]})$. Hence

$$\text{if } \sum_{k=1}^{n}[d_k - c_k] < \delta, \text{ then } \sum_{k=1}^{n} \left| TV(f_{[a, d_k]}) - TV(f_{[a, c_k]}) \right| < \epsilon. \tag{24}$$

Therefore the total variation function for f is absolutely continuous on $[a, b]$. □

Theorem 9 *Let the function f be continuous on the closed, bounded interval $[a, b]$. Then f is absolutely continuous on $[a, b]$ if and only if the family of divided difference functions $\{\text{Diff}_h f\}_{0 < h \leq 1}$ is uniformly integrable over $[a, b]$.*

Proof. First assume $\{\text{Diff}_h f\}_{0 < h \leq 1}$ is uniformly integrable over $[a, b]$. Let $\epsilon > 0$. Choose $\delta > 0$ for which

$$\int_E |\text{Diff}_h f| < \epsilon/2 \text{ if } m(E) < \delta \text{ and } 0 < h \leq 1.$$

We claim that δ responds to the ϵ challenge regarding the criterion for f to be absolutely continuous. Indeed, let $\{(c_k, d_k)\}_{k=1}^{n}$ be a disjoint collection of open subintervals of (a, b) for which $\sum_{k=1}^{n}[d_k - c_k] < \delta$. For $0 < h \leq 1$ and $1 \leq k \leq n$, by (14),

$$\text{Av}_h f(d_k) - \text{Av}_h f(c_k) = \int_{c_k}^{d_k} \text{Diff}_h f.$$

Therefore

$$\sum_{k=1}^{n} |\text{Av}_h f(d_k) - \text{Av}_h f(c_k)| \leq \sum_{k=1}^{n} \int_{c_k}^{d_k} |\text{Diff}_h f| = \int_E |\text{Diff}_h f|,$$

where $E = \bigcup_{k=1}^{n}(c_k, d_k)$ has measure less than δ. Thus, by the choice of δ,

$$\sum_{k=1}^{n} |\text{Av}_h f(d_k) - \text{Av}_h f(c_k)| < \epsilon/2 \text{ for all } 0 < h \leq 1.$$

Since f is continuous, take the limit as $h \to 0^+$ to obtain

$$\sum_{k=1}^{n} |f(d_k) - f(c_k)| \leq \epsilon/2 < \epsilon.$$

Hence f is absolutely continuous.

To prove the converse, suppose f is absolutely continuous. The preceding theorem tells us that f is the difference of increasing absolutely continuous functions. We may therefore assume that f is increasing, so that the divided difference functions are nonnegative. To verify the uniformly integrability of $\{\text{Diff}_h f\}_{0<h\leq 1}$, let $\epsilon > 0$. We must show that there is a $\delta > 0$ such that for each measurable subset E of (a, b),

$$\int_E \text{Diff}_h f < \epsilon \text{ if } m(E) < \delta \text{ and } 0 < h \leq 1. \tag{25}$$

According to Theorem 11 of Chapter 2, a measurable set E is contained in a G_δ set G for which $m(G \sim E) = 0$. But every G_δ set is the intersection of a descending sequence of open sets. Moreover, every open set is the disjoint union of a countable collection of open intervals, and therefore every open set is the union of an ascending sequence of open sets, each of which is the union of a finite disjoint collection of open intervals. Therefore, by the continuity of integration, to verify (25) it suffices to find a $\delta > 0$ such that for $\{(c_k, d_k)\}_{k=1}^n$ a disjoint collection of open subintervals of (a, b),

$$\int_E \text{Diff}_h f < \epsilon/2 \text{ if } m(E) < \delta, \text{ where } E = \bigcup_{k=1}^n (c_k, d_k), \text{ and } 0 < h \leq 1. \tag{26}$$

Choose $\delta > 0$ as the response to the $\epsilon/2$ challenge regarding the criterion for the absolute continuity of f on $[a, b + 1]$. By a change of variables for the Riemann integral and cancellation,

$$\int_u^v \text{Diff}_h f = \frac{1}{h} \cdot \int_0^h g(t)\,dt, \text{ where } g(t) = f(v+t) - f(u+t) \text{ for } 0 \leq t \leq 1 \text{ and } a \leq u < v \leq b.$$

Therefore, if $\{(c_k, d_k)\}_{k=1}^n$ is a disjoint collection of open subintervals of (a, b),

$$\int_E \text{Diff}_h f = \frac{1}{h} \cdot \int_0^h g(t)\,dt,$$

where

$$E = \bigcup_{k=1}^n (c_k, d_k) \text{ and } g(t) = \sum_{k=1}^n [f(d_k + t) - f(c_k + t)] \text{ for all } 0 \leq t \leq 1.$$

If $\sum_{k=1}^n [d_k - c_k] < \delta$, then, for $0 \leq t \leq 1$, $\sum_{k=1}^n [(d_k + t) - (c_k + t)] < \delta$, and therefore $g(t) < \epsilon/2$. Thus

$$\int_E \text{Diff}_h f = \frac{1}{h} \cdot \int_0^h g(t)\,dt < \epsilon/2.$$

Hence (26) is verified for this choice of δ.   □

Remark *For a nondegenerate closed, bounded interval $[a, b]$, let $\mathcal{F}_{Lip}$, $\mathcal{F}_{AC}$, and $\mathcal{F}_{BV}$ denote the families of functions on $[a, b]$ that are Lipschitz, absolutely continuous, and of bounded variation, respectively. We have the following strict inclusions:*

$$\mathcal{F}_{Lip} \subseteq \mathcal{F}_{AC} \subseteq \mathcal{F}_{BV}. \tag{27}$$

Proposition 7 tells us of the first inclusion, and the second inclusion was established in Theorem 7. Each of these collections is closed with respect to the formation of linear combinations. Moreover a function in one of these collections has its total variation function in the same collection. Therefore, by (23), a function in one of these collections may be expressed as the difference of two increasing functions in the same collection (see Problem 46).

PROBLEMS

37. Let f be a continuous function on $[0, 1]$ that is absolutely continuous on $[\epsilon, 1]$ for each $0 < \epsilon < 1$.

   (i) Show that f may not be absolutely continuous on $[0, 1]$.

   (ii) Show that f is absolutely continuous on $[0, 1]$ if it is increasing.

   (iii) Show that the function f on $[0, 1]$, defined by $f(x) = \sqrt{x}$ for $0 \le x \le 1$, is absolutely continuous, but not Lipschitz, on $[0, 1]$.

38. Show that f is absolutely continuous on $[a, b]$ if and only if for each $\epsilon > 0$, there is a $\delta > 0$ such that for every countable disjoint collection $\{(a_k, b_k)\}_{k=1}^{\infty}$ of open intervals in (a, b),

$$\sum_{k=1}^{\infty} |f(b_k) - f(a_k)| < \sum_{k=1}^{\infty} [b_k - a_k] < \delta.$$

39. Use the preceding problem to show that if f is increasing on $[a, b]$, then f is absolutely continuous on $[a, b]$ if and only if for each ϵ, there is a $\delta > 0$ such that for a measurable subset E of $[a, b]$,

$$m^*(f(E)) < \epsilon \text{ if } m(E) < \delta.$$

40. Use the preceding problem to show that an increasing absolutely continuous function f on $[a, b]$ maps sets of measure zero onto sets of measure zero. Conclude that the Cantor-Lebesgue function φ is not absolutely continuous on $[0, 1]$ since the function ψ, defined by $\psi(x) = x + \varphi(x)$ for $0 \le x \le 1$, maps the Cantor set to a set of measure 1 (page 52).

41. Let f be an increasing absolutely continuous function on $[a, b]$. Use (i) and (ii) below to conclude that f maps measurable sets to measurable sets.

   (i) Infer from the continuity of f and the compactness of $[a, b]$ that f maps closed sets to closed sets and therefore maps F_σ sets to F_σ sets.

   (ii) The preceding problem tells us that f maps sets of measure zero to sets of measure zero.

42. Show that both the sum and product of absolutely continuous functions are absolutely continuous.

43. Define the functions f and g on $[-1, 1]$ by $f(x) = x^{\frac{1}{3}}$ for $-1 \le x \le 1$ and

$$g(x) = \begin{cases} x^2 \cos(\pi/2x) & \text{if } x \ne 0, x \in [-1, 1] \\ 0 & \text{if } x = 0. \end{cases}$$

   (i) Show that both f and g are absolutely continuous on $[-1, 1]$.

   (ii) For the partition $P_n = \{-1, 0, 1/2n, 1/[2n - 1], \ldots, 1/3, 1/2, 1\}$ of $[-1, 1]$, examine $V(f \circ g, P_n)$.

   (iii) Show that $f \circ g$ fails to be of bounded variation, and hence also fails to be absolutely continuous, on $[-1, 1]$.

44. Let f be Lipschitz on $\mathbf{R}$ and g be absolutely continuous on $[a, b]$. Show that the composition $f \circ g$ is absolutely continuous on $[a, b]$.

45. Let f be absolutely continuous on $\mathbf{R}$ and g be absolutely continuous and strictly monotone on $[a, b]$. Show that the composition $f \circ g$ is absolutely continuous on $[a, b]$.

46. Verify the assertions made in the final remark of this section.

47. Show that a function f is absolutely continuous on $[a, b]$ if and only if for each $\epsilon > 0$, there is a $\delta > 0$ such that for every finite disjoint collection $\{(a_k, b_k)\}_{k=1}^{n}$ of open intervals in (a, b),

$$\left| \sum_{k=1}^{n} [f(b_k) - f(a_k)] \right| < \epsilon \text{ if } \sum_{k=1}^{n} [b_k - a_k] < \delta.$$

6.5 INTEGRATING DERIVATIVES: DIFFERENTIATING INDEFINITE INTEGRALS

Let f be a continuous function on the closed, bounded interval $[a, b]$. In (14), take $a = u$ and $b = v$ to arrive at the following discrete formulation of the fundamental theorem of integral calculus:

$$\int_{a}^{b} \text{Diff}_h f = \text{Av}_h f(b) - \text{Av}_h f(a).$$

Since f is continuous, the limit of the right-hand side as $h \to 0^+$ equals $f(b) - f(a)$. We now show that if f is absolutely continuous, then the limit of the left-hand side as $h \to 0^+$ equals $\int_{a}^{b} f'$ and thereby establish the fundamental theorem of integral calculus for the Lebesgue integral.[4]

Theorem 10 *Let the function f be absolutely continuous on the closed, bounded interval $[a, b]$. Then f is differentiable almost everywhere on (a, b), its derivative f' is integrable over $[a, b]$, and*

$$\int_{b}^{a} f' = f(b) - f(a). \tag{28}$$

Proof We infer from the discrete formulation of the fundamental theorem of integral calculus that

$$\lim_{n \to \infty} \left[\int_{a}^{b} \text{Diff}_{1/n} f \right] = f(b) - f(a). \tag{29}$$

Theorem 8 tells us that f is the difference of increasing functions on $[a, b]$ and therefore, by Lebesgue's Theorem, is differentiable almost everywhere on (a, b). Therefore $\{\text{Diff}_{1/n} f\}$ converges pointwise almost everywhere on (a, b) to f'. On the other hand, according to Theorem 9, $\{\text{Diff}_{1/n} f\}$ is uniformly integrable over $[a, b]$. The Vitali Convergence Theorem (page 95) permits passage of the limit under the integral sign in order to conclude that

$$\lim_{n \to \infty} \left[\int_{a}^{b} \text{Diff}_{1/n} f \right] = \int_{a}^{b} \lim_{n \to \infty} \text{Diff}_{1/n} f = \int_{a}^{b} f'. \tag{30}$$

Formula (28) follows from (29) and (30).   □

---

[4]This approach to the proof of the fundamental theorem of integral calculus for the Lebesgue integral is taken in a note by Patrick Fitzpatrick and Brian Hunt in which Theorem 9 is proven (see *www-users.math.umd.edu/~pmf/huntpmf*).

In the study of calculus, indefinite integrals are defined with respect to the Riemann integral. We here call a function f on a closed, bounded interval $[a, b]$ the **indefinite integral** of g over $[a, b]$ provided g is Lebesgue integrable over $[a, b]$ and

$$f(x) = f(a) + \int_a^x g \text{ for all } x \in [a, b].$$ (31)

Theorem 11 *A function f on a closed, bounded interval $[a, b]$ is absolutely continuous on $[a, b]$ if and only if it is an indefinite integral over $[a, b]$.*

Proof First suppose f is absolutely continuous on $[a, b]$. For each $x \in (a, b]$, f is absolutely continuous over $[a, x]$ and hence, by the preceding theorem, in the case $[a, b]$ is replaced by $[a, x]$,

$$f(x) = f(a) + \int_a^x f'.$$

Thus f is the indefinite integral of f' over $[a, b]$.

Conversely, suppose that f is the indefinite integral over $[a, b]$ of g. For a disjoint collection $\{(a_k, b_k)\}_{k=1}^n$ of open intervals in (a, b), if we define $E = \cup_{k=1}^n (a_k, b_k)$, then, by the monotonicity and additivity over domains properties of the integral,

$$\sum_{k=1}^n |f(b_k) - f(a_k)| = \sum_{k=1}^n \left| \int_{b_k}^{a_k} g \right| \leq \sum_{k=1}^n \int_{b_k}^{a_k} |g| = \int_E |g|.$$ (32)

Let $\epsilon > 0$. Since $|g|$ is integrable over $[a, b]$, according to Proposition 23 of Chapter 4, there is a $\delta > 0$ such that $\int_E |g| < \epsilon$ if $E \subseteq [a, b]$ is measurable and $m(E) < \delta$. It follows from (32) that this same δ responds to the ϵ challenge regarding the criterion for f to be absolutely continuous on $[a, b]$. $\square$

Corollary 12 *Let the function f be monotone on the closed, bounded interval $[a, b]$. Then f is absolutely continuous on $[a, b]$ if and only if*

$$\int_a^b f' = f(b) - f(a).$$ (33)

Proof Theorem 10 is the assertion that (33) holds if f is absolutely continuous, irrespective of any monotonicity assumption. Conversely, assume f is increasing and (33) holds. Let x belong to $[a, b]$. By the additivity over domains of integration,

$$0 = \int_a^b f' - [f(b) - f(a)] = \left\{ \int_a^x f' - [f(x) - f(a)] \right\} + \left\{ \int_x^b f' - [f(b) - f(x)] \right\}.$$

According to Corollary 4,

$$\int_a^x f' - [f(x) - f(a)] \leq 0 \text{ and } \int_x^b f' - [f(b) - f(x)] \leq 0.$$

If the sum of two nonnegative numbers is zero, then they both are zero. Therefore

$$f(x) = f(a) + \int_a^x f'.$$

Thus f is the indefinite integral of f'. The preceding theorem tells us that f is absolutely continuous.   □

Lemma 13 *Let f be integrable over the closed, bounded interval $[a, b]$. Then*

$$f(x) = 0 \text{ for almost all } x \in [a, b] \tag{34}$$

if and only if

$$\int_{x_1}^{x_2} f = 0 \text{ for all } (x_1, x_2) \subseteq [a, b]. \tag{35}$$

Proof Clearly (34) implies (35). Conversely, suppose (35) holds. We claim that

$$\int_E f = 0 \text{ for all measurable sets } E \subseteq [a, b]. \tag{36}$$

Indeed, (36) holds for all open sets contained in (a, b) since integration is countably additive and every open set is the union of countable disjoint collection of open intervals. The continuity of integration then tells us that (36) also holds for all G_δ sets contained in (a, b) since every such set is the intersection of a countable descending collection of open sets. But every measurable subset of $[a, b]$ is of the form $G \sim E_0$, where G is a G_δ subset of (a, b) and $m(E_0) = 0$ (see page 40). We conclude from the additivity over domains of integration that (36) is verified. Define

$$E^+ = \{x \in [a, b] \mid f(x) \geq 0\} \text{ and } E^- = \{x \in [a, b] \mid f(x) \leq 0\}.$$

These are two measurable subsets of $[a, b]$ and therefore, by (36),

$$\int_a^b f^+ = \int_{E^+} f = 0 \text{ and } \int_a^b (-f^-) = -\int_{E^-} f = 0.$$

According to Proposition 9 of Chapter 4, a nonnegative integrable function with zero integral must vanish almost everywhere on its domain. Thus f^+ and f^- vanish almost everywhere on $[a, b]$ and hence so does f.   □

Theorem 14 *Let f be integrable over the closed, bounded interval $[a, b]$. Then*

$$\frac{d}{dx}\left[\int_a^x f\right] = f(x) \text{ for almost all } x \in (a, b). \tag{37}$$

Proof Define the function F on $[a, b]$ by $F(x) = \int_a^x f$ for all $x \in [a, b]$. Theorem 18 tells us that since F is an indefinite integral, it is absolutely continuous. Therefore, by Theorem 10, F

is differentiable almost everywhere on (a, b) and its derivative F' is integrable. According to the preceding lemma, to show that the integrable function $F' - f$ vanishes almost everywhere on $[a, b]$ it suffices to show that its integral over every closed subinterval of $[a, b]$ is zero. Let $[x_1, x_2]$ be contained in $[a, b]$. According to Theorem 10, in the case $[a, b]$ is replaced by $[x_1, x_2]$, and the linearity and additivity over domains properties of integration,

$$\int_{x_1}^{x_2} [F' - f] = \int_{x_1}^{x_2} F' - \int_{x_1}^{x_2} f = F(x_2) - F(x_1) - \int_{x_1}^{x_2} f$$

$$= \int_a^{x_2} f - \int_a^{x_1} f - \int_{x_1}^{x_2} f = 0.$$

□

A function of bounded variation is said to be **singular** provided its derivative vanishes almost everywhere. The Cantor-Lebesgue function is a non-constant singular function. We infer from Theorem 10 that an absolutely continuous function is singular if and only if it is constant. Let f be of bounded variation on $[a, b]$. According to Corollary 6, f' is integrable over $[a, b]$. Define

$$g(x) = \int_a^x f' \text{ and } h(x) = f(x) - \int_a^x f' \text{ for all } x \in [a, b],$$

so that

$$f = g + h \text{ on } [a, b].$$

According to Theorem 11, the function g is absolutely continuous. We infer from Theorem 14 that the function h is singular. The above decomposition of a function of bounded variation f as the sum $g + h$ of two functions of bounded variation, where g is absolutely continuous and h is singular, is called a **Lebesgue decomposition** of f.

PROBLEMS

48. The Cantor-Lebesgue function φ is continuous and increasing on $[0, 1]$. Conclude from Theorem 10 that φ is not absolutely continuous on $[0, 1]$. Compare this reasoning with that proposed in Problem 40.

49. Let f be continuous on $[a, b]$ and differentiable almost everywhere on (a, b). Show that

$$\int_a^b f' = f(b) - f(a)$$

if and only if

$$\int_a^b \left[\lim_{n \to \infty} \text{Diff}_{1/n} f \right] = \lim_{n \to \infty} \left[\int_a^b \text{Diff}_{1/n} f \right].$$

50. Let f be continuous on $[a, b]$ and differentiable almost everywhere on (a, b). Show that if $\{\text{Diff}_{1/n} f\}$ is uniformly integrable over $[a, b]$, then

$$\int_a^b f' = f(b) - f(a).$$

51. Let f be continuous on $[a, b]$ and differentiable almost everywhere on (a, b). Suppose there is a nonnegative function g that is integrable over $[a, b]$ and

$$\left|\text{Diff}_{1/n} f\right| \le g \text{ a.e. on } [a, b] \text{ for all } n.$$

Show that

$$\int_a^b f' = f(b) - f(a).$$

52. Let f and g be absolutely continuous on $[a, b]$. Show that

$$\int_a^b f \cdot g' = f(b)g(b) - f(a)g(a) - \int_a^b f' \cdot g.$$

53. Let the function f be absolutely continuous on $[a, b]$. Show that f is Lipschitz on $[a, b]$ if and only if there is a $c > 0$ for which $|f'| \le c$ a.e. on $[a, b]$.

54. (i) Let f be a singular increasing function on $[a, b]$. Use the Vitali Covering Lemma to show that f has the following property: Given $\epsilon > 0, \delta > 0$, there is a finite disjoint collection $\{(a_k, b_k)\}_{k=1}^n$ of open intervals in (a, b) for which

$$\sum_{k=1}^n [b_k - a_k] < \delta \text{ and } \sum_{k=1}^n [f(b_k) - f(a_k)] > f(b) - f(a) - \epsilon.$$

(ii) Let f be an increasing function on $[a, b]$ with the property described in part (i). Show that f is singular.

(iii) Let $\{f_n\}$ be a sequence of singular increasing functions on $[a, b]$ for which the series $\sum_{n=1}^\infty f_n(x)$ converges to a finite value for each $x \in [a, b]$. Define

$$f(x) = \sum_{n=1}^\infty f_n(x) \text{ for } x \in [a, b].$$

Show that f is also singular.

55. Let f be of bounded variation on $[a, b]$, and define $v(x) = TV(f_{[a, x]})$ for all $x \in [a, b]$.

(i) Show that $|f'| \le v'$ a.e on $[a, b]$, and infer from this that

$$\int_a^b |f'| \le TV(f).$$

(ii) Show that the above is an equality if and only if f is absolutely continuous on $[a, b]$.

(iii) Compare parts (i) and (ii) with Corollaries 4 and 12, respectively.

56. Let g be strictly increasing and absolutely continuous on $[a, b]$.

(i) Show that for any open subset $\mathcal{O}$ of (a, b),

$$m(g(\mathcal{O})) = \int_{\mathcal{O}} g'(x) \, dx.$$

(ii) Show that for any G_δ subset E of (a, b),

$$m(g(E)) = \int_E g'(x) \, dx.$$

(iii) Show that for any subset E of $[a, b]$ that has measure 0, its image $g(E)$ also has measure 0, so that

$$m(g(E)) = 0 = \int_E g'(x)\,dx.$$

(iv) Show that for any measurable subset A of $[a, b]$,

$$m(g(A)) = \int_A g'(x)\,dx.$$

(v) Let $c = g(a)$ and $d = g(b)$. Show that for any simple function φ on $[c, d]$,

$$\int_c^d \varphi(y)\,dy = \int_a^b \varphi(g(x))g'(x)\,dx.$$

(vi) Show that for any nonnegative integrable function f over $[c, d]$,

$$\int_c^d f(y)\,dy = \int_a^b f(g(x))g'(x)\,dx.$$

(vii) Show that part (i) follows from (vi) in the case that f is the characteristic function of $\mathcal{O}$ and the composition is defined.

57. Is the change of variables formula in the last part of the preceding problem true if we just assume g is increasing, not necessarily strictly?

58. Construct an absolutely continuous strictly increasing function f on $[0, 1]$ for which $f' = 0$ on a set of positive measure. (Hint: Let E be the relative complement in $[0, 1]$ of a generalized Cantor set of positive measure and f the indefinite integral of χ_E. See Problem 39 of Chapter 2 for the construction of such a Cantor set.)

59. For a nonnegative integrable function f over $[c, d]$, and a strictly increasing absolutely continuous function g on $[a, b]$ such that $g([a, b]) \subseteq [c, d]$, is it possible to justify the change of variables formula

$$\int_{g(a)}^{g(b)} f(y)\,dy = \int_a^b f(g(x))g'(x)\,dx$$

by showing that

$$\frac{d}{dx}\left[\int_{g(a)}^{g(x)} f(s)\,ds - \int_a^x f(g(t))g'(t)\,dt\right] = 0 \text{ for almost all } x \in (a, b)?$$

60. Let f be absolutely continuous and singular on $[a, b]$. Show that f is constant. Also show that the Lebesgue decomposition of a function of bounded variation is unique if the singular function is required to vanish at $x = a$.

6.6 CONVEX FUNCTIONS

Throughout this section (a, b) is an open interval that may be bounded or unbounded.

Definition *A real-valued function φ on (a, b) is said to be* **convex** *provided for each pair of points x_1, x_2 in (a, b) and each λ with $0 \leq \lambda \leq 1$,*

$$\varphi(\lambda x_1 + (1 - \lambda)x_2) \leq \lambda\varphi(x_1) + (1 - \lambda)\varphi(x_2). \tag{38}$$

If we look at the graph of φ, the convexity inequality can be formulated geometrically by saying that each point on the chord between $(x_1, \varphi(x_1))$ and $(x_2, \varphi(x_2))$ is above the graph of φ.

Observe that for two points $x_1 < x_2$ in (a, b), each point x in (x_1, x_2) may be expressed as

$$x = \lambda x_1 + (1 - \lambda)x_2 \text{ where } \lambda = \frac{x_2 - x}{x_2 - x_1}.$$

Thus the convexity inequality may be written as

$$\varphi(x) \leq \left[\frac{x_2 - x}{x_2 - x_1}\right]\varphi(x_1) + \left[\frac{x - x_1}{x_2 - x_1}\right]\varphi(x_2) \text{ for } x_1 < x < x_2 \text{ in } (a, b).$$

Regathering terms, this inequality may also be rewritten as

$$\frac{\varphi(x) - \varphi(x_1)}{x - x_1} \leq \frac{\varphi(x_2) - \varphi(x)}{x_2 - x} \text{ for } x_1 < x < x_2 \text{ in } (a, b). \tag{39}$$

Therefore convexity may also be formulated geometrically by saying that for $x_1 < x < x_2$, the slope of the chord from $(x_1, \varphi(x_1))$ to $(x, \varphi(x))$ is no greater than the slope of the chord from $(x, \varphi(x))$ to $(x_2, \varphi(x_2))$.

Proposition 15 *If φ is differentiable on (a, b) and its derivative φ' is increasing, then φ is convex. In particular, φ is convex if it has a nonnegative second derivative φ'' on (a, b).*

Proof Let x_1, x_2 be in (a, b) with $x_1 < x_2$, and let x belong to (x_1, x_2). We must show that

$$\frac{\varphi(x) - \varphi(x_1)}{x - x_1} \leq \frac{\varphi(x_2) - \varphi(x)}{x_2 - x}.$$

However, apply the Mean Value Theorem to the restriction of φ to each of the intervals $[x_1, x]$ and $[x, x_2]$ to choose points $c_1 \in (x_1, x)$ and $c_2 \in (x, x_2)$ for which

$$\varphi'(c_1) = \frac{\varphi(x) - \varphi(x_1)}{x - x_1} \text{ and } \varphi'(c_2) = \frac{\varphi(x_2) - \varphi(x)}{x_2 - x}.$$

Thus, since φ' is increasing,

$$\frac{\varphi(x) - \varphi(x_1)}{x - x_1} = \varphi'(c_1) \leq \varphi'(c_2) = \frac{\varphi(x_2) - \varphi(x)}{x_2 - x}. \qquad \square$$

Example Each of the following three functions is convex since each has a nonnegative second derivative:

$$\varphi(x) = x^p \text{ on } (0, \infty) \text{ for } p \geq 1; \quad \varphi(x) = e^{ax} \text{ on } (-\infty, \infty); \quad \varphi(x) = \ln(1/x) \text{ on } (0, \infty).$$

The following final geometric reformulation of convexity will be useful in the establishment of differentiability properties of convex functions.

The Chordal Slope Lemma *Let φ be convex on (a, b). If $x_1 < x < x_2$ belong to (a, b), then for $p_1 = (x_1, \varphi(x_1)), \quad p = (x, \varphi(x)), \quad p_2 = (x_2, \varphi(x_2))$,*

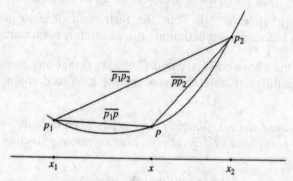

Slope of $\overline{p_1 p}$ $\leq$ slope of $\overline{p_1 p_2}$ $\leq$ slope of $\overline{p p_2}$.

Proof Regather terms in the inequality (39) to rewrite it in the following two equivalent forms:

$$\frac{\varphi(x_1) - \varphi(x)}{x_1 - x} \leq \frac{\varphi(x_2) - \varphi(x_1)}{x_2 - x_1} \text{ for } x_1 < x < x_2 \text{ in } (a, b);$$

$$\frac{\varphi(x_2) - \varphi(x_1)}{x_2 - x_1} \leq \frac{\varphi(x_2) - \varphi(x)}{x_2 - x} \text{ for } x_1 < x < x_2 \text{ in } (a, b). \qquad \square$$

For a function g on an open interval (a, b), and point $x_0 \in (a, b)$, if

$$\lim_{h \to 0, \, h < 0} \frac{g(x_0 + h) - g(x_0)}{h} \text{ exists and is finite,}$$

we denote this limit by $g'(x_0^-)$ and call it the left-hand derivative of g at x_0. Similarly, we define $g'(x_0^+)$ and call it the right-hand derivative of g at x_0. Of course, g is differentiable at x_0 if and only if it has left-hand and right-hand derivatives at x_0 that are equal. The continuity and differentiability properties of convex functions follow from the following lemma, whose proof follows directly from the Chordal Slope Lemma.

Lemma 16 *Let φ be a convex function on (a, b). Then φ has left-hand and right-hand derivatives at each point $x \in (a, b)$. Moreover, for points u, v in (a, b) with $u < v$, these one-sided derivatives satisfy the following inequality:*

$$\varphi'(u^-) \leq \varphi'(u^+) \leq \frac{\varphi(v) - \varphi(u)}{v - u} \leq \varphi'(v^-) \leq \varphi'(v^+). \tag{40}$$

Corollary 17 *Let φ be a convex function on (a, b). Then φ is Lipschitz, and therefore absolutely continuous, on each closed, bounded subinterval $[c, d]$ of (a, b).*

Proof According to the preceding lemma, for $c \le u < v \le d$,

$$\varphi'(c^+) \le \varphi'(u^+) \le \frac{\varphi(v) - \varphi(u)}{v - u} \le \varphi'(v^-) \le \varphi'(d^-) \tag{41}$$

and therefore

$$|\varphi(u) - \varphi(v)| \le M|u - v| \text{ for all } u, v \in [c, d],$$

where $M = \max\{|\varphi'(c^+)|, |\varphi'(d^-)|\}$. Thus the restriction of φ to $[u, v]$ is Lipschitz. A Lipschitz function on a closed, bounded interval is absolutely continuous. $\square$

We infer from the above corollary and Corollary 6 that any convex function defined on an open interval is differentiable almost everywhere on its domain. In fact, much more can be said.

Theorem 18 *Let φ be a convex function on (a, b). Then φ is differentiable except at a countable number of points and its derivative φ' is an increasing function.*

Proof We infer from the inequalities (40) that the functions

$$x \mapsto f'(x^-) \text{ and } x \mapsto f'(x^+)$$

are increasing real-valued functions on (a, b). But, according to Theorem 1, an increasing real-valued function is continuous except at a countable number of points. Thus, except on a countable subset C of (a, b), both the left-hand and right-hand derivatives of φ are continuous. Let x_0 belong to $(a, b) \sim C$. Choose a sequence $\{x_n\}$ of points greater than x_0 that converges to x_0. Apply Lemma 16, with $x_0 = u$ and $x_n = v$, and take limits to conclude that

$$\varphi'(x_0^-) \le \varphi'(x_0^+) \le \varphi'(x_0^-).$$

Then $\varphi'(x_0^-) = \varphi'(x_0^+)$ so that φ is differentiable at x_0. To show that φ' is an increasing function on $(a, b) \sim C$, let u, v belong to $(a, b) \sim C$ with $u < v$. Then by Lemma 16,

$$\varphi'(u) \le \frac{\varphi(u) - \varphi(v)}{u - v} \le \varphi'(v). \qquad \square$$

Let φ be a convex function on (a, b) and x_0 belong to (a, b). For a real number m, the line $y = m(x - x_0) + \varphi(x_0)$, which passes through the point $(x_0, \varphi(x_0))$, is called a **supporting line** at x_0 for the graph of φ provided this line always lies below the graph of φ, that is, if

$$\varphi(x) \ge m(x - x_0) + \varphi(x_0) \text{ for all } x \in (a, b).$$

It follows from Lemma 16 that such a line is supporting if and only if its slope m lies between the left- and right-hand derivatives of φ at x_0. Thus, in particular, there is always at least one supporting line at each point. This notion enables us to give a short proof of the following inequality:

Jensen's Inequality *Let φ be a convex function on $(-\infty, \infty)$, f an integrable function over $[0, 1]$, and $\varphi \circ f$ also integrable over $[0, 1]$. Then*

$$\varphi\left(\int_0^1 f(x)\,dx\right) \leq \int_0^1 (\varphi \circ f)(x)\,dx. \qquad (42)$$

Proof Define $\alpha = \int_0^1 f(x)\,dx$. Choose m to lie between the left-hand and right-hand derivative of φ at the point α. Then $y = m(t - \alpha) + \varphi(\alpha)$ is the equation of a supporting line at $(\alpha, \varphi(\alpha))$ for the graph of φ. Hence

$$\varphi(t) \geq m(t - \alpha) + \varphi(\alpha) \text{ for all } t \in \mathbf{R}.$$

Since f is integrable over $[0, 1]$, it is finite a.e. on $[0, 1]$ and therefore, substituting $f(x)$ for t in this inequality, we have

$$\varphi(f(x)) \geq m(f(x) - \alpha) + \varphi(\alpha) \text{ for almost all } x \in [0, 1].$$

Integrate across this inequality, using the monotonicity of the Lebesgue integral and the assumption that both f and $\varphi \circ f$ are integrable over $[a, b]$, to obtain

$$\int_0^1 \varphi(f(x))\,dx \geq \int_0^1 \left[m(f(x) - \alpha) + \varphi(\alpha)\right] dx$$

$$= m\left[\int_0^1 f(x)\,dx - \alpha\right] + \varphi(\alpha) = \varphi(\alpha). \qquad \square$$

A few words regarding the assumption, for Jensen's Inequality, of the integrability of $\varphi \circ f$ over $[0, 1]$ are in order. We have shown that a convex function is continuous and therefore Proposition 7 of Chapter 3 tells us that the composition $\varphi \circ f$ is measurable if φ is convex and f is integrable. If $\varphi \circ f$ is nonnegative, then it is unnecessary to assume the $\varphi \circ f$ is integrable since equality (42) trivially holds if the right-hand integral equals $+\infty$. In the case $\varphi \circ f$ fails to be nonnegative, if there are constants c_1 and c_2 for which

$$|\varphi(x)| \leq c_1 + c_2 |x| \text{ for all } x \in \mathbf{R}, \qquad (43)$$

then we infer from the integral comparison test that $\varphi \circ f$ is integrable over $[0, 1]$ if f is. In the absence of the growth assumption (43), the function $\varphi \circ f$ may not be integrable over $[0, 1]$ (see Problem 71).

PROBLEMS

61. Show that a real-valued function φ on (a, b) is convex if and only if for points $x_1, \ldots, x_n$ in (a, b) and nonnegative numbers $\lambda_1, \ldots, \lambda_n$ such that $\sum_{k=1}^n \lambda_k = 1$,

$$\varphi\left(\sum_{k=1}^n \lambda_k x_k\right) \leq \sum_{k=1}^n \lambda_k \varphi(x_k).$$

Use this to directly prove Jensen's Inequality for f a simple function.

62. Show that a continuous function on (a, b) is convex if and only if

$$\varphi\left(\frac{x_1 + x_2}{2}\right) \leq \frac{\varphi(x_1) + \varphi(x_2)}{2} \text{ for all } x_1, x_2 \in (a, b).$$

63. A function on a general interval I is said to be convex provided it is continuous on I and (38) holds for all $x_1, x_2 \in I$. Is a convex function on a closed, bounded interval $[a, b]$ necessarily Lipschitz on $[a, b]$?

64. Let φ have a second derivative at each point in (a, b). Show that φ is convex if and only if φ'' is nonnegative.

65. Suppose $a \geq 0$ and $b > 0$. Show that the function $\varphi(t) = (a + bt)^p$ is convex on $[0, \infty)$ for $1 \leq p < \infty$.

66. For what functions φ is Jensen's Inequality always an equality?

67. State and prove a version of Jensen's Inequality on a general closed, bounded interval $[a, b]$.

68. Let f be integrable over $[0, 1]$. Show that

$$\exp\left[\int_0^1 f(x)\, dx\right] \leq \int_0^1 \exp(f(x))\, dx$$

69. Let $\{\alpha_n\}$ be a sequence of nonnegative numbers whose sum is 1 and $\{\zeta_n\}$ a sequence of positive numbers. Show that

$$\prod_{n=1}^{\infty} \zeta_n^{\alpha_n} \leq \sum_{n=1}^{\infty} \alpha_n \zeta_n.$$

70. Let g be a positive measurable function on $[0, 1]$. Show that $\log\left(\int_0^1 g(x)\, dx\right) \geq \int_0^1 \log(g(x))\, dx$ whenever each side is defined.

71. (Nemytskii) Let φ be a continuous function on $\mathbf{R}$. Show that if there are constants for which (45) holds, then $\varphi \circ f$ is integrable over $[0, 1]$ whenever f is. Then show that if $\varphi \circ f$ is integrable over $[0, 1]$ whenever f is, then there are constants c_1 and c_2 for which (45) holds.

CHAPTER 7

The L^p Spaces: Completeness and Approximation

Contents

Completeness of the real numbers may be formulated by asserting that if $\{a_n\}$ is a sequence of real numbers for which $\lim_{n, m \to \infty} |a_n - a_m| = 0$, there is a real number a for which $\lim_{n \to \infty} |a_n - a| = 0$. There is a corresponding completeness property for the Lebesgue integral. For E measurable and $1 \leq p < \infty$, define $L^p(E)$ to be the collection of measurable functions f for which $|f|^p$ is integrable over E; thus $L^1(E)$ is the collection of integrable functions. If $\{f_n\}$ is a sequence of functions in $L^p(E)$ for which

$$\lim_{n, m \to \infty} \int_E |f_n - f_m|^p = 0,$$

there is a function f belonging to $L^p(E)$ for which

$$\lim_{n \to \infty} \int_E |f_n - f|^p = 0.$$

This is the Riesz-Fischer Theorem, the centerpiece of this chapter. A collection $\mathcal{F}$ of functions in $L^p(E)$ is said to be dense in $L^p(E)$ provided for each g in $L^p(E)$ and $\epsilon > 0$, there is a function f belonging to $\mathcal{F}$ for which $\int_E |g - f|^p < \epsilon$. We prove that there is a countable collection of functions that is dense in $L^p(E)$, and that both the continuous functions and the simple functions are dense in $L^p(E)$. The proofs of the Riesz-Fischer Theorem and the denseness results are framed in the context of normed linear spaces of functions. In order to construct this frame we prove two basic inequalities, Hölder's Inequaliy and Minkowski's Inequality.

7.1 NORMED LINEAR SPACES

Throughout this chapter E denotes a measurable set of real numbers. Define $\mathcal{F}$ to be the collection of all measurable extended real-valued functions on E that are finite a.e. on E. Define two functions f and g in $\mathcal{F}$ to be equivalent, and write $f \cong g$, provided

$$f(x) = g(x) \text{ for almost all } x \in E.$$

This is an equivalence relation, that is, it is reflexive, symmetric, and transitive. Therefore it induces a partition of $\mathcal{F}$ into a disjoint collection of equivalence classes, which we denote by $\mathcal{F}/_\cong$. There is a natural linear structure on $\mathcal{F}/_\cong$: given two functions f and g in $\mathcal{F}$, their equivalence classes $[f]$ and $[g]$ and real numbers α and β, we define the linear combination $\alpha\cdot[f]+\beta\cdot[g]$ to be the equivalence class of the functions in $\mathcal{F}$ that take the value $\alpha f(x)+\beta g(x)$ at points x in E at which both f and g are finite. These linear combinations are properly defined in that they are independent of the choice of representatives of the equivalence classes. The zero element of this linear space is the equivalence class of functions that vanish a.e. on E.

A subset of a linear space is called a subspace provided it is closed with respect to the formation of linear combinations. There is a natural family $\{L^p(E)\}_{1\leq p \leq\infty}$ of subspaces of $\mathcal{F}/_\cong$. For $1\leq p<\infty$, we define $L^p(E)$ to be the collection of equivalence classes $[f]$ for which

$$\int_E |f|^p < \infty.$$

This is properly defined since if $f\cong g$, then $\int_E |f|^p = \int_E |g|^p$. For any two numbers a and b,

$$|a+b| \leq |a| + |b| \leq 2\max\{|a|, |b|\},$$

and hence

$$|a+b|^p \leq 2^p\{|a|^p + |b|^p\}. \tag{1}$$

We infer from this inequality, together with the linearity and monotonicity of integration, that if $[f]$ and $[g]$ belong to $L^p(E)$, so also does the linear combination $\alpha\cdot[f] + \beta\cdot[g]$. Therefore $L^p(E)$ is a linear space. Of course, $L^1(E)$ comprises equivalence classes of integrable functions.

We call a function $f\in\mathcal{F}$ **essentially bounded** provided there is some $M\geq 0$, called an **essential upper bound** for f, for which

$$|f(x)| \leq M \text{ for almost all } x\in E.$$

We define $L^\infty(E)$ to be the collection of equivalence classes $[f]$ for which f is essentially bounded. It is easy to see that this is properly defined and $L^\infty(E)$ also is a linear subspace of $\mathcal{F}/_\cong$

For simplicity and convenience, we refer to the equivalence classes in $\mathcal{F}/_\cong$ as functions and denote them by f rather than $[f]$. Thus to write $f = g$ means that $f - g$ vanishes a.e. on E. This simplification imposes the obligation to check consistency when defining concepts for the $L^p(E)$ spaces. For instance, it is meaningful to assert that a sequence $\{f_n\}$ in $L^p(E)$ converges pointwise a.e. on E to a function $f\in L^p(E)$ since if $g_n\cong f_n$, for all n and $f\cong g$, then, since the union of a countable collection of sets of measure zero also is of measure zero, the sequence $\{g_n\}$ also converges pointwise a.e. on E to g. To state that a function f in $L^p[a, b]$ is continuous means that there is a continuous function that agrees with f a.e. on $[a, b]$. Since complements of sets of measure zero are dense in **R**, there is only one such continuous function and it is often convenient to consider this unique continuous function as the representative of $[f]$.

In the late nineteenth century it was observed that while real-valued functions of one or several real variables were the rudimentary ingredients of classical analysis, it is also useful to consider real-valued functions that have as their domain linear spaces of functions: such functions were called **functionals**. It became apparent that in order to systematically study such fruitful concepts as convergence of a sequence (and maintain the linearity property of convergent sequences) and thereby define the concept of continuous functional, it would be useful to extend the concept of absolute value from the real numbers to general linear spaces.[1] The notion that emerged from these investigations is called a **norm**.

Definition   *Let X be a linear space. A real-valued functional $\| \cdot \|$ on X is called a* **norm** *provided for each f and g in X and each real number α,*

(The Triangle Inequality)

$$\| f + g \| \leq \| f \| + \| g \|$$

(Positive Homogeneity)

$$\| \alpha f \| = |\alpha| \| f \|$$

(Nonnegativity)

$$\| f \| \geq 0 \text{ and } \| f \| = 0 \text{ if and only if } f = 0.$$

By a **normed linear space** we mean a linear space together with a norm. If X is a linear space normed by $\| \cdot \|$ we say that a function in X is a **unit function** provided $\| f \| = 1$. For any $f \in X$, $f \neq 0$, the function $f / \| f \|$ is a unit function: it is a scalar multiple of f which we call the **normalization** of f.

Example (the Normed Linear Space $L^1(E)$)   For a function f in $L^1(E)$, define

$$\| f \|_1 = \int_E |f|.$$

Then $\| \cdot \|_1$ is a norm on $L^1(E)$. Indeed, for $f, g \in L^1(E)$, since f and g are finite a.e. on E, we infer from the triangle inequality for real numbers that

$$|f + g| \leq |f| + |g| \text{ a.e. on } E.$$

Therefore, by the monotonicity and linearity of integration,

$$\| f + g \|_1 = \int_E |f + g| \leq \int_E [|f| + |g|] = \int_E |f| + \int_E |g| = \| f \|_1 + \| g \|_1.$$

Clearly, $\| \cdot \|_1$ is positively homogeneous. Finally, if $f \in L^1(E)$ and $\| f \|_1 = 0$, then $f = 0$ a.e. on E. Therefore $[f]$ is the zero element of the linear space $L^1(E) \subseteq \mathcal{F}/_{\cong}$, that is, $f = 0$.

Example (the Normed Linear Space $L^\infty(E)$)   For a function f in $L^\infty(E)$, define $\| f \|_\infty$ to be the infimum of the essential upper bounds for f. We call $\| f \|_\infty$ the **essential supremum**

---

[1]We will see later that continuity can also be examined in relation to metric structures, or, more generally, topological structures, on a domain and range of a mapping.

of f and claim that $\| \cdot \|_\infty$ is a norm on $L^\infty(E)$. The positivity and positive homogeneity properties follow by the same arguments used in the preceding example. To verify the triangle inequality, we first show that $\|f\|_\infty$ is an essential upper bound for f on E, that is,

$$|f| \leq \|f\|_\infty \text{ a.e. on } E. \tag{2}$$

Indeed, for each natural number n, there is a subset E_n of E for which

$$|f| \leq \|f\|_\infty + 1/n \text{ on } E \sim E_n \text{ and } m(E_n) = 0.$$

Hence, if we define $E_\infty = \bigcup_{n=1}^\infty E_n$,

$$|f| \leq \|f\|_\infty \text{ on } E \sim E_\infty \text{ and } m(E_\infty) = 0.$$

Thus the essential supremum of f is the smallest essential upper bound for f, that is, (2) holds. Now for $f, g \in L^\infty(E)$,

$$|f(x) + g(x)| \leq |f(x)| + |g(x)| \leq \|f\|_\infty + \|g\|_\infty \text{ for almost all } x \in E.$$

Therefore, $\|f\|_\infty + \|g\|_\infty$ is an essential upper bound for $f + g$ and hence

$$\|f + g\|_\infty \leq \|f\|_\infty + \|g\|_\infty.$$

Example (The Normed Linear Spaces ℓ_1 and ℓ_∞)   There is a collection of normed linear spaces of sequences that have simpler structure but many similarities with the $L^p(E)$ spaces. For $1 \leq p < \infty$, define ℓ^p to be the collection of real sequences $a = (a_1, a_2, \ldots)$ for which

$$\sum_{k=1}^\infty |a_k|^p < \infty.$$

Inequality (1) shows that the sum of two sequences in ℓ^p also belongs to ℓ^p and clearly a real multiple of a sequence in ℓ^p also belongs to ℓ^p. Thus ℓ^p is a linear space. We define ℓ^∞ to be the linear space of real bounded sequences. For a sequence $a = (a_1, a_2, \ldots)$ in ℓ^1, define

$$\|\{a_k\}\|_1 = \sum_{k=1}^\infty |a_k|.$$

This is a norm on ℓ^1. For a sequence $\{a_k\}$ in ℓ^∞, define

$$\|\{a_k\}\|_\infty = \sup_{1 \leq k < \infty} |a_k|.$$

It is also easy to see that $\| \cdot \|_\infty$ is a norm on ℓ^∞.

Example (The Normed Linear Space $C[a, b]$)   Let $[a, b]$ be a closed, bounded interval. Then the linear space of continuous real-valued functions on $[a, b]$ is denoted by $C[a, b]$. Since each continuous function on $[a, b]$ takes a maximum value, for $\in C[a, b]$, we can define

$$\|f\|_{\max} = \max_{x \in [a, b]} |f(x)|.$$

We leave it as an exercise to show that this defines a norm that we call the **maximum norm**.

PROBLEMS

1. For f in $C[a, b]$, define

$$\|f\|_1 = \int_a^b |f|.$$

Show that this is a norm on $C[a, b]$. Also show that there is no number $c \geq 0$ for which

$$\|f\|_{max} \leq c\|f\|_1 \text{ for all } f \text{ in } C[a, b],$$

but there is a $c \geq 0$ for which

$$\|f\|_1 \leq c\|f\|_{max} \text{ for all } f \text{ in } C[a, b].$$

2. Let X be the family of all polynomials with real coefficients defined on $\mathbf{R}$. Show that this is a linear space. For a polynomial p, define $\|p\|$ to the sum of the absolute values of the coefficients of p. Is this a norm?

3. For f in $L^1[a, b]$, define $\|f\| = \int_a^b x^2|f(x)|\, dx$. Show that this is a norm on $L^1[a, b]$.

4. For f in $L^\infty[a, b]$, show that

$$\|f\|_\infty = \min\left\{M \mid m\left\{x \text{ in } [a, b] \mid |f(x)| > M\right\} = 0\right\}$$

and if, furthermore, f is continuous on $[a, b]$, that

$$\|f\|_\infty = \|f\|_{max}.$$

5. Show that ℓ^∞ and ℓ^1 are normed linear spaces.

7.2   THE INEQUALITIES OF YOUNG, HÖLDER, AND MINKOWSKI

In the preceding section we introduced the linear spaces $L^p(E)$ for $1 \leq p \leq \infty$ and E a measurable set of real numbers. In the cases $p = 1$ and $p = \infty$, we defined a norm on these spaces. We now define a norm on $L^p(E)$ for $1 < p < \infty$.

Definition   *For E a measurable set, $1 < p < \infty$, and a function f in $L^p(E)$, define*

$$\|f\|_p = \left[\int_E |f|^p\right]^{1/p}$$

We will show that the functional $\|\cdot\|_p$ is a norm on $L^p(E)$. Indeed, positive homogeneity is clear. Moreover, according to Proposition 9 of Chapter 4, $\|f\|_p = 0$ if and only if f vanishes a.e. on E. Therefore $[f]$ is the zero element of the linear space $L^1(E) \subseteq \mathcal{F}/\approx$, that is, $f = 0$. It remains to establish the Triangle Inequality, that is, to show that

$$\|f + g\|_p \leq \|f\|_p + \|g\|_p \text{ for all } f, g \text{ in } L^p(E).$$

This inequality in not obvious. It is called Minkowski's Inequality.

Definition *The conjugate of a number $p \in (1, \infty)$ is the number $q = p/(p-1)$, which is the unique number $q \in (1, \infty)$ for which*

$$\frac{1}{p} + \frac{1}{q} = 1.$$

The conjugate of 1 is defined to be ∞ and the conjugate of ∞ defined to be 1.

Young's Inequality *For $1 < p < \infty$, q the conjugate of p, and any two positive numbers a and b,*

$$ab \le \frac{a^p}{p} + \frac{b^q}{q}.$$

Proof The function g, defined by $g(x) = [1/p] x^p + 1/q - x$ for $x > 0$, has a positive derivative on $(1, \infty)$, a negative derivative on $(0, 1)$, and takes the value 0 at $x = 1$. The function g therefore is nonnegative on $(0, \infty)$, that is,

$$x \le [1/p] x^p + 1/q \text{ if } x > 0.$$

In particular,

$$x_0 \le [1/p] x_0^p + 1/q \text{ if } x_0 = \frac{a}{b^{q-1}}.$$

However, this inequality is equivalent to Young's Inequality, since, because $p(q-1) = q$, it is the inequality obtained by dividing each side of Young's Inequality by b^q.   □

Theorem 1 *Let E be a measurable set, $1 \le p < \infty$, and q the conjugate of p. If f belongs to $L^p(E)$ and g belongs to $L^q(E)$, then their product $f \cdot g$ is integrable over E and*

Hölder's Inequality

$$\int_E |f \cdot g| \le \|f\|_p \cdot \|g\|_q. \tag{3}$$

Moreover, if $f \ne 0$, the function[2] $f^* = \|f\|_p^{1-p} \cdot \text{sgn}(f) \cdot |f|^{p-1}$ belongs to $L^q(X, \mu)$,

$$\int_E f \cdot f^* = \|f\|_p \text{ and } \|f^*\|_q = 1. \tag{4}$$

Proof First consider the case $p = 1$. Then Hölder's Inequality follows from the monotonicity of integration and the observation (2) that $\|f\|_\infty$ is an essential upper bound for f on E. Observe that since $f^* = \text{sgn}(f)$, (4) holds with $p = 1$, $q = \infty$. Now consider $p > 1$. Assume $f \ne 0$ and $g \ne 0$, for otherwise there is nothing to prove. It is clear that if Hölder's Inequality is true when f is replaced by its normalization $f/\|f\|_p$ and g is replaced by its normalization $g/\|g\|_q$, then it is true for f and g. We therefore assume that $\|f\|_p = \|g\|_q = 1$, that is,

$$\int_E |f|^p = 1 \text{ and } \int_E |g|^q = 1,$$

---

[2]The function $\text{sgn}(f)$ takes the value 1 if $f(x) \ge 0$ and -1 if $f(x) < 0$. Therefore $\text{sgn}(f) \cdot f = |f|$ a.e. on E since f is finite a.e. on E.

in which case Hölder's Inequality becomes

$$\int_E |f \cdot g| \le 1.$$

Since $|f|^p$ and $|g|^q$ are integrable over E, f and g are finite a.e. on E. Thus, by Young's Inequality,

$$|fg| = |f| \cdot |g| \le \frac{|f|^p}{p} + \frac{|g|^q}{q} \text{ a.e. on } E.$$

We infer from the linearity of integration and the integral comparison test that $f \cdot g$ is integrable over E and

$$\int_E |f \cdot g| \le \frac{1}{p} \int_E |f|^p + \frac{1}{q} \int_E |g|^q = \frac{1}{p} + \frac{1}{q} = 1.$$

It remains to prove (4). Observe that

$$f \cdot f^* = \|f\|_p^{1-p} \cdot |f|^p \text{ a.e. on } E.$$

Therefore

$$\int_E f \cdot f^* = \|f\|_p^{1-p} \cdot \int_E |f|^p = \|f\|_p^{1-p} \cdot \|f\|_p^p = \|f\|_p.$$

Since $q(p-1) = p$, $\|f^*\|_q = 1$.   □

It is convenient, for $f \in L^p(E)$, $f \ne 0$, to call the function f^* defined above the **conjugate function** of f.

Minkowski's Inequality   *Let E be a measurable set and $1 \le p \le \infty$. If the functions f and g belong to $L^p(E)$, then so does their sum $f + g$ and, moreover,*

$$\|f + g\|_p \le \|f\|_p + \|g\|_p.$$

Proof In the preceding section we considered the cases $p = 1$ and $p = \infty$. So we here consider the case $p \in (1, \infty)$. We already inferred from (1) that $f + g$ belongs to $L^p(E)$. Assume $f + g \ne 0$. Consider $(f + g)^*$, the conjugate function of $f + g$. We infer from the linearity of integration and Hölder's Inequality that

$$\|f + g\|_p = \int_E (f + g) \cdot (f + g)^*$$

$$= \int_E f \cdot (f + g)^* + \int_E g \cdot (f + g)^*$$

$$\le \|f\|_p \cdot \|(f + g)^*\|_q + \|g\|_p \cdot \|(f + g)^*\|_q$$

$$= \|f\|_p + \|g\|_p.$$

                   □

The special case of Hölder's Inequality when $p = q = 2$ has its own name.

The Cauchy-Schwarz Inequality *Let E be a measurable set and f and g measurable functions on E for which f^2 and g^2 are integrable over E. Then their product $f \cdot g$ also is integrable over E and*

$$\int_E |fg| \leq \sqrt{\int_E f^2} \cdot \sqrt{\int_E g^2}.$$

Corollary 2 *Let E be a measurable set and $1 < p < \infty$. Suppose $\mathcal{F}$ is a family of functions in $L^p(E)$ that is bounded in $L^p(E)$ in the sense that there is a constant M for which*

$$\|f\|_p \leq M \text{ for all } f \text{ in } \mathcal{F}.$$

Then the family $\mathcal{F}$ is uniformly integrable over E.

Proof Let $\epsilon > 0$. We must show there is a $\delta > 0$ such that for any f in $\mathcal{F}$,

$$\int_A |f| < \epsilon \text{ if } A \subseteq E \text{ is measurable and } m(A) < \delta.$$

Let A be a measurable subset of E of finite measure. Consider $L^p(A)$ and $L^q(A)$ where q is the conjugate of p. Define g to be identically equal to 1 on A. Since $m(A) < \infty$, g belongs to $L^q(A)$. We infer from Hölder's Inequality, applied to this g and the restriction of f to A, that

$$\int_A |f| = \int_A |f| \cdot g \leq \left[\int_A |f|^p\right]^{1/p} \cdot \left[\int_A |g|^q\right]^{1/q}.$$

But for all f in $\mathcal{F}$,

$$\left[\int_A |f|^p\right]^{1/p} \leq \left[\int_E |f|^p\right]^{1/p} \leq M \text{ and } \left[\int_A |g|^q\right]^{1/q} = [m(A)]^{1/q}.$$

Therefore, for all f in $\mathcal{F}$,

$$\int_A |f| \leq M \cdot [m(A)]^{1/q}.$$

Therefore for each $\epsilon > 0$, $\delta = [\epsilon/M]^q$ responds to the ϵ challenge regarding the criterion for $\mathcal{F}$ to be uniformly integrable. $\qquad \square$

Corollary 3 *Let E be a measurable set of finite measure and $1 \leq p_1 < p_2 \leq \infty$. Then $L^{p_2}(E) \subseteq L^{p_1}(E)$. Furthermore,*

$$\|f\|_{p_1} \leq c\|f\|_{p_2} \text{ for all } f \text{ in } L^{p_2}(E), \tag{5}$$

where $c = [m(E)]^{\frac{p_2 - p_1}{p_1 p_2}}$ if $p_2 < \infty$ and $c = [m(E)]^{\frac{1}{p_1}}$ if $p_2 = \infty$.

Proof We leave the case $p_2 = \infty$ as an exercise. Assume $p_2 < \infty$. Define $p = p_2/p_1 > 1$ and let q be the conjugate of p. Let f belong to $L^{p_2}(E)$. Observe that f^{p_1} belongs to $L^p(E)$ and $g = \chi_E$ belongs to $L^q(E)$ since $m(E) < \infty$. Apply Hölder's Inequality. Then

$$\int_E |f|^{p_1} = \int_E |f|^{p_1} \cdot g \leq \|f\|_{p_2}^{p_1} \cdot \left[\int_E |g|^q\right]^{1/q} = \|f\|_{p_2}^{p_1} [m(E)]^{1/q}.$$

Take the $1/p_1$ power of each side to obtain (5).   □

Example In general, for E of finite measure and $1 \leq p_1 < p_2 \leq \infty$, $L^{p_2}(E)$ is a proper subspace of $L^{p_1}(E)$. For instance, let $E = (0, 1]$ and f be defined by $f(x) = x^\alpha$ for $0 < x \leq 1$, where $-1/p_1 < \alpha < -1/p_2$. Then $f \in L^{p_1}(E) \sim L^{p_2}(E)$.

Example In general, for E of infinite measure, there are no inclusion relationships among the $L^p(E)$ spaces. For instance, for $E = (1, \infty)$ and f defined by

$$f(x) = \frac{x^{-1/2}}{1 + \ln x} \text{ for } x > 1,$$

f belongs to $L^p(E)$ if and only if $p = 2$.

PROBLEMS

6. Show that if Hölder's Inequality is true for normalized functions it is true in general.

7. Verify the assertions in the above two examples regarding the membership of the function f in $L^p(E)$.

8. Let f and g belong to $L^2(E)$. From the linearity of integration show that for any number λ,

$$\lambda^2 \int_E f^2 + 2\lambda \int_E f \cdot g + \int_E g^2 = \int_E (\lambda f + g)^2 \geq 0.$$

From this and the quadratic formula directly derive the Cauchy-Schwarz Inequality.

9. Show that in Young's Inequality there is equality if and only if $a = b = 1$.

10. Show that in Hölder's Inequality there is equality if and only if there are constants α and β, not both zero, for which

$$\alpha |f|^p = \beta |g|^q \text{ a.e. on } E.$$

11. For a point $x = (x_1, x_2, \ldots, x_n)$ in $\mathbf{R}^n$, define T_x to be the step function on the interval $[1, n + 1)$ that takes the value x_k on the interval $[k, k + 1)$, for $1 \leq k \leq n$. For $p \geq 1$, define $\|x\|_p = \|T_x\|_p$, the norm of the function T_x in $L^p[1, n + 1)$. Show that this defines a norm on $\mathbf{R}^n$. State and prove the Hölder and Minkowski Inequalities for this norm.

12. For $1 \leq p < \infty$ and a sequence $a = (a_1, a_2, \ldots) \in \ell^p$, define T_a to be the function on the interval $[1, \infty)$ that takes the value a_k on $[k, k + 1)$, for $k = 1, 2, \ldots$. Show that T_a belongs to $L^p[1, \infty)$ and that $\|a\|_p = \|T_a\|_p$. Use this to state and prove the Hölder and Minkowski Inequalities in ℓ^p.

13. Show that if f is a bounded function on E that belongs to $L^{p_1}(E)$, then it belongs to $L^{p_2}(E)$ for any $p_2 > p_1$.

14. Show that if $f(x) = \ln(1/x)$ for $x \in (0, 1]$, then f belongs to $L^p(0, 1]$ for all $1 \leq p < \infty$ but does not belong to $L^\infty(0, 1]$.

15. Formulate and prove an extension of Hölder's Inequality for the product of three functions.

16. Suppose that $\{f_n\}$ is bounded in $L^1[0, 1]$. Is $\{f_n\}$ uniformly integrable over $[0, 1]$?

17. For $1 < p < \infty$, suppose that $\{f_n\}$ is bounded in $L^p(\mathbf{R})$. Is $\{f_n\}$ tight?

18. Assume $m(E) < \infty$. For $f \in L^\infty(E)$, show that $\lim_{p \to \infty} \|f\|_p = \|f\|_\infty$.

19. For $1 \leq p < \infty$, q the conjugate of p, and $f \in L^p(E)$, show that

$$\|f\|_p = \max_{g \in L^q(E), \|g\|_q \leq 1} \int_E f \cdot g.$$

20. For $1 \leq p < \infty$, q the conjugate of p, and $f \in L^p(E)$, show that $f = 0$ if and only if

$$\int_E f \cdot g = 0 \text{ for all } g \in L^q(E).$$

21. For $1 \leq p \leq \infty$, find the values of the parameter λ for which

$$\lim_{\epsilon \to 0^+} \frac{1}{\epsilon^\lambda} \int_0^\epsilon f = 0 \text{ for all } f \in L^p[0, 1].$$

22. (Riesz) For $1 < p < \infty$, show that if the absolutely continuous function F on $[a, b]$ is the indefinite integral of an $L^p[a, b]$ function, then there is a constant $M > 0$ such that for any partition $\{x_0, \ldots, x_n\}$ of $[a, b]$,

$$\sum_{k=1}^n \frac{|F(x_k) - F(x_{k-1})|^p}{|x_k - x_{k-1}|^{p-1}} \leq M.$$

7.3 L^p IS COMPLETE: THE RIESZ-FISCHER THEOREM

The concepts of convergent sequence and Cauchy sequence are defined for a sequence in a normed linear space in exactly the same way they are for sequences in $\mathbf{R}$, normed by the absolute value.

Definition *A sequence $\{f_n\}$ in a linear space X that is normed by $\| \cdot \|$ is said to* **converge to** f *in X provided*

$$\lim_{n \to \infty} \|f - f_n\| = 0.$$

We write

$$\{f_n\} \to f \text{ in } X \text{ or } \lim_{n \to \infty} f_n = f \text{ in } X$$

to mean that each f_n and f belong to X and $\lim_{n \to \infty} \|f - f_n\| = 0$.

It is clear that for a sequence $\{f_n\}$ and function f in $C[a, b]$, $\{f_n\} \to f$ in $C[a, b]$, normed by the maximum norm, if and only if $\{f_n\} \to f$ uniformly on $[a, b]$. Furthermore, since the essential supremum of a function in $L^\infty(E)$ is an essential upper bound, for a sequence $\{f_n\}$ and function f in $L^\infty(E)$, $\{f_n\} \to f$ in $L^\infty(E)$ if and only if $\{f_n\} \to f$ uniformly on the complement of a set of measure zero. For a sequence $\{f_n\}$ and function f in $L^p(E)$, $1 \le p < \infty$, $\{f_n\} \to f$ in $L^p(E)$ if and only if

$$\lim_{n \to \infty} \int_E |f_n - f|^p = 0.$$

Definition *A sequence $\{f_n\}$ in a linear space X that is normed by $\|\cdot\|$ is said to be **Cauchy** in X provided for each $\epsilon > 0$, there is a natural number N such that*

$$\|f_n - f_m\| < \epsilon \text{ for all } m, n \ge N.$$

*A normed linear space X is said to be **complete** provided every Cauchy sequence in X converges to a function in X. A complete normed linear space is called a **Banach space**.*

The completeness axiom for the real numbers is equivalent to the assertion that $\mathbf{R}$, normed by the absolute value, is complete. This immediately implies that each Euclidean space $\mathbf{R}^n$ also is complete. In a first course in mathematical analysis it is always proven that $C[a, b]$, normed by the maximum norm, is complete (see Problem 31). The same argument, together with the measurability of pointwise limits of measurable functions, shows that $L^\infty(E)$ also is complete (see Problem 33).

Proposition 4 *Let X be a normed linear space. Then every convergent sequence in X is Cauchy. Moreover, a Cauchy sequence in X converges if it has a convergent subsequence.*

Proof Let $\{f_n\} \to f$ in X. By the triangle inequality for the norm,

$$\|f_n - f_m\| = \|[f_n - f] + [f - f_m]\| \le \|f_n - f\| + \|f_m - f\| \text{ for all } m, n.$$

Therefore $\{f_n\}$ is Cauchy.

Now let $\{f_n\}$ be a Cauchy sequence in X that has a subsequence $\{f_{n_k}\}$ which converges in X to f. Let $\epsilon > 0$. Since $\{f_n\}$ is Cauchy, we may choose N such that $\|f_n - f_m\|_p < \epsilon/2$ for all $n, m \ge N$. Since $\{f_{n_k}\}$ converges to f we may choose k such that $n_k > N$ and $\|f_{n_k} - f\|_p < \epsilon/2$. Then, by the triangle inequality for the norm,

$$\|f_n - f\|_p = \|[f_n - f_{n_k}] + [f_{n_k} - f]\|_p$$
$$= \|f_n - f_{n_k}\|_p + \|f_{n_k} - f\|_p < \epsilon \text{ for } n \ge N.$$

Therefore $\{f_n\} \to f$ in X $\qquad\qquad\qquad\qquad\qquad\qquad\qquad\qquad\qquad\qquad\qquad\square$

In view of the above lemma, a useful strategy to establish the completeness of a particular normed linear space is to show that a particular type of Cauchy sequence, tailored to the properties of the space, converges and also show that every Cauchy sequence has a subsequence of this particular type (see Problems 30 and 32). In the $L^p(E)$ spaces, $1 \leq p < \infty$, so-called rapidly Cauchy sequences,[3] defined as follows, are useful.

Definition *Let X be a linear space normed by* $\| \cdot \|$. *A sequence* $\{f_n\}$ *in X is said to be* **rapidly Cauchy** *provided there is a convergent series of positive numbers* $\sum_{k=1}^{\infty} \epsilon_k$ *for which*

$$\| f_{k+1} - f_k \| \leq \epsilon_k^2 \text{ for all } k.$$

It is useful to observe that if $\{f_n\}$ is a sequence in a normed linear space and the sequence of nonnegative numbers $\{a_k\}$ has the property that

$$\| f_{k+1} - f_k \| \leq a_k \text{ for all } k,$$

then, since

$$f_{n+k} - f_n = \sum_{j=n}^{n+k-1} [f_{j+1} - f_j] \text{ for all } n, k,$$

$$\| f_{n+k} - f_n \| \leq \sum_{j=n}^{n+k-1} \| f_{j+1} - f_j \| \leq \sum_{j=n}^{\infty} a_j \text{ for all } n, k. \tag{6}$$

Proposition 5 *Let X be a normed linear space. Then every rapidly Cauchy sequence in X is Cauchy. Furthermore, every Cauchy sequence has a rapidly Cauchy subsequence.*

Proof Let $\{f_n\}$ be a rapidly Cauchy sequence in X and $\sum_{k=1}^{\infty} \epsilon_k$ a convergent series of nonnegative numbers for which

$$\| f_{k+1} - f_k \| \leq \epsilon_k^2 \text{ for all } k. \tag{7}$$

We infer from (6) that

$$\| f_{n+k} - f_n \| \leq \sum_{j=n}^{\infty} \epsilon_j^2 \text{ for all } n, k. \tag{8}$$

Since the series $\sum_{k=1}^{\infty} \epsilon_k$ converges, the series $\sum_{k=1}^{\infty} \epsilon_k^2$ also converges. We infer from (8) that $\{f_n\}$ is Cauchy. Now assume that $\{f_n\}$ is a Cauchy sequence in X. We may inductively choose a strictly increasing sequence of natural numbers $\{n_k\}$ for which

$$\| f_{n_{k+1}} - f_{n_k} \| \leq (1/2)^k \text{ for all } k.$$

The subsequence $\{f_{n_k}\}$ is rapidly Cauchy since the geometric series with ratio $1/\sqrt{2}$ converges. $\square$

Theorem 6 *Let E be a measurable set and* $1 \leq p \leq \infty$. *Then every rapidly Cauchy sequence in* $L^p(E)$ *converges both with respect to the* $L^p(E)$ *norm and pointwise a.e. on E to a function in* $L^p(E)$.

---

[3] In the article "Rethinking the Lebesgue Integral" (*American Math Monthly*, December, 2009), Peter Lax singles out pointwise limits of sequences of continuous functions that are rapidly Cauchy with respect to the L^1 norm as primary objects in the construction of the complete space L^1. He defends the viewpoint that the principal object of desire in the program to use theorems about Banach spaces in the study of integration is the identification of L^1. Lax constructs functions in L^1 as limits of rapidly Cauchy sequences of continuous functions without first making a separate study of measure theory.

Proof We leave the case $p = \infty$ as an exercise (Problem 33). Assume $1 \leq p < \infty$. Let $\{f_n\}$ be a rapidly convergent sequence in $L^p(E)$. By possibly excising from E a set of measure zero, we may assume that each of the f_n's takes real values. Choose $\sum_{k=1}^{\infty} \epsilon_k$ to be a convergent series of positive numbers such that

$$\|f_{k+1} - f_k\|_p \leq \epsilon_k^2 \text{ for all } k, \tag{9}$$

and therefore

$$\int_E |f_{k+1} - f_k|^p \leq \epsilon_k^{2p} \text{ for all } k. \tag{10}$$

Fix a natural number k. Since, for $x \in E$, $|f_{k+1}(x) - f_k(x)| \geq \epsilon_k$ if and only if $|f_{k+1}(x) - f_k(x)|^p \geq \epsilon_k^p$, we infer from (10) and Chebychev's Inequality that

$$m\left\{x \in E \mid |f_{k+1}(x) - f_k(x)| \geq \epsilon_k\right\} = m\left\{x \in E \mid |f_{k+1}(x) - f_k(x)|^p \geq \epsilon_k^p\right\}$$

$$\leq \frac{1}{\epsilon_k^p} \cdot \int_E |f_{k+1} - f_k|^p$$

$$\leq \epsilon_k^p.$$

Since $p \geq 1$, the series $\sum_{k=1}^{\infty} \epsilon_k^p$ converges. The Borel-Cantelli Lemma tells us that there is a subset E_0 of E that has measure zero and for each $x \in E \sim E_0$, there is an index $K(x)$ such that

$$|f_{k+1}(x) - f_k(x)| < \epsilon_k \text{ for all } k \geq K(x).$$

Let x belong to $E \sim E_0$. Then

$$|f_{n+k}(x) - f_n(x)| \leq \sum_{j=n}^{n+k-1} |f_{j+1}(x) - f_j(x)|$$

$$\leq \sum_{j=n}^{\infty} \epsilon_j \text{ for all } n \geq K(x) \text{ and all } k. \tag{11}$$

The series $\sum_{j=1}^{\infty} \epsilon_j$ converges, and therefore the sequence of real numbers $\{f_k(x)\}$ is Cauchy. The real numbers are complete. Denote the limit of $\{f_k(x)\}$ by $f(x)$. It follows from (9) and (6) that

$$\int_E |f_{n+k} - f_n|^p \leq \left[\sum_{j=n}^{\infty} \epsilon_j^2\right]^p \text{ for all } n, k. \tag{12}$$

Since $\{f_n\} \to f$ pointwise a.e. on E, take the limit as $k \to \infty$ in this inequality and infer from Fatou's Lemma that

$$\int_E |f - f_n|^p \leq \left[\sum_{j=n}^{\infty} \epsilon_j^2\right]^p \text{ for all } n.$$

Since the series $\sum_{k=1}^{\infty} \epsilon_k^2$ converges, f belongs to $L^p(E)$ and $\{f_n\} \to f$ in $L^p(E)$. The proof is complete since we constructed f as the pointwise limit a.e. on E of $\{f_n\}$.   ☐

The Riesz-Fischer Theorem *Let E be a measurable set and $1 \le p \le \infty$. Then $L^p(E)$ is a Banach space. Moreover, if $\{f_n\} \to f$ in $L^p(E)$, a subsequence of $\{f_n\}$ converges pointwise a.e. on E to f.*

Proof Let $\{f_n\}$ be a Cauchy sequence $L^p(E)$. According to Proposition 5, there is a subsequence $\{f_{n_k}\}$ of $\{f_n\}$ that is rapidly Cauchy. The preceding theorem tells us that $\{f_{n_k}\}$ converges to a function f in $L^p(E)$ both with respect to the $L^p(E)$ norm and pointwise a.e. on E. According to Proposition 4 the whole Cauchy sequence converges to f with respect to the $L^p(E)$ norm.   ☐

As the following example shows, a sequence $\{f_n\}$ in $L^p(E)$ that converges pointwise a.e. on E to f in $L^p(E)$ will not in general converge in $L^p(E)$.

Example For $E = [0, 1]$, $1 \le p < \infty$, and each natural number n, let $f_n = n^{1/p} \chi_{(0, 1/n]}$. The sequence converges pointwise on $[0, 1]$ to the function that is identically zero but does not converge to this function with respect to the $L^p[0, 1]$ norm.

The next two theorems provide necessary and sufficient conditions for convergence in $L^p(E)$ for a sequence that converges pointwise.

Theorem 7 *Let E be a measurable set and $1 \le p < \infty$. Suppose $\{f_n\}$ is a sequence in $L^p(E)$ that converges pointwise a.e. on E to the function f which belongs to $L^p(E)$. Then*

$$\{f_n\} \to f \text{ in } L^p(E) \text{ if and only } \lim_{n \to \infty} \int_E |f_n|^p = \int_E |f|^p.$$

Proof By possibly excising from E a set of measure zero, we may assume f and each f_n is real-valued and the convergence is pointwise on all of E. We infer from Minkowski's Inequality that, for each n, $|\, \|f_n\|_p - \|f\|_p\,| \le \|f_n - f\|_p$. Hence, if $\{f_n\} \to f$ in $L^p(E)$, then $\lim_{n \to \infty} \int_E |f_n|^p = \int_E |f_n|^p$. To prove the converse, assume $\lim_{n \to \infty} \int_E |f_n|^p = \int_E |f_n|^p$. Define $\psi(t) = t^p$ for all t. Then ψ is convex since its second derivative is nonnegative and thus

$$\psi\left(\frac{a+b}{2}\right) \le \frac{\psi(a) + \psi(b)}{2} \text{ for all } a, b.$$

Hence

$$0 \le \frac{|a|^p + |b|^p}{2} - \left|\frac{a-b}{2}\right|^p \text{ for all } a, b.$$

Therefore, for each n, a nonnegative measurable function h_n is defined on E by

$$h_n(x) = \frac{|f_n(x)|^p + |f(x)|^p}{2} - \left|\frac{f_n(x) - f(x)}{2}\right|^p \text{ for all } x \in E.$$

Since $\{h_n\} \to |f|^p$ pointwise on E, we infer from Fatou's Lemma that

$$\int_E |f|^p \le \liminf \left[\int_E h_n \right]$$

$$= \liminf \left[\int_E \frac{|f_n(x)|^p + |f(x)|^p}{2} - \left| \frac{f_n(x) - f(x)}{2} \right|^p \right]$$

$$= \int_E |f|^p - \limsup \left[\int_E \left| \frac{f_n(x) - f(x)}{2} \right|^p \right].$$

Thus

$$\limsup \left[\int_E \left| \frac{f_n(x) - f(x)}{2} \right|^p \right] \le 0,$$

that is, $\{f_n\} \to f$ in $L^p(E)$.   □

Theorem 8 *Let E be a measurable set and $1 \le p < \infty$. Suppose $\{f_n\}$ is a sequence in $L^p(E)$ that converges pointwise a.e. on E to the function f which belongs to $L^p(E)$. Then*

$$\{f_n\} \to f \text{ in } L^p(E)$$
if and only if
$\{|f|^p\}$ is uniformly integrable and tight over E.

Proof The sequence of nonnegative integrable functions $\{|f_n - f|^p\}$ converges pointwise a.e. on E to zero. According to Corollary 2 of Chapter 5, a corollary of the Vitali Convergence Theorem,

$$\lim_{n \to \infty} \int_E |f_n - f|^p = 0 \text{ if and only if } \{|f_n - f|^p\} \text{ is uniformly integrable and tight over } E.$$

However, we infer from the inequality (1) that for all n,

$$|f_n - f|^p \le 2^p \{|f_n|^p + |f|^p\} \text{ and } |f_n|^p \le 2^p \{|f_n - f|^p + |f|^p\} \text{ a.e. on } E.$$

By assumption, $|f|^p$ is integrable over E, and therefore $\{|f_n - f|^p\}$ is uniformly integrable and tight over E if and only if the sequence $\{|f_n|^p\}$ is uniformly integrable and tight over E.   □

PROBLEMS

23. Provide an example of a Cauchy sequence of real numbers that is not rapidly Cauchy.

24. Let X be normed linear space. Assume that $\{f_n\} \to f$ in X, $\{g_n\} \to g$ in X, and α and β are real numbers. Show that

$$\{\alpha f_n + \beta g_n\} \to \alpha f + \beta g \text{ in } X.$$

25. Assume that E has finite measure and $1 \le p_1 < p_2 \le \infty$. Show that if $\{f_n\} \to f$ in $L^{p_2}(E)$, then $\{f_n\} \to f$ in $L^{p_1}(E)$.

26. (The L^p Dominated Convergence Theorem) Let $\{f_n\}$ be a sequence of measurable functions that converges pointwise a.e. on E to f. For $1 \le p < \infty$, suppose there is a function g in $L^p(E)$ such that for all n, $|f_n| \le g$ a.e. on E. Prove that $\{f_n\} \to f$ in $L^p(E)$.

27. For E a measurable set and $1 \le p < \infty$, assume $\{f_n\} \to f$ in $L^p(E)$. Show that there is a subsequence $\{f_{n_k}\}$ and a function $g \in L^p(E)$ for which $|f_{n_k}| \le g$ a.e. on E for all k.

28. Assume E has finite measure and $1 \le p < \infty$. Suppose $\{f_n\}$ is a sequence of measurable functions that converges pointwise a.e. on E to f. For $1 \le p < \infty$, show that $\{f_n\} \to f$ in $L^p(E)$ if there is a $\theta > 0$ such that $\{f_n\}$ belongs to and is bounded as a subset of $L^{p+\theta}(E)$.

29. Consider the linear space of polynomials on $[a, b]$ normed by $\| \cdot \|_{max}$ norm. Is this normed linear space a Banach space?

30. Let $\{f_n\}$ be a sequence in $C[a, b]$ and $\sum_{k=1}^{\infty} a_k$ a convergent series of positive numbers such that
$$\|f_{k+1} - f_k\|_{max} \le a_k \text{ for all } k.$$
Prove that
$$|f_{n+k}(x) - f_k(x)| \le \|f_{n+k} - f_k\|_{max} \le \sum_{j=n}^{\infty} a_j \text{ for all } k, n \text{ and all } x \in [a, b].$$
Conclude that there is a function $f \in C[a, b]$ such that $\{f_n\} \to f$ uniformly on $[a, b]$

31. Use the preceding problem to show that $C[a, b]$, normed by the maximum norm, is a Banach space.

32. Let $\{f_n\}$ be a sequence in $L^\infty(E)$ and $\sum_{k=1}^{\infty} a_k$ a convergent series of positive numbers such that
$$\|f_{k+1} - f_k\|_\infty \le a_k \text{ for all } k.$$
Prove that there is a subset E_0 of E which has measure zero and
$$|f_{n+k}(x) - f_k(x)| \le \|f_{n+k} - f_k\|_\infty \le \sum_{j=n}^{\infty} a_j \text{ for all } k, n \text{ and all } x \in E \sim E_0.$$
Conclude that there is a function $f \in L^\infty(E)$ such that $\{f_n\} \to f$ uniformly on $E \sim E_0$.

33. Use the preceding problem to show that $L^\infty(E)$ is a Banach space.

34. Prove that for $1 \le p \le \infty$, l^p is a Banach space.

35. Show that the space of c of all convergent sequences of real numbers and the space c_0 of all sequences that converge to zero are Banach spaces with respect to the l^∞ norm.

7.4 APPROXIMATION AND SEPARABILITY

We here elaborate on the general theme of Littlewood's second principle, namely, the approximation of functions in one class by ones in a better class. We consider approximation with respect to the $L^p(E)$ norm. It is useful to introduce the general concept of denseness.

Definition *Let X be a normed linear space with norm $\| \cdot \|$. Given two subsets $\mathcal{F}$ and $\mathcal{G}$ of X with $\mathcal{F} \subseteq \mathcal{G}$, we say that $\mathcal{F}$ is **dense** in $\mathcal{G}$, provided for each function g in $\mathcal{G}$ and $\epsilon > 0$, there is a function f in $\mathcal{F}$ for which $\|f - g\| < \epsilon$.*

It is not difficult to see that the set $\mathcal{F}$ is dense in $\mathcal{G}$ if and only if for each g in $\mathcal{G}$ there is a sequence $\{f_n\}$ in $\mathcal{F}$ for which

$$\lim_{n \to \infty} f_n = g \text{ in } X.$$

Moreover, it is also useful to observe that for $\mathcal{F} \subseteq \mathcal{G} \subseteq \mathcal{H} \subseteq X$,

$$\text{if } \mathcal{F} \text{ is dense in } \mathcal{G} \text{ and } \mathcal{G} \text{ is dense in } \mathcal{H}, \text{ then } \mathcal{F} \text{ is dense in } \mathcal{H}. \tag{13}$$

We have already encountered dense sets: the rational numbers are dense in $\mathbf{R}$, as are the irrational numbers. Moreover, the Weierstrass Approximation Theorem[4] may be stated in our present vocabulary of normed linear spaces as follows: the family of polynomials restricted to $[a, b]$ is dense in the linear space $C[a, b]$, normed by the maximum norm.

Proposition 9 *Let E be a measurable set and $1 \leq p \leq \infty$. Then the subspace of simple functions in $L^p(E)$ is dense in $L^p(E)$.*

Proof Let g belong to $L^p(E)$. First consider $p = \infty$. There is a subset E_0 of E of measure zero for which g is bounded on $E \sim E_0$. We infer from the Simple Approximation Lemma that there is a sequence of simple functions on $E \sim E_0$ that converge uniformly on $E \sim E_0$ to g and therefore with respect to the $L^\infty(E)$ norm. Thus the simple functions are dense in $L^\infty(E)$.

Now suppose $1 \leq p < \infty$. The function g is measurable and therefore, by the Simple Approximation Theorem, there is a sequence $\{\varphi_n\}$ of simple functions on E such that $\{\varphi_n\} \to g$ pointwise on E and

$$|\varphi_n| \leq |g| \text{ on } E \text{ for all } n.$$

It follows from the integral comparison test that each φ_n belongs to $L^p(E)$. We claim that $\{\varphi_n\} \to g$ in $L^p(E)$. Indeed, for all n,

$$|\varphi_n - g|^p \leq 2^p \{|\varphi_n|^p + |g|^p\} \leq 2^{p+1}|g|^p \text{ on } E.$$

Since $|g|^p$ is integrable over E, we infer from the Lebesgue Dominated Convergence Theorem that $\{\varphi_n\} \to g$ in $L^p(E)$. $\qquad\square$

Proposition 10 *Let $[a, b]$ be a closed, bounded interval and $1 \leq p < \infty$. Then the subspace of step functions on $[a, b]$ is dense in $L^p[a, b]$.*

Proof The preceding proposition tells us that the simple functions are dense in $L^p[a, b]$. Therefore it suffices to show that the step functions are dense in the simple functions, with respect to the $\| \cdot \|_p$ norm. Each simple function is a linear combination of characteristic functions of measurable sets. Therefore, if each such characteristic function can be arbitrarily closely approximated, in the $\| \cdot \|_p$ norm, by a step function, since the step functions are a linear space, so can any simple function. Let $g = \chi_A$, where A is a measurable subset of $[a, b]$ and let $\epsilon > 0$, and seek a step function f on $[a, b]$ for which $\|f - g\|_p < \epsilon$. According to Theorem 12 of Chapter 2, there is a finite disjoint collection of open intervals, $\{I_k\}_{k=1}^n$, for

---

[4]See Patrick Fitzpatrick's *Advanced Calculus* [Fit09] for a proof.

which, if we define $\mathcal{U} = \bigcup_{k=1}^{n} I_k$, then the symmetric difference $A \Delta \mathcal{U} = [A \sim \mathcal{U}] \cup [\mathcal{U} \cap A]$ has the property that

$$m(A \Delta \mathcal{U}) < \epsilon^p.$$

Since $\mathcal{U}$ is the union of a finite disjoint collection of open intervals, $\chi_{\mathcal{U}}$ is a step function. Moreover,

$$\|\chi_A - \chi_{\mathcal{U}}\|_p = [m(A \Delta \mathcal{U})]^{1/p}. \tag{14}$$

Therefore $\|\chi_A - \chi_{\mathcal{U}}\|_p < \epsilon$ and the proof is complete. $\square$

Definition *A normed linear space X is said to be **separable** provided there is a countable subset that is dense in X.*

The real numbers are separable since the rational numbers are a countable dense subset. For $[a, b]$ a closed, bounded interval, $C[a, b]$, normed by the maximum norm, is separable since we infer from the Weierstrass Approximation Theorem that the polynomials with rational coefficients are a countable set that is dense in $C[a, b]$.

Theorem 11 *Let E be a measurable set and $1 \le p < \infty$. Then the normed linear space $L^p(E)$ is separable.*

Proof Let $[a, b]$ be a closed, bounded interval and $S[a, b]$ the collection of step functions on $[a, b]$. Define $S'[a, b]$ to be subcollection of $S[a, b]$ comprising step functions ψ on $[a, b]$ that take rational values and for which there is a partition $P = \{x_0, \ldots, x_n\}$ of $[a, b]$ with ψ constant on (x_{k-1}, x_k), for $1 \le k \le n$, and x_k rational for $1 \le k \le n - 1$. We infer from the density of the rational numbers in the real numbers that $S'[a, b]$ is dense in $S[a, b]$, with respect to the $L^p(E)$ norm. We leave it as an exercise to verify that $S'[a, b]$ is a countable set. There are the following two inclusions, each of which is dense with respect to the $L^p[a, b]$ norm:

$$S'[a, b] \subseteq S[a, b] \subseteq L^p[a, b].$$

Therefore, by (13), $S'[a, b]$ is dense in $L^p[a, b]$. For each natural number n, define $\mathcal{F}_n$ to be the functions on $\mathbf{R}$ that vanish outside $[-n, n]$ and whose restrictions to $[-n, n]$ belong to $S'[-n, n]$. Define $\mathcal{F} = \bigcup_{n \in \mathbf{N}} \mathcal{F}_n$. Then $\mathcal{F}$ is a countable collection of functions in $L^p(\mathbf{R})$. By the Monotone Convergence Theorem,

$$\lim_{n \to \infty} \int_{[-n, n]} |f|^p = \int_{\mathbf{R}} |f|^p \text{ for all } f \in L^p(\mathbf{R}).$$

Therefore, by the choice of each $\mathcal{F}_n$, $\mathcal{F}$ is a countable collection of functions that is dense in $L^p(\mathbf{R})$. Finally, let E be a general measurable set. Then the collection of restrictions to E of functions in $\mathcal{F}$ is a countable dense subset of $L^p(E)$, and therefore $L^p(E)$ is separable. $\square$

As the following example shows, in general $L^\infty(E)$ is not separable.

Example Let $[a, b]$ be a nondegenerate closed, bounded interval. We claim that the normed linear space $L^\infty[a, b]$ is not separable. To verify this claim, we argue by contradiction.

Suppose there is a countable set $\{f_n\}_{n=1}^{\infty}$ that is dense in $L^{\infty}[a, b]$. For each number $x \in [a, b]$, select a natural number $\eta(x)$ for which

$$\|\chi_{[a, x]} - f_{\eta(x)}\|_{\infty} < 1/2.$$

Observe that

$$\|\chi_{[a, x_1]} - \chi_{[a, x_2]}\|_{\infty} = 1 \text{ if } a \le x_1 < x_2 \le b.$$

Therefore η is a one-to-one mapping of $[a, b]$ onto a set of natural numbers. But a set of natural numbers is countable and $[a, b]$ is not countable. We conclude from this contradiction that $L^{\infty}[a, b]$ is not separable.

For a measurable subset E of $\mathbf{R}$, we denote by $C_c(E)$ the linear space of continuous real-valued functions on E that vanish outside a bounded set. In the proof of the above theorem, for $1 \le p < \infty$, we presented a dense subset $\mathcal{F}$ of $L^p(\mathbf{R})$ with the property that for each $f \in \mathcal{F}$, there is a closed, bounded interval $[a, b]$ for which the restriction of f to $[a, b]$ is a step function and f vanishes outside $[a, b]$. It is not difficult to see that each $f \in \mathcal{F}$ is the limit in $L^p(\mathbf{R})$ of a sequence of continuous, piecewise linear functions, each of which vanish outside a bounded set. Define $\mathcal{F}'$ to be the union of all such approximating sequences of functions in $\mathcal{F}$. Then $\mathcal{F}'$ is dense in $L^p(\mathbf{R})$. Moreover, for E a measurable set, the collection of restriction to E of functions belonging to $\mathcal{F}'$ is a dense subset of $L^p(E)$ consisting of continuous functions on E that vanish outside a bounded set. This proves the following theorem.

Theorem 12 *Let E be a measurable set and $1 \le p < \infty$. Then $C_c(E)$ is dense in $L^p(E)$.*

PROBLEMS

36. Let S be a subset of a normed linear space X. Show that S is dense in X if and only if each $g \in X$ is the limit of a sequence in S.

37. Verify (13).

38. Prove that the collection of polynomials with rational coefficients is countable.

39. Let E be a measurable set, $1 \le p < \infty$, q the conjugate of p, and S a dense subset of $L^q(E)$. Show that if $g \in L^p(E)$ and $\int_E f \cdot g = 0$ for all $f \in S$, then $g = 0$.

40. Verify the details in the proof of Theorem 11.

41. Let E be a measurable set of finite measure and $1 \le p_1 < p_2 < \infty$. Consider the linear space $L^{p_2}(E)$ normed by $\|\cdot\|_{p_1}$. Is this normed linear space a Banach space?

42. Exhibit a measurable set E for which $L^{\infty}(E)$ is separable. Show that $L^{\infty}(E)$ is not separable if the set E contains a nondegenerate interval.

43. Suppose that X is a Banach space with norm $\|\cdot\|$. Let X_0 be a dense subspace of X. Assume that X_0, when normed by the norm it inherits from X, is also a Banach space. Prove that $X = X_0$.

44. For $1 \le p < \infty$, show that the sequence space ℓ^p is separable. Show that the collection of sets of natural numbers is uncountable and conclude that ℓ^{∞} is not separable.

45. Prove Theorem 12.

46. Show that for $1 < p < \infty$ and any two numbers a and b,

$$\left| \text{sgn}(a) \cdot |a|^{1/p} - \text{sgn}(b) \cdot |b|^{1/p} \right|^p \le 2^p \cdot |a - b|.$$

47. Show that for $1 < p < \infty$ and any two numbers a and b,

$$\left| \text{sgn}(a) \cdot |a|^p - \text{sgn}(b) \cdot |b|^p \right| \le p \cdot |a - b|(|a| + |b|)^{p-1}.$$

48. (Mazur) Let E be a measurable set and $1 < p < \infty$. For f in $L^1(E)$, define the function $\Phi(f)$ on E by

$$\Phi(f)(x) = \text{sgn}(f(x))|f(x)|^{1/p}.$$

Show that $\Phi(f)$ belongs to $L^p(E)$. Moreover, use Problem 46 to show that

$$\|\Phi(f) - \Phi(g)\|_p \le 2^p \cdot \|f - g\|_1 \text{ for all } f, g \text{ in } L^1(E).$$

From this conclude that Φ is a continuous mapping of $L^1(E)$ into $L^p(E)$ in the sense that if $\{f_n\} \to f$ in $L^1(E)$, then $\{\Phi(f_n)\} \to \Phi(f)$ in $L^p(E)$. Then show that Φ is one-to-one and its image is $L^p(E)$. Find a formula for the inverse mapping. Use the preceding problem to conclude that the inverse mapping Φ^{-1} is a continuous mapping from $L^p(E)$ to $L^1(E)$.

49. Use the preceding problem to show that the separability of $L^1(E)$ implies the separability of $L^p(E)$, for $1 < p < \infty$.

50. For $[a, b]$ a nondegenerate closed, bounded interval, show that there is no continuous mapping Φ from $L^1[a, b]$ onto $L^\infty[a, b]$.

51. Use Lusin's Theorem to prove Theorem 12.

CHAPTER 8

The L^p Spaces: Duality and Weak Convergence

Contents

For a measurable set E, $1 \leq p < \infty$, and q conjugate to p, let g belong to $L^q(E)$. Define the real-valued functional T on $L^p(E)$ by

$$T(f) = \int_E f \cdot g \text{ for all } f \in L^p(E). \tag{i}$$

Hölder's Inequality tells us that $f \cdot g$ is integrable and therefore T is properly defined. The functional T inherits linearity from the linearity of integration. Furthermore, there is a $M \geq 0$ for which

$$|T(f)| \leq M \cdot \|f\|_p \text{ for all } f \in L^p(E). \tag{ii}$$

Indeed, by Hölder's Inequality, this holds for $M = \|g\|_q$. The Riesz Representation Theorem asserts that if T is any real-valued linear functional on $L^p(E)$ with the property that there is an M for which (ii) holds, then there is a unique g in $L^q(E)$ for which T is given by (i). A sequence $\{f_n\}$ of functions in $L^p(E)$ to said to converge weakly to a function f in $L^p(E)$ provided

$$\lim_{n \to \infty} \int_E f_n \cdot g = \int_E f \cdot g \text{ for all } g \in L^q(E). \tag{iii}$$

We use the Riesz Representation Theorem and a theorem of Helley to show that, for $1 < p < \infty$, any bounded sequence in $L^p(E)$ has a weakly convergent subsequence. As an example of just one of the many consequences of this result, we prove the existence of minimizers for certain convex functionals.

8.1 THE RIESZ REPRESENTATION FOR THE DUAL OF L^p, $1 \leq P < \infty$

Definition *A* **linear functional** *on a linear space X is a real-valued function T on X such that for g and h in X and α and β real numbers,*

$$T(\alpha \cdot g + \beta \cdot h) = \alpha \cdot T(g) + \beta \cdot T(h).$$

It is easy to verify that the linear combination of linear functionals, defined pointwise, is also linear. Thus the collection of linear functionals on a linear space is itself a linear space.

Example Let E be a measurable set, $1 \leq p < \infty$, q the conjugate of p, and g belong to $L^q(E)$. Define the functional T on $L^p(E)$ by

$$T(f) = \int_E g \cdot f \text{ for all } f \in L^p(E). \tag{1}$$

Hölder's Inequality tells us that for $f \in L^p(E)$, the product $g \cdot f$ is integrable over E so the functional T is properly defined. By the linearity of integration, T is linear. Observe that Hölder's Inequality is the statement that

$$|T(f)| \leq \|g\|_q \cdot \|f\|_p \text{ for all } f \in L^p(E). \tag{2}$$

Example Let $[a, b]$ be a closed, bounded interval and the function g be of bounded variation on $[a, b]$. Define the functional T on $C[a, b]$ by

$$T(f) = \int_a^b f(x) \, dg(x) \text{ for all } f \in C[a, b], \tag{3}$$

where the integral is in the sense of Riemann-Stieltjes. The functional T is properly defined and linear.[1] Moreover, it follows immediately from the definition of this integral that

$$|T(f)| \leq TV(g) \cdot \|f\|_{\max} \text{ for all } f \in C[a, b], \tag{4}$$

where $TV(g)$ is the total variation of g over $[a, b]$.

Definition *For a normed linear space X, a linear functional T on X is said to be **bounded** provided there is an $M \geq 0$ for which*

$$|T(f)| \leq M \cdot \|f\| \text{ for all } f \in X. \tag{5}$$

*The infimum of all such M is called the **norm** of T and denoted by $\|T\|_*$.*

The inequalities (2) tell us that the linear functional in the first example is bounded, while inequalities (4) do the same for the second example.

Let T be a bounded linear functional on the normed linear space X. It is easy to see that (5) holds for $M = \|T\|_*$. Hence, by the linearity of T,

$$|T(f) - T(h)| \leq \|T\|_* \cdot \|f - h\| \text{ for all } f, h \in X. \tag{6}$$

From this we infer the following continuity property of a bounded linear functional T:

$$\text{if } \{f_n\} \to f \text{ in } X, \text{ then } \{T(f_n)\} \to T(f). \tag{7}$$

---

[1] See Chapter 2 of Richard Wheedon and Antoni Zygmund's book *Measure and Integral* [WZ77] regarding Riemann-Stieltjes integration.

We leave it as an exercise to show that

$$\|T\|_* = \sup \{T(f) \mid f \in X, \ \|f\| \leq 1\}, \tag{8}$$

and use this characterization of $\| \cdot \|_*$ to prove the following proposition.

Proposition 1 *Let X be a normed linear space. Then the collection of bounded linear functionals on X is a linear space on which $\| \cdot \|_*$ is a norm. This normed linear space is called the **dual space** of X and denoted by X^*.*

Proposition 2 *Let E be a measurable set, $1 \leq p < \infty$, q the conjugate of p, and g belong to $L^q(E)$. Define the functional T on $L^p(E)$ by*

$$T(f) = \int_E g \cdot f \ \text{for all } f \in L^p(E).$$

Then T is a bounded linear functional on $L^p(E)$ and $\|T\|_* = \|g\|_q$.

Proof We infer from (2) that T is a bounded linear functional on $L^p(E)$ and $\|T\|_* \leq \|g\|_q$. On the other hand, according to Theorem 1 of the preceding chapter (with p and q interchanged), the conjugate function of g, $g^* = \|g\|_q^{q-1} \, \text{sgn}(g)|g|^{q-1}$, belongs to $L^p(E)$,

$$T(g^*) = \|g\|_q \text{ and } \|g^*\|_p = 1.$$

It follows from (8) that $\|T\|_* = \|g\|_q$. $\qquad\square$

Our goal now is to prove that for $1 \leq p < \infty$, every bounded linear functional on $L^p(E)$ is given by integration against a function in $L^q(E)$, where q is the conjugate of p.

Proposition 3 *Let T and S be bounded linear functionals on a normed linear space X. If $T = S$ on a dense subset X_0 of X, then $T = S$.*

Proof Let g belong to X. Since X_0 is dense in X, there is a sequence $\{g_n\}$ in X_0 that converges in X to g. We infer from (7) that $\{S(g_n)\} \to S(g)$ and $\{T(g_n)\} \to T(g)$. But $S(g_n) = T(g_n)$ for all n, and hence $S(g) = T(g)$. $\qquad\square$

Lemma 4 *Let E be a measurable set and $1 \leq p < \infty$. Suppose the function g is integrable over E and there is an $M \geq 0$ for which*

$$\left| \int_E g \cdot f \right| \leq M \|f\|_p \text{ for every simple function } f \text{ in } L^p(E). \tag{9}$$

Then g belongs to $L^q(E)$, where q is the conjugate of p. Moreover, $\|g\|_q \leq M$.

Proof Since g is integrable over E, it is finite a.e. on E. By possibly excising a set of measure zero from E, we assume g is finite on all of E. We first consider the case $p > 1$. Since $|g|$ is a nonnegative measurable function, according to the Simple Approximation Theorem, there is a sequence of simple functions $\{\varphi_n\}$ that converges pointwise on E to $|g|$ and $0 \leq \varphi_n \leq |g|$ on E for all n. Since $\{\varphi_n^q\}$ is a sequence of nonnegative measurable functions that converges pointwise on E to $|g|^q$, by Fatou's Lemma, to show that $|g|^q$ is integrable over E and $\|g\|_q \leq M$ it suffices to show that

$$\int_E \varphi_n^q \leq M^q \text{ for all } n. \tag{10}$$

Fix a natural number n. To verify (10) we estimate the functional values of φ_n^q on E as follows:

$$\varphi_n^q = \varphi_n \cdot \varphi_n^{q-1} \leq |g| \cdot \varphi_n^{q-1} = g \cdot \text{sgn}(g) \cdot \varphi_n^{q-1} \text{ on } E. \tag{11}$$

We define the simple function f_n by

$$f_n = \text{sgn}(g) \cdot \varphi_n^{q-1} \text{ on } E.$$

The function φ_n is integrable over E since it is dominated on E by the integrable function g. Therefore, since φ_n is simple, it has finite support, and hence f_n belongs to $L^p(E)$. We infer from (11) and (9) that

$$\int_E \varphi_n^q \leq \int_E g \cdot f_n \leq M \|f_n\|_p. \tag{12}$$

Since q is the conjugate of p, $p(q-1) = q$ and therefore

$$\int_E |f_n|^p = \int_E \varphi_n^{p(q-1)} = \int_E \varphi_n^q.$$

We rewrite (12) as

$$\int_E \varphi_n^q \leq M \cdot \left[\int_E \varphi_n^q \right]^{1/p}.$$

Since $|\varphi|_n^q$ is integrable over E, we may regather this integral inequality as

$$\left[\int_E \varphi_n^q \right]^{1-1/p} \leq M,$$

which, since $1 - 1/p = 1/q$, is a restatement of (10).

It remains to consider the case $p = 1$. We must show that M is an essential upper bound for g. We argue by contradiction. If M is not an essential upper bound, then, by the continuity of measure, there is some $\epsilon > 0$, for which the set $E_\epsilon = \{x \in E \mid |g(x)| > M + \epsilon\}$ has nonzero measure. If we let f be the characteristic function of a measurable subset of E_ϵ that has finite positive measure, we contradict (9). $\qquad\square$

Theorem 5 *Let $[a, b]$ be a closed, bounded interval and $1 \le p < \infty$. Suppose T is a bounded linear functional on $L^p[a, b]$. Then there is a function g in $L^q[a, b]$, where q is the conjugate of p, for which*

$$T(f) = \int_I g \cdot f \text{ for all } f \text{ in } L^p[a, b].$$

Proof We consider the case $p > 1$. The proof of the case $p = 1$ is similar. For x in $[a, b]$, define

$$\Phi(x) = T(\chi_{[a, x)}).$$

We claim that this real-valued function Φ is absolutely continuous on $[a, b]$. Indeed, by the linearity of T, for each $[c, d] \subseteq [a, b]$, since $\chi_{[c, d)} = \chi_{[a, d)} - \chi_{[a, c)}$,

$$\Phi(d) - \Phi(c) = T(\chi_{[a, d)}) - T(\chi_{[a, c)}) = T(\chi_{[c, d)}).$$

Thus if $\{(a_k, b_k)\}_{k=1}^n$ is a finite disjoint collection of intervals in (a, b), by the linearity of T,

$$\sum_{k=1}^n |\Phi(b_k) - \Phi(a_k)| = \sum_{k=1}^n \epsilon_k \cdot T(\chi_{[a_k, b_k)}) = T\left(\sum_{k=1}^n \epsilon_k \cdot \chi_{[a_k, b_k)}\right), \tag{13}$$

where each $\epsilon_k = \text{sgn}[\Phi(b_k) - \Phi(a_k)]$. Moreover, for the simple function $f = \sum_{k=1}^n \epsilon_k \cdot \chi_{[a_k, b_k)}$,

$$|T(f)| \le \|T\|_* \cdot \|f\|_p \text{ and } \|f\|_p = \left[\sum_{k=1}^n (b_k - a_k)\right]^{1/p}.$$

Thus

$$\sum_{k=1}^n |\Phi(b_k) - \Phi(a_k)| \le \|T\|_* \cdot \left[\sum_{k=1}^n (b_k - a_k)\right]^{1/p}.$$

Therefore, $\delta = (\epsilon/\|T\|_*)^p$ responds to any $\epsilon > 0$ challenge regarding the criterion for Φ to be absolutely continuous on $[a, b]$.

According to Theorem 10 of Chapter 6, the function $g = \Phi'$ is integrable over $[a, b]$ and

$$\Phi(x) = \int_0^x g \text{ for all } x \in [a, b].$$

Therefore, for each $[c, d] \subseteq (a, b)$,

$$T(\chi_{[c, d)}) = \Phi(d) - \Phi(c) = \int_a^b g \cdot \chi_{[c, d)}.$$

Since the functional T^2 and the functional $f \mapsto \int_a^b g \cdot f$ are linear on the linear space of step functions, it follows that

$$T(f) = \int_a^b g \cdot f \text{ for all step functions } f \text{ on } [a, b].$$

---

[2]The functional T must respect the equivalence relation of equality a.e. on $[a, b]$ among functions in $L^p[a, b]$. In particular, for $a \le c \le d \le b$, $T(\chi_{[c, d)}) = T(\chi_{(c, d)}) = T(\chi_{[c, d]})$.

By Proposition 10 of the preceding chapter and its proof, if f is a simple function on $[a, b]$, there is a sequence of step functions $\{\varphi_n\}$ that converges to f in $L^p[a, b]$ and also is uniformly pointwise bounded on $[a, b]$. Since the linear functional T is bounded on $L^p[a, b]$, it follows from the continuity property (7) that

$$\lim_{n \to \infty} T(\varphi_n) = T(f).$$

On the other hand, by the Lebesgue Dominated Convergence Theorem,

$$\lim_{n \to \infty} \int_a^b g \cdot \varphi_n = \int_a^b g \cdot f.$$

Therefore

$$T(f) = \int_a^b g \cdot f \text{ for all simple functions } f \text{ on } [a, b].$$

Since T is bounded,

$$\left| \int_a^b g \cdot f \right| = |T(f)| \leq \|T\|_* \cdot \|f\|_p \text{ for all simple functions } f \text{ on } [a, b].$$

According to Lemma 4, g belongs to $L^q[a, b]$. It follows from Proposition 2 that the linear functional $f \mapsto \int_a^b g \cdot f$ is bounded on $L^p[a, b]$. This functional agrees with the bounded functional T on the simple functions, which, by Proposition 9 of the preceding chapter, is a dense subspace of $L^p[a, b]$. We infer from Proposition 3 that these two functionals agree on all of $L^p[a, b]$.   □

The Riesz Representation Theorem for the Dual of $L^p(E)$ *Let E be a measurable set, $1 \leq p < \infty$, and q the conjugate of p. For each $g \in L^q(E)$, define the bounded linear functional $\mathcal{R}_g$ on $L^p(E)$ by*

$$\mathcal{R}_g(f) = \int_E g \cdot f \text{ for all } f \text{ in } L^p(E). \tag{14}$$

Then for each bounded linear functional T on $L^p(E)$, there is a unique function $g \in L^q(E)$ for which

$$\mathcal{R}_g = T, \text{ and } \|T\|_* = \|g\|_q. \tag{15}$$

Proof Proposition 2 tells us that for each $g \in L^q(E)$, $\mathcal{R}_g$ is a bounded linear functional on $L^p(E)$ for which $\|\mathcal{R}_g\|_* = \|g\|_q$. By the linearity of integration, for each $g_1, g_2 \in L^q(E)$,

$$\mathcal{R}_{g_1} - \mathcal{R}_{g_2} = \mathcal{R}_{g_1 - g_2}.$$

Thus if $\mathcal{R}_{g_1} = \mathcal{R}_{g_2}$, then $\mathcal{R}_{g_1 - g_2} = 0$ and hence $\|g_1 - g_2\|_q = 0$ so that $g_1 = g_2$. Therefore, for a bounded linear functional T on $L^p(E)$, there is at most one function $g \in L^q(E)$ for which $\mathcal{R}_g = T$. It remains to show that for each bounded linear functional T on $L^p(E)$, there is a function $g \in L^q(E)$ for which $T = \mathcal{R}_g$. The preceding theorem tells us that this is so for E

a closed, bounded interval. We now verify this for $E = \mathbf{R}$ and then for general measurable sets E.

Let T be a bounded linear functional on $L^p(\mathbf{R})$. Fix a natural number n. Define the linear functional T_n on $L^p[-n, n]$ by

$$T_n(f) = T(\hat{f}) \text{ for all } f \in L^p[-n, n],$$

where $\hat{f}$ is the extension of f to all of $\mathbf{R}$ that vanishes outside $[-n, n]$. Then, since $\|f\|_p = \|\hat{f}\|_p$,

$$|T_n(f)| \leq \|T\|_* \|f\|_p \text{ for all } f \in L^p[-n, n].$$

Thus $\|T_n\|_* \leq \|T\|_*$. The preceding theorem tells us there is a function $g_n \in L^q[-n, n]$ for which

$$T_n(f) = \int_{-n}^{n} g_n \cdot f \text{ for all } f \in L^p[-n, n] \text{ and } \|g_n\|_q = \|T_n\|_* \leq \|T\|_*. \tag{16}$$

By the remarks regarding uniqueness at the beginning of this proof, the restriction of g_{n+1} to $[-n, n]$ agrees with g_n a.e. on $[-n, n]$. Define g to be a measurable function on $\mathbf{R}$ which, for each n, agrees with g_n a.e. on $[-n, n]$. We infer from the definitions of T_n and g_n, together with the left-hand equality in (16), that for all functions $f \in L^p(\mathbf{R})$ that vanish outside a bounded set,

$$T(f) = \int_{\mathbf{R}} g \cdot f.$$

By the right-hand inequality in (16),

$$\int_{-n}^{n} |g|^q \leq (\|T\|_*)^q \text{ for all } n$$

and hence, by Fatou's Lemma, g belongs to $L^q(\mathbf{R})$. Since the bounded linear functionals $\mathcal{R}_g$ and T agree on the dense subspace of $L^p(\mathbf{R})$ comprising the $L^p(\mathbf{R})$ functions that vanish outside a bounded set, it follows from Proposition 3 that $\mathcal{R}_g$ agrees with T on all of $L^p(\mathbf{R})$.

Finally, consider a general measurable set E and T a bounded linear functional on $L^p(E)$. Define the linear functional $\widehat{T}$ on $L^p(\mathbf{R})$ by $\widehat{T}(f) = T(f|_E)$. Then T is a bounded linear functional on $L^p(\mathbf{R})$. We have just shown that there is a function $\hat{g} \in L^q(\mathbf{R})$ for which $\widehat{T}$ is represented by integration over $\mathbf{R}$ against $\hat{g}$. Define g to be the restriction of $\hat{g}$ to E. Then $T = \mathcal{R}_g$. $\qquad\square$

Remark *In the second example of this section, we exhibited Lebesgue-Stieltjes integration against a function of bounded variation as an example of a bounded linear functional on $C[a, b]$. A theorem of Riesz, which we prove in Chapter 21, tells us that all the bounded linear functionals on $C[a, b]$ are of this form. In Section 5 of Chapter 21, we characterize the bounded linear functionals on $C(K)$, the linear space of continuous real-valued functions on a compact topological space K, normed by the maximum norm.*

Remark *Let $[a, b]$ be a nondegenerate closed, bounded interval. We infer from the linearity of integration and Hölder's Inequality that if f belongs to $L^1[a, b]$, then the functional $g \mapsto \int_a^b f \cdot g$*

is a bounded linear functional on $L^\infty[a, b]$. It turns out, however, that there are bounded linear functionals on $L^\infty[a, b]$ that are not of this form. In Section 3 of Chapter 19, we prove a theorem of Kantorovitch which characterizes the dual of L^∞.

PROBLEMS

1. Verify (8).

2. Prove Propositon 1.

3. Let T be a linear functional on a normed linear space X. Show that T is bounded if and only if the continuity property (7) holds.

4. A functional T on a normed linear space X is said to be Lipschitz provided there is a $c \geq 0$ such that
$$|T(g) - T(h)| \leq c\|g - h\| \text{ for all } g, h \in X.$$
The infimum of such c's is called the Lipschitz constant for T. Show that a linear functional is bounded if and only if it is Lipschitz, in which case its Lipschitz constant is $\|T\|_*$.

5. Let E be a measurable set and $1 \leq p < \infty$. Show that the functions in $L^p(E)$ that vanish outside a bounded set are dense in $L^p(E)$. Show that this is false for $L^\infty(\mathbf{R})$.

6. Establish the Riesz Representation Theorem in the case $p = 1$ by first showing, in the notation of the proof of the theorem, that the function Φ is Lipschitz and therefore it is absolutely continuous. Then follow the $p > 1$ proof.

7. State and prove a Riesz Representation Theorem for the bounded linear functionals on l^p, $1 \leq p < \infty$.

8. Let c be the linear space of real sequences that converge to a real number and c_0 the subspace of c comprising sequences that converge to 0. Norm each of these linear spaces with the ℓ^∞ norm. Determine the dual space of c and of c_0.

9. Let $[a, b]$ be a closed, bounded interval and $C[a, b]$ be normed by the maximum norm. Let x_0 belong to $[a, b]$. Define the linear functional T on $C[a, b]$ by $T(f) = f(x_0)$. Show that T is bounded and is given by Riemann-Stieltjes integration against a function of bounded variation.

10. Let f belong to $C[a, b]$. Show that there is a function g that is of bounded variation on $[a, b]$ for which
$$\int_a^b f\, dg = \|f\|_{\max} \text{ and } TV(f) = 1.$$

11. Let $[a, b]$ be a closed, bounded interval and $C[a, b]$ be normed by the maximum norm. Let T be a bounded linear functional on $C[a, b]$. For $x \in [a, b]$, let g_x be the member of $C[a, b]$ that is linear on $[a, x]$ and on $[x, b]$ with $g_x(a) = 0$, $g_x(x) = x - a$ and $g_x(b) = x - a$. Define $\Phi(x) = T(g_x)$ for $x \in [a, b]$. Show that Φ is Lipschitz on $[a, b]$.

8.2 WEAK SEQUENTIAL CONVERGENCE IN L^p

The Bolzano-Weierstrass Theorem for the real numbers is the assertion that every bounded sequence of real numbers has a convergent sequence. This property immediately extends to bounded sequences in each Euclidean space $\mathbf{R}^n$. This property fails in an infinite dimensional normed linear space.[3] In particular, the following example shows that for $1 \leq p \leq \infty$, there are bounded sequences in $L^p[0, 1]$ that fail to have any subsequences that converge in $L^p[0, 1]$. The functions defined in the following example are called **Radamacher functions**.

Example For $I = [0, 1]$ and a natural number n, consider the step function f_n defined on I by

$$f_n(x) = (-1)^k \text{ for } k/2^n \leq x < (k+1)/2^n \text{ where } 0 \leq k < 2^n - 1.$$

Fix $1 \leq p \leq \infty$. Then $\{f_n\}$ is a bounded sequence in $L^p(I)$: indeed, $\|f_n\|_p \leq 1$ for every index n. On the other hand, since, for $n \neq m$, $|f_n - f_m|$ takes the value 2 on a set of measure $1/2$, $\|f_n - f_m\|_p \geq (2)^{1-1/p}$. Therefore no subsequence of $\{f_n\}$ is Cauchy in $L^p(I)$ and hence no subsequence can converge in $L^p(I)$. We also note that no subsequence can converge pointwise almost everywhere on I since, for $1 \leq p < \infty$, if there were such a subsequence, by the Bounded Convergence Theorem it would converge in $L^p(I)$.

Definition *Let X be a normed linear space. A sequence $\{f_n\}$ in X is said to* **converge weakly** *in X to f in X provided*

$$\lim_{n \to \infty} T(f_n) = T(f) \text{ for all } T \in X^*.$$

We write

$$\{f_n\} \rightharpoonup f \text{ in } X$$

to mean that f and each f_n belong to X and $\{f_n\}$ converges weakly in X to f.

We continue to write $\{f_n\} \to f$ in X to mean that $\lim_{n \to \infty} \|f_n - f\| = 0$ and, to distinguish this mode of convergence from weak convergence, often refer to this mode of convergence as **strong convergence** in X. Since

$$|T(f_n) - T(f)| = |T(f_n - f)| \leq \|T\|_* \cdot \|f_n - f\| \text{ for all } T \in X^*,$$

if a sequence converges strongly, then it converges weakly. The converse is false.

Proposition 6 *Let E be a measurable set, $1 \leq p < \infty$, and q the conjugate of p. Then $\{f_n\} \rightharpoonup f$ in $L^p(E)$ if and only if*

$$\lim_{n \to \infty} \int_E g \cdot f_n = \int_E g \cdot f \text{ for all } g \in L^q(E).$$

Proof The Riesz Representation Theorem tells us that every bounded linear functional on $L^p(E)$ is given by integration against a function in $L^q(E)$. $\qquad \square$

For E a measurable set and $1 \leq p < \infty$, a sequence in $L^p(E)$ can converge weakly to at most one function in $L^p(E)$. Indeed, suppose $\{f_n\}$ converges weakly in $L^p(E)$ to both f_1 and f_2. Consider the conjugate function of $f_1 - f_2$, $(f_1 - f_2)^*$. Then

$$\int_E (f_1 - f_2)^* \cdot f_2 = \lim_{n \to \infty} \int_E (f_1 - f_2)^* \cdot f_n = \int_E (f_1 - f_2)^* \cdot f_1.$$

---

[3]Riesz's Theorem, which we prove in Section 3 of Chapter 13, tells us that in every infinite dimensional normed linear space X, there is a bounded sequence that has no subsequence that converges in X.

Therefore

$$\|f_1 - f_2\|_p = \int_E (f_1 - f_2)^* (f_1 - f_2) = 0.$$

Thus $f_1 = f_2$ and therefore weak sequential limits are unique.

Theorem 7 *Let E be a measurable set and $1 \leq p < \infty$. Suppose $\{f_n\} \rightharpoonup f$ in $L^p(E)$. Then*

$$\{f_n\} \text{ is bounded in } L^p(E) \text{ and } \|f\|_p \leq \liminf \|f_n\|_p. \tag{17}$$

Proof Let q be the conjugate of p and f^* the conjugate function of f. We first establish the right-hand inequality of (17). We infer from Hölder's Inequality that

$$\int_E f^* \cdot f_n \leq \|f^*\|_q \cdot \|f_n\|_p = \|f_n\|_p \text{ for all } n.$$

Since $\{f_n\}$ converges weakly to f and f^* belongs to $L^q(E)$,

$$\|f\|_p = \int_E f^* \cdot f = \lim_{n \to \infty} \int_E f^* \cdot f_n \leq \liminf \|f_n\|_p.$$

We argue by contradiction to show that $\{f_n\}$ is bounded in $L^p(E)$. Assume $\{\|f_n\|_p\}$ is unbounded. Without loss of generality (see Problem 18), by possibly taking scalar multiples of a subsequence, we suppose

$$\|f_n\|_p = n \cdot 3^n \text{ for all } n. \tag{18}$$

We inductively select a sequence of real numbers $\{\epsilon_k\}$ for which $\epsilon_k = \pm 1/3^k$ for each k. Define $\epsilon_1 = 1/3$. If n is a natural number for which $\epsilon_1, \ldots, \epsilon_n$ have been defined, define

$$\epsilon_{n+1} = 1/3^{n+1} \text{ if } \int_E \left[\sum_{k=1}^{n} \epsilon_k (f_n)^* \right] \cdot f_{n+1} \geq 0,$$

and $\epsilon_{n+1} = -1/3^{n+1}$ if the above integral is negative. Therefore, by (18) and the definition of conjugate function,

$$\left| \int_E \left[\sum_{k=1}^{n} \epsilon_k (f_k)^* \right] \cdot f_n \right| \geq 1/3^n \|f_n\|_p = n \text{ and } \|\epsilon_n \cdot (f_n)^*\|_q = 1/3^n \text{ for all } n. \tag{19}$$

Since $\|\epsilon_k \cdot (f_k)^*\|_q = 1/3^k$ for all k, the sequence of partial sums of the series $\sum_{k=1}^{\infty} \epsilon_k \cdot (f_k)^*$ is a Cauchy sequence in $L^q(E)$. The Riesz-Fischer Theorem tells us that $L^q(E)$ is complete. Define the function $g \in L^q(E)$ by

$$g = \sum_{k=1}^{\infty} \epsilon_k \cdot (f_k)^*.$$

Fix a natural number n. We infer from the triangle inequality, (19), and Hölder's Inequality that

$$\left| \int_E g \cdot f_n \right| = \left| \int_E \left[\sum_{k=1}^{\infty} \epsilon_k \cdot (f_k)^* \right] \cdot f_n \right|$$

$$\geq \left| \int_E \left[\sum_{k=1}^{n} \epsilon_k \cdot (f_k)^* \right] \cdot f_n \right| - \left| \int_E \left[\sum_{k=n+1}^{\infty} \epsilon_k \cdot (f_k)^* \right] \cdot f_n \right|$$

$$\geq n - \left| \int_E \left[\sum_{k=n+1}^{\infty} \epsilon_k \cdot (f_k)^* \right] \cdot f_n \right|$$

$$\geq n - \left[\sum_{k=n+1}^{\infty} 1/3^k \right] \cdot \| f_n \|_p$$

$$= n - 1/3^n \cdot 1/2 \cdot \| f_n \|_p$$

$$= n/2.$$

This is a contradiction because, since the sequence $\{f_n\}$ converges weakly in $L^p(E)$ and g belongs to $L^q(E)$, the sequence of real numbers $\{\int_E g \cdot f_n\}$ converges and therefore is bounded. Hence $\{f_n\}$ is bounded in L^p. □

Corollary 8 *Let E be a measurable set, $1 \leq p < \infty$, and q the conjugate of p. Suppose $\{f_n\}$ converges weakly to f in $L^p(E)$ and $\{g_n\}$ converges strongly to g in $L^q(E)$. Then*

$$\lim_{n \to \infty} \int_E g_n \cdot f_n = \int_E g \cdot f. \tag{20}$$

Proof For each index n,

$$\int_E g_n \cdot f_n - \int_E g \cdot f = \int_E [g_n - g] \cdot f_n + \int_E g \cdot f_n - \int_E g \cdot f.$$

According to the preceding theorem, there is a constant $C \geq 0$ for which

$$\| f_n \|_p \leq C \text{ for all } n.$$

Therefore, by Hölder's Inequality,

$$\left| \int_E g_n \cdot f_n - \int_E g \cdot f \right| \leq C \cdot \| g_n - g \|_q + \left| \int_E g \cdot f_n - \int_E g \cdot f \right| \text{ for all } n.$$

From these inequalities and the fact that both

$$\lim_{n \to \infty} \| g_n - g \|_q = 0 \text{ and } \lim_{n \to \infty} \int_E g \cdot f_n = \int_E g \cdot f$$

it follows that (20) holds. □

By the **linear span** of a subset S of a linear space X we mean the linear space consisting of all linear combinations of functions in S, that is, the linear space of functions of the form

$$f = \sum_{k=1}^{n} \alpha_k \cdot f_k,$$

where each α_k is a real number and each f_k belongs to S.

Proposition 9 *Let E be a measurable set, $1 \leq p < \infty$, and q the conjugate of p. Assume $\mathcal{F}$ is a subset of $L^q(E)$ whose linear span is dense in $L^q(E)$. Let $\{f_n\}$ be a bounded sequence in $L^p(E)$ and f belong to $L^p(E)$. Then $\{f_n\} \to f$ in $L^p(E)$ if and only if*

$$\lim_{n \to \infty} \int_E f_n \cdot g = \int_E f \cdot g \text{ for all } g \in \mathcal{F}. \tag{21}$$

Proof Proposition 6 characterizes weak convergence in $L^p(E)$. Assume (21) holds. To verify weak convergence, let g_0 belong to $L^q(E)$. We show that $\lim_{n \to \infty} \int_E f_n \cdot g_0 = \int_E f \cdot g_0$. Let $\epsilon > 0$. We must find a natural number N for which

$$\left| \int_E f_n \cdot g_0 - \int_E f \cdot g_0 \right| < \epsilon \text{ if } n \geq N. \tag{22}$$

Observe that for any $g \in L^q(E)$ and natural number n,

$$\int_E f_n \cdot g_0 - \int_E f \cdot g_0 = \int_E (f_n - f) \cdot (g_0 - g) + \int_E (f_n - f) \cdot g,$$

and therefore, by Hölder's Inequality,

$$\left| \int_E f_n \cdot g_0 - \int_E f \cdot g_0 \right| \leq \|f_n - f\|_p \cdot \|g - g_0\|_q + \left| \int_E f_n \cdot g - \int_E f \cdot g \right|.$$

Since $\{f_n\}$ is bounded in $L^p(E)$ and the linear span of $\mathcal{F}$ is dense in $L^q(E)$, there is a function g in this linear span for which

$$\|f_n - f\|_p \cdot \|g - g_0\|_q < \epsilon/2 \text{ for all } n.$$

We infer from (21), the linearity of integration, and the linearity of convergence for sequences of real numbers, that

$$\lim_{n \to \infty} \int_E f_n \cdot g = \int_E f \cdot g.$$

Therefore there is a natural number N for which

$$\left| \int_E f_n \cdot g - \int_E f \cdot g \right| < \epsilon/2 \text{ if } n \geq N.$$

By the preceding estimates it is clear that (22) holds for this choice of N. $\qquad\square$

According to Proposition 9 of the preceding chapter, for $1 < q \leq \infty$, the simple functions in $L^q(E)$ are dense in $L^q(E)$, and these functions have finite support if $q < \infty$. Moreover, Proposition 10 of the same chapter tells us that for a closed, bounded interval $[a, b]$ and $1 < q < \infty$, the step functions are dense in $L^q[a, b]$. Therefore the following two characterizations of weak continuity follow from the preceding proposition.

Theorem 10 *Let E be a measurable set and $1 \leq p < \infty$. Suppose $\{f_n\}$ is a bounded sequence in $L^p(E)$ and f belongs to $L^p(E)$. Then $\{f_n\} \to f$ in $L^p(E)$ if and only if for every measurable subset A of E,*

$$\lim_{n \to \infty} \int_A f_n = \int_A f. \tag{23}$$

If $p > 1$, it is sufficient to consider sets A of finite measure.

Theorem 11 *Let $[a, b]$ be a closed, bounded interval and $1 < p < \infty$. Suppose $\{f_n\}$ is a bounded sequence in $L^p[a, b]$ and f belongs to $L^p[a, b]$. Then $\{f_n\} \to f$ in $L^p[a, b]$ if and only if*

$$\lim_{n \to \infty} \left[\int_a^x f_n \right] = \int_a^x f \text{ for all } x \text{ in } [a, b]. \tag{24}$$

Theorem 11 is false for $p = 1$, since the step functions are not dense in $L^\infty[a, b]$: see Problem 44.

Example (the Riemann-Lebesgue Lemma) Let $I = [-\pi, \pi]$ and $1 < p < \infty$. For each natural number n, define $f_n(x) = \sin nx$ for x in I. Then $|f_n| \leq 1$ on I for each n, so $\{f_n\}$ is a bounded sequence in $L^p(I)$. The preceding corollary tells us that the sequence $\{f_n\}$ converges weakly in $L^p(I)$ to $f \equiv 0$ if and only if

$$\lim_{n \to \infty} \int_{-\pi}^x \sin nt \, dt = 0 \text{ for all } x \in I.$$

Explicit calculation of these integrals shows that this is true. On the other hand, observe that for each n,

$$\int_{-\pi}^\pi |\sin nt|^2 \, dt = \int_{-\pi}^\pi \sin^2 nt \, dt = \pi.$$

Thus no subsequence of $\{f_n\}$ converges strongly in $L^2(I)$ to $f \equiv 0$. A similar estimate shows no subsequence converges strongly in any $L^p(I)$. Therefore by the Bounded Convergence Theorem, no subsequence of $\{f_n\}$ converges pointwise almost everywhere on I to $f \equiv 0$.

Example For a natural number n, define $f_n = n \cdot \chi_{(0, 1/n]}$ on $[0, 1]$. Define f to be identically zero on $[0, 1]$. Then $\{f_n\}$ is a sequence of unit functions in $L^1[0, 1]$ that converges pointwise to f on $[0, 1]$. But $\{f_n\}$ does not converge weakly to f in $L^1[0, 1]$ since, taking $g = \chi_{[0, 1]} \in L^\infty[0, 1]$,

$$\lim_{n \to \infty} \int_0^1 g \cdot f_n = \lim_{n \to \infty} \int_0^1 f_n = 1 \text{ while } \int_0^1 g \cdot f = \int_0^1 f = 1.$$

Example Define the tent function f_0 on $\mathbf{R}$ to vanish outside $(-1, 1)$, be linear on the intervals $[-1, 0]$ and $[0, 1]$ and take the value 1 at $x = 0$. For each natural number n, define

$f_n(x) = f_0(x - n)$ and let $f \equiv 0$ on $\mathbf{R}$. Then $\{f_n\} \to f$ pointwise on $\mathbf{R}$. Let $1 \leq p < \infty$. The sequence $\{f_n\}$ is bounded in $L^p(\mathbf{R})$. We leave it as an exercise in the use of continuity of measure to show that for a set of finite measure A,

$$\lim_{n \to \infty} \int_A f_n = \int_A f, \tag{25}$$

and thereby infer from Theorem 10 that, for $1 < p < \infty$, $\{f_n\} \rightharpoonup f$ in $L^p(\mathbf{R})$. But $\{f_n\}$ does not converge weakly to f in $L^1(\mathbf{R})$ since for $g \equiv 1$ on $\mathbf{R}$, g belongs to $L^\infty(\mathbf{R})$, while $\{\int_{\mathbf{R}} f_n\}$ does not converge to $\int_{\mathbf{R}} f$.

The preceding two examples exhibit bounded sequences in $L^1(E)$ that converge pointwise to a function in $L^1(E)$ and yet do not converge weakly in $L^1(E)$. This does not occur in $L^p(E)$ if $1 < p < \infty$.

Theorem 12 *Let E be a measurable set and $1 < p < \infty$. Suppose $\{f_n\}$ is a bounded sequence in $L^p(E)$ that converges pointwise a.e. on E to f. Then $\{f_n\} \rightharpoonup f$ in $L^p(E)$.*

Proof We infer from Fatou's Lemma, applied to the sequence $\{|f_n|^p\}$, that f belongs to $L^p(E)$. Theorem 11 tells us that to verify weak sequential convergence it is necessary and sufficient to show that for each measurable subset A of E of finite measure,

$$\lim_{n \to \infty} \int_A f_n = \int_A f. \tag{26}$$

Let A be such a set. According to Corollary 2 of the preceding chapter, since the sequence $\{f_n\}$ is bounded in $L^p(E)$, it is uniformly integrable over E. But $m(A) < \infty$. Therefore, by the Vitali Convergence Theorem, (26) holds. $\square$

The Radon-Riesz Theorem *Let E be a measurable set and $1 < p < \infty$. Suppose $\{f_n\} \rightharpoonup f$ in $L^p(E)$. Then*

$$\{f_n\} \to f \text{ in } L^p(E) \text{ if and only if } \lim_{n \to \infty} \|f_n\|_p = \|f\|_p.$$

Proof It is always that case, in any linear space X normed by $\| \cdot \|$, that strong convergence implies convergence of the norms. Indeed, this follows from the following consequence of the triangle inequality:

$$\big|\|g\| - \|h\|\big| \leq \|g - h\| \text{ for all } g, h \text{ in } X.$$

It remains to show that in the $L^p(E)$ spaces, $1 < p < \infty$, weak convergence and convergence of the norms implies strong convergence in $L^p(E)$. We present the proof for the case $p = 2$.[4] Let $\{f_n\}$ be a sequence in $L^2(E)$ for which

$$\{f_n\} \rightharpoonup f \text{ in } L^2(E) \text{ and } \lim_{n \to \infty} \int_E f_n^2 = \int_E f^2.$$

---

[4] For the proof for general $p > 1$, a substitute is needed for the identity $(a - b)^2 = a^2 - 2ab + b^2$. A detailed proof is provided in Frigyes Riesz and Béla Sz.-Nagy's *Functional Analysis* [RSN90], pages 78–80.

Observe that for each n,

$$\| f_n - f \|_2^2 = \int_E |f_n - f|^2 = \int_E (f_n - f)^2 = \int_E |f_n|^2 - 2 \cdot \int_E f_n \cdot f + \int_E |f|^2.$$

Since f belongs to $L^q(E) = L^2(E)$,

$$\lim_{n \to \infty} \int_E f_n \cdot f = \int_E f^2.$$

Therefore $\{f_n\} \to f$ in $L^2(E)$. $\square$

Corollary 13 *Let E be a measurable set and $1 < p < \infty$. Suppose $\{f_n\} \to f$ in $L^p(E)$. Then a subsequence of $\{f_n\}$ converges strongly in $L^p(E)$ to f if and only if*

$$\| f \|_p = \liminf \| f_n \|_p.$$

Proof If $\| f \|_p = \liminf \| f_n \|_p$, then there is a subsequence $\{f_{n_k}\}$ for which $\lim_{k \to \infty} \| f_{n_k} \|_p = \| f \|_p$. The Radon-Riesz Theorem tells us that $\{f_{n_k}\}$ converges strongly to f in $L^p(E)$. Conversely, if there is a subsequence $\{f_{n_k}\}$ that converges strongly to f, then $\lim_{k \to \infty} \| f_{n_k} \|_p = \| f \|_p$. Thus $\liminf \| f_n \|_p \leq \| f \|_p$. The right-hand inequality in (17) is this inequality in the opposite direction. $\square$

As the following example shows, the Radon-Riesz Theorem does not extend to the case $p = 1$.

Example For each natural number n, define $f_n(x) = 1 + \sin(nx)$ on $I = [-\pi, \pi]$. It follows from the Riemann-Lebesgue Lemma that the sequence $\{f_n\}$ converges weakly in $L^1(I)$ to the function $f \equiv 1$. Since each f_n is nonnegative, we therefore also have $\lim_{n \to \infty} \| f_n \|_1 = \| f \|_1$. Since $\{\sin(nx)\}$ does not converge strongly in $L^1(I)$, $\{f_n\}$ does not converge strongly in $L^1(I)$.

Remark *For E a measurable set, $1 \leq p < \infty$, $f \in L^p(E)$, and f^* the conjugate function of f, define $T \in (L^p(E))^*$ by*

$$T(h) = \int_E f^* \cdot h \text{ for all } h \in L^p(E).$$

Rewrite (17) as

$$T(f) = \| f \|_p \text{ and } \| T \|_* = 1. \qquad (27)$$

In Section 2 of Chapter 14, we prove the Hahn-Banach Theorem and as a corollary of this theorem show that if X is any normed linear space and f belonging to X, there is a bounded linear operator T in X^* for which $T(f) = \| f \|$ and $\| T \|_* = 1$. For the $L^p(E)$ spaces, the conjugate function is a concrete presentation of this abstract functional.

PROBLEMS

12. Show that the sequence defined in the first example of this section does not converge strongly to $f \equiv 0$ in $L^p[0, 1]$ for all $1 \leq p < \infty$.

13. Fix real numbers α and β. For each natural number n, consider the step function f_n defined on $I = [0, 1]$ by

$$f_n(x) = (1 - (-1)^k)\alpha/2 + (1 + (-1)^k)\beta/2 \text{ for } k/2^n \leq x < (k+1)/2^n, \ 0 \leq k < 2^n - 1.$$

For $1 < p < \infty$, show that $\{f_n\}$ converges weakly in $L^p(I)$ to the constant function that takes the value $(\alpha + \beta)/2$. For $\alpha \neq \beta$, show that no subsequence of $\{f_n\}$ converges strongly in $L^p(I)$.

14. Let h be a continuous function defined on all of $\mathbf{R}$ that is periodic of period T and $\int_0^T h = 0$. Let $[a, b]$ be a closed, bounded interval and for each natural number n, define the function f_n on $[a, b]$ by $f_n(x) = h(nx)$. Define $f \equiv 0$ on $[a, b]$. Show that for $1 \leq p < \infty$, $\{f_n\} \rightharpoonup f$ in $L^p[a, b]$.

15. Let $1 < p < \infty$ and f_0 belong to $L^p(\mathbf{R})$. For each natural number n, define $f_n(x) = f_0(x - n)$ for all x. Define $f \equiv 0$ on $\mathbf{R}$. Show that $\{f_n\} \rightharpoonup f$ in $L^p(\mathbf{R})$. Is this true for $p = 1$?

16. Let E be a measurable set, $\{f_n\}$ a sequence in $L^2(E)$ and f belong to $L^2(E)$. Suppose

$$\lim_{n \to \infty} \int_E f_n \cdot f = \lim_{n \to \infty} \int_E f_n^2 = \int_E f^2.$$

Show that $\{f_n\}$ converges strongly to f in $L^2(E)$.

17. Let E be a measurable set and $1 < p < \infty$. Suppose $\{f_n\}$ is a bounded sequence in $L^p(E)$ and f belongs to $L^p(E)$. Consider the following four properties: (i) $\{f_n\}$ converges pointwise to f almost everywhere on E, (ii) $\{f_n\} \rightharpoonup f$ in $L^p(E)$, (iii) $\{\|f_n\|_p\}$ converges to $\{\|f\|_p\}$, and (iv) $\{f_n\} \to f$ in $L^p(E)$. If $\{f_n\}$ possesses two of these properties, does a subsequence possess all four properties?

18. Let X be a normed linear space and $\{f_n\} \rightharpoonup f$ in X. Suppose $\{\|f_n\|\}$ is unbounded. Show that, by possibly taking a subsequence and relabeling, we may suppose $\|f_n\| \geq \alpha_n = n \cdot 3^n$ for all n. Then show that, by possibly taking a further subsequence and relabeling, we may suppose $\{\|f_n\|/\alpha_n\} \to \alpha \in [1, \infty]$. Define $g_n = \alpha_n/\|f_n\| \cdot f_n$ for each n. Show that $\{g_n\}$ converges weakly and $\|g_n\| = n \cdot 3^n$ for all n.

19. For $1 \leq p < \infty$, let $\{\zeta_n\}$ be a bounded sequence in ℓ^p and ζ belong in ℓ^p. Show that $\{\zeta_n\} \rightharpoonup \zeta$ in ℓ^p if and only if it converges componentwise, that is, for each index k,

$$\lim_{n \to \infty} \zeta_n^k = \zeta^k \text{ where } \zeta_n = (\zeta_n^1, \zeta_n^2, \ldots) \text{ and } \zeta = (\zeta^1, \zeta^2, \ldots).$$

20. Let $1 \leq p_1 < p_2 < \infty$, $\{f_n\}$ be a sequence in $L^{p_2}[0, 1]$ and f belong to $L^{p_2}[0, 1]$. What is the relationship between $\{f_n\} \rightharpoonup f$ in $L^{p_2}[0, 1]$ and $\{f_n\} \rightharpoonup f$ in $L^{p_1}[0, 1]$?

21. For $1 \leq p < \infty$ and each index n, let $e_n \in \ell^p$ have nth component 1 and other components vanish. Show that if $p > 1$, then $\{e_n\}$ converges weakly to 0 in ℓ^p, but no subsequence converges strongly to 0. Show that $\{e_n\}$ does not converge weakly in ℓ^1.

22. State and prove the Radon-Riesz Theorem in ℓ^2.

23. Let $[a, b]$ be a closed, bounded interval. Suppose $\{f_n\} \rightharpoonup f$ in $C[a, b]$. Show that $\{f_n\}$ converges pointwise on $[a, b]$ to f.

24. Let $[a, b]$ be a closed, bounded interval. Suppose $\{f_n\} \rightharpoonup f$ in $L^\infty[a, b]$. Show that

$$\lim_{n \to \infty} \int_a^x f_n = \int_a^x f \text{ for all } x \in [a, b].$$

25. Let X be a normed linear space. Suppose that for each $f \in X$ there is bounded linear functional $T \in X^*$ for which $T(f) = \|f\|$ and $\|T\|_* = 1$.

    (i) Prove that if $\{f_n\}$ converges weakly in X to both f_1 and f_2, then $f_1 = f_2$.

    (ii) Prove that if $\{f_n\} \to f$ in X, then $\|f\| \leq \liminf \|f_n\|$.

26. (Uniform Boundedness Principle) Let E be a measurable set, $1 \leq p < \infty$, and q the conjugate of p. Suppose $\{f_n\}$ is a sequence in $L^p(E)$ such that for each $g \in L^q(E)$, the sequence $\{\int_E g \cdot f_n\}$ is bounded. Show that $\{f_n\}$ is bounded in $L^p(E)$.

8.3 WEAK SEQUENTIAL COMPACTNESS

As we observed in the beginning of the preceding section, for $[a, b]$ a closed, bounded interval and $1 \leq p \leq \infty$, there are bounded sequences in $L^p[a, b]$ that fail to have any strongly convergent subsequences. However, for $1 < p < \infty$, there is the following seminal theorem regarding weak sequential convergence.

Theorem 14 *Let E be a measurable set and $1 < p < \infty$. Then every bounded sequence in $L^p(E)$ has a subsequence that converges weakly in $L^p(E)$ to a function in $L^p(E)$.*

Our proof of this weak sequential compactness result is based on the following theorem.[5]

Helley's Theorem *Let X be a separable normed linear space and $\{T_n\}$ a sequence in its dual space X^* that is bounded, that is, there is an $M \geq 0$ for which*

$$|T_n(f)| \leq M \cdot \|f\| \text{ for all } f \text{ in } X \text{ and all } n. \tag{28}$$

Then there is a subsequence $\{T_{n_k}\}$ of $\{T_n\}$ and T in X^* for which

$$\lim_{k \to \infty} T_{n_k}(f) = T(f) \text{ for all } f \text{ in } X. \tag{29}$$

Proof Let $\{f_j\}_{j=1}^\infty$ be a countable subset of X that is dense in X. We infer from (28) that the sequence of real numbers $\{T_n(f_1)\}$ is bounded. Therefore, by the Bolzano-Weierstrass Theorem, there is a strictly increasing sequence of integers $\{s(1, n)\}$ and a number a_1 for which

$$\lim_{n \to \infty} T_{s(1,n)}(f_1) = a_1.$$

We again use (28) to conclude that the sequence of real numbers $\{T_{s(1,n)}(f_2)\}$ is bounded, and so again by the Bolzano-Weierstrass Theorem, there is a subsequence $\{s(2, n)\}$ of $\{s(1, n)\}$ and a number a_2 for which

$$\lim_{n \to \infty} T_{s(2,n)}(f_2) = a_2 \text{ for all } j.$$

---

[5] This theorem was proved by Eduard Helley in 1912 for the special case $X = C[a, b]$, normed by the maximum norm. In his 1932 book, Stefan Banach observed, providing a one-sentence proof, that the result holds for any separable normed linear space.

We inductively continue this selection process to obtain a countable collection of strictly increasing sequences of natural numbers $\{\{s(j,n)\}\}_{j=1}^{\infty}$ and a sequence of real numbers $\{a_j\}$ such that for each j,

$$\{s(j+1,n)\} \text{ is a subsequence of } \{s(j,n)\},$$

and

$$\lim_{n \to \infty} T_{s(j,n)}(f_j) = a_j.$$

For each index k, define $n_k = s(k,k)$. Then for each j, $\{n_k\}_{k=j}^{\infty}$ is a subsequence of $\{s(j,k)\}$ and hence

$$\lim_{k \to \infty} T_{n_k}(f_j) = a_j \text{ for all } j.$$

Since $\{T_{n_k}\}$ is bounded in X^* and $\{T_{n_k}(f)\}$ is a Cauchy sequence for each f is a dense subset of X, $\{T_{n_k}(f)\}$ is Cauchy for all f in X. The real numbers are complete. Therefore we may define

$$T(f) = \lim_{k \to \infty} T_{n_k}(f) \text{ for all } f \in X.$$

Since each T_{n_k} is linear, the limit functional T is linear. Since

$$|T_{n_k}(f)| \leq M \cdot \|f\| \text{ for all } k \text{ and all } f \in X,$$

$$|T(f)| = \lim_{k \to \infty} |T_{n_k}(f)| \leq M \cdot \|f\| \text{ for all } f \in X.$$

Therefore T is bounded. $\square$

Proof of Theorem 14 Let q be the conjugate of p. Let $\{f_n\}$ be a bounded sequence in $L^p(E)$. Define $X = L^q(E)$. Let n be a natural number. Define the functional T_n on X by

$$T_n(g) = \int_E f_n \cdot g \text{ for } g \text{ in } X = L^q(E).$$

Proposition 2, with p and q interchanged and the observation that p is the conjugate of q, tells us that each T_n is a bounded linear functional on X and $\|T_n\|_* = \|f_n\|_p$. Since $\{f_n\}$ is a bounded sequence in $L^p(E)$, $\{T_n\}$ is a bounded sequence in X^*. Moreover, according to Theorem 11 of Chapter 6, since $1 < q < \infty$, $X = L^q(E)$ is separable. Therefore, by Helley's Theorem, there is a subsequence $\{T_{n_k}\}$ and $T \in X^*$ such that

$$\lim_{k \to \infty} T_{n_k}(g) = T(g) \text{ for all } g \text{ in } X = L^q(E). \tag{30}$$

The Riesz Representation Theorem, with p and q interchanged, tells us that there is a function f in $L^p(E)$ for which

$$T(g) = \int_E f \cdot g \text{ for all } g \text{ in } X = L^q(E).$$

But (30) means that

$$\lim_{k \to \infty} \int_E f_{n_k} \cdot g = \int_E f \cdot g \text{ for all } g \text{ in } L^q(E),$$

According to Proposition 6, $\{f_{n_k}\}$ converges weakly to f in $L^p(E)$ $\square$

As we see in the following example, for $[a, b]$ a nondegenerate closed, bounded interval, a bounded sequence in $L^1[a, b]$ may fail to have a weakly convergent subsequence.

Example For $I = [0, 1]$ and a natural number n, define $I_n = [0, 1/n]$ and $f_n = n \cdot \chi_{I_n}$. Then $\{f_n\}$ is a bounded sequence in $L^1[0, 1]$ since $\|f_n\|_1 = 1$ for all n. We claim that $\{f_n\}$ fails to have a subsequence that converges weakly in $L^1[0, 1]$. Indeed, suppose otherwise. Then there is a subsequence $\{f_{n_k}\}$ that converges weakly in $L^1[0, 1]$ to $f \in L^1[0, 1]$. For each $[c, d] \subseteq [0, 1]$, integration against $\chi_{[c, d]}$ is a bounded linear functional on $L^1[0, 1]$. Thus

$$\int_c^d f = \lim_{k \to \infty} \int_c^d f_{n_k}.$$

Therefore

$$\int_c^d f = 0 \text{ for all } 0 < c < d \leq 1.$$

It follows from Lemma 13 of Chapter 5 that $f = 0$ almost everywhere on $[0, 1]$. Therefore

$$0 = \int_0^1 f = \lim_{k \to \infty} \int_0^1 f_{n_k} = 1.$$

This contradiction shows that $\{f_n\}$ has no weakly convergent subsequence.

Definition *A subset K of a normed linear space X is said to be **weakly sequentially compact** in X provided every sequence $\{f_n\}$ in K has a subsequence that converges weakly to $f \in K$.*

Theorem 15 *Let E be a measurable set and $1 < p < \infty$. Then*

$$\{f \in L^p(E) \mid \|f\|_p \leq 1\} \text{ is weakly sequentially compact in } L^p(E).$$

Proof Let $\{f_n\}$ be a sequence in $L^p(E)$ for which $\|f_n\|_p \leq 1$ for all n. Theorem 14 tells us that there is a subsequence $\{f_{n_k}\}$ which converges weakly to $f \in L^p(E)$. Moreover, $\|f\|_p \leq 1$ since, by (17),

$$\|f\|_p \leq \liminf \|f_n\|_p \leq 1. \qquad \square$$

Remark *While a general bounded sequence in $L^1(E)$, does not have a weakly convergent subsequence, a theorem of Dunford and Pettis, which we prove in Section 5 of Chapter 19, tells us that any bounded sequence in $L^1(E)$ that is uniformly integrable possesses a weakly convergent subsequence.*

PROBLEMS

27. Let $[a, b]$ be a nondegenerate closed, bounded interval. In the Banach space $C[a, b]$, normed by the maximum norm, find a bounded sequence that fails to have any strongly convergent subsequence.

28. For $1 \leq p \leq \infty$, find a bounded sequence in ℓ^p that fails to have any strongly convergent subsequence.

29. Let E be a measurable set that contains a nondegenerate interval. Show that there is a bounded sequence in $L^1(E)$ that fails to have a weakly convergent subsequence. Exhibit a measurable set E for which every bounded sequence in $L^1(E)$ has a weakly convergent subsequence.

30. Let X be a normed linear space, $\{T_n\}$ be a sequence in X^*, and T belong to X^*. Show that $\{T_n\} \to T$ with respect to the $\|\cdot\|_*$ norm if and only if

$$\lim_{n \to \infty} T_n(f) = T(f) \text{ uniformly on } \{f \in X \mid \|f\| \le 1\}.$$

31. Is the sequence defined in the last example of this section uniformly integrable?

32. For $p = 1$, at what point does the proof of Theorem 14 fail?

33. Show that in $\ell^p, 1 \le p < \infty$, every bounded sequence in ℓ^p has a weakly convergent subsequence.

34. Let $\{f_n\}$ be a sequence of functions on $[0, 1]$, each of which is of bounded variation and for which $\{TV(f_n)\}$ is bounded. Show that there is a subsequence $\{f_{n_k}\}$ with the property that for each continuous function g on $[0, 1]$, the sequence of integrals $\{\int_0^1 g(x) \, df_{n_k}(x) \, dx\}$ is Cauchy.

35. Let X be a normed linear space and $\{T_n\}$ a sequence in X^* for which there is an $M \ge 0$ such that $\|T_n\|_* \le M$ for all n. Let S be a dense subset of X such that $\{T_n(g)\}$ is Cauchy for all $g \in S$.
   (i) Show that $\{T_n(g)\}$ is Cauchy for all $g \in X$.
   (ii) Define $T(g) = \lim_{n \to \infty} T_n(g)$ for all $g \in X$. Show that T is linear. Then show that T is bounded.

36. Show that the conclusion of Helley's Theorem is not true for $X = L^\infty[0, 1]$.

37. Let E have finite measure and $1 \le p < \infty$. Suppose $\{f_n\}$ is a bounded sequence in $L^p(E)$ and f belongs to $L^p(E)$. If one of the following properties holds, determine, for each of the other properties, if a subsequence has that other property. The cases $p = 1$ and $p > 1$ should be considered.
   (i) $\{f_n\} \to f$ in $L^p(E)$.
   (ii) $\{f_n\} \rightharpoonup f$ in $L^p(E)$.
   (iii) $\{f_n\} \to f$ pointwise a.e. on E.
   (iv) $\{f_n\} \to f$ in measure.

8.4   THE MINIMIZATION OF CONVEX FUNCTIONALS

The L^p spaces were introduced by Frigyes Riesz as part of a program to formulate for functionals and mappings defined on infinite dimensional spaces appropriate versions of properties possessed by functionals and mappings defined on finite dimensional spaces. The initial goal was to provide tools with which to analyze integral equations. This program was particularly successful for linear functionals and mappings and indeed the subject of linear algebra matured into the subject called linear functional analysis. However, beyond linear functionals, just as convex functions defined on convex sets of real numbers possess quite special properties, convex functionals defined on convex subsets of the L^p spaces also possess special features. In this section we consider a minimization principle for such convex functionals.

Let E be a measurable set and $1 \leq p < \infty$. We have exhibited sequences in $L^p(E)$ that converge weakly but have no subsequences that converge strongly. In view of this, the following theorem is somewhat surprising.

The Banach-Saks Theorem *Let E be a measurable set and $1 < p < \infty$. Suppose $\{f_n\} \rightharpoonup f$ in $L^p(E)$. Then there is a subsequence $\{f_{n_k}\}$ for which the sequence of arithmetic means converges strongly to f in $L^p(E)$, that is,*

$$\lim_{k \to \infty} \frac{f_{n_1} + f_{n_2} + \ldots + f_{n_k}}{k} = f \text{ strongly in } L^p(E).$$

Proof We present the proof for the case $p = 2$.[6] By replacing each f_n with $f_n - f$, we suppose $f = 0$. Theorem 7 tells us that $\{f_n\}$ is bounded in $L^2(E)$. Choose $M \geq 0$ for which

$$\int_E f_n^2 \leq M \text{ for all } n.$$

Define $n_1 = 1$. Since $\{f_n\}$ converges weakly in $L^2(E)$ to 0 and f_{n_1} belongs to $L^2(E)$ (here, of course, $p = q = 2$), we can choose a natural number $n_2 > n_1$ for which $\left| \int_E f_{n_1} \cdot f_{n_2} \right| \leq 1$. Suppose we have chosen natural numbers $n_1 < n_2 < \ldots < n_k$ such that

$$\int_E (f_{n_1} + \ldots + f_{n_j})^2 \leq 2j + Mj \text{ for } j = 1, \ldots, k.$$

Since $f_{n_1} + \ldots + f_{n_k}$ belongs to $L^2(E)$ and $\{f_n\}$ converges weakly in $L^2(E)$ to 0, we may choose a natural $n_{k+1} > n_k$ for which

$$\int_E (f_{n_1} + \ldots + f_{n_k}) \cdot f_{n_{k+1}} \leq 1. \tag{31}$$

However,

$$\int_E (f_{n_1} + \ldots + f_{n_{k+1}})^2 = \int_E (f_{n_1} + \ldots + f_{n_k})^2$$
$$+ 2 \int_E (f_{n_1} + \ldots + f_{n_k}) \cdot f_{n_{k+1}} + \int_E f_{n_{k+1}}^2,$$

and therefore

$$\int_E (f_{n_1} + \ldots + f_{n_{k+1}})^2 \leq 2k + Mk + 2 + M = 2(k+1) + M(k+1).$$

The subsequence $\{f_{n_k}\}$ has been inductively chosen so that

$$\int_E \left[\frac{f_{n_1} + f_{n_2} + \ldots + f_{n_k}}{k} \right]^2 \leq \frac{(2+M)}{k} \text{ for all } k,$$

Therefore the sequence of arithmetic means of $\{f_{n_k}\}$ converges strongly to $f \equiv 0$ in $L^2(E)$. □

[6]For the proof for $p \neq 2$, see the original paper by S. Banach and S. Saks in Studia Math., vol 2, 1930.

Definition *A subset C of a linear space X is said to be **convex** provided whenever f and g belong to C and $\lambda \in [0, 1]$, then $\lambda f + (1 - \lambda)g$ also belongs to C.*

Definition *A subset C of a normed linear space X is said to be **closed** provided whenever $\{f_n\}$ is a sequence in X that converges strongly in X to f, then if each f_n belongs to C, the limit f also belongs to C.*

Example Let E be a measurable set, $1 \le p < \infty$, and g nonnegative function in $L^p(E)$, define

$$C = \{f \text{ measurable on } E \mid |f| \le g \text{ a.e. on } E\}.$$

We claim that C is a closed, convex subset of $L^p(E)$. Indeed, we infer from the integral comparison test that each function in C belongs to $L^p(E)$. It is clear that C is convex. To verify that C is closed, let $\{f_n\}$ be a sequence in $L^p(E)$ that converges in $L^p(E)$ to f. By the Riesz-Fischer Theorem, there is a subsequence of $\{f_n\}$ that converges pointwise almost everywhere on E to f. From this pointwise convergence it follows that f belongs to C.

Example Let E be a measurable set and $1 \le p < \infty$. Then $B = \{f \in L^p(E) \mid \|f\|_p \le 1\}$ is closed and convex. To see it is convex just observe that if f and g belong to B and $\lambda \in [0, 1]$, then, by the Minkowski Inequality,

$$\|\lambda f + (1 - \lambda)g\|_p \le \lambda \|f\|_p + (1 - \lambda)\|g\|_p \le 1.$$

To see that B is closed observe that if $\{f_n\}$ is a sequence in B that converges in $L^p(E)$ to $f \in L^p(E)$, then it follows from Minkowski's Inequality that for each n, $\left| \|f_n\|_p - \|f\|_p \right| \le \|f_n - f\|_p$, so that $\{\|f_n\|_p\}$ converges to $\|f\|_p$. Thus $\|f\|_p \le 1$.

Definition *A real-valued functional T defined on a subset C of a normed linear space X is said to be **continuous** provided whenever a sequence $\{f_n\}$ in C converges strongly to $f \in C$, then $\{T(f_n)\} \to T(f)$.*

In the very special case of a linear functional, continuity is equivalent to boundedness. In general, these concepts are unrelated.

Definition *A real-valued functional T defined on a convex subset C of a normed linear space X is said to be **convex** provided whenever f and g belong to C and $\lambda \in [0, 1]$,*

$$T(\lambda f + (1 - \lambda)g) \le \lambda T(f) + (1 - \lambda)T(g).$$

In any normed linear space, the triangle inequality is equivalent to the convexity of the norm.

Example Let E be a measurable set and $1 \le p < \infty$. Suppose φ is a continuous, convex real-valued function defined on **R** for which there are constants a and b such that $|\varphi(s)| \le a + b|s|^p$ for all real numbers s. Define the functional T on $L^p(E)$ by

$$T(f) = \int_E \varphi \circ f \text{ for all } f \in L^p(E).$$

We leave it as an exercise (see Problem 42) to show that T is properly defined, continuous, and convex.

Lemma 16 *Let E be a measurable set and $1 < p < \infty$. Suppose C is a closed, bounded convex subset of $L^p(E)$ and T is a continuous convex functional on C. If $\{f_n\}$ is a sequence in C that converges weakly in $L^p(E)$ to f, then f also belongs to C. Moreover,*

$$T(f) \leq \liminf T(f_n).$$

Proof By the Banach-Saks Theorem, there is a subsequence of $\{f_n\}$ whose sequence of arithmetic means converges strongly in $L^p(E)$ to f. The arithmetic means belong to C since C is convex and therefore, since C is closed, the function f belongs to C. Moreover, there is a further subsequence of $\{T(f_n)\}$ that converges to $\alpha = \liminf T(f_n)$. Therefore, we may choose a subsequence such that

$$\lim_{k \to \infty} \frac{f_{n_1} + f_{n_2} + \cdots + f_{n_k}}{k} = f \text{ strongly in } L^p(E)$$

and

$$\lim_{k \to \infty} T(f_{n_k}) = \alpha.$$

Since the functional T is continuous,

$$T(f) = \lim_{k \to \infty} T\left(\frac{f_{n_1} + f_{n_2} + \cdots + f_{n_k}}{k} \right).$$

Moreover, the arithmetic means of a convergent sequence of real numbers converge to the same limit and therefore

$$\lim_{k \to \infty} \frac{T(f_{n_1}) + T(f_{n_2}) + \cdots + T(f_{n_k})}{k} = \alpha.$$

On the other hand, since T is convex, for each k,

$$T\left(\frac{f_{n_1} + f_{n_2} + \cdots + f_{n_k}}{k} \right) \leq \frac{T(f_{n_1}) + T(f_{n_2}) + \cdots + T(f_{n_k})}{k}.$$

Thus

$$T(f) = \lim_{k \to \infty} T\left(\frac{f_{n_1} + f_{n_2} + \cdots + f_{n_k}}{k} \right)$$

$$\leq \lim_{k \to \infty} \frac{T(f_{n_1}) + T(f_{n_2}) + \cdots + T(f_{n_k})}{k} = \alpha.$$

$\square$

Theorem 17 *Let E be a measurable set and $1 < p < \infty$. Suppose C is a closed, bounded convex subset of $L^p(E)$ and T is a continuous convex functional on C. Then T takes on a minimum value on C, that is, there is a function $f_0 \in C$ such that*

$$T(f_0) \leq T(f) \text{ for all } f \in C.$$

Proof We first show that the image $T(C)$ is bounded below. Indeed, otherwise there is a sequence $\{f_n\}$ in C such that $\lim_{n \to \infty} T(f_n) = -\infty$. Since C is bounded, by possibly taking a subsequence, we use Theorem 14 to suppose that $\{f_n\}$ converges weakly in $L^p(E)$ to a function f in $L^p(E)$. We infer from the preceding lemma that f belongs to C and that

$$T(f) \leq \liminf T(f_n) = -\infty.$$

This is a contradiction. Thus T is bounded below on C. Define

$$c = \inf \{T(f) \mid f \in C\}.$$

Choose a sequence $\{f_n\}$ in C such that $\lim_{n \to \infty} T(f_n) = c$. Again, by possibly taking a subsequence we may invoke Theorem 14 to suppose that $\{f_n\}$ converges weakly in $L^p(E)$ to a function f_0 in $L^p(E)$. We infer from the preceding lemma that f_0 belongs to C and

$$T(f_0) \leq \liminf T(f_n) = c.$$

Thus $T(f_0) = c$. $\qquad\qquad\qquad\qquad\qquad\qquad\qquad\qquad\qquad\qquad\qquad\qquad\qquad\qquad\square$

Corollary 18 *Let E be a measurable set of finite measure and $1 < p < \infty$. Suppose φ is a real-valued continuous convex function on $\mathbf{R}$ for which there are constants $c_1 \geq 0$ and $c_2 \geq 0$ such that*

$$|\varphi(s)| \leq c_1 + c_2 \cdot |s|^p \text{ for all } s. \tag{32}$$

Then there is a function $f_0 \in L^p(E)$ with $\|f_0\|_p \leq 1$ for which

$$\int_E \varphi \circ f_0 = \min_{f \in L^p(E), \|f\|_p \leq 1} \int_E \varphi \circ f. \tag{33}$$

Proof If f is a measurable real-valued function on E, since φ is continuous, the composition $\varphi \circ f$ is measurable. Let f belong to $L^p(E)$. Since f is finite a.e. on E, we infer from (32) that

$$|\varphi \circ f| \leq c_1 + c_2 \cdot |f|^p \text{ a.e. on } E.$$

Thus, by the integral comparison test, $\varphi \circ f$ is integrable over E. Define the functional T on $L^p(E)$ by

$$T(f) = \int_E \varphi \circ f \text{ for all } f \in L^p(E).$$

Then T is properly defined and it inherits convexity from φ. We already noted that the set $C = \{f \in L^p(E) \mid \|f\|_p \leq 1\}$ is strongly closed, bounded, and convex. The existence of a minimizer for T on C will be a consequence of the preceding theorem if we show that T is continuous in $L^p(E)$. Let $\{f_n\}$ be a sequence in $L^p(E)$ that converges strongly to f in $L^p(E)$. By taking a subsequence if necessary and relabeling, we suppose $\{f_n\}$ is rapidly Cauchy. Therefore, according to Theorem 6 of Chapter 7, $\{f_n\}$ converges pointwise a.e. on E to f. Since φ is continuous, $\{\varphi \circ f_n\}$ converges pointwise a.e. on E to $\varphi \circ f$. Moreover, by the completeness of $L^q(E)$, since $\{f_n\}$ is rapidly Cauchy in $L^p(E)$, the function

$$g = \sum_{k=1}^{\infty} |f_k|$$

belongs to $L^p(E)$. It is clear that

$$|f_n| \leq g \text{ a.e. on } E \text{ for all } n,$$

and hence, by the inequality (33),

$$|\varphi \circ f_n| \leq c_1 + c_2 \cdot |f_n|^p \leq c_1 + c_2 \cdot g^p \text{ a.e. on } E \text{ for all } n.$$

We infer from the Dominated Convergence Theorem that

$$\lim_{n \to \infty} \int_E \varphi \circ f_n = \int_E \varphi \circ f.$$

Therefore T is continuous on $L^p(E)$.   □

Remark *We proved the Bolzano-Weierstrass Theorem in Chapter 1: every bounded sequence of real numbers has a convergent subsequence. This theorem is the basis of the argument that every continuous real-valued function on a closed, bounded interval takes a minimum value. In the mid nineteenth century it was uncritically assumed that a similar argument was valid for establishing minimum values of real-valued functionals on spaces of functions. Karl Weierstrass observed the fallacy in this argument. Given a sequence of continuous functions* $\{f_n\}$ *on* $[0, 1]$ *for which*

$$\int_0^1 |f_n|^2 \leq 1 \text{ for all } n,$$

there may not exist a subsequence $\{f_{n_k}\}$ *and* $f \in L^2[0, 1]$ *for which*

$$\lim_{k \to \infty} \int_0^1 |f_{n_k} - f|^2 = 0:$$

(see Problem 45). Many mathematicians, including David Hilbert, turned their attention to investigating specific classes of functionals for which it is possible to prove the existence of minimizers.[7] *Theorem 17 exhibits one such class of functionals.*

PROBLEMS

38. For $1 < p < \infty$ and each index n, let $e_n \in \ell^p$ have nth component 1 and other components 0. Show that $\{e_n\}$ converges weakly to 0 in ℓ^p, but no subsequence converges strongly to 0. Find a subsequence whose arithmetic means converge strongly to 0 in ℓ^p.

39. Show that if a sequence of real numbers $\{a_n\}$ converges to a, then the sequence of arithmetic means also converges to a.

40. State and prove the Banach-Saks Theorem in ℓ^2.

41. Let E be a measurable set and $1 \leq p < \infty$. Let T be a continuous linear functional on $L^p[a, b]$ and $K = \{f \in L^p(E) \mid \|f\|_p \leq 1\}$. Find a function $f_0 \in K$ for which

$$T(f_0) \geq T(f) \text{ for all } f \text{ in } K.$$

---

[7]Hilbert's article *On the Dirichlet Principle* is translated in *A Source Book in Classical Analysis* by Garrett Birkhoff (Harvard University Press, 1973).

42. (Nemytskii) Let E be a measurable set and p_1, p_2 belong to $[1, \infty)$. Suppose φ is a continuous real-valued function defined on $\mathbf{R}$ for which there are constants c_1 and c_2 such that $|\varphi(s)| \leq c_1 + c_2|s|^{p_1/p_2}$ for all real numbers s. Let $\{f_n\}$ be a sequence in $L^{p_1}(E)$. Show that

$$\text{if } \{f_n\} \to f \text{ in } L^{p_1}(E), \text{ then } \{\varphi \circ f_n\} \to \varphi \circ f \text{ in } L^{p_2}.$$

43. (Beppo Levi) Let E be a measurable set, $1 \leq p < \infty$, and C a closed bounded convex subset of $L^p(E)$. Show that for any function $f_0 \in L^p(E)$, there is a function g_0 in C for which

$$\|g_0 - f_0\|_p \leq \|g - f_0\|_p \text{ for all } g \text{ in } C.$$

44. (Banach-Saks) For a natural number n, define the function f_n on $[0, 1]$ by setting

$$f_n(x) = 1 \text{ for } k/2^n + 1/2^{2n+1} \leq x < (k+1)/2^n \text{ and } 0 \leq k \leq 2^n - 1,$$

and $f_n(x) = 1 - 2^{n+1}$ elsewhere on $[0, 1]$. Define $f \equiv 0$ on $[0, 1]$.

(i) Show that

$$\left| \int_0^x f_n \right| \leq 1/2^n \text{ for all } x \in [0, 1] \text{ and all } n,$$

and therefore

$$\lim_{n \to \infty} \int_0^x f_n = \int_0^x f \text{ for all } x \in [0, 1].$$

(ii) Define E to be the subset of $[0, 1]$ on which $f_n = 1$ for all n. Show that

$$\int_E f_n = m(E) > 0 \text{ for all } n.$$

(iii) Show that $\|f_n\|_1 \leq 2$ for all n. Infer from part (ii) that $\{f_n\}$ is a bounded sequence in $L^1[0, 1]$ that does not converge weakly in $L^1[0, 1]$ to f. Does this and part (i) contradict Theorem 11.

(iv) For $1 < p < \infty$, infer from part (ii) that $\{f_n\}$ is a sequence in $L^p[0, 1]$ that does not converge weakly in $L^p[0, 1]$ to f. Does this and part (i) contradict Theorem 11?

45. Find a sequence $\{g_n\}$ in $L^2[0, 1]$ that has no Cauchy subsequence. Use this subsequence and the denseness of the continuous functions in $L^2[0, 1]$ to find a sequence of continuous functions on $[0, 1]$ for which no subsequence converges in $L^2[0, 1]$ to a function in $L^2[0, 1]$.

PART TWO

ABSTRACT SPACES: METRIC, TOPOLOGICAL, BANACH, AND HILBERT SPACES

CHAPTER 9

Metric Spaces: General Properties

Contents

In Chapter 1 we established three types of properties of the real numbers. The first type are the algebraic properties related to addition and multiplication. The second are the properties of the positive numbers by way of which the concepts of order and absolute value are defined. Using the algebraic and order properties, the distance between two real numbers is defined to be the absolute value of their difference. The final property possessed by the real numbers is completeness: the Completeness Axiom for the real numbers is equivalent to the property that every Cauchy sequence of real numbers converges to a real number. In the study of normed linear spaces, which was begun in Chapter 7, the algebraic structure of the real numbers is extended to that of a linear space; the absolute value is extended to the concept of a norm, which induces a concept of distance between points; and the order properties of the real numbers are left aside. We now proceed one step further in generalization. The object of the present chapter is to study general spaces called metric spaces for which the notion of distance between two points is fundamental. There is no linear structure. The concepts of open set and closed set in Euclidean space extend naturally to general metric spaces, as do the concepts of convergence of a sequence and continuity of a function or mapping. We first consider these general concepts. We then study metric spaces which possess finer structure: those that are complete, compact, or separable.

9.1 EXAMPLES OF METRIC SPACES

Definition *Let X be a nonempty set. A function $\rho: X \times X \to \mathbf{R}$ is called a **metric** provided for all x, y, and z in X,*

(i) $\rho(x, y) \geq 0$;

(ii) $\rho(x, y) = 0$ if and only if $x = y$;

(iii) $\rho(x, y) = \rho(y, x)$;

(iv) $\rho(x, y) \leq \rho(x, z) + \rho(z, y)$.

*A nonempty set together with a metric on the set is called a **metric space**.*

We often denote a metric space by (X, ρ). Property (iv) is known as the **triangle inequality** for the metric. The quintessential example of a metric space is the set **R** of all real numbers with $\rho(x, y) = |x - y|$.

Normed Linear Spaces   In Section 7.1 we extended the concept of absolute value to a general linear space. Recall that a nonnegative real-valued function $\| \cdot \|$ on a linear space X is called a **norm** provided for each $u, v \in X$ and real number α,

(i) $\|u\| = 0$ if and only if $u = 0$.

(ii) $\|u + v\| \leq \|u\| + \|v\|$.

(iii) $\|\alpha u\| = |\alpha| \|u\|$.

We called a linear space with a norm a normed linear space. A norm $\| \cdot \|$ on a linear space X induces a metric ρ on X by defining

$$\rho(x, y) = \|x - y\| \text{ for all } x, y \in X. \tag{1}$$

Property (ii) of a norm is called the triangle inequality for the norm. It is equivalent to the triangle inequality for the induced metric. Indeed, for $x, y, z \in X$, set $u = x - z$ and $v = z - y$ and observe that

$$\|u + v\| \leq \|u\| + \|v\| \text{ if and only if } \rho(x, y) \leq \rho(x, z) + \rho(z, y).$$

Three prominent examples of normed linear spaces are Euclidean spaces $\mathbf{R}^n$, the $L^p(E)$ spaces, and $C[a, b]$. For a natural number n, consider the linear space $\mathbf{R}^n$ whose points are n-tuples of real numbers. For $x = (x_1, \ldots, x_n)$ in $\mathbf{R}^n$ the Euclidean norm of x, $\|x\|$, is defined by

$$\|x\| = [x_1^2 + \ldots + x_n^2]^{1/2}.$$

We devoted Chapters 7 and 8 to the study of the normed linear spaces $L^p(E)$, for $1 \leq p \leq \infty$ and E a Lebesgue measurable set of real numbers. For $1 \leq p < \infty$, the triangle inequality for the $L^p(E)$ norm is called the Minkowski Inequality. For a closed bounded interval of real numbers $[a, b]$, consider the linear space $C[a, b]$ of continuous real-valued functions on $[a, b]$. The maximum norm $\| \cdot \|_{max}$ is defined for $f \in C[a, b]$ by

$$\|f\|_{max} = \max \{|f(x)| \mid x \in [a, b]\}.$$

The triangle inequality for the maximum norm follows from this inequality for the absolute values on the real numbers.

The Discrete Metric   For any nonempty set X, the discrete metric ρ is defined by setting $\rho(x, y) = 0$ if $x = y$ and $\rho(x, y) = 1$ if $x \neq y$.

Metric Subspaces   For a metric space (X, ρ), let Y be a nonempty subset of X. Then the restriction of ρ to $Y \times Y$ defines a metric on Y and we call such a metric space a metric **subspace**. Therefore every nonempty subset of Euclidean space, of an $L^p(E)$ space, $1 \leq p \leq \infty$, and of $C[a, b]$ is a metric space.

Metric Products   For metric spaces (X_1, ρ_1) and (X_2, ρ_2), we define the **product metric** τ on the *Cartesian product* $X_1 \times X_2$ by setting, for (x_1, x_2) and (y_1, y_2) in $X_1 \times X_2$,

$$\tau((x_1, x_2), (y_1, y_2)) = \left\{ [\rho_1(x_1, y_1)]^2 + [\rho_2(x_2, y_2)]^2 \right\}^{1/2}.$$

It is readily verified that τ has all the properties required of a metric. This construction extends to countable products (see Problem 10).

A particularly interesting and useful example of a metric space that is not directly presented as a metric subspace of a normed linear space is the Nikodym metric on the collection of measurable subsets of a Lebesgue measurable subset of **R** (see Problem 5).

On any nonempty set X consisting of more than one point there are different metrics. For instance, if X is a nonempty collection of continuous functions on the closed, bounded interval $[a, b]$, then X is a metric space with respect to the discrete metric, with respect to the metric induced by the maximum norm and, for $1 \le p < \infty$, with respect to the metric induced by the $L^p[a, b]$ norm. The following relation of equivalence between metrics on a set is useful.

Definition *Two metrics ρ and σ on a set X are said to be* **equivalent** *provided there are positive numbers c_1 and c_2 such that for all $x_1, x_2 \in X$,*

$$c_1 \cdot \sigma(x_1, x_2) \le \rho(x_1, x_2) \le c_2 \cdot \sigma(x_1, x_2).$$

Definition *A mapping f from a metric space (X, ρ) to a metric space (Y, σ) is said to be an* **isometry** *provided it maps X onto Y and for all $x_1, x_2 \in X$,*

$$\sigma(f(x_1), f(x_2)) = \rho(x_1, x_2).$$

Two metric spaces are called **isometric** provided there is an isometry from one onto the other. To be isometric is an equivalence relation among metric spaces. From the viewpoint of metric spaces, two isometric metric spaces are exactly the same, an isometry amounting merely to a relabeling of the points.

In the definition of a metric ρ on a set X it is sometimes convenient to relax the condition that $\rho(x, y) = 0$ only if $x = y$. When we allow the possibility that $\rho(x, y) = 0$ for some $x \ne y$, we call ρ a **pseudometric** and (X, ρ) a pseudometric space. On such a space, define the relation $x \cong y$ provided $\rho(x, y) = 0$. This is an equivalence relation that separates X into a disjoint collection of equivalence classes $X/\cong$. For equivalence classes $[x]$ and $[y]$, define $\tilde{\rho}([x], [y]) = \rho(x, y)$. It is easily seen that this properly defines a metric $\tilde{\rho}$ on $X/\cong$. Similar considerations apply when we allow the possibility, in the definition of a norm, that $\|u\| = 0$ for $u \ne 0$. Some examples of pseudometrics and pseudonorms are considered in Problems 5, 7, 9, and 49.

PROBLEMS

1. Show that two metrics ρ and τ on the same set X are equivalent if and only if there is a $c > 0$ such that for all $u, v \in X$,

$$\frac{1}{c} \tau(u, v) \le \rho(u, v) \le c \tau(u, v).$$

2. Show that the following define equivalent metrics on $\mathbf{R}^n$:

$$\rho^*(x, y) = |x_1 - y_1| + \ldots + |x_n - y_n|;$$

$$\rho^+(x, y) = \max\{|x_1 - y_1|, \ldots, |x_n - y_n|\}.$$

3. Find a metric on $\mathbf{R}^n$ that fails to be equivalent to either of those defined in the preceding problem.

4. For a closed, bounded interval $[a, b]$, consider the set $X = C[a, b]$ of continuous real-valued functions on $[a, b]$. Show that the metric induced by the maximum norm and that induced by the $L^1[a, b]$ norm are not equivalent.

5. *The Nikodym Metric.* Let E be a Lebesgue measurable set of real numbers of finite measure, X the set of Lebesgue measurable subsets of E, and m Lebesgue measure. For $A, B \in X$, define $\rho(A, B) = m(A \Delta B)$, where $A \Delta B = [A \sim B] \cup [B \sim A]$, the symmetric difference of A and B. Show that this is a pseudometric on X. Define two measurable sets to be equivalent provided their symmetric difference has measure zero. Show that ρ induces a metric on the collection of equivalence classes. Finally, show that for $A, B \in X$,

$$\rho(A, B) = \int_E |\chi_A - \chi_B|,$$

where χ_A and χ_B are the characteristic functions of A and B, respectively.

6. Show that for $a, b, c \geq 0$,

$$\text{if } a \leq b + c, \text{ then } \frac{a}{1+a} \leq \frac{b}{1+b} + \frac{c}{1+c}.$$

7. Let E be a Lebesgue measurable set of real numbers that has finite measure and X the set of Lebesgue measurable real-valued functions on E. For $f, g \in X$, define

$$\rho(f, g) = \int_E \frac{|f - g|}{1 + |f - g|}.$$

Use the preceding problem to show that this is a pseudometric on X. Define two measurable functions to be equivalent provided they are equal a.e. on E. Show that ρ induces a metric on the collection of equivalence classes.

8. For $0 < p < 1$, show that

$$(a + b)^p \leq a^p + b^p \text{ for all } a, b \geq 0.$$

9. For E a Lebesgue measurable set of real numbers, $0 < p < 1$, and g and h Lebesgue measurable functions on E that have integrable pth powers, define

$$\rho_p(h, g) = \int_E |g - h|^p.$$

Use the preceding problem to show that this is a pseudometric on the collection of Lebesgue measurable functions on E that have integrable pth powers. Define two such functions to be equivalent provided they are equal a.e. on E. Show that $\rho_p(\cdot, \cdot)$ induces a metric on the collection of equivalence classes.

10. Let $\{(X_n, \rho_n)\}_{n=1}^{\infty}$ be a countable collection of metric spaces. Use Problem 6 to show that ρ_* defines a metric on the Cartesian product $\prod_{n=1}^{\infty} X_n$, where for points $x = \{x_n\}$ and $y = \{y_n\}$ in $\prod_{n=1}^{\infty} X_n$,

$$\rho_*(x, y) = \sum_{n=1}^{\infty} \frac{1}{2^n} \cdot \frac{\rho_n(x_n, y_n)}{1 + \rho_n(x_n, y_n)}.$$

11. Let (X, ρ) be a metric space and A any set for which there is a one-to-one mapping f of A onto the set X. Show that there is a unique metric on A for which f is an isometry of metric spaces. (This is the sense in which an isometry amounts merely to a relabeling of the points in a space.)

12. Show that the triangle inequality for Euclidean space $\mathbf{R}^n$ follows from the triangle inequality for $L^2[0, 1]$.

9.2 OPEN SETS, CLOSED SETS, AND CONVERGENT SEQUENCES

Many concepts studied in Euclidean spaces and general normed linear spaces can be naturally and usefully extended to general metric spaces. They do not depend on linear structure.

Definition *Let (X, ρ) be a metric space. For a point x in X and $r > 0$, the set*

$$B(x, r) \equiv \{x' \in X \mid \rho(x', x) < r\}$$

is called the **open ball** *centered at x of radius r. A subset $\mathcal{O}$ of X is said to be* **open** *provided for every point $x \in \mathcal{O}$, there is an open ball centered at x that is contained in $\mathcal{O}$. For a point $x \in X$, an open set that contains x is called a* **neighborhood** *of x.*

We should check that we are consistent here, namely, that an open ball is open. By the definition of open set, to show that $B(x, r)$ is open it suffices to show that

$$\text{if } x' \in B(x, r) \text{ and } r' = r - \rho(x', x), \text{ then } B(x', r') \subseteq B(x, r).$$

To verify this, let $y \in B(x', r')$. Then $\rho(y, x') < r'$, so that, by the triangle inequality,

$$\rho(y, x) \leq \rho(y, x') + \rho(x', x) < r' + \rho(x', x) = r.$$

Therefore $B(x', r') \subseteq B(x, r)$.

Proposition 1 *Let X be a metric space. The whole set X and the empty-set $\emptyset$ are open; the intersection of any two open subsets of X is open; and the union of any collection of open subsets of X is open.*

Proof It is clear that X and $\emptyset$ are open and the union of a collection of open sets is open. Let $\mathcal{O}_1$ and $\mathcal{O}_2$ be open subsets of X. If these two sets are disjoint, then the intersection is the empty-set, which is open. Otherwise, let x belong to $\mathcal{O}_1 \cap \mathcal{O}_2$. Since $\mathcal{O}_1$ and $\mathcal{O}_2$ are open sets containing x, there are positive numbers δ_1 and δ_2 for which $B(x, \delta_1) \subseteq \mathcal{O}_1$ and $B(x, \delta_2) \subseteq \mathcal{O}_2$. Define $\delta = \min\{\delta_1, \delta_2\}$. Then the open ball $B(x, \delta)$ is contained $\mathcal{O}_1 \cap \mathcal{O}_2$. Therefore $\mathcal{O}_1 \cap \mathcal{O}_2$ is open. $\square$

The following proposition, whose proof we leave as an exercise, provides a description, in the case the metric space X is a subspace of the metric space Y, of the open subsets of X in terms of the open subsets of Y.

Proposition 2 *Let X be a subspace of the metric space Y and E a subset of X. Then E is open in X if and only if $E = X \cap \mathcal{O}$, where $\mathcal{O}$ is open in Y.*

Definition *For a subset E of a metric space X, a point $x \in X$ is called a **point of closure** of E provided every neighborhood of x contains a point in E. The collection of points of closure of E is called the **closure** of E and is denoted by $\overline{E}$.*

It is clear that we always have $E \subseteq \overline{E}$. If E contains all of its points of closure, that is, $E = \overline{E}$, then the set E is said to be **closed**. For a point x in the metric space (X, ρ) and $r > 0$, the set $\overline{B}(x, r) \equiv \{x' \in X \mid \rho(x', x) \leq r\}$ is called the **closed ball** centered at x of radius r. It follows from the triangle inequality for the metric that $\overline{B}(x, r)$ is a closed set that contains $B(x, r)$. In a normed linear space X we refer to $B(0, 1)$ as the **open unit ball** and $\overline{B}(0, 1)$ as the **closed unit ball**.

Proposition 3 *For E a subset of a metric space X, its closure $\overline{E}$ is closed. Moreover, $\overline{E}$ is the smallest closed subset of X containing E in the sense that if F is closed and $E \subseteq F$, then $\overline{E} \subseteq F$.*

Proof The set $\overline{E}$ is closed if it contains all its points of closure. Let x be a point of closure of $\overline{E}$. Consider a neighborhood $\mathcal{U}_x$ of x. There is a point $x' \in \overline{E} \cap \mathcal{U}_x$. Since x' is a point of closure of E and $\mathcal{U}_x$ is a neighborhood of x', there is a point $x'' \in E \cap \mathcal{U}_x$. Therefore every neighborhood of x contains a point of E and hence $x \in \overline{E}$. So the set $\overline{E}$ is closed. It is clear that if $A \subseteq B$, then $\overline{A} \subseteq \overline{B}$, and hence if F is closed and contains E, then $\overline{E} \subseteq \overline{F} = F$. $\square$

Proposition 4 *A subset of a metric space X is open if and only if its complement in X is closed.*

Proof First suppose E is open in X. Let x be a point of closure of $X \sim E$. Then x cannot belong to E because otherwise there would be a neighborhood of x that is contained in E and thus disjoint from $X \sim E$. Thus x belongs to $X \sim E$ and hence $X \sim E$ is closed. Now suppose $X \sim E$ is closed. Let x belong to E. Then there must be a neighborhood of x that is contained in E, for otherwise every neighborhood of x contains points in $X \sim E$ and therefore x is a point of closure of $X \sim E$. Since $X \sim E$ is closed, x also belongs to $X \sim E$. This is a contradiction. $\square$

Since $X \sim [X \sim E] = E$, it follows from the preceding proposition that *a set is closed if and only if its complement is open*. Therefore, by De Morgan's Identities, Proposition 1 may be reformulated in terms of closed sets as follows.

Proposition 5 *Let X be a metric space. The empty-set $\emptyset$ and the whole set X are closed; the union of any two closed subsets of X is closed; and the intersection of any collection of closed subsets of X is closed.*

We have defined what it means for a sequence in a normed linear space to converge. The following is the natural generalization of convergence to metric spaces.

Definition *A sequence $\{x_n\}$ in a metric space (X, ρ) is said to **converge** to the point $x \in X$ provided*

$$\lim_{n \to \infty} \rho(x_n, x) = 0,$$

*that is, for each $\epsilon > 0$, there is an index N such that for every $n \geq N$, $\rho(x_n, x) < \epsilon$. The point to which the sequence converges is called the **limit** of the sequence and we often write $\{x_n\} \to x$ to denote the convergence of $\{x_n\}$ to x.*

A sequence in a metric space can converge to at most one point. Indeed, given two points u, v in a metric space X, set $r = \rho(u, v)/2$. We infer from the triangle inequality for the metric ρ that $B(u, r)$ and $B(v, r)$ are disjoint. So it is not possible for a sequence to converge to both u and v. Moreover, convergence can be rephrased as follows: a sequence $\{x_n\}$ converges to the limit x provided that for any neighborhood $\mathcal{O}$ of X, all but at most finitely many terms of the sequence belong to $\mathcal{O}$. Naturally, for a subset E of X and a sequence $\{x_n\}$ such that x_n belongs to E for all n, we say that $\{x_n\}$ is a sequence in E.

Proposition 6 *For a subset E of a metric space X, a point $x \in X$ is a point of closure of E if and only if x is the limit of a sequence in E. Therefore, E is closed if and only if whenever a sequence in E converges to a limit $x \in X$, the limit x belongs to E.*

Proof It suffices to prove the first assertion. First suppose x belongs to $\overline{E}$. For each natural number n, since $B(x, 1/n) \cap E \neq \emptyset$, we may choose a point, which we label x_n, that belongs to $B(x, 1/n) \cap E$. Then $\{x_n\}$ is a sequence in E and we claim that it converges to x. Indeed, let $\epsilon > 0$. Choose an index N for which $1/N < \epsilon$. Then

$$\rho(x_n, x) < 1/n < 1/N < \epsilon \text{ if } n \geq N.$$

Thus $\{x_n\}$ converges to x. Conversely, if a sequence in E converges to x, then every ball centered at x contains infinitely many terms of the sequence and therefore contains points in E. So $x \in \overline{E}$. ☐

In general, a change in the metric on a set will change what it means for a subset to be open and therefore what it means for a subset to be closed. It will also change what it means for a sequence to converge. For instance, for the discrete metric on a set X, every subset is open, every subset is closed, and a sequence converges to a limit if and only if all but a finite number of terms of the sequence are equal to the limit. The following proposition, the proof of which we leave as an exercise, tells us that for equivalent metrics on a set, the open sets are the same, and therefore the closed sets are the same and convergence of a sequence is the same.

Proposition 7 *Let ρ and σ be equivalent metrics on a nonempty set X. Then a subset of X is open in the metric space (X, ρ) if and only if it is open in the metric space (X, σ).*

PROBLEMS

13. In a metric space X, is it possible for $r > 0$ and two distinct points u and v in X to have $B(u, r) = B(v, r)$? Is this possible in Euclidean space $\mathbf{R}^n$? Is it possible in a normed linear space?

14. Let (X, ρ) be a metric space in which $\{u_n\} \to u$ and $\{v_n\} \to v$. Show that $\{\rho(u_n, v_n)\} \to \rho(u, v)$.

15. Let X be a metric space, x belong to X and $r > 0$.
    (i) Show that $\overline{B}(x, r)$ is closed and contains $B(x, r)$.
    (ii) Show that in a normed linear space X the closed ball $\overline{B}(x, r)$ is the closure of the open ball $B(x, r)$, but this is not so in a general metric space.

16. Prove Proposition 2.

17. Prove Proposition 7.

18. Let X be a subspace of the metric space Y and A a subset of X. Show that A is closed in X if and only if $A = X \cap F$, where F is closed in Y.

19. Let X be a subspace of the metric space Y.
    (i) If $\mathcal{O}$ is an open subset of the metric subspace X, is $\mathcal{O}$ an open subset of Y? What if X is an open subset of Y?
    (ii) If F is a closed subset of the metric subspace X, is F a closed subset of Y? What if X is a closed subset of Y?

20. For a subset E of a metric space X, a point $x \in X$ is called an interior point of E provided there is an open ball centered at x that is contained in E: the collection of interior points of E is called the interior of E and denoted by int E. Show that int E is always open and E is open if and only if $E = \text{int } E$.

21. For a subset E of a metric space X, a point $x \in X$ is called an exterior point of E provided there is an open ball centered at x that is contained in $X \sim E$: the collection of exterior points of E is called the exterior of E and denoted by ext E. Show that ext E is always open. Show that E is closed if and only if $X \sim E = \text{ext } E$.

22. For a subset E of a metric space X, a point $x \in X$ is called a boundary point of E provided every open ball centered at x contains points in E and points in $X \sim E$: the collection of boundary points of E is called the boundary of E and denoted by bd E. Show (i) that bd E is always closed, (ii) that E is open if and only if $E \cap \text{bd } E = \emptyset$, and (iii) that E is closed if and only if bd $E \subseteq E$.

23. Let A and B be subsets of a metric space X. Show that if $A \subseteq B$, then $\overline{A} \subseteq \overline{B}$. Also, show that $(\overline{A \cup B}) = \overline{A} \cup \overline{B}$ and $(\overline{A \cap B}) \subseteq \overline{A} \cap \overline{B}$.

24. Show that for a subset E of a metric space X, the closure of E is the intersection of all closed subsets of X that contain E.

9.3 CONTINUOUS MAPPINGS BETWEEN METRIC SPACES

The following is the natural generalization of continuity for real-valued functions of a real variable.

Definition *A mapping f from a metric space X to a metric space Y is said to be continuous at the point $x \in X$ provided for any sequence $\{x_n\}$ in X,*

$$\text{if } \{x_n\} \to x, \text{ then } \{f(x_n)\} \to f(x).$$

The mapping f is said to be **continuous** *provided it is continuous at every point in X.*

The following three propositions are generalizations of corresponding results for real-valued functions of a real variable and the proofs of the general results are essentially the same as the special cases.

The ϵ–δ Criterion for Continuity *A mapping f from a metric space (X, ρ) to a metric space (Y, σ) is continuous at the point $x \in X$ if and only if for every $\epsilon > 0$, there is a $\delta > 0$ for which if $\rho(x, x') < \delta$, then $\sigma(f(x), f(x')) < \epsilon$, that is,*

$$f(B(x, \delta)) \subseteq B(f(x), \epsilon).$$

Proof First suppose $f: X \to Y$ is continuous at x. We establish the ϵ–δ criterion by arguing by contradiction. Suppose there is some $\epsilon_0 > 0$ for which there is no positive number δ for which $f(B(x, \delta)) \subseteq B(f(x), \epsilon_0)$. In particular, if n is a natural number, it is not true that $f(B(x, 1/n)) \subseteq B(f(x), \epsilon_0)$. This means that there is a point in X, which we label x_n, such that $\rho(x, x_n) < 1/n$ while $\sigma(f(x), f(x_n)) \geq \epsilon_0$. This defines a sequence $\{x_n\}$ in X that converges to x, but whose image sequence $\{f(x_n)\}$ does not converge to $f(x)$. This contradicts the continuity of the mapping $f: X \to Y$ at the point x.

To prove the converse, suppose the ϵ–δ criterion holds. Let $\{x_n\}$ be a sequence in X that converges to x. We must show that $\{f(x_n)\}$ converges to $f(x)$. Let $\epsilon > 0$. We can choose a positive number δ for which $f(B(x, \delta)) \subseteq B(f(x), \epsilon)$. Moreover, since the sequence $\{x_n\}$ converges to x, we can select an index N such that $x_n \in B(x, \delta)$ for $n \geq N$. Hence $f(x_n) \in B(f(x), \epsilon)$ for $n \geq N$. Thus the sequence $\{f(x_n)\}$ converges to $f(x)$ and therefore $f: X \to Y$ is continuous at the point x. $\quad\square$

Proposition 8 *A mapping f from a metric space X to a metric space Y is continuous if and only if for each open subset $\mathcal{O}$ of Y, the inverse image under f of $\mathcal{O}$, $f^{-1}(\mathcal{O})$, is an open subset of X.*

Proof First assume the mapping f is continuous. Let $\mathcal{O}$ be an open subset of Y. Let x be a point in $f^{-1}(\mathcal{O})$; we must show that an open ball centered at x is contained in $f^{-1}(\mathcal{O})$. But $f(x)$ is a point in $\mathcal{O}$, which is open in Y, so there is some positive number r for which $B((f(x), r)) \subseteq \mathcal{O}$. Since $f: X \to Y$ is continuous at the point x, by the ϵ–δ criterion for continuity at a point, we can select a positive number δ for which $f(B(x, \delta)) \subseteq B(f(x), r) \subseteq \mathcal{O}$. Thus $B(x, \delta) \subseteq f^{-1}(\mathcal{O})$ and therefore $f^{-1}(\mathcal{O})$ is open in X.

To prove the converse, suppose the inverse image under f of each open set is open. Let x be a point in X. To show that f is continuous at x, we use the ϵ–δ criterion for continuity. Let $\epsilon > 0$. The open ball $B(f(x), \epsilon)$ is an open subset of Y. Thus $f^{-1}(B(f(x), \epsilon))$ is open in X. Therefore we can choose a positive number δ with $B(x, \delta) \subseteq f^{-1}(B(f(x), \epsilon))$, that is, $f(B(x, \delta)) \subseteq B(f(x), \epsilon)$. $\quad\square$

Proposition 9 *The composition of continuous mappings between metric spaces, when defined, is continuous.*

Proof Let $f: X \to Y$ be continuous and $g: Y \to Z$ be continuous, where X, Y, and Z are metric spaces. We use the preceding proposition. Let $\mathcal{O}$ be open in Z. Since g is continuous, $g^{-1}(\mathcal{O})$ is open in Y and therefore, since f is continuous, $f^{-1}(g^{-1}(\mathcal{O})) = (g \circ f)^{-1}(\mathcal{O})$ is open in X. Therefore $g \circ f$ is continuous. $\square$

Definition *A mapping from a metric space (X, ρ) to a metric space (Y, σ) is said to be* **uniformly continuous,** *provided for every $\epsilon > 0$, there is a $\delta > 0$ such that for $u, v \in X$,*

$$\text{if } \rho(u, v) < \delta, \text{ then } \sigma(f(u), f(v)) < \epsilon.$$

We infer from the ϵ–δ criterion for continuity at a point that a uniformly continuous mapping is continuous. The converse is not true.

Example A mapping f from a metric space (X, ρ) to a metric space (Y, σ) is said to be **Lipschitz** provided there is a $c \geq 0$ such that for all $u, v \in X$,

$$\sigma(f(u), f(v)) \leq c \cdot \rho(u, v).$$

A Lipschitz mapping is uniformly continuous since, regarding the criterion for uniform continuity, $\delta = \epsilon/c$ responds to any $\epsilon > 0$ challenge.

PROBLEMS

25. Exhibit a continuous mapping that is not uniformly continuous and a uniformly continuous mapping that is not Lipschitz.

26. Show that every mapping from a metric space (X, ρ) to a metric space (Y, σ) is continuous if ρ is the discrete metric.

27. Suppose there is a continuous, one-to-one mapping from a metric space (X, ρ) to a metric space (Y, σ), where σ is the discrete metric. Show that every subset of X is open.

28. For a metric space (X, ρ), show that the metric $\rho: X \times X \to \mathbf{R}$ is continuous, where $X \times X$ has the product metric.

29. Let z be a point in the metric space (X, ρ). Define the function $f: X \to \mathbf{R}$ by $f(x) = \rho(x, z)$. Show that f is uniformly continuous.

30. Show that the composition of uniformly continuous mappings between metric spaces, when defined, is uniformly continuous.

31. Show that a continuous mapping between metric spaces remains continuous if an equivalent metric is imposed on the domain and an equivalent metric is imposed on the range.

32. For a nonempty subset E of the metric space (X, ρ) and a point $x \in X$, define the distance from x to E, $\text{dist}(x, E)$, as follows:

$$\text{dist}(x, E) = \inf \{\rho(x, y) \mid y \in E\}.$$

   (i)   Show that the distance function $f: X \to \mathbf{R}$ defined by $f(x) = \text{dist}(x, E)$, for $x \in X$, is continuous.

   (ii) Show that $\{x \in X \mid \text{dist}(x, E) = 0\} = \overline{E}$.

33. Show that a subset E of a metric space X is open if and only if there is a continuous real-valued function f on X for which $E = \{x \in X \mid f(x) > 0.\}$.

34. Show that a subset E of a metric space X is closed if and only if there is a continuous real-valued function f on X for which $E = f^{-1}(0)$.

35. Let X and Y be metric spaces. Prove that $f : X \to Y$ is continuous if and only if $f^{-1}(C)$ is closed in X whenever C is closed in Y.

36. Let $X = C[a, b]$. Define the function $\psi : X \to \mathbf{R}$ by

$$\psi(f) = \int_a^b f(x)\,dx \quad \text{for each } f \text{ in } X.$$

Show that ψ is Lipschitz on the metric space X, where X has the metric induced by the maximum norm.

9.4 COMPLETE METRIC SPACES

By itself, the structure of a metric space is too barren to be fruitful in the study of interesting problems in mathematical analysis. It is remarkable, however, that by considering metric spaces that possess just one additional property, namely completeness, we can establish an abundance of interesting and important results. We devote the next chapter to three fundamental theorems for complete metric spaces.

Definition *A sequence $\{x_n\}$ in a metric space (X, ρ) is said to be a* **Cauchy sequence** *provided for each $\epsilon > 0$, there is an index N for which*

$$\text{if } n, m \geq N, \text{ then } \rho(x_n, x_m) < \epsilon.$$

This generalizes the concept of Cauchy sequence we first considered, in Chapter 1, for sequences of real numbers and then, in Chapter 7, for sequences in a normed linear space. For general metric spaces, as in the case of a normed linear space, a convergent sequence is Cauchy and a Cauchy sequence is bounded (see Problem 37).

Definition *A metric space X is said to be* **complete** *provided every Cauchy sequence in X converges to a point in X.*

The completeness axiom for the real numbers is equivalent to the completeness of the metric space $\mathbf{R}$. From this we infer that each Euclidean space $\mathbf{R}^n$ is complete. Moreover, the Riesz-Fischer Theorem, proved in Section 7.3, tells us that for E a Lebesgue measurable set of real numbers and $1 \leq p \leq \infty$, $L^p(E)$ is complete.

Proposition 10 *Let $[a, b]$ be a closed, bounded interval of real numbers. Then $C[a, b]$, with the metric induced by the maximum norm, is complete.*

Proof Let $\{f_n\}$ be a Cauchy sequence in $C[a, b]$. First suppose there is a convergent series $\sum_{k=1}^{\infty} a_k$ such that

$$\|f_{k+1} - f_k\|_{\max} \leq a_k \text{ for all } k. \tag{2}$$

Since

$$f_{n+k} - f_n = \sum_{j=n}^{n+k-1} [f_{j+1} - f_j] \text{ for all } n, k,$$

$$\| f_{n+k} - f_n \|_{\max} \le \sum_{j=n}^{n+k-1} \| f_{j+1} - f_j \|_{\max} \le \sum_{j=n}^{\infty} a_j \text{ for all } n, k.$$

Let x belong to $[a, b]$. Then

$$|f_{n+k}(x) - f_n(x)| \le \sum_{j=n}^{\infty} a_j \text{ for all } n, k. \tag{3}$$

The series $\sum_{k=1}^{\infty} a_k$ converges, and therefore $\{f_n(x)\}$ is a Cauchy sequence of real numbers. The real numbers are complete. Denote the limit of $\{f_n(x)\}$ by $f(x)$. Take the limit as $k \to \infty$ in (3) to conclude that

$$|f(x) - f_n(x)| \le \sum_{j=n}^{\infty} a_j \text{ for all } n \text{ and all } x \in [a, b].$$

We infer from this estimate that $\{f_n\}$ converges uniformly on $[a, b]$ to f. Since each f_n is continuous, so is f. The general case follows from the particular case by noting that a Cauchy sequence converges if is has a convergent sequence and every Cauchy sequence in $C[a, b]$ has a subsequence for which (2) holds.   □

In general, a subspace of a complete metric space is not complete. For instance, an open, bounded interval of real numbers is not complete, while **R** is complete. However, there is the following simple characterization of those subspaces that are complete.

Proposition 11 *Let E be a subset of the complete metric space X. Then the metric subspace E is complete if and only if E is a closed subset of X.*

Proof First suppose E is a closed subset of X. Let $\{x_n\}$ be a Cauchy sequence in E. Then $\{x_n\}$ can be considered as a Cauchy sequence in X and X is complete. Thus $\{x_n\}$ converges to a point x in X. According to Proposition 6, since E is a closed subset of X, the limit of a convergent sequence in E belongs to E. Thus x belongs to E and hence E is a complete metric space.

To prove the converse, suppose E is complete. According to Proposition 6, to show E is a closed subset of X we must show that the limit of a convergent sequence in E also belongs to E. Let $\{x_n\}$ be a sequence in E that converges to $x \in X$. But a convergent sequence is Cauchy. Thus, by the completeness of E, $\{x_n\}$ converges to a point in E. But a convergent sequence in a metric space has only one limit. Thus x belongs to E.   □

Theorem 12 *The following are complete metric spaces:*

(i) *Each nonempty closed subset of Euclidean space $\mathbf{R}^n$.*

(ii) *For E a measurable set of real numbers and $1 \le p \le \infty$, each nonempty closed subset of $L^p(E)$.*

(iii) *Each nonempty closed subset of $C[a, b]$.*

Definition *For a nonempty subset E of a metric space (X, ρ), we define the **diameter** of E, diam E, by*

$$\text{diam } E = \sup \{\rho(x, y) \mid x, y \in E\}.$$

*We say E is **bounded** provided it has finite diameter. A descending sequence $\{E_n\}_{n=1}^\infty$ of nonempty subsets of X is called a **contracting sequence** provided*

$$\lim_{n \to \infty} \text{diam}(E_n) = 0.$$

The Nested Set Theorem of Chapter 1 tells us that the intersection of a contracting sequence of nonempty closed sets of real numbers consists of a single point. This generalizes as follows.

The Cantor Intersection Theorem *Let X be a metric space. Then X is complete if and only if whenever $\{F_n\}_{n=1}^\infty$ is a contracting sequence of nonempty closed subsets of X, there is a point $x \in X$ for which $\bigcap_{n=1}^\infty F_n = \{x\}$.*

Proof First assume X is complete. Let $\{F_n\}_{n=1}^\infty$ be a contracting sequence of nonempty closed subsets of X. For each index n, select $x_n \in F_n$. We claim that $\{x_n\}$ is a Cauchy sequence. Indeed, let $\epsilon > 0$. There is an index N for which diam $F_N < \epsilon$. Since $\{F_n\}_{n=1}^\infty$ is descending, if $n, m \geq N$, then x_n and x_m belong to F_N and therefore $\rho(x_n, x_m) \leq$ diam $F_N < \epsilon$. Thus $\{x_n\}$ is a Cauchy sequence. Since X is complete, this sequence converges to some $x \in X$. However, for each index n, F_n is closed and $x_k \in F_n$ for $k \geq n$ so that x belongs to F_n. Thus x belongs to $\bigcap_{n=1}^\infty F_n$. It is not possible for the intersection to contain two points for, if it did, $\lim_{n \to \infty}$ diam $F_n \neq 0$.

To prove the converse, suppose that for any contracting sequence $\{F_n\}_{n=1}^\infty$ of nonempty closed subsets of X, there is a point $x \in X$ for which $\bigcap_{n=1}^\infty F_n = \{x\}$. Let $\{x_n\}$ be a Cauchy sequence in X. For each index n define F_n to be the closure of the nonempty set $\{x_k \mid k \geq n\}$. Then $\{F_n\}$ is a descending sequence of nonempty closed sets. Since $\{x_n\}$ is Cauchy, the sequence $\{F_n\}$ is contracting. Thus, by assumption, there is a point x in X for which $\{x\} = \bigcap_{n=1}^\infty F_n$. For each index n, x is a point of closure of $\{x_k \mid k \geq n\}$ and therefore any ball centered at x has nonempty intersection with $\{x_k \mid k \geq n\}$. Hence we may inductively select a strictly increasing sequence of natural numbers $\{n_k\}$ such that for each index k, $\rho(x, x_{n_k}) < 1/k$. The subsequence $\{x_{n_k}\}$ converges to x. Since $\{x_n\}$ is Cauchy, the whole sequence $\{x_n\}$ converges to x (see Problem 38). Therefore X is complete. □

A very rough geometric interpretation of the Cantor Intersection Theorem is that a metric space fails to be complete because it has "holes." If X is an incomplete metric space, it can always be suitably minimally enlarged to become complete. For example, the set of rational numbers is not complete, but it is a dense metric subspace of the complete space $\mathbf{R}$. As a further example, let $X = C[a, b]$, now considered with the norm $\| \cdot \|_1$, which it inherits from $L^1[a, b]$. The metric space (X, ρ_1) is not complete. But it is a dense metric subspace of the complete metric space $L^1[a, b]$. These are two specific examples of a construction that has a quite abstract generalization. We outline a proof of the following theorem in Problem 49.

Theorem 13 *Let (X, ρ) be a metric space. Then there is a complete metric space $(\widetilde{X}, \widetilde{\rho})$ for which X is a dense subset of $\widetilde{X}$ and*

$$\rho(u, v) = \widetilde{\rho}(u, v) \text{ for all } u, v \in X.$$

We call the metric space described above the **completion** of (X, ρ). In the context of metric spaces the completion is unique in the sense that any two completions are isometric by way of an isometry that is the identity mapping on X.

PROBLEMS

37. In a metric space X, show (i) that a convergent sequence is Cauchy and (ii) that a Cauchy sequence is bounded.

38. In a metric space X, show that a Cauchy sequence converges if and only if it has a convergent subsequence.

39. Suppose that $\{x_n\}$ is a sequence in a complete metric space (X, ρ) and for each index n, $\rho(x_n, x_{n+1}) < 1/2^n$. Show that $\{x_n\}$ converges. Does $\{x_n\}$ converge if for each index n, $\rho(x_n, x_{n+1}) < 1/n$?

40. Provide an example of a descending countable collection of closed, nonempty sets of real numbers whose intersection is empty. Does this contradict the Cantor Intersection Theorem?

41. Let ρ and σ be equivalent metrics on a nonempty set X. Show that (X, ρ) is complete if and only if (X, σ) is complete.

42. Prove that the product of two complete metric spaces is complete.

43. For a mapping f of the metric space (X, ρ) to the metric space (Y, σ), show that f is uniformly continuous if and only if for any two sequences $\{u_n\}$ and $\{v_n\}$ in X,

$$\text{if } \lim_{n \to \infty} \rho(u_n, v_n) = 0, \text{ then } \lim_{n \to \infty} \sigma(f(u_n), f(v_n))) = 0.$$

44. Use the outline below to prove the following extension property for uniformly continuous mappings: Let X and Y be metric spaces, with Y complete, and f a uniformly continuous mapping from a subset E of X to Y. Then f has a unique uniformly continuous extension to a mapping $\overline{f}$ of $\overline{E}$ to Y.

   (i) Show that f maps Cauchy sequences in E to Cauchy sequences in Y.

   (ii) For $x \in \overline{E}$, choose a sequence $\{x_n\}$ in E that converges to x and define $\overline{f}(x)$ to be the limit of $\{f(x_n)\}$. Use Problem 43 to show that $\overline{f}(x)$ is properly defined.

   (iii) Show that $\overline{f}$ is uniformly continuous on $\overline{E}$.

   (iv) Show that the above extension is unique since any two such extensions are continuous mappings on $\overline{E}$ that take the same values on the dense subset E of $\overline{E}$.

45. Consider the countable collection of metric spaces $\{(X_n, \rho_n)\}_{n=1}^{\infty}$. For the Cartesian product of these sets $Z = \prod_{n=1}^{\infty} X_n$, define σ on $Z \times Z$ by setting, for $x = \{x_n\}, y = \{y_n\}$,

$$\sigma(x, y) = \sum_{n=1}^{\infty} 2^{-n} \rho_n^*(x_n, y_n) \text{ where each } \rho_n^* = \rho_n/(1 + \rho_n).$$

   (i) Show that σ is a metric.

   (ii) Show that (Z, σ) is complete if and only if each (X_n, ρ_n) is complete.

46. For each index n, define $f_n(x) = \alpha x^n + \beta \cos(x/n)$ for $0 \leq x \leq 1$. For what values of the parameters α and β is the sequence $\{f_n\}$ a Cauchy sequence in the metric space $C[0, 1]$?

47. Let $\mathcal{D}$ be the subspace of $C[0, 1]$ consisting of the continuous functions $f \colon [0, 1] \to \mathbf{R}$ that are differentiable on $(0, 1)$. Is $\mathcal{D}$ complete?

48. Define $\mathcal{L}$ to be the subspace of $C[0, 1]$ consisting of the functions $f \colon [0, 1] \to \mathbf{R}$ that are Lipschitz. Is $\mathcal{L}$ complete?

49. For a metric space (X, ρ), complete the following outline of a proof of Theorem 13:

   (i)   If $\{x_n\}$ and $\{y_n\}$ are Cauchy sequences in X, show that $\{\rho(x_n, y_n)\}$ is a Cauchy sequence of real numbers and therefore converges.

   (ii) Define X' to be the set of Cauchy sequences in X. For two Cauchy sequences in X, $\{x_n\}$ and $\{y_n\}$, define $\rho'(\{x_n\}, \{y_n\}) = \lim \rho(x_n, y_n)$. Show that this defines a pseudometric ρ' on X'.

   (iii) Define two members of X', that is, two Cauchy sequences $\{x_n\}$ and $\{y_n\}$ in X, to be equivalent, provided $\rho'(\{x_n\}, \{y_n\}) = 0$. Show that this is an equivalence relation in X' and denote by $\widehat{X}$ the set of equivalence classes. Define the distance $\widehat{\rho}$ between two equivalence classes to be the ρ' distance between representatives of the classes. Show that $\widehat{\rho}$ is properly defined and is a metric on $\widehat{X}$.

   (iv) Show that the metric space $(\widehat{X}, \widehat{\rho})$ is complete. (Hint: If $\{x_n\}$ is a Cauchy sequence from X, we may assume [by taking subsequences] that $\rho(x_n, x_{n+1}) < 2^{-n}$ for all n. If $\{\{x_{n,m}\}_{n=1}^{\infty}\}_{m=1}^{\infty}$ is a sequence of such Cauchy sequences that represents a Cauchy sequence in $\widehat{X}$, then the sequence $\{x_{n,n}\}_{n=1}^{\infty}$ is a Cauchy sequence from X that represents the limit of the Cauchy sequences from $\widehat{X}$.)

   (v)   Define the mapping h from X to $\widehat{X}$ by defining, for $x \in X$, $h(x)$ to be the equivalence class of the constant sequence all of whose terms are x. Show that $h(X)$ is dense in $\widehat{X}$ and that $\widehat{\rho}(h(u), h(v)) = \rho(u, v)$ for all $u, v \in X$.

   (vi) Define the set $\widetilde{X}$ to be the disjoint union of X and $\widehat{X} \sim h(X)$. For $u, v \in \widetilde{X}$, define $\widetilde{\rho}(u, v)$ as follows: $\widetilde{\rho}(u, v) = \rho(u, v)$ if $u, v \in X$; $\widetilde{\rho}(u, v) = \widehat{\rho}(u, v)$ for $u, v \in \widehat{X} \sim h(X)$; and $\widetilde{\rho}(u, v) = \widehat{\rho}(h(u), v)$ for $u \in X$, $v \in \widehat{X} \sim h(X)$. From the preceding two parts conclude that the metric space $(\widetilde{X}, \widetilde{\rho})$ is a complete metric space containing (X, ρ) as a dense subspace.

50. Show that any two completions of a metric space X are isometric by way of an isometry that is the identity mapping on X.

9.5   COMPACT METRIC SPACES

Recall that a collection of sets $\{E_\lambda\}_{\lambda \in \Lambda}$ is said to be a **cover** of a set E provided $E \subseteq \bigcup_{\lambda \in \Lambda} E_\lambda$. By a subcover of a cover of E we mean a subcollection of the cover which itself also is a cover of E. If E is a subset of a metric space X, by an **open cover** of E we mean a cover of E consisting of open subsets of X. The concept of compactness, examined in Chapter 1 for sets of real numbers, generalizes as follows to the class of metric spaces.

Definition   *A metric space X is called* **compact** *provided every open cover of X has a finite subcover. A subset K of X is called* **compact** *provided K, considered as a metric subspace of X, is compact.*

An open subset of the subspace K of a metric space X is the intersection of K with an open subset of X. Therefore a subset K of a metric space X is compact if and only if each cover of K by a collection of open subsets of X has a finite subcover.

If T is a collection of open subsets of a metric space X, then the collection F of complements of sets in T is a collection of closed sets. Moreover, T is a cover if and only if F has empty intersection. Thus, by De Morgan's Identities, a metric space X is compact if and only if every collection of closed sets with a nonempty intersection has a finite subcollection whose intersection also is nonempty. A collection F of sets in X is said to have the **finite intersection property** provided any finite subcollection of F has a nonempty intersection. Thus we may formulate compactness in terms of collections of closed sets as follows.

Proposition 14 *A metric space X is compact if and only if every collection F of closed subsets of X with the finite intersection property has nonempty intersection.*

Definition *A metric space X is said to be* **totally bounded** *provided for each $\epsilon > 0$, the space X can be covered by a finite number of open balls of radius ϵ. A subset E of X is called* **totally bounded** *provided that E, considered as a subspace of the metric space X, is totally bounded.*

For a subset E of a metric space X, by an ϵ-**net** for E we mean a finite collection of open balls $\{B(x_k, \epsilon)\}_{k=1}^n$ with centers x_k in X whose union covers E. We leave it as an exercise to show that the metric subspace E is totally bounded if and only if for each $\epsilon > 0$, there is a finite ϵ-**net** for E. The point of this observation is that regarding the criterion for a metric subspace E to be totally bounded it is not necessary to require that the centers of the balls in the net belong to E.

If a metric space X is totally bounded, then it is bounded in the sense that its diameter is finite. Indeed, if X is covered by a finite number of balls of radius 1, then we infer from the triangle inequality that diam $X \leq c$, where $c = 2 + d$, d being the maximum distance between the centers of the covering balls. However, as is seen in the following example, a bounded metric space need not be totally bounded.

Example Let X be the Banach space ℓ^2 of square summable sequences. Consider the closed unit ball $B = \{\{x_n\} \in \ell^2 \,|\, \|\{x_n\}\|_2 \leq 1\}$. Then B is bounded. We claim that B is not totally bounded. Indeed, for each natural number n, let e_n have nth component 1 and other components 0. Then $\|e_n - e_m\|_2 = \sqrt{2}$ if $m \neq n$. Then B cannot be contained in a finite number of balls of radius $r < 1/2$ since one of these balls would contain two of the e_n's, which are distance $\sqrt{2}$ apart and yet the ball has diameter less than 1.

Proposition 15 *A subset of Euclidean space $\mathbf{R}^n$ is bounded if and only if it is totally bounded.*

Proof It is always the case that a totally bounded metric space is bounded. So let E be a bounded subset of $\mathbf{R}^n$. For simplicity take $n = 2$. Let $\epsilon > 0$. Since E is bounded, we may take $a > 0$ large enough so that E is contained in the square $[-a, a] \times [-a, a]$. Let P_k be a partition of $[-a, a]$ for which each partition interval has length less than $1/k$. Then $P_k \times P_k$ induces a partition of $[-a, a] \times [-a, a]$ into closed rectangles of diameter at most $\sqrt{2}/k$. Choose k such that $\sqrt{2}/k < \epsilon$. Consider the finite collection of balls of radius ϵ with centers (x, y) where x and y are partition points of P_k. Then this finite collection of balls of radius ϵ covers the square $[-a, a] \times [-a, a]$ and therefore also covers E. $\qquad \square$

Definition *A metric space X is said to be* **sequentially compact** *provided every sequence in X has a subsequence that converges to a point in X.*

Theorem 16 (Characterization of Compactness for a Metric Space) *For a metric space X, the following three assertions are equivalent:*

(i) *X is complete and totally bounded;*

(ii) *X is compact;*

(iii) *X is sequentially compact.*

For clarity we divide the proof into three propositions.

Proposition 17 *If a metric space X is complete and totally bounded, then it is compact.*

Proof We argue by contradiction. Suppose $\{\mathcal{O}_\lambda\}_{\lambda \in \Lambda}$ is an open cover of X for which there is no finite subcover. Since X is totally bounded, we may choose a finite collection of open balls of radius less than $1/2$ that cover X. There must be one of these balls that cannot be covered by a finite subcollection of $\{\mathcal{O}_\lambda\}_{\lambda \in \Lambda}$. Select such a ball and label its closure F_1. Then F_1 is closed and diam $F_1 \leq 1$. Once more using the total boundedness of X, there is a finite collection of open balls of radius less than $1/4$ that cover X. This collection also covers F_1. There must be one of these balls whose intersection with F_1 cannot be covered by a finite subcollection of $\{\mathcal{O}_\lambda\}_{\lambda \in \Lambda}$. Define F_2 to be the closure of the intersection of such a ball with F_1. Then F_1 and F_2 are closed, $F_2 \subseteq F_1$, and diam $F_1 \leq 1$, diam $F_2 \leq 1/2$. Continuing in this way we obtain a contracting sequence of nonempty, closed sets $\{F_n\}$ with the property that each F_n cannot be covered by a finite subcollection of $\{\mathcal{O}_\lambda\}_{\lambda \in \Lambda}$. But X is complete. According to the Cantor Intersection Theorem there is a point x_0 in X that belongs to the intersection $\bigcap_{n=1}^{\infty} F_n$. There is some λ_0 such that $\mathcal{O}_{\lambda_0}$ contains x_0 and since $\mathcal{O}_{\lambda_0}$ is open, there is a ball centered at x_0, $B(x_0, r)$, such that $B(x_0, r) \subseteq \mathcal{O}_{\lambda_0}$. Since $\lim_{n \to \infty}$ diam $F_n = 0$ and $x_0 \in \bigcap_{n=1}^{\infty} F_n$, there is an index n such that $F_n \subseteq \mathcal{O}_{\lambda_0}$. This contradicts the choice of F_n as being a set that cannot be covered by a finite subcollection of $\{\mathcal{O}_\lambda\}_{\lambda \in \Lambda}$. This contradiction shows that X is compact. $\square$

Proposition 18 *If a metric space X is compact, then it is sequentially compact.*

Proof Let $\{x_n\}$ be a sequence in X. For each index n, let F_n be the closure of the nonempty set $\{x_k \mid k \geq n\}$. Then $\{F_n\}$ is a descending sequence of nonempty closed sets. According to the Cantor Intersection Theorem there is a point x_0 in X that belongs to the intersection $\bigcap_{n=1}^{\infty} F_n$. Since for each n, x_0 belongs to the closure of $\{x_k \mid k \geq n\}$, the ball $B(x_0, 1/k)$ has nonempty intersection with $\{x_k \mid k \geq n\}$. By induction we may select a strictly increasing sequence of indices $\{n_k\}$ such that for each index k, $\rho(x_0, x_{n_k}) < 1/k$. The subsequence $\{x_{n_k}\}$ converges to x_0. Thus X is sequentially compact. $\square$

Proposition 19 *If a metric space X is sequentially compact, then it is complete and totally bounded.*

Proof We argue by contradiction to establish total boundedness. Suppose X is not totally bounded. Then for some $\epsilon > 0$ we cannot cover X by a finite number of open balls of radius ϵ.

Select a point x_1 in X. Since X is not contained in $B(x_1, \epsilon)$, we may choose $x_2 \in X$ for which $\rho(x_1, x_2) \geq \epsilon$. Now since X is not contained in $B(x_1, \epsilon) \cup B(x_2, \epsilon)$, we may choose $x_3 \in X$ for which $\rho(x_3, x_2) \geq \epsilon$ and $\rho(x_3, x_1) \geq \epsilon$. Continuing in this way we obtain a sequence $\{x_n\}$ in X with the property that $\rho(x_n, x_k) \geq \epsilon$ for $n > k$. Then the sequence $\{x_n\}$ can have no convergent subsequence, since any two different terms of any subsequence are a distance ϵ or more apart. Thus X is not sequentially compact. This contradiction shows that X must be totally bounded.

To show that X is complete, let $\{x_n\}$ be a Cauchy sequence in X. Since X is sequentially compact, a subsequence of $\{x_n\}$ converges to a point $x \in X$. Using the Cauchy property it is not difficult to see that the whole sequence converges to x. Thus X is complete.   □

These three propositions complete the proof of the Characterization of Compactness Theorem.

Since Euclidean space $\mathbf{R}^n$ is complete, each closed subset is complete as a metric subspace. Moreover, Proposition 15 asserts that a subset of Euclidean space is bounded if and only if it is totally bounded. Therefore from our Characterization of Compactness Theorem we have the following characterization of compactness for a subspace of Euclidean space.

Theorem 20 *For a subset K of $\mathbf{R}^n$, the following three assertions are equivalent:*

   (i) *K is closed and bounded;*

   (ii) *K is compact;*

   (iii) *K is sequentially compact.*

Regarding this theorem, the equivalence of (i) and (ii) is known as the Heine-Borel Theorem and that of (i) and (iii) the Bolzano-Weierstrass Theorem. In Chapter 1, we proved each of these in $\mathbf{R} = \mathbf{R}^1$, because we needed both of them for the development of the Lebesgue integral for functions of a real variable.

Proposition 21 *Let f be a continuous mapping from a compact metric space X to a metric space Y. Then its image $f(X)$ also is compact.*

Proof Let $\{\mathcal{O}_\lambda\}_{\lambda \in \Lambda}$ be an open covering of $f(X)$. Then, by the continuity of f, $\{f^{-1}(\mathcal{O}_\lambda)\}_{\lambda \in \Lambda}$ is an open cover of X. By the compactness of X, there is a finite subcollection $\{f^{-1}(\mathcal{O}_{\lambda_1}), \ldots, f^{-1}(\mathcal{O}_{\lambda_n})\}$ that also covers X. Since f maps X onto $f(X)$, the finite collection $\{\mathcal{O}_{\lambda_1}, \ldots, \mathcal{O}_{\lambda_n}\}$ covers $f(X)$.   □

One of the first properties of functions of a real variable that is established in a calculus course and which we proved in Chapter 1 is that a continuous function on a closed, bounded interval takes maximum and minimum values. It is natural to attempt to classify the metric spaces for which this extreme value property holds.

Theorem 22 (Extreme Value Theorem) *Let X be a metric space. Then X is compact if and only if every continuous real-valued function on X takes a maximum and a minimum value.*

Proof First assume X is compact. Let the function $f: X \to \mathbf{R}$ be continuous. The preceding proposition tells us that $f(X)$ is a compact set of real numbers. According to Corollary 20, $f(X)$ is closed and bounded. We infer from the completeness of $\mathbf{R}$ that a closed and bounded nonempty set of real numbers has a largest and smallest member.

To prove the converse, assume every continuous real-valued function on X takes a maximum and minimum value. According to Theorem 20, to show that X is compact it is necessary and sufficient to show it is totally bounded and complete. We argue by contradiction to show that X is totally bounded. If X is not totally bounded, then there is an $r > 0$ and a countably infinite subset of X, which we enumerate as $\{x_n\}_{n=1}^{\infty}$, for which the collection of open balls $\{B(x_n, r)\}_{n=1}^{\infty}$ is disjoint. For each natural number n, define the function $f_n: X \to \mathbf{R}$ by

$$f_n(x) = \begin{cases} r/2 - \rho(x, x_n) & \text{if } \rho(x, x_n) \le r/2 \\ 0 & \text{otherwise.} \end{cases}$$

Define the function $f: X \to \mathbf{R}$ by

$$f(x) = \sum_{n=1}^{\infty} n \cdot f_n(x) \text{ for all } x \in X.$$

Since each f_n is continuous and vanishes outside $B(x_n, r/2)$ and the collection $\{B(x_n, r)\}_{n=1}^{\infty}$ is disjoint, f is properly defined and continuous. But for each natural number n, $f(x_n) = n \cdot r/2$, and hence f is unbounded above and therefore does not take a maximum value. This is a contradiction. Therefore X is totally bounded. It remains to show that X is complete. Let $\{x_n\}$ be a Cauchy sequence in X. Then for each $x \in X$, we infer from the triangle inequality that $\{\rho(x, x_n)\}$ is a Cauchy sequence of real numbers that, since $\mathbf{R}$ is complete, converges to a real number. Define the function $f: X \to \mathbf{R}$ by

$$f(x) = \lim_{n \to \infty} \rho(x, x_n) \text{ for all } x \in X.$$

Again by use of the triangle inequality we conclude that f is continuous. By assumption, there is a point x in X at which f takes a minimum value. Since $\{x_n\}$ is Cauchy, the infimum of f on X is 0. Therefore $f(x) = 0$ and hence $\{x_n\}$ converges to x. Thus X is complete. $\qquad\Box$

If $\{\mathcal{O}_\lambda\}_{\lambda \in \Lambda}$ is an open cover of a metric space X, then each point $x \in X$ is contained in a member of the cover, $\mathcal{O}_\lambda$, and since $\mathcal{O}_\lambda$ is open, there is some $\epsilon > 0$, such that

$$B(x, \epsilon) \subseteq \mathcal{O}_\lambda. \tag{4}$$

In general, the ϵ depends on the choice of x. The following proposition tells us that for a compact metric space this containment holds uniformly in the sense that we can find ϵ independently of $x \in X$ for which the inclusion (4) holds. A positive number ϵ with this property is called a **Lebesgue number** for the cover $\{\mathcal{O}_\lambda\}_{\lambda \in \Lambda}$.

The Lebesgue Covering Lemma *Let $\{\mathcal{O}_\lambda\}_{\lambda \in \Lambda}$ be an open cover of a compact metric space X. Then there is a number $\epsilon > 0$, such that for each $x \in X$, the open ball $B(x, \epsilon)$ is contained in some member of the cover.*

Proof We argue by contradiction. Assume there is no such positive Lebesgue number. Then for each natural number n, $1/n$ fails to be a Lebesgue number. Thus there is a point in X, which we label x_n, for which $B(x_n, 1/n)$ fails to be contained in a single member of the cover. This defines a sequence $\{x_n\}$ in X. By the Characterization of Compactness Theorem, X is sequentially compact. Thus a subsequence $\{x_{n_k}\}$ converges to a point $x_0 \in X$. Now there is some $\lambda_0 \in \Lambda$ for which $\mathcal{O}_{\lambda_0}$ contains x_0 and since $\mathcal{O}_{\lambda_0}$ is open, there is a ball centered at x_0, $B(x_0, r_0)$, for which

$$B(x_0, r_0) \subseteq \mathcal{O}_{\lambda_0}.$$

We may choose an index k for which $\rho(x_0, x_{n_k}) < r_0/2$ and $1/n_k < r_0/2$. By the triangle inequality, $B(x_{n_k}, 1/n_k) \subseteq \mathcal{O}_{\lambda_0}$ and this contradicts the choice of x_{n_k} as being a point for which $B(x_{n_k}, 1/n_k)$ fails to be contained in a single member of the cover. $\square$

Proposition 23 *A continuous mapping from a compact metric space (X, ρ) into a metric space (Y, σ) is uniformly continuous.*

Proof Let f be a continuous mapping from X to Y. Let $\epsilon > 0$. By the ϵ–δ criterion for continuity at a point, for each $x \in X$, there is a $\delta_x > 0$ for which if $\rho(x, x') < \delta_x$, then $\sigma(f(x), f(x')) < \epsilon/2$. Therefore, setting $\mathcal{O}_x = B(x, \delta_x)$, by the triangle inequality for σ,

$$\sigma(f(u), f(v)) \leq \sigma(f(u), f(x)) + \sigma(f(x), f(v)) < \epsilon \text{ if } u, v \in \mathcal{O}_x. \tag{5}$$

Let δ be a Lebesgue number for the open cover $\{\mathcal{O}_x\}_{x \in X}$. Then for $u, v \in X$, if $\rho(u, v) < \delta$ there is some x for which $u \in B(v, \delta) \subseteq \mathcal{O}_x$ and therefore, by (5), $\sigma(f(u), f(v)) < \epsilon$. $\square$

PROBLEMS

51. Consider the metric space $\mathbf{Q}$ consisting of the rational numbers with the metric induced by the absolute value. Which subspaces of $\mathbf{Q}$ are complete and which are compact?

52. Let $B = B(x, r)$ be an open ball in Euclidean space $\mathbf{R}^n$. Show that B fails to be compact by (i) showing B is not sequentially compact, (ii) finding an open cover of B without any finite subcover, and (iii) showing B is not closed.

53. When is a nonempty set X with the discrete metric a compact metric space?

54. Let ρ and σ be equivalent metrics on a nonempty set X. Show that the metric space (X, ρ) is compact if and only if the metric space (X, σ) is compact.

55. Show that the Cartesian product of two compact metric spaces also is compact.

56. Show that the Cartesian product of two totally bounded metric spaces also is totally bounded.

57. For E contained in a metric space X, show that the subspace E is totally bounded if and only if for each $\epsilon > 0$, E can be covered by a finite number of open balls (open in X) of radius ϵ which have centers belonging to X.

58. Let E be a subset of the compact metric space X. Show the metric subspace E is compact if and only if E is a closed subset of X.

59. (Fréchet Intersection Theorem). Let $\{F_n\}_{n=1}^{\infty}$ be a descending countable collection of nonempty closed subsets of a compact metric space X. Show that $\bigcap_{n=1}^{\infty} F_n \neq \emptyset$.

60. For a subset E of a metric space X, show that E is totally bounded if and only if its closure $\overline{E}$ is totally bounded.

61. For a subset E of a complete metric space X, show that E is totally bounded if and only if its closure $\overline{E}$ is compact.

62. Let $B = \{\{x_n\} \in \ell^2 \mid \sum_{n=1}^{\infty} x_n^2 \leq 1\}$ be the closed unit ball in ℓ^2. Show that B fails to be compact by (i) showing B is not sequentially compact, (ii) finding an open cover of B without any finite subcover, and (iii) showing B is not totally bounded.

63. Let $B = \{f \in L^2[a, b] \mid \|f\|_2 \leq 1\}$ be the closed unit ball in $L^2[a, b]$. Show that B fails to be compact by (i) showing B is not sequentially compact, (ii) finding an open cover of B without any finite subcover, and (iii) showing B is not totally bounded.

64. Let X be a totally bounded metric space.
    (i) If f is a uniformly continuous mapping from X to a metric space Y, show that $f(X)$ is totally bounded.
    (ii) Is (i) still true if f is only required to be continuous?

65. Let ρ be a metric on a set X. Define

$$\tau(u, v) = \frac{\rho(u, v)}{1 + \rho(u, v)} \text{ for all } u, v \in X.$$

Verify that τ is a bounded metric on X and convergence of sequences with respect to the ρ metric and the τ metric is the same. Conclude that sets that are closed with respect to the ρ metric are closed with respect to the τ metric and that sets that are open with respect to the ρ metric are open with respect to the τ metric. Are the metrics ρ and τ equivalent?

66. Let E be a subset of Euclidean space $\mathbf{R}^n$. Assume every continuous real-valued function of E takes a minimum value. Prove that E is closed and bounded.

67. Let E be a subset of Euclidean space $\mathbf{R}^n$. Assume every continuous real-valued function of E is uniformly continuous. Prove that E is closed and bounded.

68. Suppose f is a continuous real-valued function on Euclidean space $\mathbf{R}^n$ with the property that there is a number c such that $|f(x)| \geq c \cdot \|x\|$ for all $x \in \mathbf{R}^n$. Show that if K is a compact set of real numbers, then its inverse image under f, $f^{-1}(K)$, also is compact. (Mappings with this property are called **proper**.)

69. For a compact metric space (X, ρ), show that there are points $u, v \in X$ for which $\rho(u, v) = \operatorname{diam} X$.

70. Let K be a compact subset of the metric space (X, ρ) and x_0 belong to X. Show that there is a point $z \in K$ for which

$$\rho(z, x_0) \leq \rho(x, x_0) \text{ for all } x \in K.$$

71. Let K be a compact subset of the metric space X. For a point $x \in X \sim K$, show that there is a open set $\mathcal{U}$ containing K and an open set $\mathcal{O}$ containing x for which $\mathcal{U} \cap \mathcal{O} = \emptyset$.

72. Let A and B be subsets of a metric space (X, ρ). Define

$$\operatorname{dist}(A, B) = \inf \{\rho(u, v) \mid u \in A, v \in B\}.$$

If A is compact and B is closed, show that $A \cap B = \emptyset$ if and only if $\operatorname{dist}(A, B) > 0$.

73. Let K be a compact subset of a metric space X and $\mathcal{O}$ an open set containing K. Use the preceding problem to show that there is an open set $\mathcal{U}$ for which $K \subseteq \mathcal{U} \subseteq \overline{\mathcal{U}} \subseteq \mathcal{O}$.

9.6   SEPARABLE METRIC SPACES

Definition *A subset D of a metric space X is said to be* **dense** *in X provided every nonempty open subset of X contains a point of D. A metric space X is said to be* **separable** *provided there is a countable subset of X that is dense in X.*

Observe that D is dense in X if and only if every point in X is a point of closure of D, that is, $\overline{D} = X$. One of the first results of mathematical analysis is that the rational numbers are countable and dense in $\mathbf{R}$ (see Theorem 2 of Chapter 1). Therefore $\mathbf{R}$ is separable. From this we infer that every Euclidean space $\mathbf{R}^n$ is separable. The Weierstrass Approximation Theorem tells us that the polynomials are dense in $C[a, b]$. Thus the set of polynomials with rational coefficients is countable and dense in $C[a, b]$. Therefore $C[a, b]$ is separable. Theorem 11 of Chapter 7 tells us that for E a Lebesgue measurable set of real numers and $1 \leq p < \infty$, the normed linear space $L^p(E)$ is separable. We showed that $L^\infty[0, 1]$ is not separable.

Proposition 24 *A compact metric space is separable.*

Proof Let X be a compact metric space. Then X is totally bounded. For each natural number n, cover X by a finite number of balls of radius $1/n$. Let D be the collection of points that are centers of one of this countable collection of covers. Then D is countable and dense. $\qquad\square$

Proposition 25 *A metric space X is separable if and only if there is a countable collection* $\{\mathcal{O}_n\}_{n=1}^\infty$ *of open subsets of X such that any open subset of X is the union of a subcollection of* $\{\mathcal{O}_n\}_{n=1}^\infty$.

Proof First suppose X is separable. Let D be a countable dense subset of X. If D is finite, then $X = D$. Assume D is countably infinite. Let $\{x_n\}$ be an enumeration of D. Then $\{B(x_n, 1/m)\}_{n,m \in N}$ is a countable collection of open subsets of X. We claim that every open subset of X is the union of a subcollection of $\{B(x_n, 1/m)\}_{n,m \in N}$. Indeed, let $\mathcal{O}$ be an open subset of X. Let x belong to $\mathcal{O}$. We must show there are natural numbers n and m for which

$$x \in B(x_n, 1/m) \subseteq \mathcal{O}. \qquad (6)$$

Since $\mathcal{O}$ is open, there is a natural number m for which $B(x, 1/m)$ is contained in $\mathcal{O}$. Since x is a point of closure of D, we may choose a natural number n for which x_n belongs to $D \cap B(x, 1/2m)$. Thus (6) holds for this choice of n and m.

To prove the converse, suppose there is a countable collection $\{\mathcal{O}_n\}_{n=1}^\infty$ of open sets such that any open subset of X is the union of a subcollection of $\{\mathcal{O}_n\}_{n=1}^\infty$. For each index n, choose a point in $\mathcal{O}_n$ and label it x_n. Then the set $\{x_n\}_{n=1}^\infty$ is countable and is dense since every nonempty open subset of X is the union of a subcollection of $\{\mathcal{O}_n\}_{n=1}^\infty$ and therefore contains points in the set $\{x_n\}_{n=1}^\infty$. $\qquad\square$

Proposition 26 *Every subspace of a separable metric space is separable.*

Proof Let E be a subspace of the separable metric space X. By the preceding proposition, there is a countable collection $\{\mathcal{O}_n\}_{n=1}^\infty$ of open sets in X for which each open set in X

is a union of some subcollection of $\{\mathcal{O}_n\}_{n=1}^\infty$. Thus $\{\mathcal{O}_n \cap E\}_{n=1}^\infty$ is a countable collection of subsets of E, each one of which, by Proposition 2, is open. Since each open subset of E is the intersection of E with an open subset of X, every open subset of E is a union of a subcollection of $\{\mathcal{O}_n \cap E\}_{n=1}^\infty$. We infer from the preceding proposition that E is separable. $\qquad\square$

Theorem 27 *The following are separable metric spaces:*

- (i) *Each nonempty subset of Euclidean space $\mathbf{R}^n$.*
- (ii) *For E a Lebesgue measurable set of real numbers and $1 \le p < \infty$, each nonempty subset of $L^p(E)$.*
- (iii) *Each nonempty subset of $C[a, b]$.*

PROBLEMS

74. Let X be a metric space that contains a finite dense subset D. Show that $X = D$.

75. Show that for a subset D of a metric space X, D is dense in the subspace $\overline{D}$.

76. Show that if two continuous mappings defined on a metric space X take the same values on a dense subset, then they are equal.

77. Show that the product of two separable metric spaces is again separable.

78. Let ρ and σ be equivalent metrics on a nonempty set X. Show that (X, ρ) is separable if and only if (X, σ) is separable.

79. Show that on any uncountable set X there is a metric on X with respect to which X is not separable.

CHAPTER 10

Metric Spaces: Three Fundamental Theorems

Contents

In this chapter we establish three theorems that are widely used in mathematical analysis. These theorems will be essential tools in our later study of linear operators between Banach spaces and Hilbert spaces and of integration on general measure spaces.

10.1 THE ARZELÀ-ASCOLI THEOREM

In many important problems in analysis, given a sequence of continuous real-valued functions it is useful to know that there is a subsequence that converges uniformly. In this section, our main result is the Arzelà–Ascoli Theorem, which provides a criterion for a uniformly bounded sequence of continuous real-valued functions on a compact metric space X to have a uniformly convergent subsequence. After we prove this theorem, we relate it to the general problem of finding criteria for a subset of a metric space to be compact.

For a metric space X, we denote by $C(X)$ the linear space of continuous real-valued functions on X. If X is compact, according to Theorem 22 of the preceding chapter, every continuous function on X takes a maximum value. For a function f in $C(X)$, define

$$\|f\|_{\max} = \max_{x \in X} |f(x)|.$$

This defines a norm, as it did in the special case $X = [a, b]$ we first considered in Chapter 7. This maximum norm induces a metric by

$$\rho_{\max}(g, h) = \|g - h\|_{\max} \text{ for all } g, h \in C(X).$$

We call this metric the **uniform metric** because a sequence in $C(X)$ converges with respect to this metric if and only if it converges uniformly on X. A sequence that is Cauchy with respect to this metric is called **uniformly Cauchy**. The proof of the completeness of $C(X)$ for a general compact metric space X is no different than the proof for the case $X = [a, b]$ (see the proof of Proposition 10 of the preceding chapter).

Proposition 1 *If X is a compact metric space, then $C(X)$ is complete.*

Definition *A collection $\mathcal{F}$ of real-valued functions on a metric space X is said to be* **equicontinuous** *at the point $x \in X$ provided for each $\epsilon > 0$, there is a $\delta > 0$ such that for every $f \in \mathcal{F}$ and $x' \in X$,*

$$\text{if } \rho(x', x) < \delta, \text{ then } |f(x') - f(x)| < \epsilon.$$

The collection $\mathcal{F}$ is said to be equicontinuous on X provided it is equicontinuous at every point in X.

Of course, each function in an equicontinuous collecton of functions is continuous and any finite collection of continuous functions is equicontinuous. In general, an infinite collection of continuous functions will not be equicontinuous. For instance, for each natural number n, define $f_n(x) = x^n$ for $0 \le x \le 1$. Then $\{f_n\}$ is a countable collection of continuous functions on $[0, 1]$ that is not equicontinuous at $x = 0$ and is equicontinuous at the other points in $[0, 1]$.

Example For $M \ge 0$, let $\mathcal{F}$ be the collection of continuous real-valued functions on the closed, bounded interval $[a, b]$ that are differentiable on the open interval (a, b) and for which

$$|f'| \le M \text{ on } (a, b)$$

We infer from the the Mean Value Theorem that

$$|f(u) - f(v)| \le M \cdot |u - v| \text{ for all } u, v \in [a, b].$$

Therefore $\mathcal{F}$ is equicontinuous since, regarding the criterion for equicontinuity at each point in X, $\delta = \epsilon / M$ responds to the $\epsilon > 0$, challenge.

A sequence $\{f_n\}$ of real-valued functions on a set X is said to be **pointwise bounded** provided for each $x \in X$, the sequence $\{f_n(x)\}$ is bounded and is said to be **uniformly bounded** on X provided there is some $M \ge 0$ for which

$$|f_n| \le M \text{ on } X \text{ for all } n.$$

Lemma 2 (The Arzelà–Ascoli Lemma) *Let X be a separable metric space and $\{f_n\}$ an equicontinuous sequence in $C(X)$ that is pointwise bounded. Then a subsequence of $\{f_n\}$ converges pointwise on all of X to a real-valued function f on X.*

Proof Let $\{x_j\}_{j=1}^{\infty}$ be an enumeration of a dense subset D of X. The sequence of real numbers defined by $n \mapsto f_n(x_1)$ is bounded. Therefore, by the Bolzano-Weierstrass Theorem, this sequence has a convergent subsequence, that is, there is a strictly increasing sequence of integers $\{s(1, n)\}$ and a number a_1 for which

$$\lim_{n \to \infty} f_{s(1,n)}(x_1) = a_1.$$

Using the same argument, the sequence defined by $n \mapsto f_{s(1,n)}(x_2)$ is bounded and therefore there is a subsequence $\{s(2, n)\}$ of $\{s(1, n)\}$ and a number a_2 for which $\lim_{n \to \infty} f_{s(2,n)}(x_2) = a_2$. We inductively continue this selection process to obtain a countable collection of strictly increasing sequences of natural numbers $\{\{s(j,n)\}\}_{j=1}^{\infty}$ and a sequence of numbers $\{a_j\}$ such that for each j,

$$\{s(j+1,n)\} \text{ is a subsequence of } \{s(j,n)\} \text{ and } \lim_{n \to \infty} f_{s(j,n)}(x_j) = a_j.$$

For each index j, define $f(x_j) = a_j$. Consider the "diagonal" subsequence $\{f_{n_k}\}$ obtained by setting $n_k = s(k,k)$ for each index k. For each j, $\{n_k\}_{k=j}^{\infty}$ is a subsequence of the j-th subsequence of natural numbers selected above and therefore

$$\lim_{k \to \infty} f_{n_k}(x_j) = a_j = f(x_j).$$

Thus $\{f_{n_k}\}$ converges pointwise on D to f.

For notational convenience, assume the whole sequence of $\{f_n\}$ converges pointwise on D to f. Let x_0 be any point in X. We claim that $\{f_n(x_0)\}$ is Cauchy. Indeed, let $\epsilon > 0$. By the equicontinuity of $\{f_n\}$ at x_0, we may choose $\delta > 0$ such that $|f_n(x) - f_n(x_0)| < \epsilon/3$ for all indices n and all $x \in X$ for which $\rho(x, x_0) < \delta$. Since D is dense, there is a point $x \in D$ such that $\rho(x, x_0) < \delta$. Moreover, since $\{f_n(x)\}$ converges, it must be a Cauchy sequence, and so we may choose N so large that

$$|f_n(x) - f_m(x)| < \epsilon/3 \text{ for all } m, n \geq N.$$

Then for all $m, n \geq N$,

$$|f_n(x_0) - f_m(x_0)| \leq |f_n(x_0) - f_n(x)| + |f_n(x) - f_m(x)| \\ + |f_m(x_0) - f_m(x)| < \epsilon/3 + \epsilon/3 + \epsilon/3 = \epsilon.$$

Thus $\{f_n(x_0)\}$ is a Cauchy sequence of real numbers. Since $\mathbf{R}$ is complete, $\{f_n(x_0)\}$ converges. Denote the limit by $f(x_0)$. The sequence $\{f_n\}$ converges pointwise on all of X to $f: X \to \mathbf{R}$. $\qquad \square$

We proved that a continuous real-valued function on a compact metric space is uniformly continuous. The exact same proof shows that if X is a compact metric space and $\mathcal{F}$ is an equicontinuous collection of real-valued functions on X, then $\mathcal{F}$ is **uniformly equicontinuous** in the sense that for each $\epsilon > 0$, there is a $\delta > 0$ such that for $u, v \in X$ and any $f \in \mathcal{F}$,

$$\text{if } \rho(u, v) < \delta, \text{ then } |f(u) - f(v)| < \epsilon.$$

The Arzelà–Ascoli Theorem *Let X be a compact metric space and $\{f_n\}$ a uniformly bounded, equicontinuous sequence of real-valued functions on X. Then $\{f_n\}$ has a subsequence that converges uniformly on X to a continuous function f on X.*

Proof Since X is a compact metric space, according to Proposition 24 of the preceding chapter, it is separable. The Arzelà-Ascoli Lemma tells us that a subsequence of $\{f_n\}$ converges pointwise on all of X to a real-valued function f. For notational convenience, assume the whole sequence $\{f_n\}$ converges pointwise on X. Therefore, in particular, for each x in X, $\{f_n(x)\}$ is a Cauchy sequence of real numbers. We use this and equicontinuity to show that $\{f_n\}$ is a Cauchy sequence in $C(X)$.

Let $\epsilon > 0$. By the uniform equicontinuity of $\{f_n\}$ on X, there is a $\delta > 0$ such that for all n,

$$|f_n(u) - f_n(v)| < \epsilon/3 \text{ for all } u, v \in X \text{ such that } \rho(u, v) < \delta. \tag{1}$$

Since X is a compact metric space, according to Theorem 16 of the preceding chapter, it is totally bounded. Therefore there are a finite number of points $x_1, \ldots, x_k$ in X for which X is covered by $\{B(x_i, \delta)\}_{i=1}^{k}$. For $1 \leq i \leq k$, $\{f_n(x_i)\}$ is Cauchy, so there is an index N such that

$$|f_n(x_i) - f_m(x_i)| < \epsilon/3 \text{ for } 1 \leq i \leq k \text{ and all } n, m \geq N. \tag{2}$$

Now for any x in X, there is an i, $1 \leq i \leq k$, such that $\rho(x, x_i) < \delta$, and therefore for $n, m \geq N$,

$$|f_n(x) - f_m(x)| \leq |f_n(x) - f_n(x_i)| + |f_n(x_i) - f_m(x_i)|$$
$$+ |f_m(x_i) - f_m(x)| < \epsilon/3 + \epsilon/3 + \epsilon/3 = \epsilon.$$

Thus $\{f_n\}$ is uniformly Cauchy. Therefore, since $C(X)$ is complete, $\{f_n\}$ converges uniformly on X to a continuous function. $\square$

We proved that a metric space is compact if and only if it is sequentially compact. Furthermore, for a subspace K of Euclidean space $\mathbf{R}^n$, the Heine-Borel Theorem tells us that K is compact if and only if K is a closed, bounded subset of $\mathbf{R}^n$. In a general metric space, being closed and bounded is a necessary condition for compactness (see Problem 1), but it is not sufficient. For example, the closed unit ball $\{f \in C[0, 1] \mid \|f\|_{\max} \leq 1\}$ of $C[0, 1]$ is a closed, bounded subset of $C[0, 1]$ which fails to be sequentially compact. Indeed, the sequence $\{f_n\}$, defined by $f_n(x) = x^n$ on $[0, 1]$ for all n, fails to have a subsequence that converges uniformly to a continuous function on $[0, 1]$. The Arzelà-Ascoli Theorem may be reformulated as a criterion for the determination of the closed, bounded subsets of $C(X)$ that are compact.

Theorem 3 *Let X be a compact metric space and $\mathcal{F}$ a subset of $C(X)$. Then $\mathcal{F}$ is a compact subspace of $C(X)$ if and only if $\mathcal{F}$ is closed, uniformly bounded, and equicontinuous.*

Proof First suppose that $\mathcal{F}$ is closed, bounded, and equicontinuous. Let $\{f_n\}$ be a sequence in $\mathcal{F}$. According to the Arzelà-Ascoli Theorem, a subsequence of $\{f_n\}$ converges uniformly to a function in $f \in C(X)$. Since $\mathcal{F}$ is closed, f belongs to $\mathcal{F}$. Thus $\mathcal{F}$ is a sequentially compact metric space and therefore is compact.

Now assume $\mathcal{F}$ is compact. We leave it as an exercise to show that $\mathcal{F}$ is bounded and is a closed subset of $C(X)$. We argue by contradiction to show that $\mathcal{F}$ is equicontinuous. Suppose that $\mathcal{F}$ is not equicontinuous at a point x in X. Then there is an $\epsilon_0 > 0$ such that for each natural number n, there is a function in $\mathcal{F}$ that we label f_n and a point X we label x_n for which

$$|f_n(x_n) - f_n(x)| \geq \epsilon_0 \text{ while } \rho(x_n, x) < 1/n. \tag{3}$$

Since $\mathcal{F}$ is a compact metric space, it is sequentially compact. Therefore there is a subsequence $\{f_{n_k}\}$ that converges uniformly on X to a continuous function f. Choose an index K such that $\rho_{\max}(f, f_{n_k}) < \epsilon_0/3$ for $k \geq K$. We infer from (3) that for $k \geq K$,

$$|f(x_{n_k}) - f(x)| > \epsilon_0/3 \text{ while } \rho(x_{n_k}, x) < 1/n_k. \tag{4}$$

This contradicts the continuity of f at the point x. Therefore $\mathcal{F}$ is equicontinuous. $\square$

Remark *The proof of the Arzelà–Ascoli Lemma is very similar to the proof we provided in Chapter 7 of Helley's Theorem. The common technique underlying both proofs is called a Cantor diagonalization argument (see Problem 14).*

Remark *The forthcoming Riesz's Theorem of Chapter 13 tells us that the closed unit ball of a normed linear space is compact if and only if the linear space is finite dimensional. Therefore, given a particular infinite dimensional normed linear space, it is interesting to characterize the closed, bounded subsets that are compact. The compactness criterion provided by the Arzelà-Ascoli Theorem for subsets of $C(X)$ has a ℓ^p counterpart. It is not difficult to show that, for $1 \le p < \infty$, a closed, bounded subset of ℓ^p is compact if and only if it is equisummable in the sense that for each $\epsilon > 0$, there is an index N for which*

$$\sum_{k=N}^{\infty} |x_k|^p < \epsilon \text{ for all } x = \{x_n\} \in S.$$

PROBLEMS

1. Let E be a compact subspace of a metric space Y. Show that E is a closed, bounded subset of Y.

2. Show that an equicontinuous sequence of real-valued functions on a compact metric space is pointwise bounded if and only if it is uniformly bounded.

3. Show that an equicontinuous family of continuous functions on a compact metric space is uniformly equicontinuous.

4. Let X be a metric space and $\{f_n\}$ a sequence in $C(X)$ that converges uniformly on X to $f \in C(X)$. Show that $\{f_n\}$ is equicontinuous.

5. A real-valued function f on $[0, 1]$ is said to be Hölder continuous of order α provided there is a constant C for which

$$|f(x) - f(y)| \le C|x - y|^{\alpha} \text{ for all } x, y \in [0, 1].$$

   Define the Hölder norm

$$\|f\|_{\alpha} = \max\left\{|f(x)| + |f(x) - f(y)|/|x - y|^{\alpha} \mid x, y \in [0, 1], x \neq y\right\}.$$

   Show that for $0 < \alpha \le 1$, the set of functions for which $\|f\|_{\alpha} \le 1$ has compact closure as a subset of $C[0,1]$.

6. Let X be a compact metric space and $\mathcal{F}$ a subset of $C(X)$. Show that $\mathcal{F}$ is equicontinuous if and only if its closure in $C(X)$, $\overline{\mathcal{F}}$, is equicontinuous. Conclude that a subset of $C(X)$ has compact closure if and only if it is equicontinuous and uniformly bounded.

7. For a closed, bounded interval $[a, b]$, let $\{f_n\}$ be a sequence in $C[a, b]$. If $\{f_n\}$ is equicontinuous, does $\{f_n\}$ necessarily have a uniformly convergent subsequence? If $\{f_n\}$ is uniformly bounded, does $\{f_n\}$ necessarily have a uniformly convergent subsequence?

8. Let X be a compact metric space and Y be a general metric space. Denote by $C(X, Y)$ the set of continuous mappings from X to Y. State and prove a version of the Arzelà-Ascoli Theorem for a sequence in $C(X, Y)$ in which the assumption that $\{f_n\}$ is pointwise bounded is replaced by the assumption that for each $x \in X$, the closure of the set $\{f_n(x) \mid n \text{ a natural number}\}$ is a compact subspace of Y.

9. Let $\{f_n\}$ be an equicontinuous, uniformly bounded sequence of continuous real-valued functions on $\mathbf{R}$. Show that there is a subsequence of $\{f_n\}$ that converges pointwise on $\mathbf{R}$ to a continuous function on $\mathbf{R}$ and that the convergence is uniform on each bounded subset of $\mathbf{R}$.

10. For $1 \le p < \infty$, show that a subspace of ℓ^p is compact if and only if it is closed, bounded, and equisummable.

11. For a sequence of nonnegative real numbers $\{c_n\}$, let S be the subset of ℓ^2 consisting of those $x = \{x_n\} \in \ell^2$ such that $|x_n| \le c_n$ for all n. Show that S is equisummable if $\{c_n\}$ belongs to ℓ^2.

12. For $1 \le p \le \infty$, show that the closed unit ball in the Banach space ℓ^p is not compact.

13. For $1 \le p \le \infty$, show that the closed unit ball in the Banach space $L^p[0, 1]$ is not compact.

14. Let S be a countable set and $\{f_n\}$ a sequence of real-valued functions on S that is pointwise bounded on S. Show that there is a subsequence of $\{f_n\}$ that converges pointwise on S to a real-valued function.

10.2 THE BAIRE CATEGORY THEOREM

Let E be a subset of a metric space X. A point $x \in E$ is called an **interior point** of E provided there is an open ball centered at x that is contained in E: the collection of interior points of E is called the **interior** of E and denoted by int E. A point $x \in X \sim E$ is called an **exterior point** of E provided there is an open ball centered at x that is contained in $X \sim E$: the collection of exterior points of E is called the **exterior** of E and denoted by ext E. If a point $x \in X$ has the property that every ball centered at x contains points in E and points in $X \sim E$, it is called a **bounday point** of E: the collection of boundary points of E is called the **boundary** of E and denoted by bd E. We leave it as an exercise to verify that for any subset E of X:

$$X = \text{int } E \cup \text{ext } E \cup \text{bd } E \text{ and the union is disjoint.} \tag{5}$$

Recall that a subset of A of a metric space X is said to be **dense** (in X) provided every nonempty open subset of X contains a point on A. We call a subset of a metric space **hollow** (in X) provided it has empty interior.[1] Observe that for a subset E of a metric space X,

$$E \text{ is hollow in } X \text{ if and only if its complement, } X \sim E, \text{ is dense in } X. \tag{6}$$

For a metric space X, a point $x \in X$ and $0 < r_1 < r_2$, we have the inclusion $\overline{B}(x, r_1) \subseteq B(x, r_2)$. From the continuity of the metric we infer that $\overline{B}(x, r_1)$ is closed and it contains $B(x, r_1)$. Thus the closure of $B(x, r_1)$ is contained in $B(x, r_2)$. Therefore, if $\mathcal{O}$ is an open subset of a metric space X, for each point $x \in \mathcal{O}$, there is an open ball centered at x whose closure is contained in $\mathcal{O}$.

The Baire Category Theorem *Let X be a complete metric space.*

(i) *Let $\{\mathcal{O}_n\}_{n=1}^\infty$ be a countable collection of open dense subsets of X. Then the intersection $\bigcap_{n=1}^\infty \mathcal{O}_n$ also is dense.*

(ii) *Let $\{F_n\}_{n=1}^\infty$ be a countable collection of closed hollow subsets of X. Then the union $\bigcup_{n=1}^\infty F_n$ also is hollow.*

Proof A set is dense if and only if its complement is hollow. A set is open if and only if its complement is closed. We therefore infer from De Morgan's Identities that (i) and (ii) are equivalent. We establish (i). Let x_0 belong to X and $r_0 > 0$. We must show that $B(x_0, r_0)$ contains a point of $\bigcap_{n=1}^\infty \mathcal{O}_n$. The set $B(x_0, r_0) \cap \mathcal{O}_1$ is nonempty since $\mathcal{O}_1$ is dense in X.

---

[1] The adjective "hollow" was suggested by Adam Ross.

Let x_1 belong to the open set $B(x_0, r_0) \cap \mathcal{O}_1$. Choose $r_1, 0 < r_1 < 1$, for which, if we define $B_1 = B(x_1, r_1)$, then

$$\overline{B}_1 \subseteq B(x_0, r_0) \cap \mathcal{O}_1. \tag{7}$$

Suppose n is a natural number and the descending collection of open balls $\{B_k\}_{k=1}^n$ has been chosen with the property that for $1 \le k \le n$, B_k has radius less than $1/k$ and $\overline{B}_k \subseteq \mathcal{O}_k$. The set $B_n \cap \mathcal{O}_{n+1}$ is nonempty since $\mathcal{O}_{n+1}$ is dense in X. Let x_{n+1} belong to the open set $B(x_n, r_n) \cap \mathcal{O}_n$. Choose $r_{n+1}, 0 < r_{n+1} < 1/(n+1)$, for which, if we define $B_{n+1} = B(x_{n+1}, r_{n+1})$, $\overline{B}_{n+1} \subseteq B_n \cap \mathcal{O}_{n+1}$. This inductively defines a contracting sequence of closed sets $\{\overline{B}_n\}_{n=1}^\infty$ with the property that for each n, $\overline{B}_n \subseteq \mathcal{O}_n$. The metric space X is complete. We therefore infer from the Cantor Intersection Theorem that $\bigcap_{n=1}^\infty \overline{B}_n$ is nonempty. Let x_* belong to this intersection. Then x_* belongs to $\bigcap_{n=1}^\infty \mathcal{O}_n$. On the other hand, by (7), x_* also belongs to $B(x_0, r_0)$. This completes the proof of (i). $\square$

A subset E of a metric space X is called **nowhere dense** provided its closure $\overline{E}$ is hollow. A subset E of X is nowhere dense if and only if for each open subset $\mathcal{O}$ of X, $E \cap \mathcal{O}$ is not dense in $\mathcal{O}$ (see Problem 16). The Baire Category Theorem has the following equivalent formulation: In a complete metric space, the union of a countable collection of nowhere dense sets is hollow.

Corollary 4 *Let X be a complete metric space and $\{F_n\}_{n=1}^\infty$ a countable collection of closed subsets of X. If $\bigcup_{n=1}^\infty F_n$ has nonempty interior, then at least one of the F_n's has nonempty interior. In particular, if $X = \bigcup_{n=1}^\infty F_n$, then at least one of the F_n's has nonempty interior.*

Corollary 5 *Let X be a complete metric space and $\{F_n\}_{n=1}^\infty$ a countable collection of closed subsets of X. Then $\bigcup_{n=1}^\infty \operatorname{bd} F_n$ is hollow.*

Proof We leave it as an exercise to show that for any closed subset E of X, the boundary of E, $\operatorname{bd} E$, is hollow. The boundary of any subset of X is closed. Therefore, for each natural number n, $\operatorname{bd} F_n$ is closed and hollow. According to the Baire Category Theorem, $\bigcup_{n=1}^\infty \operatorname{bd} F_n$ is hollow. $\square$

Theorem 6 *Let $\mathcal{F}$ be a family of continuous real-valued functions on a complete metric space X that is pointwise bounded in the sense that for each $x \in X$, there is a constant M_x for which*

$$|f(x)| \le M_x \text{ for all } f \in \mathcal{F}.$$

Then there is a nonempty open subset $\mathcal{O}$ of X on which $\mathcal{F}$ is uniformly bounded in the sense that there is a constant M for which

$$|f| \le M \text{ on } \mathcal{O} \text{ for all } f \in \mathcal{F}. \tag{8}$$

Proof For each index n, define $E_n = \{x \in X \mid |f(x)| \le n \text{ for all } f \in \mathcal{F}\}$. Then E_n is closed since each function in $\mathcal{F}$ is continuous and the interection of a collection of closed sets is closed. Since $\mathcal{F}$ is pointwise bounded, for each $x \in X$, there is an index n such that $|f(x)| \le n$ for all $f \in \mathcal{F}$; that is, x belongs to E_n. Hence $X = \bigcup_{n=1}^\infty E_n$. Since X is a complete metric space, we conclude from Corollary 4 that there is a natural number n for which E_n contains an open ball $B(x, r)$. Thus (8) holds for $\mathcal{O} = B(x, r)$ and $M = n$. $\square$

We have seen that if a sequence of continuous real-valued functions converges uniformly, then the limit function is continuous and this is false for pointwise convergence. However, under pointwise convergence to a real-valued function of a sequence of continuous real-valued functions on a complete metric space, the limit function is continuous at each point in a dense subset of its domain.

Theorem 7 *Let X be a complete metric space and $\{f_n\}$ a sequence of continuous real-valued functions on X that converges pointwise on X to the real-valued function f. Then there is a dense subset D of X for which $\{f_n\}$ is equicontinuous and f is continuous at each point in D.*

Proof Let m and n be natural numbers, Define

$$E(m, n) = \{x \in X \mid \ |f_j(x) - f_k(x)| \leq 1/m \text{ for all } j, k \geq n\}.$$

Since each function $x \mapsto |f_j(x) - f_k(x)|$ is continuous, the set $E(m, n)$, being the intersection of a collection of closed sets, is closed. According to Corollary 5,

$$D = X \sim \left[\bigcup_{n,m \in \mathbf{N}} \text{bd } E_{m,n} \right]$$

is dense in X. Observe that if n and m are natural numbers and the point x in D belongs to $E(m, n)$, then x belongs to the interior of $E(m, n)$. We claim that $\{f_n\}$ is equicontinuous at each point of D. Indeed, let x_0 belong to D. Let $\epsilon > 0$. Choose a natural number m for which $1/m < \epsilon/4$. Since $\{f_n(x_0)\}$ converges to a real number, $\{f_n(x_0)\}$ is Cauchy. Choose a natural number N for which

$$|f_j(x_0) - f_k(x_0))| \leq 1/m \text{ for all } j, k \geq N. \tag{9}$$

Therefore x_0 belongs to $E_{m, N}$. As we observed above, x_0 belongs to the interior of $E(m, N)$. Choose $r > 0$ such that $B(x_0, r) \subseteq E(m, N)$, that is,

$$|f_j(x) - f_k(x))| \leq 1/m \text{ for all } j, k \geq N \text{ and all } x \in B(x_0, r). \tag{10}$$

The function f_N is continuous at x_0. Therefore there is a $\delta, 0 < \delta < r$, for which

$$|f_N(x) - f_N(x_0)| < 1/m \text{ for all } x \in B(x_0, \delta). \tag{11}$$

Observe that for every point $x \in X$ and natural number j,

$$f_j(x) - f_j(x_0) = [f_j(x) - f_N(x)] + [f_N(x) - f_N(x_0)] + [f_N(x_0) - f_j(x_0)].$$

We infer from (9), (10), (11), and the triangle inequality that

$$|f_j(x) - f_j(x_0)| \leq 3/m < [3/4]\epsilon \text{ for all } j \geq N \text{ and all } x \in B(x_0, \delta). \tag{12}$$

The finite family of continuous functions $\{f_j\}_{j=1}^{N-1}$ is clearly equicontinuous at x_0. We therefore infer from (12) that $\{f_n\}$ is equicontinuous at x_0. This implies continuity at x_0. Indeed, take the limit as $j \to \infty$ in (12) to obtain

$$|f(x) - f(x_0)| < \epsilon \text{ and all } x \in B(x_0, \delta). \tag{13}$$

$\square$

Remark *There is standard terminology associated with the ideas of this section. A subset E of a metric space X is said to be of the* **first category** *(or meager) if E is the union of a countable collection of nowhere dense subsets of X. A set that is not of the first category is said to be of the* **second category** *(or nonmeager), and the complement of a set of first category is called* **residual** *(or co-meager). The Baire Category Theorem may also be rephrased as follows: an open subset of a complete metric space is of the second category.*

Remark *The consequences of the Baire Category Theorem are surprisingly varied. In Chapter 13, we use Theorem 6 to prove the Open Mapping Theorem and the Uniform Boundedness Principle, two cornerstones for the study of linear functionals and operators. In Chapter 18, we use Theorem 7 to prove the Vitali-Hahn-Saks Theorem regarding the convergence of measures, an essential ingredient in the description of weak convergence in $L^1(E)$. In Problems 20 and 21, two interesting properties of continuous and differentiable functions are deduced from the Baire Category Theorem.*

PROBLEMS

15. Let E be a subset of a metric space X. Show that bd E is closed. Also show that if E is closed, then the interior of bd E is empty.

16. In a metric space X, show that a subset E is nowhere dense if and only if for each open subset $\mathcal{O}$ of X, $E \cap \mathcal{O}$ is not dense in $\mathcal{O}$.

17. In a complete metric space X, is the union of a countable collection of nowhere dense sets also nowhere dense?

18. Let $\mathcal{O}$ be an open subset and F be a closed subset of a metric space X. Show that both $\overline{\mathcal{O}} \sim \mathcal{O}$ and $F \sim \text{int } F$ are closed and hollow.

19. In a complete metric space, is the union of a countable collection of sets of the first category also of the first category?

20. Let F_n be the subset of $C[0, 1]$ consisting of functions for which there is a point x_0 in $[0, 1]$ such that $|f(x) - f(x_0)| \leq n|x - x_0|$ for all $x \in [0, 1]$. Show that F_n is closed. Show that F_n is hollow by observing that for $f \in C[0, 1]$ and $r > 0$ there a piecewise linear function $g \in C[0, 1]$ for which $\rho_{\max}(f, g) < r$ and the the left-hand and right-hand derivatives of g on $[0, 1]$ are greater than $n + 1$. Conclude that $C[0, 1] \neq \bigcup_{n=1}^{\infty} F_n$ and show that each $h \in C[0, 1] \sim \bigcup_{n=1}^{\infty} F_n$ fails to be differentiable at any point in $(0, 1)$.

21. Let f be a real-valued function on a metric space X. Show that the set of points at which f is continuous is the intersection of a countable collection of open sets. Conclude that there is not a real-valued function on **R** that is continuous just at the rational numbers.

22. For each natural number n, show that in $[0, 1]$ there is a nowhere dense closed set that has Lebesgue measure $1 - 1/n$. Use this to construct a set of the first category in $[0, 1]$ that has measure 1.

23. A point x in a metric space X is called isolated provided the singleton set $\{x\}$ is open in X.

   (i) Prove that a complete metric space without isolated points has an uncountable number of points.

   (ii) Use part (i) to prove that $[0, 1]$ is uncountable. Compare this with the proof that $[0, 1]$ is uncountable because it has positive Lebesgue measure.

(iii) Show that if X is a complete metric space without isolated points and $\{F_n\}_{n=1}^{\infty}$ is a countable collection of closed hollow sets, then $X \sim \bigcup_{n=1}^{\infty} F_n$ is dense and uncountable.

24. Let E be a subset of a complete metric space X. Verify the following assertions.

   (i)   If $X \sim E$ is dense and F is a closed set contained in E, then F is nowhere dense.

   (ii) If E and $X \sim E$ are both dense, then at most one of them is the union of a countable collection of closed sets.

   (iii) The set of rational numbers in $[0, 1]$ is not the intersection of a countable collection of open sets.

25. Show that under the hypotheses of Theorem 6 there is a dense open set $\mathcal{O} \subset X$ such that each $x \in \mathcal{O}$ has a neighborhood U on which $\mathcal{F}$ is uniformly bounded.

26. By Hölder's Inequality, we have $L^2[a, b] \subseteq L^1[a, b]$. Show that the set $L^2[a, b]$, considered as a subset of the complete metric space $L^1[a, b]$, is of the first category.

27. Let f be a continuous real-valued function on $\mathbf{R}$ with the property that for each real number x, $\lim_{n \to \infty} f(nx) = 0$. Show that $\lim_{x \to \infty} f(x) = 0$.

28. Let f be a continuous real-valued function on $\mathbf{R}$ that has derivatives of all orders. Suppose that for each real number x, there is an index $n = n(x)$ for which $f^{(n)}(x) = 0$. Show that f is a polynomial. (Hint: Apply the Baire Category Theorem twice.)

10.3   THE BANACH CONTRACTION PRINCIPLE

Definition *A point x in X is called a* **fixed point** *of the mapping $T \colon X \to X$ provided* $T(x) = x$.

We are interested here in finding assumptions on a mapping that ensures it has a fixed point. Of course, a mapping may or may not have any fixed points. For instance, the mapping $T \colon \mathbf{R} \to \mathbf{R}$ defined by $T(x) = x + 1$ certainly has no fixed points.

A fixed point of a real-valued function of a real variable corresponds to a point in the plane at which the graph of the function intersects the diagonal line $y = x$. This observation provides the geometric insight for the most elementary result regarding the existence of fixed points: Let $[a, b]$ be a closed, bounded interval in $\mathbf{R}$ and suppose that the image of the continuous function $f \colon [a, b] \to \mathbf{R}$ is contained in $[a, b]$. Then $f \colon [a, b] \to \mathbf{R}$ has a fixed point. This follows from the Intermediate Value Theorem by observing that if we define $g(x) = f(x) - x$ for x in $[a, b]$, then $g(a) \geq 0$ and $g(b) \leq 0$, so that $g(x_0) = 0$ for some x_0 in $[a, b]$, which means that $f(x_0) = x_0$.

A subset K of $\mathbf{R}^n$ is said to be convex provided whenever u and v belong to K, the segment $\{tu + (1 - t)v \mid 0 \leq t \leq 1\}$ is contained in K. The preceding result generalizes to mappings on subsets of Euclidean spaces as follows: If K is a compact, convex subset of $\mathbf{R}^n$ and the mapping $T \colon K \to K$ is continuous, then T has a fixed point. This is called Brouwer's Fixed Point Theorem.[2] Here we will prove an elementary fixed point result called the Banach Contraction Principle in which there is a more restrictive assumption on the mapping but a very general assumption on the underlying space.

---

[2] An analytic proof of this theorem may be found in *Linear Operators, Part I* (pp. 467–469) by Nelson Dunford and Jacob Schwartz [DS71].

Definition *A mapping T from a metric space (X, ρ) into itself is said to be* **Lipschitz** *provided there is a number $c \geq 0$, called a Lipschitz constant for the mapping, for which*

$$\rho(T(u), T(v)) \leq c\,\rho(u, v) \text{ for all } u, v \in X.$$

If $c < 1$, the Lipschitz mapping is called a **contraction**.

The Banach Contraction Principle *Let X be a complete metric space and the mapping $T: X \to X$ be a contraction. Then $T: X \to X$ has exactly one fixed point.*

Proof Let c be a number with $0 \leq c < 1$ that is a Lipschitz constant for the mapping T. Select a point in X and label it x_0. Now define the sequence $\{x_k\}$ inductively by defining $x_1 = T(x_0)$ and, if k is a natural number such that x_k is defined, defining $x_{k+1} = T(x_k)$. The sequence $\{x_n\}$ is properly defined since $T(X)$ is a subset of X. We will show that this sequence converges to a fixed point of T.

Indeed, observe that by the definition of the sequence and the Lipschitz constant c, it follows that

$$\rho(x_2, x_1) = \rho(T(x_1), T(x_0)) = \rho(T(T(x_0)), T(x_0)) \leq c\,\rho(T(x_0), x_0),$$

and that

$$\rho(x_{k+1}, x_k) = \rho(T(x_k), T(x_{k-1})) \leq c\,\rho(x_k, x_{k-1}) \text{ if } k \geq 2.$$

Using an induction argument, we infer from these two inequalities that

$$\rho(x_{k+1}, x_k) \leq c^k \rho(T(x_0), x_0) \text{ for every natural number } k.$$

Hence, if m and k are natural numbers with $m > k$, from the triangle inequality for the metric ρ and the geometric sum formula,[3] it follows that

$$\rho(x_m, x_k) \leq \rho(x_m, x_{m-1}) + \rho(x_{m-1}, x_{m-2}) + \cdots + \rho(x_{k+1}, x_k)$$

$$\leq [c^{m-1} + c^{m-2} + \cdots + c^k]\rho(T(x_0), x_0)$$

$$= c^k[1 + c + \cdots + c^{m-1-k}]\rho(T(x_0), x_0)$$

$$= c^k \cdot \frac{1 - c^{m-k}}{1 - c} \cdot \rho(T(x_0), x_0).$$

Consequently, since $0 \leq c < 1$,

$$\rho(x_m, x_k) \leq \frac{c^k}{1 - c} \cdot \rho(T(x_0), x_0) \text{ if } m > k.$$

3

$$\sum_{k=0}^{n} c^k = \frac{1 - c^{n+1}}{1 - c} \text{ if } c \neq 1.$$

But $\lim_{k \to \infty} c^k = 0$, and hence, from the preceding inequality we conclude that $\{x_k\}$ is a Cauchy sequence.

By assumption, the metric space X is complete. Thus there is a point x in X to which the sequence $\{x_k\}$ converges. Since T is Lipschitz, it is continuous. Therefore

$$T(x) = \lim_{k \to \infty} T(x_k) = \lim_{k \to \infty} x_{k+1} = x.$$

Thus the mapping $T: X \to X$ has at least one fixed point. It remains to check that there is only one fixed point. But if u and v are points in X such that $T(u) = u$ and $T(v) = v$, then

$$0 \le \rho(u, v) = \rho(T(u), T(v)) \le c\rho(u, v),$$

so that since $0 \le c < 1$, we must have $\rho(u, v) = 0$, that is, $u = v$. Thus there is exactly one fixed point. $\qquad\square$

The above proof of the Banach Contraction Principle actually proves substantially more than the *existence* of a unique fixed point. *It provides an algorithm for approximating the fixed point.* Indeed, under the assumptions of the Banach Contraction Principle, what has been proven is that if c is a number with $0 \le c < 1$ that is a Lipschitz constant for the mapping $T: X \to X$, and x_0 is any point in X, then (i) the sequence $\{x_k\}$ defined recursively by setting $x_1 = T(x_0)$ and $x_{k+1} = T(x_k)$ for $k \ge 1$ converges to a fixed point x_* of T and (ii)

$$\rho(x_*, x_k) \le \frac{c^k}{1 - c} \cdot \rho(T(x_0), x_0) \text{ for every natural number } k.$$

The Banach Contraction Principle is widely used in the study of nonlinear differential equations. We provide one example of its use. Suppose $\mathcal{O}$ is an open subset of the plane $\mathbf{R}^2$ that contains the point (x_0, y_0). Given a function $g: \mathcal{O} \to \mathbf{R}$, the problem we pose is to find an open interval of real numbers I containing the point x_0 and a differentiable function $f: I \to \mathbf{R}$ such that

$$\begin{aligned} f'(x) &= g(x, f(x)) \text{ for all } x \in I \\ f(x_0) &= y_0. \end{aligned} \tag{14}$$

A very special case of the above equation occurs if g is independent of its second variable, so $g(x, y) = h(x)$. Even in this case, if the image of the function $h: I \to \mathbf{R}$ fails to be an interval, there is no solution of equation (14) (see Problems 42 and 43). On the other hand, if h is continuous, then it follows from the Fundamental Theorem of Differential Calculus that equation (14) has a unique solution given by

$$f(x) = y_0 + \int_{x_0}^{x} h(t)\, dt \text{ for all } x \in I.$$

Therefore for a general continuous real-valued function of two variables g, if a continuous function $f: I \to \mathbf{R}$ has the property that $(x, f(x)) \in \mathcal{O}$ for each $x \in I$, then f is a solution of (14) if and only if

$$f(x) = y_0 + \int_{x_0}^{x} g(t, f(t))\, dt \text{ for all } x \in I. \tag{15}$$

As we will see in the proof of the next theorem, this equivalence between solutions of the differential equation (14) and those of the *integral equation* (15) is the observation that permits us to use fixed point theorems in the study of differential equations.

The Picard Local Existence Theorem *Let $\mathcal{O}$ be an open subset of the plane $\mathbf{R}^2$ containing the point (x_0, y_0). Suppose the function $g: \mathcal{O} \to \mathbf{R}^2$ is continuous and there is a positive number M for which the following Lipschitz property in the second variable holds, uniformly with respect to the first variable:*

$$|g(x, y_1) - g(x, y_2)| \le M|y_1 - y_2| \text{ for all points } (x, y_1) \text{ and } (x, y_2) \text{ in } \mathcal{O}. \quad (16)$$

Then there is an open interval I containing x_0 on which the differential equation (14) has a unique solution.

Proof For ℓ a positive number, define I_ℓ to be the closed interval $[x_0 - \ell, x_0 + \ell]$. In view of the equivalence noted above between solutions of (14) and (15), it suffices to show that ℓ can be chosen so that there is exactly one continuous function $f: I_\ell \to \mathbf{R}$ having the property that

$$f(x) = y_0 + \int_{x_0}^x g(t, f(t)) \, dt \text{ for all } x \in I_\ell.$$

Since $\mathcal{O}$ is open, we may choose positive numbers a and b such that the closed rectangle $R = [x_0 - a, x_0 + a] \times [y_0 - b, y_0 + b]$ is contained in $\mathcal{O}$. Now for each positive number ℓ with $\ell \le a$, define X_ℓ to be the subspace of the metric space $C(I_\ell)$ consisting of those continuous functions $f: I_\ell \to \mathbf{R}$ that have the property that

$$|f(x) - y_0| \le b \text{ for all } x \in I_\ell;$$

that is, the continuous functions on I_ℓ that have a graph contained in the rectangle $I_\ell \times [y_0 - b, y_0 + b]$.

For $f \in X_\ell$, define the function $T(f) \in C(I_\ell)$ by

$$T(f)(x) = y_0 + \int_{x_0}^x g(t, f(t)) \, dt \text{ for all } x \in I_\ell.$$

A solution of the integral equation (15) is simply a fixed point of the mapping $T: X_\ell \to C(I_\ell)$. The strategy of the proof is as follows: Since $C(I_\ell)$ is a complete metric space and X_ℓ is a closed subset of $C(I_\ell)$, X_ℓ is also a complete metric space. We will show that if ℓ is chosen sufficiently small, then

$$T(X_\ell) \subseteq X_\ell \text{ and } T: X_\ell \to X_\ell \text{ is a contraction.}$$

Hence, we infer from the Banach Contraction Principle that $T: X_\ell \to X_\ell$ has a unique fixed point.

In order to choose ℓ so that $T(X_\ell) \subseteq X_\ell$ we first use the compactness of the closed, bounded rectangle R together with the continuity of g to choose a positive number K such that

$$|g(x, y)| \le K \text{ for all points } (x, y) \text{ in } R.$$

Now for $f \in X_\ell$ and $x \in I_\ell$,

$$|T(f)(x) - y_0| = \left| \int_{x_0}^{x} g(t, f(t)) \, dt \right| \le \ell K,$$

so that

$$T(X_\ell) \subseteq X_\ell \text{ provided } \ell K \le b.$$

Observe that for functions $f_1, f_2 \in X_\ell$, and $x \in I_\ell$, we may infer from (16) that

$$|g(x, f_1(x)) - g(x, f_2(x))| \le M \rho_{max}(f_1, f_2).$$

Consequently, using the linearity and monotonicity properties of the integral, we have

$$|T(f_1)(x) - T(f_2)(x)| = \left| \int_{x_0}^{x} [g(t, f_1(t)) - g(t, f_2(t))] dt \right|$$

$$\le |x - x_0| M \rho_{max}(f_1, f_2)$$

$$\le \ell M \rho_{max}(f_1, f_2).$$

This inequality, together with the inclusion $T(X_\ell) \subseteq X_\ell$ provided $\ell K \le b$, implies that

$$T: X_\ell \to X_\ell \text{ is a contraction provided } \ell K \le b \text{ and } \ell M < 1.$$

Define $\ell = \min\{b/K, 1/2M\}$. The Banach Contraction Principle tells us that the mapping $T: X_\ell \to X_\ell$ has a unique fixed point. $\qquad \square$

PROBLEMS

29. Let p be a polynomial. Show that $p: \mathbf{R} \to \mathbf{R}$ is Lipschitz if and only if the degree of p is less than 2.

30. Fix $\alpha > 0$, define $f(x) = \alpha x(1 - x)$ for x in $[0, 1]$.
    (i) For what values of α is $f([0, 1]) \subseteq [0, 1]$?
    (ii) For what values of α is $f([0, 1]) \subseteq [0, 1]$ and $f: [0, 1] \to [0, 1]$ a contraction?

31. Does a mapping of a metric space X into itself that is Lipschitz with Lipschitz constant less than 1 necessarily have a fixed point?

32. Does a mapping of a complete metric space into itself that is Lipschitz with Lipschitz constant 1 necessarily have a fixed point?

33. Let X be a compact metric space and T a mapping from X into itself such that

$$\rho(T(u), T(v)) < \rho(u, v) \text{ for all } u, v \in X.$$

Show that T has a unique fixed point.

34. Define $f(x) = \pi/2 + x - \arctan x$ for all real numbers x. Show that

$$|f(u) - f(v)| < |u - v| \text{ for all } u, v \in \mathbf{R}.$$

Show that f does not have a fixed point. Does this contradict the preceding problem?

35. In Euclidean space $\mathbf{R}^n$ consider the closed unit ball $B = \{x \in \mathbf{R}^n \mid \|x\| \leq 1\}$. Let f map B into B and be Lipschitz with Lipschitz constant 1. Without using the Brouwer Fixed Point Theorem, show that f has a fixed point.

36. Suppose that the mapping $f: \mathbf{R}^n \to \mathbf{R}^n$ is a contraction. Define $g(x) = x - f(x)$ for all x in $\mathbf{R}^n$. Show that the mapping $g: \mathbf{R}^n \to \mathbf{R}^n$ is both one-to-one and onto. Also show that g and its inverse are continuous.

37. Let X be a complete metric space containing the point x_0 and let r be a positive real number. Define $K = \{x \text{ in } X \mid \rho(x, x_0) \leq r\}$. Suppose that the mapping $T: K \to X$ is Lipschitz with Lipschitz constant c. Suppose also that $cr + \rho(T(x_0), x_0) \leq r$. Prove that $T(K) \subseteq K$ and that $T: K \to X$ has a fixed point.

38. Show that if the function $g: \mathbf{R}^2 \to \mathbf{R}$ has continuous first-order partial derivatives, then for each point (x_0, y_0) in $\mathbf{R}^2$ there is a neighborhood $\mathcal{O}$ of (x_0, y_0) on which the Lipschitz assumption (16) holds.

39. In case the function $g: \mathcal{O} \to \mathbf{R}$ has the form $g(x, y) = h(x) + by$, where the function $h: \mathbf{R} \to \mathbf{R}$ is continuous, prove that the following is an explicit formula for the solution of (14):

$$f(x) = e^{b(x-x_0)} y_0 + \int_{x_0}^{x} e^{b(x-t)} h(t) \, dt \text{ for all } x \text{ in } I.$$

40. Consider the differential equation

$$f'(x) = 3[f(x)]^{2/3} \text{ for all } x \in \mathbf{R}$$
$$f(0) = 0.$$

Show that the function $f: \mathbf{R} \to \mathbf{R}$ that is identically 0 is a solution and the function $f: \mathbf{R} \to \mathbf{R}$ defined by $f(x) = 0$, if $x < 0$ and $f(x) = x^3$, if $x \geq 0$, is also a solution. Does this contradict the Picard Existence Theorem?

41. For a positive number ϵ, consider the differential equation

$$f'(x) = (1/\epsilon)[1 + (f(x))^2] \text{ for all } x \in \mathbf{R}$$
$$f(0) = 0.$$

Show that on the interval $I = (-\epsilon(\pi/2), \epsilon(\pi/2))$ there is a unique solution of this differential equation that is defined by $f(x) = \tan(x/\epsilon)$ and there is no solution in an interval strictly containing I.

42. Let I be an open interval in $\mathbf{R}$ and suppose that the function $h: I \to \mathbf{R}$ has the property that there are points $x_1 < x_2$ in I and a number c such that $h(x_1) < c < h(x_2)$ but c does not belong to $h(I)$. Prove that there is no solution to the differential equation (14) by arguing that if $f: I \to \mathbf{R}$ is a solution, then the continuous function $f(x) - cx$ fails to attain a minimum value on the interval $[x_1, x_2]$.

43. Use the preceding exercise to prove the following theorem of Darboux: Let I be an open interval in $\mathbf{R}$ and suppose that the function $f: I \to \mathbf{R}$ is differentiable. Then the image of the derivative $f': I \to \mathbf{R}$ is an interval.

44. State and prove a form of the Picard Existence Theorem for systems of differential equations in the following context: $\mathcal{O}$ is an open subset of $\mathbf{R} \times \mathbf{R}^n$, $\mathbf{g}: \mathcal{O} \to \mathbf{R}^n$ is continuous, the point $(x_0, \mathbf{y}_0)$ is in $\mathcal{O}$, and the system of differential equations is

$$\mathbf{f}'(x) = \mathbf{g}(x, \mathbf{f}(x)) \text{ for all } x \in I$$
$$\mathbf{f}(x_0) = \mathbf{y}_0.$$

(Hint: Approximate g by a Lipschitz mapping and then use the Arzelà-Ascoli Theorem.)

CHAPTER 11

Topological Spaces: General Properties

Contents

We devoted the preceding two chapters to the study of metric spaces. In these spaces, we first used the metric to define an open ball and then used open balls to define open sets. We found that we were able to express a number of concepts solely in terms of the open sets associated with the metric. In the present chapter we study spaces for which the notion of an open set is fundamental: other concepts are defined in terms of open sets. Such spaces are called topological spaces. They are more general than metric spaces. Perhaps you ask: Why not stick to metric spaces? From the viewpoint of analysis the main reason is that it is often necessary to study such concepts as convergence of a sequence or compactness of a set in a setting more general than that provided by a metric space. One immediate example is to consider a collection of real-valued functions on a set. The concept of uniform convergence of a sequence of functions is a metric concept. The concept of pointwise convergence is not a metric concept. Another prominent example arises for a set X that is a normed linear space. The set X, with the metric induced by the norm, is a metric space. With respect to this metric, one has the concept of convergence of a sequence and compactness of a set. But on X there are important concepts, such as weak convergence of a sequence (we studied this in Chapter 8) and weak compactness of a set, which cannot be formulated in the framework of a metric. They can be formulated as topological concepts for a topology on a normed linear space called the weak topology. Furthermore, the comparison of topologies illuminates our understanding of subtleties that arise when considering different modes of sequential convergence.

11.1 OPEN SETS, CLOSED SETS, BASES, AND SUBBASES

Definition *Let X be a nonempty set. A topology $\mathcal{T}$ for X is a collection of subsets of X, called* **open** *sets, possessing the following properties:*

   (i) The entire set X and the empty-set $\emptyset$ are open;

(ii) *The intersection of any finite collection of open sets is open;*

(iii) *The union of any collection of open sets is open.*

A nonempty set X, together wih a topology on X, is called a **topological space**. *For a point x in X, an open set that contains x is called a* **neighborhood** *of x.*

We sometimes denote a topological space by $(X, \mathcal{T})$. Often we are interested in only one topology for a given set of points, and in such cases we sometimes use the symbol X to denote both the set of points and the topological space $(X, \mathcal{T})$. When greater precision is needed, we make explicit the topology.

Proposition 1 *A subset E of a topological space X is open if and only if for each point x in X there is a neighborhood of x that is contained in E.*

Proof This follows immediately from the definition of neighborhood and the property of a topology that the union of a collection of open sets is again open.   □

Metric Topology Consider a metric space (X, ρ). Define a subset $\mathcal{O}$ of X to be open provided for each point $x \in \mathcal{O}$ there is an open ball centered at x that is contained in $\mathcal{O}$. Thus the open sets are unions of collections of open balls. Proposition 1 of Chapter 9 is the assertion that this collection of open sets is a topology for X. We call it the **metric topology** induced by the metric ρ. As a particular case of a metric topology on a set we have the topology we call the Euclidean topology induced on $\mathbf{R}^n$ by the Euclidean metric.[1]

The Discrete Topology Let X be any nonempty set. Define $\mathcal{T}$ to be the collection of all subsets of X. Then $\mathcal{T}$ is a topology for X called the discrete topology. For the discrete topology, every set containing a point is a neighborhood of that point. The discrete topology is induced by the discrete metric.

The Trivial Topology Let X be any nonempty set. Define $\mathcal{T}$ to be the collection of subsets of X consisting of $\emptyset$ and X. Then $\mathcal{T}$ is a topology for X called the trivial topology. For the trivial topology, the only neighborhood of a point is the whole set X.

Topological Subspaces Given a topological space $(X, \mathcal{T})$ and a nonempty subset E of X, we define the inherited topology $\mathcal{S}$ for E to consist of all sets of the form $E \cap \mathcal{O}$ where $\mathcal{O}$ belongs to $\mathcal{T}$. We call the topological space $(E, \mathcal{S})$ a **subspace** of $(X, \mathcal{T})$.

In elementary analysis we define what it means for a subset of $\mathbf{R}$ to be open even if we have no need to use the word "topology." In Chapter 1, we proved that the topological space $\mathbf{R}$ has the property that every open set is the union of a countable disjoint collection of open intervals. In a metric space, every open set is the union of a collection of open balls.

---

[1]Unless otherwise stated, by the topological space $\mathbf{R}^n$ we mean the set $\mathbf{R}^n$ with the Euclidean topology. In the problems we introduce more exotic topologies on $\mathbf{R}$ and $\mathbf{R}^2$ (see Problems 9 for the Sorgenfrey Line and 10 for the Moore Plane).

In a general topological space it is often useful to distinguish a collection of open sets called a **base** for the topology: they are building blocks for the topology.

Definition *For a topological space* (X, T) *and a point* x *in* X, *a collection of neighborhoods of* x, $\mathcal{B}_x$, *is called a* **base for the topology at** x *provided for any neighborhood* $\mathcal{U}$ *of* x, *there is a set* B *in the collection* $\mathcal{B}_x$ *for which* $B \subseteq \mathcal{U}$. *A collection of open sets* $\mathcal{B}$ *is called a* **base for the topology** T *provided it contains a base for the topology at each point.*

Observe that a subcollection of a topology is a base for the topology if and only if every nonempty open set is the union of a subcollection of $\mathcal{B}$. Once a base for a topology is prescribed, the topology is completely defined: it consists of $\emptyset$ and unions of sets belonging to the base. For this reason a topology is often defined by specifying a base. The following proposition describes the properties that a collection of subsets of X must possess in order for it to be a base for a topology.

Proposition 2 *For a nonempty set* X, *let* $\mathcal{B}$ *be a collection of subsets of* X. *Then* $\mathcal{B}$ *is a base for a topology for* X *if and only if*

   (i) $\mathcal{B}$ *covers* X, *that is,* $X = \bigcup_{B \in \mathcal{B}} B$.

   (ii) *if* B_1 *and* B_2 *are in* $\mathcal{B}$ *and* $x \in B_1 \cap B_2$, *then there is a set* B *in* $\mathcal{B}$ *for which* $x \in B \subseteq B_1 \cap B_2$.

The unique topology that has $\mathcal{B}$ *as its base consists of* $\emptyset$ *and unions of subcollections of* $\mathcal{B}$.

Proof Assume $\mathcal{B}$ possesses properties (i) and (ii). Define T to be the collection of unions of subcollections of $\mathcal{B}$ together with $\emptyset$. We claim that T is a topology for X. Indeed, we infer from (i) that the set X is the union of all the sets in $\mathcal{B}$ and therefore it belongs to T. Moreover, it is also clear that the union of a subcollection of T is also a union of a subcollection of $\mathcal{B}$ and therefore belongs to T. It remains to show that if $\mathcal{O}_1$ and $\mathcal{O}_2$ belong to T, then their intersection $\mathcal{O}_1 \cap \mathcal{O}_2$ belongs to T. Indeed, let x belong to $\mathcal{O}_1 \cap \mathcal{O}_2$. Then there are sets B_1 and B_2 in $\mathcal{B}$ such that $x \in B_1 \subseteq \mathcal{O}_1$ and $x \in B_2 \subseteq \mathcal{O}_2$. Using (ii), choose B_x in $\mathcal{B}$ with $x \in B_x \subseteq B_1 \cap B_2$. Then $\mathcal{O}_1 \cap \mathcal{O}_2 = \bigcup_{x \in \mathcal{O}} B_x$, the union of a subcollection of $\mathcal{B}$. Thus T is a topology for which $\mathcal{B}$ is a base. It is unique. We leave the proof of the converse as an exercise. $\square$

A base determines a unique topology. However, in general, a topology has many bases. For instance, the collection of open intervals is a base for the Euclidean topology on $\mathbf{R}$, while the collection of open, bounded intervals with rational endpoints also is a base for this topology.

Example Let (X, T) and (Y, S) be topological spaces. In the Cartesian product $X \times Y$, consider the collection of sets $\mathcal{B}$ consisting of products $\mathcal{O}_1 \times \mathcal{O}_2$, where $\mathcal{O}_1$ is open in X and $\mathcal{O}_2$ is open in Y. We leave it as an exercise to check that $\mathcal{B}$ is a base for a topology on $X \times Y$. The topology is called the **product topology** on $X \times Y$.

Definition *For a topological space* (X, T), *a subcollection* S *of* T *that covers* X *is called a* **subbase** *for the topology* T *provided intersections of finite subcollections of* S *are a base for* T.

Example   Consider a closed, bounded interval $[a, b]$ as a topological space with the topology it inherits from **R**. This space has a subbase consisting of intervals of the type $[a, c)$ or $(c, b]$ for $a < c < b$.

Any collection of subsets S of a nonempty set X that covers X is a subbase for a unique topology on X since it is not difficult to see, using Proposition 2, that intersections of finite subcollections of S is a base.

Definition   *For a subset E of a topological space X, a point $x \in X$ is called a* **point of closure** *of E provided every neighborhood of x contains a point in E. The collection of points of closure of E is called the* **closure** *of E and denoted by $\overline{E}$.*

It is clear that we always have $E \subseteq \overline{E}$. If E contains all of its points of closure, that is, $E = \overline{E}$, the set E is said to be **closed.**

Proposition 3   *For E a subset of a topological space X, its closure $\overline{E}$ is closed. Moreover, $\overline{E}$ is the smallest closed subset of X containing E in the sense that if F is closed and $E \subseteq F$, then $\overline{E} \subseteq F$.*

Proof   The set $\overline{E}$ is closed provided it contains all its points of closure. Let x be a point of closure of $\overline{E}$. Consider a neighborhood $\mathcal{U}_x$ of x. There is a point $x' \in \overline{E} \cap \mathcal{U}_x$. Since x' is a point of closure of E and $\mathcal{U}_x$ is a neighborhood of x', there is a point $x'' \in E \cap \mathcal{U}_x$. Therefore every neighborhood of X contains a point of E and hence $x \in \overline{E}$. So the set $\overline{E}$ is closed. It is clear that if $A \subseteq B$, then $\overline{A} \subseteq \overline{B}$, so that if F is closed and contains E, then $\overline{E} \subseteq \overline{F} = F$. $\square$

Proposition 4   *A subset of a topological space X is open if and only if its complement in X is closed.*

Proof   First suppose E is open in X. Let x be a point of closure of $X \sim E$. Then x cannot belong to E because otherwise there would be a neighborhood x that is contained in E and therefore does not intersect $X \sim E$. Thus x belongs to $X \sim E$ and hence $X \sim E$ is closed. Now suppose $X \sim E$ is closed. Let x belong to E. Then there must be a neighborhood of x that is contained in E, for otherwise every neighborhood of x would contain points in $X \sim E$ and therefore x would be a point of closure of $X \sim E$. Since $X \sim E$ is closed, x would belong to $X \sim E$. This is a contradiction. $\square$

Since $X \sim [X \sim E] = E$, it follows from the preceding proposition that a subset of a topological space X is closed if and only if its complement in X is open. Therefore, by De Morgan's Identities, the collection of closed subsets of a topological space possesses the following properties.

Proposition 5   *Let X be a topological space. The empty-set $\emptyset$ and the whole set X are closed; the union of any finite collection of closed subsets of X is closed; and the intersection of any collection of closed subsets of X is closed.*

PROBLEMS

1. Show that the discrete topology for a nonempty set X is a metric topology.

2. Show that the discrete topology on a set has a unique base.

3. Regarding Proposition 2, show that if $\mathcal{B}$ is a base for a topology, then properties (i) and (ii) hold.

4. Let $\mathcal{T}_1$ and $\mathcal{T}_2$ be topologies for a nonempty set X. Show that $\mathcal{T}_1 = \mathcal{T}_2$ if and only if there are bases $\mathcal{B}_1$ for $\mathcal{T}_1$ and $\mathcal{B}_2$ for $\mathcal{T}_2$ that are related as follows at each point x in X: for each neighborhood $\mathcal{N}_1$ of x belonging to $\mathcal{B}_1$, there is a neighborhood $\mathcal{N}_2$ of x belonging to $\mathcal{B}_2$ for which $\mathcal{N}_2 \subseteq \mathcal{N}_1$ and for each neighborhood $\mathcal{N}_2$ of x belonging to $\mathcal{B}_2$, there is a neighborhood $\mathcal{N}_1$ of x belonging to $\mathcal{B}_1$ for which $\mathcal{N}_1 \subseteq \mathcal{N}_2$.

5. Let E be a subset of a topological space X.
   (i) A point $x \in X$ is called an interior point of E provided there is a neighborhood of x that is contained in E: the collection of interior points of E is called the interior of E and denoted by int E. Show that int E is always open and E is open if and only if $E = $ int E.
   (ii) A point $x \in X$ is called an exterior point of E provided there is a neighborhood of x that is contained in $X \sim E$: the collection of exterior points of E is called the exterior of E and denoted by ext E. Show that ext E is always open and E is open if and only if $\overline{E} \sim E \subseteq$ ext E.
   (iii) A point $x \in X$ is called a boundary point of E provided every neighborhood of x contains points in E and points in $X \sim E$: the collection of boundary points of E is called the boundary of E and denoted by bd E. Show that (i) bd E is always closed, (ii) E is open if and only if $E \cap$ bd $E = \emptyset$, and (iii) E is closed if and only if bd $E \subseteq E$.

6. Let A and B be subsets of a topological space X. Show that if $A \subseteq B$, then $\overline{A} \subseteq \overline{B}$. Also, show that $(\overline{A \cup B}) = \overline{A} \cup \overline{B}$ and $(\overline{A \cap B}) \subseteq \overline{A} \cap \overline{B}$.

7. Let $\mathcal{O}$ be an open subset of a topological space X. For a subset E of X, show that $\mathcal{O}$ is disjoint from E if and only if it is disjoint from $\overline{E}$.

8. For a collection $\mathcal{S}$ of subsets of a nonempty set X, show that there is a topology $\mathcal{T}$ on X that contains the collection $\mathcal{S}$ and has the property that any other topology that contains $\mathcal{S}$ also contains $\mathcal{T}$: it is the topology with the fewest sets that contains $\mathcal{S}$.

9. (The Sorgenfrey Line) Show that the collection of intervals of the form $[a, b)$, where $a < b$, is a base for a topology for the set of real numbers $\mathbf{R}$. The set of real numbers $\mathbf{R}$ with this topology is called the *Sorgenfrey Line*.

10. (The Moore Plane) Consider the upper half plane, $\mathbf{R}^{2,+} = \{(x, y) \in \mathbf{R}^2 \mid y \geq 0.\}$ For points (x, y) with $y > 0$, take as a basic open neighborhood a usual Euclidean open ball centered at (x, y) and contained in the upper half plane. As a basic open neighborhood of a point $(x, 0)$ take the set consisting of the point itself and all the points in an open Euclidean ball in the upper half plane that is tangent to the real line at $(x, 0)$. Show that this collection of sets is a base. The set $\mathbf{R}^{2,+}$ with this topology is called the *Moore Plane*.

11. (Kuratowski 14-subset problem)
    (i) Let E be a subset of a topological space X. Show that at most 14 different sets can be obtained from E by repeated use of complementation and closure.
    (ii) Give an example in $\mathbf{R}^2$ where there are 14 different sets coming from a suitable E.

11.2   THE SEPARATION PROPERTIES

In order to establish interesting results for topological spaces and continuous mappings between such spaces, it is necessary to enrich the rudimentary topological structure. In this section we consider so-called separation properties for a topology on a set X, which ensure that the topology discriminates between certain disjoint pairs of sets and, as a consequence, ensure that there is a robust collection of continuous real-valued functions on X.

We have defined what we mean by a neighborhood of a point in a topological space. For a subset K of a topological space X, by a **neighborhood of K** we mean an open set that contains K. We say that two disjoint subsets A and B of X can be **separated by disjoint neighborhoods** provided there are neighborhoods of A and B, respectively, that are disjoint. For a topological space X, we consider the following four separation properties:

> **The Tychonoff Separation Property** For each two points u and v in X, there is a neighborhood of u that does not contain v and a neighborhood of v that does not contain u.
>
> **The Hausdorff Separation Property** Each two points in X can be separated by disjoint neighborhoods.
>
> **The Regular Separation Property** The Tychonoff separation property holds and, moreover, each closed set and point not in the set can be separated by disjoint neighborhoods.
>
> **The Normal Separation Property** The Tychonoff separation property holds and, moreover, each two disjoint closed sets can be separated by disjoint neighborhoods.

We naturally call a topological space Tychonoff, Hausdorff, regular, or normal, provided it satisfies the respective separation property.

Proposition 6 *A topological space X is a Tychonoff space if and only if every set consisting of a single point is closed.*

Proof Let x be in X. The set $\{x\}$ is closed if and only if $X \sim \{x\}$ is open. Now $X \sim \{x\}$ is open if and only if for each point y in $X \sim \{x\}$ there is a **neighborhood** of y that is contained in $X \sim \{x\}$, that is, there is a neighborhood of y that does not contain x.   □

Proposition 7 *Every metric space is normal.*

Proof Let (X, ρ) be a metric space. Define the distance between a subset F of X and point x in X by

$$\text{dist}(x, F) = \inf \left\{ \rho(x, x') \mid x' \text{ in } F \right\}.$$

Let F_1 and F_2 be closed disjoint subsets of X. Define

$$\mathcal{O}_1 = \left\{ x \text{ in } X \mid \text{dist}(x, F_1) < \text{dist}(x, F_2) \right\} \text{ and } \mathcal{O}_2 = \left\{ x \text{ in } X \mid \text{dist}(x, F_2) < \text{dist}(x, F_1) \right\}.$$

Since the complement of a closed set is open, $\text{dist}(x, F) > 0$ if F is closed and x does not belong to F. Therefore $F_1 \subseteq \mathcal{O}_1$ and $F_2 \subseteq \mathcal{O}_2$ and clearly, $\mathcal{O}_1 \cap \mathcal{O}_2 = \emptyset$. Moreover, using the triangle inequality for the metric, it is not difficult to see that $\mathcal{O}_1$ and $\mathcal{O}_2$ are open.   □

Using obvious notation, the preceding two propositions provide the following string of inclusions between families of topologies on a set X:

$$\mathcal{T}_{\text{metric}} \subseteq \mathcal{T}_{\text{normal}} \subseteq \mathcal{T}_{\text{regular}} \subseteq \mathcal{T}_{\text{Hausdorff}} \subseteq \mathcal{T}_{\text{Tychonoff}}.$$

We close this brief section with the following very useful reformulation of normality in terms of nested neighborhoods of closed sets.

Proposition 8 *Let X be a Tychoneff topological space. Then X is normal if and only if whenever $\mathcal{U}$ is a neighborhood of a closed subset F of X, there is another neighborhood of F whose closure is contained in $\mathcal{U}$, that is, there is an open set $\mathcal{O}$ for which*

$$F \subseteq \mathcal{O} \subseteq \overline{\mathcal{O}} \subseteq \mathcal{U}.$$

Proof First assume X is normal. Since F and $X \sim \mathcal{U}$ are disjoint closed sets, there are disjoint open sets $\mathcal{O}$ and $\mathcal{V}$ for which $F \subseteq \mathcal{O}$ and $X \sim \mathcal{U} \subseteq \mathcal{V}$. Thus $\mathcal{O} \subseteq X \sim \mathcal{V} \subseteq \mathcal{U}$. Since $\mathcal{O} \subseteq X \sim \mathcal{V}$ and $X \sim \mathcal{V}$ is closed, $\overline{\mathcal{O}} \subseteq X \sim \mathcal{V} \subseteq \mathcal{U}$.

To prove the converse, suppose the nested neighborhood property holds. Let A and B be disjoint closed subset of X. Then $A \subseteq X \sim B$ and $X \sim B$ is open. Thus there is an open set $\mathcal{O}$ for which $A \subseteq \mathcal{O} \subseteq \overline{\mathcal{O}} \subseteq X \sim B$. Therefore $\mathcal{O}$ and $X \sim \overline{\mathcal{O}}$ are disjoint neighborhoods of A and B, respectively.   □

PROBLEMS

12. Show that if F is a closed subset of a normal space X, then the subspace F is normal. Is it necessary to assume that F is closed?

13. Let X be a topological space. Show that X is Hausdorff if and only if the diagonal $D = \{(x_1, x_2) \in X \times X \mid x_1 = x_2\}$ is a closed subset of $X \times X$.

14. Consider the set of real numbers with the topology consisting of the empty-set and sets of the form $(-\infty, c), c \in \mathbf{K}$. Show that this space is Tychonoff but not Hausdorff.

15. (Zariski Topology) In $\mathbf{R}^n$ let $\mathcal{B}$ be the family of sets $\{x \in \mathbf{R}^n \mid p(x) \neq 0\}$, where p is a polynomial in n variables. Let $\mathcal{T}$ be the topology on X that has $\mathcal{B}$ as a subbase. Show that $\mathcal{T}$ is a topology for $\mathbf{R}^n$ that is Tychonoff but not Hausdorff.

16. Show the Sorgenfrey Line and the Moore Plane are Hausdorff (see Problems 9 and 10).

11.3   COUNTABILITY AND SEPARABILITY

We have defined what it means for a sequence in a metric space to converge. The following is the natural generalization of sequential convergence to topological spaces.

Definition *A sequence $\{x_n\}$ in a topological space X is said to **converge** to the point $x \in X$ provided for each neighborhood $\mathcal{U}$ of x, there is an index N such that if $n \geq N$, then x_n belongs to $\mathcal{U}$. The point x is called a **limit** of the sequence.*

In a metric space, a sequence cannot converge to two different points so we refer to *the limit* of a sequence. In a general topological space, a sequence can converge to different points. For instance, for the trivial topology on a set, every sequence converges to every point. For a Hausdorff space, a sequence has a unique limit.

Definition *A topological space X is said to be* **first countable** *provided there is a countable base at each point. The space X is said to be* **second countable** *provided there is a countable base for the topology.*

It is clear that a second countable space is first countable.

Example Every metric space X is first countable since for $x \in X$, the countable collection of open balls $\{B(x, 1/n)\}_{n=1}^{\infty}$ is a base at x for the topology induced by the metric.

We leave the proof of the following proposition as an exercise.

Proposition 9 *Let X be a first countable topological space. For a subset E of X, a point $x \in X$ is a point of closure of E if and only if x is a limit of a sequence in E. Therefore a subset E of X is closed if and only if whenever a sequence in E converges to $x \in X$, the point x belongs to E.*

In a topological space that is not first countable, it is possible for a point to be a point of closure of a set and yet no sequence in the set converges to the point (see Problem 22).

Definition *A subset E of topological space X is said to be* **dense** *in X provided every open set in X contains a point of E. We call X* **separable** *provided it has a countable dense subset.*

It is clear that a set E is dense in X if and only if every point in X is a point of closure of E, that is, $\overline{E} = X$.

In Chapter 9, we proved that a metric space is second countable if and only if it is separable. In a general topological space, a second countable space is separable, but a separable space, even one that is first countable, may fail to be second countable (see Problem 21).

A topological space is said to be **metrizable** provided the topology is induced by a metric. Not every topology is induced by a metric. Indeed, we have seen that a metric space is normal, so certainly the trivial topology on a set with more than one point is not metrizable. It is natural to ask if it is possible to identify those topological spaces that are metrizable. By this we mean to state criteria in terms of the open sets of the topology that are necessary and sufficient in order that the topology be induced by a metric. There are such criteria.[2] In the case the topological space X is second countable, there is the following simple necessary and sufficient criterion for metrizability.

The Urysohn Metrization Theorem *Let X be a second countable topological space. Then X is metrizable if and only if it is normal.*

We already have shown that a metric space is normal. We postpone until the next chapter the proof, for second countable topological spaces, of the converse.

---

[2] The Nagata–Smirnov–Bing Metrization Theorem is such a result; See page 127 of John Kelley's *General Topology* [Kel55].

PROBLEMS

17. A topological space is said to be a *Lindelöf* space or to have the *Lindelöf* property provided each open cover of X has a countable subcover. Show that if X is second countable, then it is *Lindelöf*.

18. Let X be an uncountable set of points, and let $\mathcal{T}$ consist of $\emptyset$ and all subsets of X that have finite complements. Show that $\mathcal{T}$ is a topology for X and that the space $(X, \mathcal{T})$ is not first countable.

19. Show that a second countable space is separable and every subspace of a second countable space is second countable.

20. Show that the Moore Plane is separable (see Problem 10). Show that the subspace $\mathbf{R} \times \{0\}$ of the Moore Plane is not separable. Conclude that the Moore Plane is not metrizable and not second countable.

21. Show that the Sorgenfrey Line is first countable but not second countable and yet the rationals are dense (see Problem 9). Conclude that the Sorgenfrey Line is not metrizable.

22. Let $X_1 = N \times N$, where N denotes the set of natural numbers and take $X = X_1 \cup \{\omega\}$, where ω does not belong to X_1. For each sequence $s = \{m_k\}$ of natural numbers and natural number n, define

$$B_{s.n} = \{\omega\} \cup \{(j, k) : j \geq m_k \text{ all } k \geq n\}.$$

   (i)   Show that the sets $B_{s,n}$ together with the singleton sets $\{(j, k)\}$ form a base for a topology on X.

   (ii) Show that ω is a point of closure of X_1 even though no sequence $\{x_n\}$ from X_1 converges to ω.

   (iii) Show that the space X is separable but is not first countable and so is not second countable.

   (iv) Is X a Lindelöf space?

11.4 CONTINUOUS MAPPINGS BETWEEN TOPOLOGICAL SPACES

We defined continuity for mappings between metric spaces in terms of convergent sequences: A mapping f is continuous at a point x provided whenever a sequence converges to x the image sequence converges to $f(x)$. We then showed that this was equivalent to, the ϵ-δ criterion expressed in terms of open balls. The concept of continuity extends to mappings between topological spaces in the following natural manner.

Definition *For topological spaces $(X, \mathcal{T})$ and $(Y, \mathcal{S})$, a mapping $f: X \to Y$ is said to be* **continuous** *at the point x_0 in X provided for any neighborhood $\mathcal{O}$ of $f(x_0)$, there is a neighborhood $\mathcal{U}$ of x_0 for which $f(\mathcal{U}) \subseteq \mathcal{O}$. We say f is continuous provided it is continuous at each point in X.*

Proposition 10 *A mapping $f: X \to Y$ between topological spaces X and Y is continuous if and only if for any open subset $\mathcal{O}$ in Y, its inverse image under f, $f^{-1}(\mathcal{O})$, is an open subset of X.*

Proof First suppose that f is continuous. Let $\mathcal{O}$ be open in Y. According to Proposition 1, to show that $f^{-1}(\mathcal{O})$ is open it suffices to show that each point in $f^{-1}(\mathcal{O})$ has a neighborhood that is contained in $f^{-1}(\mathcal{O})$. Let x belong to $f^{-1}(\mathcal{O})$. Then by the continuity of f at x

there is a neighborhood of x that is mapped into $\mathcal{O}$ and therefore is contained in $f^{-1}(\mathcal{O})$. Conversely, if f^{-1} maps open sets to open sets, then it is immediate that f is continuous on all of X. $\qquad\Box$

For a continuous mapping f of a topological space X to a topological space Y, by the definition of the subspace topology, the restriction of f to a subspace of X also is continuous. We leave the proof of the next proposition as an exercise.

Proposition 11 *The composition of continuous mappings between topological spaces, when defined, is continuous.*

Definition *Given two topologies T_1 and T_2 for a set X, if $T_2 \subseteq T_1$, we say that T_2 is **weaker** than T_1 and that T_1 is **stronger** than T_2.*

Given a cover S of a set X, it is useful to understand the topologies for X with respect to which the cover S is open. Of course, S is open with respect to the discrete topology on X. In fact, there is a weakest topology for X with respect to which this cover is open: it is the unique topology that has S as a subbase. We leave the proof of the following proposition as an exercise.

Proposition 12 *Let X be a nonempty set and S any collection of subsets of X that covers X. The collection of subsets of X consisting of intersections of finite subcollections of S is a base for a topology T for X. It is the weakest topology containing S in the sense that if T' is any other topology for X containing S, then $T \subseteq T'$.*

Definition *Let X be a nonempty set and consider a collection of mappings $\mathcal{F} = \{f_\alpha : X \to X_\alpha\}_{\alpha \in \Lambda}$, where each X_α is a topological space. The weakest topology for X that contains the collection of sets*

$$\mathcal{F} = \left\{ f_\alpha^{-1}(\mathcal{O}_\alpha) \;\middle|\; f_\alpha \in \mathcal{F}, \; \mathcal{O}_\alpha \text{ open in } X_\alpha \right\}$$

*is called the **weak topology** for X induced by $\mathcal{F}$.*

Proposition 13 *Let X be a nonempty set and $\mathcal{F} = \{f_\lambda : X \to X_\lambda\}_{\lambda \in \Lambda}$ a collection of mappings where each X_λ is a topological space. The weak topology for X induced by $\mathcal{F}$ is the topology on X that has the fewest number of sets among the topologies on X for which each mapping $f_\lambda : X \to X_\lambda$ is continuous.*

Proof According to Proposition 10, for each λ in Λ, $f_\lambda : X \to X_\lambda$ is continuous if and only if the inverse image under f_λ of each open set in X_λ is open in X. $\qquad\Box$

Definition *A continuous mapping from a topological space X to a topological space Y is said to be a **homeomorphism** provided it is one-to-one, maps X onto Y, and has a continuous inverse f^{-1} from Y to X.*

It is clear that the inverse of a homeomorphism is a homeomorphism and that the composition of homeomorphisms, when defined, is a homeomorphism. Two topological spaces X and Y are said to be **homeomorphic** if there is a homeomorphism between them.

This is an equivalence relation among topological spaces, that is, it is reflexive, symmetric, and transitive. From a topological point of view two homeomorphic topological spaces are indistinguishable since, according to Proposition 10, for a homeomorphism f of X onto Y, a set E is open in X if and only if its image $f(E)$ is open in Y. The concept of homeomorphism plays the same role for topological spaces that isometry plays for metric spaces and, say, group isomorphism plays for groups. But some care is needed here. In the next example we show that, for E a Lebesgue measurable set of real numbers, $L^1(E)$ is homeomorphic to $L^2(E)$.[3]

Example (Mazur) Let E be a Lebesgue measurable set of real numbers. For f in $L^1(E)$, define the function $\Phi(f)$ on E by $\Phi(f)(x) = \operatorname{sgn}(f(x))|f(x)|^{1/2}$. Then $\Phi(f)$ belongs to $L^2(E)$. We leave it as an exercise to show that for any two numbers a and b,

$$\left| \operatorname{sgn}(a) \cdot |a|^{1/2} - \operatorname{sgn}(b) \cdot |b|^{1/2} \right|^2 \leq 2 \cdot |a-b|,$$

and therefore

$$\|\Phi(f) - \Phi(g)\|_2^2 \leq 2 \cdot \|f - g\|_1 \text{ for all } f, g \text{ in } L^1(E).$$

From this we conclude that Φ is a continuous one-to-one mapping of $L^1(E)$ into $L^2(E)$. It also maps $L^1(E)$ onto $L^2(E)$ and its inverse Φ^{-1} is defined by $\Phi^{-1}(f)(x) = \operatorname{sgn}(f(x))|f(x)|^2$ for f in $L^2(E)$. Use Problem 38 to conclude that the inverse mapping Φ^{-1} is a continuous mapping from $L^2(E)$ to $L^1(E)$. Therefore $L^1(E)$ is homeomorphic to $L^2(E)$, where each of these spaces is equipped with the topology induced by its L^p norm.

PROBLEMS

23. Let f be a mapping of the topological space X to the topological space Y and S be a subbase for the topology on Y. Show that f is continuous if and only if the inverse image under f of every set in S is open in X.

24. Let X be a topological space.

    (i)   If X has the trivial topology, find all continuous mappings of X into $\mathbf{R}$.

    (ii) If X has the discrete topology, find all continuous mappings of X into $\mathbf{R}$.

    (iii) Find all continuous one-to-one mappings from $\mathbf{R}$ to X if X has the discrete topology.

    (iv) Find all continuous one-to-one mappings from $\mathbf{R}$ to X if X has the trivial topology.

25. For topological spaces X and Y, let f map X to Y. Which of the following assertions are equivalent to the continuity of f? Verify your answers.

    (i)   The inverse image under f of every closed subset of Y is closed in X.

    (ii) If $\mathcal{O}$ is open in X, then $f(\mathcal{O})$ is open in Y.

    (iii) If F is closed in X, then $f(F)$ is closed in Y.

    (iv) For each subset A of X, $f(\overline{A}) \subseteq \overline{f(A)}$.

---

[3]The same type of argument shows that any two $L^p(E)$ spaces, for $1 \leq p < \infty$, are homeomorphic. There is a remarkable theorem due to M.I. Kadets which tells us that any two separable infinite dimensional complete normed linear spaces are homeomorphic ("A Proof of the Topological Equivalence of All Separable Infinite Dimensional Banach Spaces," *Functional Analysis and Applications*, *1*, 1967). From the topological point of view, $L^2[0, 1]$ is indistinguishable from $C[0, 1]$. These spaces look very different from many other angles of vision.

26. Prove Proposition 11.

27. Prove Proposition 12.

28. Prove that the sum and product of two real-valued continuous functions defined on a topological space X are themselves continuous.

29. Let $\mathcal{F}$ be a collection of real-valued functions on a set X. Find necessary and sufficient conditions on $\mathcal{F}$ in order that X, considered as a topological space with the weak topology induced by $\mathcal{F}$, is Tychonoff.

30. For topological spaces X and Y, let the mapping $f: X \to Y$ be one-to-one and onto. Show that the following assertions are equivalent.

   (i) f is a homeomorphism of X onto Y.

   (ii) A subset E of X is open in X if and only if $f(E)$ is open in Y.

   (iii) A subset E of X is closed in X if and only if $f(E)$ is closed in Y.

   (iv) The image of the closure of a set is the closure of the image, that is, for each subset A of X, $f(\overline{A}) = \overline{f(A)}$.

31. For topological spaces X and Y, let f be a continuous mapping from X onto Y. If X is Hausdorff, is Y Hausdorff? If X is normal, is Y normal?

32. Let ρ_1 and ρ_2 be metrics on the set X that induce topologies $\mathcal{T}_1$ and $\mathcal{T}_2$, respectively. If $\mathcal{T}_1 = \mathcal{T}_2$, are the metrics necessarily equivalent?

33. Show that the inverse of a homeomorphism is a homeomorphism and the composition of two homeomorphisms, when defined, is again a homeomorphism.

34. Suppose that a topological space X has the property that every continuous real-valued function on X takes a minimum value. Show that any topological space that is homeomorphic to X also possesses this property.

35. Suppose that a topological space X has the property that every continuous real-valued function on X has an interval as its image. Show that any topological space that is homeomorphic to X also possesses this property.

36. Show that $\mathbf{R}$ is homeomorphic to the open bounded interval $(0, 1)$, but is not homeomorphic to the closed bounded interval $[0, 1]$.

37. Let X and Y be topological spaces and consider a mapping f from X to Y. Suppose $X = X_1 \cup X_2$ and the restrictions of f to the topological subspaces X_1 and to X_2 are continuous. Show that f need not be continuous at any point in X. Show that f is continuous on X if X_1 and X_2 are open. Compare this with the case of measurable functions and the inheritance of measurability from the measurability of restrictions.

38. Show that for any two numbers a and b,

$$\left| \operatorname{sgn}(a) \cdot |a|^2 - \operatorname{sgn}(b) \cdot |b|^2 \right| \le 2 \cdot |a - b|(|a| + |b|).$$

11.5 COMPACT TOPOLOGICAL SPACES

We have studied compactness for metric spaces. We provided several characterizations of compactness and established properties of continuous mappings and continuous real-valued functions defined on compact metric spaces. The concept of compactness can be naturally and usefully extended to topological spaces.

Recall that a collection of sets $\{E_\lambda\}_{\lambda \in \Lambda}$ is said to be a **cover** of a set E provided $E \subseteq \bigcup_{\lambda \in \Lambda} E_\lambda$. If each E_λ is contained in a topological space, a cover is said to be open provided each set in the cover is open.

Definition *A topological space X is said to be* **compact** *provided every open cover of X has a finite subcover. A subset K of X is called compact provided K, considered as a topological space with the subspace topology inherited from X, is compact.*

In view of the definition of the subspace topology, a subset K of X is compact provided every covering of K by a collection of open subsets of X has a finite subcover.

Certain results regarding compactness in a topological space carry over directly from the metric space setting; for example, the image of a compact topological space under a continuous mapping also is compact. Other properties of compact metric spaces, for example, the equivalence of compactness and sequential compactness, carry over to the topological setting only for spaces that possess some additional topological structure. Other properties of compact metric spaces, such as total boundedness, have no simple correspondent in the topological setting.

Recall that a collection of sets is said to have the **finite intersection property** provided every finite subcollection has nonempty intersection. Since a subset of a topological space X is closed if and only if its complement in X is open, we have, by De Morgan's Identities, the following extension to topological spaces of a result we previously established for metric spaces.

Proposition 14 *A topological space X is compact if and only if every collection of closed subsets of X that possesses the finite intersection property has nonempty intersection.*

Proposition 15 *A closed subset K of a compact topological space X is compact.*

Proof Let $\{\mathcal{O}_\lambda\}_{\lambda \in \Lambda}$ be an open cover for K by open subsets of X. Since $X \sim K$ is an open subset of X, $[X \sim F] \cup \{\mathcal{O}_\lambda\}_{\lambda \in \Lambda}$ is an open cover of X. By the compactness of X this cover has a finite subcover, and, by possibly removing the set $X \sim K$ from this finite subcover, the remaining collection is a finite subcollection of $\{\mathcal{O}_\lambda\}_{\lambda \in \Lambda}$ that covers K. Thus K is compact. $\square$

We proved that a compact subspace K of a metric space X must be a closed subset of X. This is also true for topological spaces that are Hausdorff.

Proposition 16 *A compact subspace K of a Hausdorff topological space X is a closed subset of K.*

Proof We will show that $X \sim K$ is open so that K must be closed. Let y belong to $X \sim K$. Since X is Hausdorff, for each $x \in K$ there are disjoint neighborhoods $\mathcal{O}_x$ and $\mathcal{U}_x$ of x and y, respectively. Then $\{\mathcal{O}_x\}_{x \in K}$ is an open cover of K, and so, since K is compact, there is a finite subcover $\{\mathcal{O}_{x_1}, \mathcal{O}_{x_2}, \ldots, \mathcal{O}_{x_n}\}$. Define $\mathcal{N} = \bigcap_{i=1}^n \mathcal{U}_{x_i}$. Then $\mathcal{N}$ is a neighborhood of y which is disjoint from each $\mathcal{O}_{x_i}$ and hence is contained in $X \sim K$. Therefore $X \sim K$ is open. $\square$

Definition *A topological space X is said to be* **sequentially compact** *provided each sequence in X has a subsequence that converges to a point of X.*

We have shown that a metric space is compact if and only if it is sequentially compact. The same holds for topological spaces that are second countable.

Proposition 17 *Let X be a second countable topological space. Then X is compact if and only if it is sequentially compact.*

Proof First assume X is compact. Let $\{x_n\}$ be a sequence in X. For each index n, let F_n be the closure of the nonempty set $\{x_k \mid k \geq n\}$. Then $\{F_n\}$ is a descending sequence of nonempty closed sets. Since $\{F_n\}$ has the finite intersection property, by Proposition 14, $\bigcap_{n=1}^{\infty} F_n \neq \emptyset$:, choose a point x_0 in this intersection. Since X is second countable, it is first countable. Let $\{B_n\}_{n=1}^{\infty}$ be a base for the topology at the point x_0. We may assume that each $B_{n+1} \subseteq B_n$. Since x_0 belongs to the closure of $\{x_k \mid k \geq n\}$, for each n, the neighborhood B_n has nonempty intersection with $\{x_k \mid k \geq n\}$. Therefore we may inductively select a strictly increasing sequence of indices $\{n_k\}$ such that for each index k, $x_{n_k} \in B_k$. Since for each neighborhood $\mathcal{O}$ of x_0, there is an index N for which $B_n \subseteq \mathcal{O}$ for $n \geq N$, the subsequence $\{x_{n_k}\}$ converges to x_0. Thus X is sequentially compact.

Now suppose X is sequentially compact. Since X is second countable, every open cover has a countable subcover. Therefore, to show that X is compact it suffices to show that every countable open cover of X has a finite subcover. Let $\{\mathcal{O}_n\}_{n=1}^{\infty}$ be such a cover. We argue by contradiction. Assume there is no finite subcover. Then for each index n, there is an index $m(n) > n$ for which $\mathcal{O}_{m(n)} \sim \bigcup_{i=1}^{n} \mathcal{O}_i \neq \emptyset$. For each natural number n, choose $x_n \in \mathcal{O}_{m(n)} \sim \bigcup_{i=1}^{n} \mathcal{O}_i$. Then, since X is sequentially compact, a subsequence of $\{x_n\}$ converges to $x_0 \in X$. But $\{\mathcal{O}_n\}_{n=1}^{\infty}$ is an open cover of X, so there is some $\mathcal{O}_N$ that is a neighborhood of x_0. Therefore, there are infinitely many indices n for which x_n belongs to $\mathcal{O}_N$. This is not possible since $x_n \notin \mathcal{O}_N$ for $n > N$. $\qquad \square$

Theorem 18 *A compact Hausdorff space is normal.*

Proof Let X be compact and Hausdorff. We first show it is regular, that is, each closed set and point not in the set can be separated by disjoint neighborhoods. Let F be a closed subset of X and x belong to $X \sim F$. Since X is Hausdorff, for each $y \in F$ there are disjoint neighborhoods $\mathcal{O}_y$ and $\mathcal{U}_y$ of x and y, respectively. Then $\{\mathcal{U}_y\}_{y \in F}$ is an open cover of F. But F is compact. Thus here is a finite subcover $\{\mathcal{U}_{y_1}, \mathcal{U}_{y_2}, \ldots, \mathcal{U}_{y_n}\}$. Define $\mathcal{N} = \bigcap_{i=1}^{n} \mathcal{O}_{y_i}$. Then $\mathcal{N}$ is a neighborhood of y which is disjoint from $\bigcup_{i=1}^{n} \mathcal{U}_{y_i}$, a neighborhood of F. Thus X is regular. A repeat of this argument, now using regularity, shows that X is normal. $\qquad \square$

Proposition 19 *A continuous one-to-one mapping f of a compact space X onto a Hausdorff space Y is a homeomorphism.*

Proof In order to show that f is a homeomorphism it is only necessary to show that it carries open sets into open sets or equivalently closed sets into closed sets. Let F be a closed subset of X. Then F is compact since X is compact. Therefore, by Proposition 20, $f(F)$ is compact. Hence, by Proposition 16, since Y is Hausdorff, $f(F)$ is closed. $\qquad \square$

Proposition 20 *The continuous image of a compact topological space is compact.*

Proof Let f be a continuous mapping of compact topological space X to a topological space Y. Let $\{O_\lambda\}_{\lambda \in \Lambda}$ be a covering of $f(X)$ by open subsets of Y. Then, by the continuity of f, $\{f^{-1}(O_\lambda)\}_{\lambda \in \Lambda}$ is an open cover of X. By the compactness of X, there is a finite subcollection $\{f^{-1}(O_{\lambda_1}), \ldots, f^{-1}(O_{\lambda_n})\}$ that also covers X. The finite collection $\{O_{\lambda_1}, \ldots, O_{\lambda_n}\}$ covers $f(X)$. $\qquad\square$

Corollary 21 *A continuous real-valued function on a compact topological space takes a maximum and minimum functional value.*

Proof Let X be compact and $f: X \to \mathbf{R}$ be continuous. By the preceding proposition, $f(X)$ is a compact set of real numbers. Thus $f(X)$ is closed and bounded. But a closed and bounded set of real numbers contains a smallest and largest member. $\qquad\square$

A topological space is said to be **countably compact** provided every countable open cover has a finite subcover. We explore some properties of such spaces in Problems 39 and 40.

PROBLEMS

39. For a second countable space X, show that X is compact if and only if it is countably compact.

40. (Fréchet Intersection Theorem) Let X be a topological space. Prove that X is countably compact if and only if whenever $\{F_n\}$ is a descending sequence of nonempty closed subsets of X, the intersection $\bigcap_{n=1}^{\infty} F_n$ is nonempty.

41. Let X be compact Hausdorff and $\{F_n\}_{n=1}^{\infty}$ be a descending collection of closed subsets of X. Let $\mathcal{O}$ be a neighborhood of the intersection $\bigcap_{n=1}^{\infty} F_n$. Show there is an index N such that $F_n \subseteq \mathcal{O}$ for $n \geq N$.

42. Show that it is not possible to express a closed, bounded interval of real numbers as the pairwise disjoint union of a countable collection (having more than one member) of closed, bounded intervals.

43. Let f be a continuous mapping of the compact space X onto the Hausdorff space Y. Show that any mapping g of Y into Z for which $g \circ f$ is continuous must itself be continuous.

44. Let $(X, \mathcal{T})$ be a topological space.
    (i) Prove that if $(X, \mathcal{T})$ is compact, then $(X, \mathcal{T}_1)$ is compact for any topology $\mathcal{T}_1$ weaker than $\mathcal{T}$.
    (ii) Show that if $(X, \mathcal{T})$ is Hausdorff, then $(X, \mathcal{T}_2)$ is Hausdorff for any topology $\mathcal{T}_2$ stronger than $\mathcal{T}$.
    (iii) Show that if $(X, \mathcal{T})$ is compact and Hausdorff, then any strictly weaker topology is not Hausdorff and any strictly stronger topology is not compact.

45. (The Compact-Open Topology) Let X and Y be Hausdorff topological spaces and Y^X the collection of maps from X into Y. On Y^X we define a topology, called the compact-open topology, by taking as a subbase sets of the form $\mathcal{U}_{K,\mathcal{O}} = \{f: X \to Y \mid f(K) \subseteq \mathcal{O}\}$, where K is a compact subset of X and $\mathcal{O}$ is an open subset of Y. Thus the compact-open topology is the weakest topology on Y^X such that the sets $\mathcal{U}_{K,\mathcal{O}}$ are open.
    (i) Let $\{f_n\}$ be a sequence in Y^X that converges with respect to the compact-open topology to $f \in Y^X$. Show that $\{f_n\}$ converges pointwise to f on X.

(ii) Now assume that Y is a metric space. Show that a sequence $\{f_n\}$ in Y^X converges with respect to the compact-open topology to $f \in Y^X$ if and only if $\{f_n\}$ converges to f uniformly on each compact subset K of X.

46. (Dini's Theorem) Let $\{f_n\}$ be a sequence of continuous real-valued functions on a countably compact space X. Suppose that for each $x \in X$, the sequence $\{f_n(x)\}$ decreases monotonically to zero. Show that $\{f_n\}$ converges to zero uniformly.

11.6 CONNECTED TOPOLOGICAL SPACES

Two nonempty open subsets of a topological space X are said to **separate** X if they are disjoint and their union is X. A topological space which cannot be separated by such a pair is said to be **connected**. Since the complement of an open set is closed, each of the open sets in a separation of a space is also closed. Thus a topological space is connected if and only if the only subsets that are both open and closed are the whole space and the empty-set.

A subset E of X is said to be connected provided it is a connected topological subspace. Thus a subset E of X is connected if there do not exist open subsets $\mathcal{O}_1$ and $\mathcal{O}_2$ of X for which

$$\mathcal{O}_1 \cap E \neq \emptyset, \ \mathcal{O}_2 \cap E \neq \emptyset, \ E \subseteq \mathcal{O}_1 \cup \mathcal{O}_2 \text{ and } E \cap \mathcal{O}_1 \cap \mathcal{O}_2 = \emptyset.$$

Proposition 22 *Let f be a continuous mapping of a connected space X to a topological space Y. Then its image $f(Y)$ is connected.*

Proof Observe that f is a continuous mapping of X onto the topological space $f(X)$, where $f(X)$ has the subspace topology inherited from Y. We argue by contradiction. Suppose $f(X)$ is not connected. Let $\mathcal{O}_1$ and $\mathcal{O}_2$ be a separation of $f(X)$. Then $f^{-1}(\mathcal{O}_1)$ and $f^{-1}(\mathcal{O}_2)$ are disjoint nonempty open sets in X whose union is X. Thus this pair is a separation of X in contradiction to the connectedness of X. □

We leave it as an exercise to show that for a set C of real numbers, the following are equivalent:

$$(i) \ C \text{ is an interval}; \ (ii) \ C \text{ is convex}; \ (iii) \ C \text{ is connected}. \tag{1}$$

Definition *A topological space X is said to have the intermediate value property provided the image of any continuous real-valued function on X is an interval.*

Proposition 23 *A topological space has the intermediate value property if and only if it is connected.*

Proof According to (1), a connected set of real numbers is an interval. We therefore infer from Proposition 22 that a connected topological space has the intermediate value property. To prove the converse, we suppose that X is a topological space that is not connected and conclude that it fails to have the intermediate value property. Indeed, since X is not connected, there is a pair of nonempty open subsets of X, $\mathcal{O}_1$ and $\mathcal{O}_2$, for which $X = \mathcal{O}_1 \cup \mathcal{O}_2$. Define the function f on X to take the value 0 on $\mathcal{O}_1$ and 1 on $\mathcal{O}_2$. Then f is continuous since $f^{-1}(A)$ is an open subset of X for every subset A of $\mathbf{R}$ and hence, in particular, for every open subset of $\mathbf{R}$. On the other hand, f fails to have the intermediate value property. □

If a topological space is not connected, then for any separation of the space, a subspace that has nonempty intersection with each of the sets in the separation also fails to be connected. Moreover, the image under a continuous map of an interval of real numbers is connected. Thus a topological space X is connected if for each pair of points $u, v \in X$, there is a continuous map $f: [0,1] \rightarrow X$ for which $f(0) = u$ and $f(1) = v$. A topological space possessing this property is said to be **arcwise connected.** While an arcwise-connected topological space is connected, there are connected spaces that fail to be arcwise connected (see Problem 49). However, for an open subset of a Euclidean space $\mathbf{R}^n$, connectednes is equivalent to arcwise connectedness (see Problem 50).

PROBLEMS

47. Let $\{C_\lambda\}_{\lambda \in \Lambda}$ be a collection of connected subsets of a topological space X and suppose that any two of them have a point in common. Show that the union of $\{C_\lambda\}_{\lambda \in \Lambda}$ also is connected.

48. Let A be a connected subset of a topological space X, and suppose $A \subseteq B \subseteq \overline{A}$. Show that B is connected.

49. Show that the following subset of the plane is connected but not arcwise connected.

$$X = \{(x, y) \mid x = 0, \; -1 \leq y \leq 1\} \cup \{(x, y) \mid y = \sin 1/x, \; 0 < x \leq 1\}.$$

50. Show that an arcwise connected topological space X is connected. Also show that each connected open subset $\mathcal{O}$ of a Euclidean space $\mathbf{R}^n$ is arcwise connected. (Hint: Let x belong to $\mathcal{O}$. Define C to be the set of points in $\mathcal{O}$ that can be connected in $\mathcal{O}$ to x by a piecewise linear arc. Show that C is both open and closed in $\mathcal{O}$.)

51. Consider the circle $C = \{(x, y) \mid x^2 + y^2 = 1\}$ in the plane $\mathbf{R}^2$. Show that C is connected.

52. Show that $\mathbf{R}^n$ is connected.

53. Show that a compact metric space (X, ρ) fails to be connected if and only if there are two disjoint, nonempty subsets A and B whose union is X and $\epsilon > 0$ such that $\rho(u, v) \geq \epsilon$ for all $u \in A$, $v \in B$. Show that this is not necessarily the case for noncompact metric spaces.

54. A metric space (X, ρ) is said to be **well chained** provided for each pair of points $u, v \in X$ and each $\epsilon > 0$, there is a finite number of points in X, $u = x_0, x_1, \ldots, x_{n-1}, x_n = v$ such that $\rho(x_{i-1}, x_i) < \epsilon$, for $1 \leq i \leq n$.

   (i)   Show that if X is connected, then it is well chained, but the converse is not true.

   (ii) Show that if X is compact and well chained, then it is connected.

   (iii) Show that if an open subset of $\mathbf{R}^n$ is well chained, then it is connected.

55. Show that for any point (x, y) in the plane $\mathbf{R}^2$, the subspace $\mathbf{R}^2 \sim \{(x, y)\}$ is connected. Use this to show that $\mathbf{R}$ is not homeomorphic to $\mathbf{R}^2$.

56. Verify the equivalence of the three assertions in (1).

CHAPTER 12

Topological Spaces: Three Fundamental Theorems

Contents

In the preceding chapter we considered several different topological concepts and examined relationships between these concepts. In this chapter we focus on three theorems in topology that, beyond their intrinsic interest, are indispensible tools in several areas of analysis.

12.1 URYSOHN'S LEMMA AND THE TIETZE EXTENSION THEOREM

On a metric space (X, ρ) there is an an abundance of continuous real-valued functions. Indeed, for a nonempty closed subset C of X, the function d_C, called the distance to C and defined by

$$d_C(x) = \inf_{x' \in C} \rho(x', x) \text{ for all } x \in X,$$

is continuous and C is the inverse image under d_C of 0. Continuity follows from the triangle inequality. Moreover, if A and B are disjoint closed subsets of X, there is a continuous real-valued function f on X for which

$$f(X) \subseteq [0, 1], \ f = 0 \text{ on } A \text{ and } f = 1 \text{ on } B.$$

The function f is given by

$$f = \frac{d_A}{d_A + d_B} \text{ on } X.$$

This explicit construction of f depends on the metric on X. However, the next fundamental lemma tells us that there exist such functions on any normal topological space and, in particular, on any compact Hausdorff space.

Urysohn's Lemma *Let A and B be disjoint closed subsets of a normal topological space X. Then for any closed, bounded interval of real numbers $[a, b]$, there is a continuous real-valued function f defined on X that takes values in $[a, b]$, while $f = a$ on A and $f = b$ on B.*

This lemma may be considered to be an extension result: Indeed, define the real-valued function f on $A \cup B$ by setting $f = a$ on A and $f = b$ on B. This is a continuous function on the closed subset $A \cup B$ of X which takes values in $[a, b]$. Urysohn's Lemma asserts that this function can be extended to a continuous function on all of X which also takes values in $[a, b]$. We note that if a Tychonoff topological space X possesses the property described in Urysohn's Lemma, then X must be normal. Indeed, for A and B nonempty disjoint closed subsets of X and a continuous real-valued function f on X that takes the value 0 on A and 1 on B, if I_1 and I_2 are disjoint open intervals containing 0 and 1, respectively, then $f^{-1}(I_1)$ and $f^{-1}(I_1)$ are disjoint neighborhoods of A and B, respectively.

The proof of Urysohn's Lemma becomes clearer if we introduce the following concept and then establish two preliminary results.

Definition *Let X be a topological space and Λ a set of real numbers. A collection of open subsets of X indexed by Λ, $\{\mathcal{O}_\lambda\}_{\lambda \in \Lambda}$, is said to be **normally ascending** provided for any $\lambda_1, \lambda_2 \in \Lambda$,*

$$\overline{\mathcal{O}}_{\lambda_1} \subseteq \mathcal{O}_{\lambda_2} \text{ if } \lambda_1 < \lambda_2.$$

Example Let f be a continuous real-valued function on the topological space X. Let Λ be any set of real numbers and define, for $\lambda \in \Lambda$,

$$\mathcal{O}_\lambda = \{x \in X \mid f(x) < \lambda\}.$$

By continuity it is clear that if $\lambda_1 < \lambda_2$, then

$$\overline{\mathcal{O}}_{\lambda_1} \subseteq \{x \in X \mid f(x) \le \lambda_1\} \subseteq \{x \in X \mid f(x) < \lambda_2\} = \mathcal{O}_{\lambda_2}$$

and therefore the collection of open sets $\{\mathcal{O}_\lambda\}_{\lambda \in \Lambda}$ is normally ascending.

We leave the proof of the following lemma as an exercise.

Lemma 1 *Let X be a topological space. For Λ a dense subset of the open, bounded interval of real numbers (a, b), let $\{\mathcal{O}_\lambda\}_{\lambda \in \Lambda}$ be a normally ascending collection of open subsets of X. Define the function $f: X \to \mathbf{R}$ by setting $f = b$ on $X \sim \bigcup_{\lambda \in \Lambda} \mathcal{O}_\lambda$ and otherwise setting*

$$f(x) = \inf \{\lambda \in \Lambda \mid x \in \mathcal{O}_\lambda\}. \tag{1}$$

Then $f: X \to [a, b]$ is continuous.

We next provide a strong generalization of Proposition 8 of the preceding chapter.

Lemma 2 *Let X be a normal topological space, F a closed subset of X, and $\mathcal{U}$ a neighborhood of F. Then for any open, bounded interval (a, b), there is a dense subset Λ of (a, b) and a normally ascending collection of open subsets of X, $\{\mathcal{O}_\lambda\}_{\lambda \in \Lambda}$, for which*

$$F \subseteq \mathcal{O}_\lambda \subseteq \overline{\mathcal{O}}_\lambda \subseteq \mathcal{U} \text{ for all } \lambda \in \Lambda. \tag{2}$$

Proof Since there is a strictly increasing continuous function of $(0, 1)$ onto (a, b) we may assume that $(a, b) = (0, 1)$. For the dense subset of $(0, 1)$ we choose the set of dyadic rationals belonging to $(0, 1)$:

$$\Lambda = \{m/2^n \mid m \text{ and } n \text{ natural numbers}, 1 \le m \le 2^n - 1\}.$$

For each natural number n, let Λ_n be the subset of Λ whose elements have denominator 2^n. We will inductively define a sequence of collections of normally ascending open sets $\{\mathcal{O}_\lambda\}_{\lambda \in \Lambda_n}$, where each indexing is an extension of its predecessor.

By Proposition 8 of the preceding chapter, we may choose an open set $\mathcal{O}_{1/2}$ for which

$$F \subseteq \mathcal{O}_{1/2} \subseteq \overline{\mathcal{O}_{1/2}} \subseteq \mathcal{U}.$$

Thus we have defined $\{\mathcal{O}_\lambda\}_{\lambda \in \Lambda_1}$. Now we use Proposition 8 twice more, first with F the same and $\mathcal{U} = \mathcal{O}_{1/2}$ and then with $F = \overline{\mathcal{O}}_{1/2}$ and $\mathcal{U}$ the same, to find open sets $\mathcal{O}_{1/4}$ and $\mathcal{O}_{3/4}$ for which

$$F \subseteq \mathcal{O}_{1/4} \subseteq \overline{\mathcal{O}}_{1/4} \subseteq \mathcal{O}_{1/2} \subseteq \overline{\mathcal{O}}_{1/2} \subseteq \mathcal{O}_{3/4} \subseteq \overline{\mathcal{O}}_{3/4} \subseteq \mathcal{U}.$$

Thus we have extended the normally ascending collection $\{\mathcal{O}_\lambda\}_{\lambda \in \Lambda_1}$ to the normally ascending collection $\{\mathcal{O}_\lambda\}_{\lambda \in \Lambda_2}$. It is now clear how to proceed inductively to define for each natural number n, the normally ascending collection of open sets $\{\mathcal{O}_\lambda\}_{\lambda \in \Lambda_n}$. Observe that the union of this countable collection is a normally ascending collection of open sets parametrized by Λ, each of which is a neighborhood of F that has compact closure contained in $\mathcal{U}$. $\square$

Proof of Urysohn's Lemma By Lemma 2, applied with $F = A$ and $\mathcal{U} = X \sim B$, we can choose a dense subset Λ of (a, b) and a normally ascending collection of open subsets of X, $\{\mathcal{O}_\lambda\}_{\lambda \in \Lambda}$, for which

$$A \subseteq \mathcal{O}_\lambda \subseteq X \sim B \text{ for all } \lambda \in \Lambda.$$

Define the function $f : X \to [a, b]$ by setting $f = b$ on $X \sim \bigcup_{\lambda \in \Lambda} \mathcal{O}_\lambda$ and otherwise setting

$$f(x) = \inf \{ \lambda \in \Lambda \mid x \in \mathcal{O}_\lambda \} .$$

Then $f = a$ on A and $f = b$ on B. Lemma 1 tells us that f is continuous. $\square$

We mentioned above that Urysohn's Lemma may be considered to be an extension result. We now use this lemma to prove a much stronger extension theorem.

The Tietze Extension Theorem *Let X be a normal topological space, F a closed subset of X, and f a continuous real-valued function on F that takes values in the closed, bounded interval $[a, b]$. Then f has a continuous extension to all of X that also takes values in $[a, b]$.*

Proof Since the closed, bounded intervals $[a, b]$ and $[-1, 1]$ are homeomorphic, it is sufficient, and also convenient, to consider the case $[a, b] = [-1, 1]$. We proceed by constructing a sequence $\{g_n\}$ of continuous real-valued functions on X that has the following two properties: for each index n,

$$|g_n| \le (2/3)^n \text{ on } X \tag{3}$$

and

$$|f - [g_1 + \cdots + g_n]| \le (2/3)^n \text{ on } F. \tag{4}$$

Indeed, suppose, for the moment, that this sequence of functions has been constructed. Define, for each index n, the real-valued function s_n on X by

$$s_n(x) = \sum_{k=1}^{n} g_n(x) \text{ for } x \text{ in } X.$$

We infer from the estimate (3) that, for each x in X, $\{s_n(x)\}$ is a Cauchy sequence of real numbers. Since $\mathbf{R}$ is complete, this sequence converges. Define

$$g(x) = \lim_{n \to \infty} s_n(x) \text{ for } x \text{ in } X.$$

Since each g_n is continuous on X, so is each s_n. We may infer from the estimate (3) that $\{s_n\}$ converges to g uniformly on X and therefore g is continuous. From the estimate (4) it is clear that $f = g$ on F. Thus the theorem is proved provided we construct the sequence $\{g_n\}$. We do so by induction.

Claim: For each $a > 0$ and continuous function $h: F \to \mathbf{R}$ for which $|h| \le a$ on F, there is a continuous function $g: X \to \mathbf{R}$ such that

$$|g| \le (2/3)a \text{ on } X \text{ and } |h - g| \le (2/3)a \text{ on } F. \tag{5}$$

Indeed, define

$$A = \left\{x \text{ in } F \mid h(x) \le -(1/3)a\right\} \text{ and } B = \left\{x \text{ in } F \mid h(x) \ge (1/3)a\right\}.$$

Since h is continuous on F and F is a closed subset of X, A and B are disjoint closed subsets of X. Therefore, by Urysohn's Lemma, there is a continuous real-valued function g on X for which

$$|g| \le (1/3)a \text{ on } X, \ g(A) = -(1/3)a \text{ and } g(B) = (1/3)a.$$

It is clear that (5) holds for this choice of g. Apply the above approximation claim with $h = f$ and $a = 1$ to find a continuous function $g_1: X \to \mathbf{R}$ for which

$$|g_1| \le (2/3) \text{ on } X \text{ and } |f - g_1| \le (2/3) \text{ on } F.$$

Now apply the claim once more with $h = f - g_1$ and $a = 2/3$ to find a continuous function $g_2: X \to \mathbf{R}$ for which

$$|g_2| \le (2/3)^2 \text{ on } X \text{ and } |f - [g_1 + g_2]| \le (2/3)^2 \text{ on } F.$$

It is now clear how to proceed to inductively choose the sequence $\{g_n\}$ which possesses properties (3) and (4). $\qquad \square$

The Tietze Extension Theorem has a generalization to real-valued functions on X that are not necessarily bounded (see Problem 8).

As a second application of Urysohn's Lemma, we present the following necessary and sufficient criterion for the metrizability of a second countable topological space.

The Urysohn Metrization Theorem *Let X be a second countable topological space: Then X is metrizable if and only if it is normal.*

Proof We have already shown that a metric space is normal. Now let X be a second countable and normal topological space. Choose a countable base $\{\mathcal{U}_n\}_{n \in \mathbf{N}}$ for the topology. Let A be the subset of the product $\mathbf{N} \times \mathbf{N}$ defined by

$$A = \left\{(n, m) \text{ in } \mathbf{N} \times \mathbf{N} \mid \overline{\mathcal{U}}_n \subseteq \mathcal{U}_m\right\}.$$

Since X is normal, according to Urysohn's Lemma, for each pair (n, m) in A, there is a continuous real-valued function $f_{n,m} \colon X \to [0, 1]$ for which

$$f_{n,m} = 0 \text{ on } \overline{\mathcal{U}}_n \text{ and } f_{n,m} = 1 \text{ on } X \sim \mathcal{U}_m.$$

For x, y in X, define

$$\rho(x, y) = \sum_{(n, m) \in A} \frac{1}{2^{n+m}} |f_{n,m}(x) - f_{n,m}(y)|. \qquad (6)$$

The set A is countable so this sum converges. It is not difficult to see that this is a metric. We claim that the topology induced by ρ is the given topology on X. To verify this it is necessary to compare bases. Specifically, it is necessary to verify the following two properties at each point $x \in X$:

(i) If $\mathcal{U}_n$ contains x, then there is an $\epsilon > 0$ for which $B_\rho(x, \epsilon) \subseteq \mathcal{U}_n$.

(ii) For each $\epsilon > 0$, there is a $\mathcal{U}_n$ that contains x and $\mathcal{U}_n \subseteq B_\rho(x, \epsilon)$.

We leave the verification of these assertions as an exercise. ☐

PROBLEMS

1. Let C be a closed subset of a metric space (X, ρ). Show that the distance to C function d_C is continuous and $d_C(x) = 0$ if and only if x belongs to C.

2. Provide an example of a continuous real-valued function on the open interval $(0, 1)$ that is not extendable to a continuous function on $\mathbf{R}$. Does this contradict the Tietze Extension Theorem?

3. Deduce Urysohn's Lemma as a consequence of the Tietze Extension Theorem.

4. State and prove a version of the Tietze Extension Theorem for functions with values in $\mathbf{R}^n$.

5. Suppose that a topological space X has the property that every continuous, bounded real-valued function on a closed subset has a continuous extension to all of X. Show that if X is Tychonoff, then it is normal.

6. Let $(X, \mathcal{T})$ be a normal topological space and $\mathcal{F}$ the collection of continuous real-valued functions on X. Show that $\mathcal{T}$ is the weak topology induced by $\mathcal{F}$.

7. Show that the function ρ defined in the proof of the Urysohn Metrization Theorem is a metric that defines the same topology as the given topology.

8. Let X be a normal topological space, F a closed subset of X, and f a continuous real-valued function on F. Then f has a continuous extension to a real-valued function $\overline{f}$ on all of X. Prove this as follows:

   (i) Apply the Tietze Extension Theorem to obtain a continuous extension $h \colon X \to [0, \cdot 1]$ of the function $f \cdot (1 + |f|)^{-1} \colon F \to [0, 1]$;

   (ii) Once more, apply the Tietze Extension Theorem to obtain a function $\phi \colon X \to [0, 1]$ such that $\phi = 1$ on F and $\phi = 0$ on $h^{-1}(1)$;

   (iii) Consider the function $\overline{f} = \phi \cdot h / (1 - \phi \cdot h)$.

9. Show that a mapping f from a topological space X to a topological space Y is continuous if and only if there is a subbase $\mathcal{S}$ for the topology on Y such that the preimage under f of each set in $\mathcal{S}$ is open in X. Use this to show that if Y is a closed, bounded interval $[a, b]$, then f

is continuous if and only if for each real number $c \in (a, b)$, the sets $\{x \in X \mid f(x) < c\}$ and $\{x \in X \mid f(x) > c\}$ are open.

10. Use the preceding problem to prove Lemma 1.

12.2   THE TYCHONOFF PRODUCT THEOREM

For a collection of sets indexed by a set Λ, $\{X_\lambda\}_{\lambda \in \Lambda}$, we defined the Cartesian product $\Pi_{\lambda \in \Lambda} X_\lambda$ to be the collection of mappings from the index set Λ to the union $\bigcup_{\lambda \in \Lambda} X_\lambda$ such that each index $\lambda \in \Lambda$ is mapped to a member of X_λ. For a member x of the Cartesian product and an index $\lambda \in \Lambda$, it is customary to denote $x(\lambda)$ by x_λ and call x_λ the λ-th component of x. For each parameter $\lambda_0 \in \Lambda$, we define the λ_0 projection mapping $\pi_{\lambda_0} : \Pi_{\lambda \in \Lambda} X_\lambda \to X_{\lambda_0}$ by

$$\pi_{\lambda_0}(x) = x_{\lambda_0} \text{ for } x \in \Pi_{\lambda \in \Lambda} X_\lambda.$$

We have defined the product metric on the Cartesian product of two metric spaces. This extends in an obvious manner to a metric on the Cartesian product of a finite number of metric spaces. Moreover, there is a natural metric on the Cartesian product of a countable number of metric spaces (see Problem 16).

There is a natural definition of a topology on the Cartesian product of a finite collection of topological spaces. Given a collection $\{(X_k, \mathcal{T}_k)\}_{k=1}^n$ of topological spaces, the collection of products

$$\mathcal{O}_1 \times \ldots \mathcal{O}_k \ldots \times \mathcal{O}_n,$$

where each $\mathcal{O}_k$ belongs to $\mathcal{T}_k$, is a base for a topology on $\Pi_{1 \le k \le n} X_k$. The topology on the Cartesian product consisting of unions of these basic sets is called the **product topology** on $\Pi_{1 \le k \le n} X_k$.

What is novel for topological spaces is that a product topology can be defined on an arbitrary Cartesian product $\Pi_{\lambda \in \Lambda} X_\lambda$ of topological spaces. The index set is not required to be finite or even countable.

Definition *Let $\{(X_\lambda, \mathcal{T}_\lambda)\}_{\lambda \in \Lambda}$ be a collection of topological spaces indexed by a set Λ. The* **product topology** *on the Cartesian product $\Pi_{\lambda \in \Lambda} X_\lambda$ is the topology that has as a base sets of the form $\Pi_{\lambda \in \Lambda} \mathcal{O}_\lambda$, where each $\mathcal{O}_\lambda \in \mathcal{T}_\lambda$ and $\mathcal{O}_\lambda = X_\lambda$, except for finitely many λ.*

If all the X_λ's are the same space X, it is customary to denote $\Pi_{\lambda \in \Lambda} X_\lambda$ by X^Λ. In particular, if **N** denotes the set on natural numbers, then $X^{\mathbf{N}}$ is the collection of sequences in X while $\mathbf{R}^X$ is the collection of real-valued functions that have domain X. If X is a metric space and Λ is countable, then the product topology on X^Λ is induced by a metric (see Problem 16). In general, if X is a metric space but Λ is uncountable, the product topology is not induced by a metric. For example, the product topology on $\mathbf{R}^{\mathbf{R}}$ is not induced by a metric (see Problem 17). We leave it as an exercise to verify the following two propositions.

Proposition 3 *Let X be a topological space. A sequence $\{f_n : \Lambda \to X\}$ converges to f in the product space X^Λ if and only if $\{f_n(\lambda)\}$ converges to $f(\lambda)$ for each λ in Λ. Thus, convergence of a sequence with respect to the product topology is pointwise convergence.*

Proposition 4 *The product topology on the Cartesian product of topological spaces $\Pi_{\lambda \in \Lambda} X_\lambda$ is the weak topology associated to the collection of projections $\{\pi_\lambda : \Pi_{\lambda \in \Lambda} X_\lambda \to X_\lambda\}_{\lambda \in \Lambda}$.*

that is, it is the topology on the Cartesian product that has the fewest number of sets among the topologies for which all the projection mappings are continuous.

The centerpiece of this section is the Tychonoff Product Theorem, which tells us that the product $\Pi_{\lambda \in \Lambda} X_\lambda$ of compact topological spaces is compact. There are no restrictions on the index space Λ. In preparation for the proof of this theorem we first establish two lemmas regarding collections of sets that possess the finite intersection property.

Lemma 5 *Let A be a collection of subsets of a set X that possesses the finite intersection property. Then there is a collection B of subsets of X which contains A, has the finite intersection property, and is maximal with respect to this property; that is, no collection of subsets of X that properly contains B possesses the finite intersection property.*

Proof Consider the family $\mathcal{F}$ of all collections of subsets of X containing A and possessing the finite intersection property. Order $\mathcal{F}$ by inclusion. Every linearly ordered subfamily $\mathcal{F}_0$ of $\mathcal{F}$ has an upper bound consisting of the sets belonging to any collection in $\mathcal{F}_0$. According to Zorn's Lemma, there is maximal member of $\mathcal{F}$. This maximal member is a collection of sets that has the properties described in the conclusion of the lemma. $\square$

Lemma 6 *Let B be a collection of subsets of X that is maximal with respect to the finite intersection property. Then each intersection of a finite number of sets in B is again in B, and each subset of X that has nonempty intersection with each set in B is itself in B.*

Proof Let B' be the collection of all sets that are finite intersections of sets in B. Then B' is a collection having the finite intersection property and containing B. Thus $B' = B$ by the maximality, with respect to inclusion, of B. Now suppose that C is a subset of X that has nonempty intersection with each member of B. Since B contains each finite intersection of sets in B, it follows that $B \cup \{C\}$ has the finite intersection property. By the maximality, with respect to inclusion, of B, $B \cup \{C\} = B$, and so C is a member of B. $\square$

The Tychonoff Product Theorem *Let $\{X_\lambda\}_{\lambda \in \Lambda}$ be a collection of compact topological spaces indexed by a set Λ. Then the Cartesian product $\Pi_{\lambda \in \Lambda} X_\lambda$, with the product topology, also is compact.*

Proof Let $\mathcal{F}$ be a collection of closed subsets of $X = \Pi_{\lambda \in \Lambda} X_\lambda$ possessing the finite intersection property. We must show $\mathcal{F}$ has nonempty intersection. By Lemma 5, there is a collection B of (not necessarily closed) subsets of X that contains $\mathcal{F}$ and is maximal with respect to the finite intersection property. Fix $\lambda \in \Lambda$. Define

$$B_\lambda = \{\pi_\lambda(B) \mid B \in B\}.$$

Then B_λ is a collection of subsets of the set X_λ that has the finite intersection property, as does the collection of closures of members of B_λ. By the compactness of X_λ there is a point $x_\lambda \in X_\lambda$ for which

$$x_\lambda \in \bigcap_{B \in B} \overline{\pi_\lambda(B)}.$$

Define x to be the point in X whose λ-th coordinate is x_λ. We claim that

$$x \in \bigcap_{F \in \mathcal{F}} F. \tag{7}$$

Indeed, the point x has the property that for each index λ, x_λ is a point of closure of $\pi_\lambda(B)$ for every $B \in \mathcal{B}$. Thus [1]

> every subbasic neighborhood $\mathcal{N}_x$ of x has nonempty intersection
>
> with every set B in $\mathcal{B}$. $\hspace{3cm}$ (8)

From the maximality of $\mathcal{B}$ and Lemma 6, we conclude that every subbasic neighborhood of x belongs to $\mathcal{B}$. Once more using Lemma 6, we conclude that every basic neighborhood of x belongs to $\mathcal{B}$. But $\mathcal{B}$ has the finite intersection property and contains the collection $\mathcal{F}$. Let F be a set in $\mathcal{F}$. Then every basic neighborhood of x has nonempty intersection with F. Hence x is a point of closure of the closed set F, so that x belongs to F. Thus (7) holds. $\hspace{1cm}$ $\square$

PROBLEMS

11. Show that the product of an arbitrary collection of Tychonoff spaces, with the product topology, also is Tychonoff.

12. Show that the product of an arbitrary collection of Hausdorff spaces, with the product topology, also is Hausdorff.

13. Consider the Cartesian product of n copies of $\mathbf{R}$,

$$\mathbf{R}^n = \overbrace{\mathbf{R} \times \mathbf{R} \times \cdots \times \mathbf{R}}^{n}.$$

Show that the product topology is the same as the metric topology on $\mathbf{R}^n$ induced by the Euclidean metric.

14. Let (X, ρ_1) and (Y, ρ_2) be metric spaces. Show that the product topology on $X \times Y$, where X and X have the topologies induced by their respective metrics, is the same as the topology induced by the product metric

$$\rho((x_1, y_1), (x_2, y_2)) = \sqrt{[\rho_1(x_1, x_2)]^2 + [\rho_2(y_1, y_2)]^2}.$$

15. Show that if X is a metric space with metric ρ, then

$$\rho^*(x, y) = \frac{\rho(x, y)}{1 + \rho(x, y)}$$

also is a metric on X and it induces the same topology as the metric ρ.

16. Consider the countable collection of metric spaces $\{(X_n, \rho_n)\}_{n=1}^\infty$. For the Cartesian product of these sets $X = \prod_{n=1}^\infty X_n$, define $\rho: X \times X \to \mathbf{R}$ by

$$\rho(x, y) = \sum_{n=1}^\infty \frac{\rho_n(x_n, y_n)}{2^n[1 + \rho_n(x_n, y_n)]}.$$

---

[1] It is convenient here to call an open set $\mathcal{O}$ set of the form $\mathcal{O} = \prod_{\lambda \in \Lambda} \mathcal{O}_\lambda$. where each $\mathcal{O}_\lambda$ is an open subset of X_λ and $\mathcal{O}_\lambda = X_\lambda$ except for one λ, a *subbasic set* and the finite intersection of such sets a *basic set*.

Use the preceding problem to show that ρ is a metric on $X = \prod_{n=1}^{\infty} X_n$ which induces the product topology on X, where each X_n has the topology induced by the metric ρ_n.

17. Consider the set $X = \mathbf{R}^{\mathbf{R}}$ with the product topology. Let E be the subset of X consisting of functions that take the value 0 on a countable set and elsewhere take the value 1. Let f_0 be the function that is identically zero. Then it is clear that f_0 is a point of closure of E. But there is no sequence $\{f_n\}$ in E that converges to f_0, since for any sequence $\{f_n\}$ in E there is some $x_0 \in \mathbf{R}$ such that $f_n(x_0) = 1$ for all n and so the sequence $\{f_n(x_0)\}$ does not converge to $f_0(x_0)$. This shows, in particular, that $X = \mathbf{R}^{\mathbf{R}}$ is not first countable and therefore not metrizable.

18. Let X denote the discrete topological space with two elements. Show that X^N is homeomorphic to the Cantor set.

19. Using the Tychonoff Product Theorem and the compactness of each closed, bounded interval of real numbers prove that any closed, bounded subset of $\mathbf{R}^n$ is compact.

20. Provide a direct proof of the assertion that if X is compact and I is a closed, bounded interval, then $X \times I$ is compact. (Hint: Let $\mathcal{U}$ be an open covering of $X \times I$, and consider the smallest value of $t \in I$ such that for each $t' < t$ the set $X \times [0, t']$ can be covered by a finite number of sets in $\mathcal{U}$. Use the compactness of X to show that $X \times [0, t]$ can also be covered by a finite number of sets in $\mathcal{U}$ and that if $t < 1$, then for some $t'' > t$, $X \times [0, t'']$ can be covered by a finite number of sets in $\mathcal{U}$.)

21. Prove that the product of a countable number of sequentially compact topological spaces is sequentially compact.

22. A product I^A of unit intervals is called a (generalized) cube. Prove that every compact Hausdorff space X is homeomorphic to a closed subset of some cube. (Let $\mathcal{F}$ be the family of continuous real-valued functions on X with values in $[0, 1]$. Let $Q = \prod_{f \in \mathcal{F}} I_f$. Then, since X is normal, the mapping g of X onto Q that takes x into the point whose f-th coordinate is $f(x)$ is one-to-one, continuous, and has closed image.)

23. Let $Q = I^A$ be a cube, and let f be a continuous real-valued function on Q. Then, given $\epsilon > 0$, there is a continuous real-valued function g on Q for which $|f - g| < \epsilon$ and g is a function of only a finite number of coordinates. (Hint: Cover the range of f by a finite number of intervals of length ϵ and look at the inverse images of these intervals.)

12.3 THE STONE-WEIERSTRASS THEOREM

The following theorem is one of the jewels of classical analysis.

The Weierstrass Approximation Theorem *Let f be a continuous real-valued function on a closed, bounded interval $[a, b]$. Then for each $\epsilon > 0$, there is a polynomial p for which*

$$|f(x) - p(x)| < \epsilon \text{ for all } x \in [a, b].$$

In this section we provide a far-reaching extension of this theorem. For a compact Hausdorff space X, consider the linear space $C(X)$ of continuous real-valued functions on X with the maximum norm. The Weierstrass Approximation Theorem tells us that the polynomials are dense in $C[a, b]$.

Now $C(X)$ has a product structure not possessed by all linear spaces, namely, the product fg of two functions f and g in $C(X)$ is again in $C(X)$. A linear subspace $\mathcal{A}$ of $C(X)$

is called an **algebra** provided the product of any two functions in A also belongs to A. A collection A of real-valued functions on X is said to **separate points** in X provided for any two distinct points u and v in X, there is an f in A for which $f(u) \neq f(v)$. Observe that since X is compact and Hausdorff, according to Theorem 18 of the preceding chapter, it is normal and therefore we may infer from Urysohn's Lemma that the whole algebra $C(X)$ separates points in X.

The Stone-Weierstrass Approximation Theorem *Let X be a compact Hausdorff space. Suppose A is an algebra of continuous real-valued functions on X that separates points in X and contains the constant functions. Then A is dense in $C(X)$.*

Observe that this is a generalization of the Weierstrass Approximation Theorem since the closed, bounded interval $[a, b]$ is compact and Hausdorff and the collection of polynomials is an algebra that contains the constant functions and separates points.

Before we prove the theorem, a few words concerning strategy are in order.[2] Since X is compact and Hausdorff, it is normal. We infer from Urysohn's Lemma that for each pair of disjoint closed subsets A and B of X and $\epsilon \in (0, 1/2)$, there is a function $f \in C(X)$ for which

$$f = \epsilon/2 \text{ on } A, f = 1 - \epsilon/2 \text{ on } B, \text{ and } \epsilon/2 \leq f \leq 1 - \epsilon/2 \text{ on } X.$$

Therefore, if $|h - f| < \epsilon/2$ on X,

$$h < \epsilon \text{ on } A, h > 1 - \epsilon \text{ on } B, \text{ and } 0 \leq h \leq 1 \text{ on } X. \tag{9}$$

The proof will proceed in two steps. First, we show that for each pair of disjoint closed subsets A and B of X and $\epsilon \in (0, 1/2)$, there is a function h belonging to the algebra A for which (9) holds. We then show that any function f in $C(X)$ can be uniformly approximated by linear combinations of such h's.

Lemma 7 *Let X be a compact Hausdorff space and A an algebra of continuous functions on X that separates points and contains the constant functions. Then for each closed subset F of X and point x_0 belonging to $X \sim F$, there is a neighborhood U of x_0 that is disjoint from F and has the following property: for each $\epsilon > 0$, there is a function $h \in A$ for which*

$$h < \epsilon \text{ on } U, \ h > 1 - \epsilon \text{ on } F, \text{ and } 0 \leq h \leq 1 \text{ on } X. \tag{10}$$

Proof We first claim that for each point $y \in F$, there is a function g_y in A for which

$$g_y(x_0) = 0, \ g_y(y) > 0, \text{ and } 0 \leq g_y \leq 1 \text{ on } X. \tag{11}$$

Indeed, since A separates points, there is a function $f \in A$ for which $f(x_0) \neq f(y)$. The function

$$g_y = \left[\frac{f - f(x_0)}{\|f - f(x_0)\|_{max}} \right]^2$$

---

[2] The proof we present is due to B. Brasowski and F. Deutsch, *Proceedings of the American Mathematical Society, 81* (1981). Many very different-looking proofs of the Stone-Weierstrass Theorem have been given since the first proof in 1937 by Marshal Stone.

belongs to $\mathcal{A}$ and satisfies (11). By the continuity of g_y, there is a neighborhood $\mathcal{N}_y$ of y on which g_y only takes positive values. However, F is a closed subset of the compact space X and therefore F itself is compact. Thus we may choose a finite collection of these neighborhoods $\{\mathcal{N}_{y_1}, \ldots, \mathcal{N}_{y_n}\}$ that covers F. Define the function $g \in \mathcal{A}$ by

$$g = \frac{1}{n} \sum_{i=1}^{n} g_{y_i}.$$

Then

$$g(x_0) = 0, \; g > 0 \text{ on } F, \text{ and } 0 \leq g \leq 1 \text{ on } X. \tag{12}$$

But a continuous function on a compact set takes a minimum value, so we may choose $c > 0$ for which $g \geq c$ on F. By possibly multiplying g by a positive number, we may suppose $c < 1$. On the other hand, g is continuous at x_0, so there is a neighborhood $\mathcal{U}$ of x_0 for which $g < c/2$ on U. Thus g belongs to the algebra $\mathcal{A}$ and

$$g < c/2 \text{ on } \mathcal{U}, \; g \geq c \text{ on } F, \text{ and } 0 \leq g \leq 1 \text{ on } X. \tag{13}$$

We claim that (10) holds for this choice of neighborhood $\mathcal{U}$. Let $\epsilon > 0$. By the Weierstrass Approximation Theorem, we can find a polynomial p such that[3]

$$p < \epsilon \text{ on } [0, c/2], \; p > 1 - \epsilon \text{ on } [c, 1], \text{ and } 0 \leq p \leq 1 \text{ on } [0, 1]. \tag{14}$$

Since p is a polynomial and f belongs to the algebra $\mathcal{A}$, the composition $h = p \circ g$ also belongs to $\mathcal{A}$. From (13) and (14) we conclude that (10) holds. $\qquad\square$

Lemma 8 *Let X be a compact Hausdorff space and $\mathcal{A}$ an algebra of continuous functions on X that separates points and contains the constant functions. Then for each pair of disjoint closed subsets A and B of X and $\epsilon > 0$, there is a function h belonging to $\mathcal{A}$ for which*

$$h < \epsilon \text{ on } A, \; h > 1 - \epsilon \text{ on } B, \text{ and } 0 \leq h \leq 1 \text{ on } X. \tag{15}$$

Proof By the preceding lemma in the case $F = B$, for each point $x \in A$, there is a neighborhood $\mathcal{N}_x$ of x that is disjoint from B and has the property (10). However, A is compact since it is a closed subset of the compact space X, and therefore there is a finite collection of neighborhoods $\{\mathcal{N}_{x_1}, \ldots, \mathcal{N}_{x_n}\}$ that covers A. Choose ϵ_0 for which $0 < \epsilon_0 < \epsilon$ and $(1 - \epsilon_0/n)^n > 1 - \epsilon$. For $1 \leq i \leq n$, since $\mathcal{N}_{x_i}$ has property (10) with $B = F$, we choose $h_i \in \mathcal{A}$ such that

$$h_i < \epsilon_0/n \text{ on } \mathcal{N}_{x_i}, \; h_i > 1 - \epsilon_0/n \text{ on } B, \text{ and } 0 \leq h_i \leq 1 \text{ on } X.$$

Define

$$h = h_1 \cdot h_2 \cdots h_n \text{ on } X.$$

Then h belongs to the algebra $\mathcal{A}$. Since for each i, $0 \leq h_i \leq 1$ on X, we have $0 \leq h \leq 1$ on X. Also, for each i, $h_i > 1 - \epsilon_0/n$ on B, so $h \geq (1 - \epsilon_0/n)^n > 1 - \epsilon$ on B. Finally, for each point x in A there is an index i for which x belongs to $\mathcal{N}_{x_i}$. Thus $h_i(x) < \epsilon_0/n < \epsilon$ and since for the other indices j, $0 \leq h_j(x) \leq 1$, we conclude that $h(x) < \epsilon$. $\qquad\square$

---

[3] Rather than using the Weierstrass Approximation Theorem here, one can show that (14) holds for a polynomial of the form $p(x) = 1 - (1 - x^n)^m$, where n and m are suitably chosen natural numbers.

Proof of the Stone-Weierstrass Theorem Let f belong to $C(X)$. Set $c = \|f\|_{\max}$. If we can arbitrarily closely uniformly approximate the function

$$\frac{f+c}{\|f+c\|_{\max}}$$

by functions in $\mathcal{A}$, we can do the same for f. Therefore we may assume that $0 \leq f \leq 1$ on X. Let $n > 1$ be a natural number. Consider the uniform partition $\{0, 1/n, 2/n, \ldots, (n-1)/n, 1\}$ of $[0, 1]$ into n intervals, each of length $1/n$. Fix j, $1 \leq j \leq n$. Define

$$A_j = \left\{x \text{ in } X \mid f(x) \leq (j-1)/n\right\} \text{ and } B_j = \left\{x \text{ in } X \mid f(x) \geq j/n\right\}.$$

Since f is continuous, both A_j and B_j are closed subsets of X and, of course, they are disjoint. By the preceding lemma, with $A = A_j$, $B = B_j$, and $\epsilon = 1/n$, there is a function g_j in the algebra $\mathcal{A}$ for which

$$g_j(x) < 1/n \text{ if } f(x) \leq (j-1)/n, \ g_j(x) > 1 - 1/n \text{ if } f(x) \geq j/n \text{ and } 0 \leq g_j \leq 1 \text{ on } X. \quad (16)$$

Define

$$g = \frac{1}{n} \sum_{j=1}^{n} g_j.$$

Then g belongs to $\mathcal{A}$. We claim that

$$\|f - g\|_{\max} < 3/n. \qquad (17)$$

Once we establish this claim the proof is complete since, given $\epsilon > 0$, we simply select n such that $3/n < \epsilon$ and therefore $\|f - g\|_{\max} < \epsilon$. To verify (17), we first show that

$$\text{if } 1 \leq k \leq n \text{ and } f(x) \leq k/n, \text{ then } g(x) \leq k/n + 1/n. \qquad (18)$$

Indeed, for $j = k+1, \ldots, n$, since $f(x) \leq k/n$, $f(x) \leq (j-1)/n$ and therefore $g_j(x) \leq 1/n$. Thus

$$\frac{1}{n} \sum_{j=k+1}^{n} g_j \leq (n-k)/n^2 \leq 1/n.$$

Consequently, since each $g_j(x) \leq 1$, for all j,

$$g(x) = \frac{1}{n} \sum_{j=1}^{n} g_j = \frac{1}{n} \sum_{j=1}^{k} g_j + \frac{1}{n} \sum_{j=k+1}^{n} g_j \leq \frac{1}{n} \sum_{j=1}^{k} g_j + 1/n \leq k/n + 1/n.$$

Thus (18) holds. A similar argument shows that

$$\text{if } 1 \leq k \leq n \text{ and } (k-1)/n \leq f(x), \text{ then } (k-1)/n - 1/n \leq g(x). \qquad (19)$$

For $x \in X$, choose k, $1 \leq k \leq n$, such that $(k-1)/n \leq f(x) \leq k/n$. From (18) and (19) we infer that $|f(x) - g(x)| < 3/n$. $\square$

We conclude this chapter with the following elegant consequence of Urysohn's Lemma and the Stone-Weierstrass Theorem.

Riesz's Theorem *Let X be a compact Hausforff topological space. Then $C(X)$ is separable if and only if X is metrizable.*

Proof First assume X is metrizable. Let ρ be a metric that induces the topology on X. Then X, being a compact metric space, is separable. Choose a countable dense subset $\{x_n\}$ of X. For each natural number n, define $f_n(x) = \rho(x, x_n)$ for all $x \in X$. Since ρ induces the topology, f_n is continuous. We infer from the denseness of $\{x_n\}$ that $\{f_n\}$ separates points in X. Define $f_0 \equiv 1$ on X. Now let $\mathcal{A}$ to be the collection of polynomials, with real coefficients, in a finite number of the $f_k, 0 \leq k < \infty$. Then $\mathcal{A}$ is an algebra that contains the constant functions, and it separates points in X since it contains each f_k. According to the Stone-Weierstrass Theorem, $\mathcal{A}$ is dense in $C(X)$. But the collection of functions f in $\mathcal{A}$ that are polynomials with rational coefficients is a countable set that is dense in $\mathcal{A}$. Therefore $C(X)$ is separable.

Conversely, suppose $C(X)$ is separable. Let $\{g_n\}$ be a countable dense subset of $C(X)$. For each natural number n, define $\mathcal{O}_n = \{x \in X \mid g_n(x) > 1/2\}$. Then $\{\mathcal{O}_n\}_{1 \leq n < \infty}$ is a countable collection of open sets. We claim that every open set is the union of a subcollection of $\{\mathcal{O}_n\}_{1 \leq n < \infty}$, and therefore X is second countable. But X is normal, since it is compact and Hausdorff. The Urysohn Metrization Theorem tells us that X is metrizable. To verify second countability, let the point x belong to the open set $\mathcal{O}$. Since X is normal, there is an open set $\mathcal{U}$ for which $x \in \mathcal{U} \subseteq \overline{\mathcal{U}} \subseteq \mathcal{O}$. By Urysohn's Lemma, there is a g in $C(X)$ such that $g(x) = 1$ on $\mathcal{U}$ and $g = 0$ on $X \sim \mathcal{O}$. By the denseness of $\{g_n\}$ in $C(X)$, there is a natural number n for which $|g - g_n| < 1/2$ on X. Therefore $x \in \mathcal{O}_n \subseteq \mathcal{O}$. This completes the proof. $\square$

PROBLEMS

24. Suppose that X is a topological space for which there is a collection of continuous real-valued functions on X that separates points in X. Show that X must be Hausdorff.

25. Let X be a compact Hausdorff space and $\mathcal{A} \subseteq C(X)$ an algebra that contains the constant functions. Show that $\mathcal{A}$ is dense in $C(X)$ if and only if $\mathcal{A}$ separates points in X.

26. Let $\mathcal{A}$ be an algebra of continuous real-valued functions on a compact space X that contains the constant functions. Let $f \in C(X)$ have the property that for some constant function c and real number α, the function $\alpha(f + c)$ belongs to $\overline{\mathcal{A}}$. Show that f also belongs to $\overline{\mathcal{A}}$.

27. For $f, g \in C[a, b]$, show that $f = g$ if and only if $\int_a^b x^n f(x)\, dx = \int_a^b x^n g(x)\, dx$ for all n.

28. For $f \in C[a, b]$ and $\epsilon > 0$, show that there are real numbers $c_0, c_1, \ldots, c_n$ for which

$$|f(x) - c_0 - \sum_{k=1}^{n} c_k \cdot e^{kx}| < \epsilon \text{ for all } x \in [a, b].$$

29. For $f \in C[0, \pi]$ and $\epsilon > 0$, show that there are real numbers $c_0, c_1, \ldots, c_n$ for which

$$|f(x) - c_0 - \sum_{k=1}^{n} c_k \cdot \cos kx| < \epsilon \text{ for all } x \in [0, \pi].$$

30. Let f be a continuous real-valued function on **R** that is periodic with period 2π. For $\epsilon > 0$, show that there are real numbers, $c_0, a_1, \ldots, a_n, b_1, \ldots, b_n$, such that

$$|f(x) - c_0 - \sum_{k=1}^{n} [a_k \cos kx + b_k \sin kx]| < \epsilon \text{ for all } x \in \mathbf{R}.$$

(Hint: A periodic function may be identified with a continuous function on the unit circle in the plane and the unit circle is compact and Hausdorff with the topology it inherits from the plane.)

31. Let X and Y be compact Hausdorff spaces and f belong to $C(X \times Y)$. Show that for each $\epsilon > 0$, there are functions $f_1, \ldots, f_n$ in $C(X)$ and $g_1, \ldots, g_n$ in $C(Y)$ such that

$$|f(x, y) - \sum_{k=1}^{n} f_k(x) \cdot g_k(y)| < \epsilon \text{ for all } (x, y) \in X \times Y.$$

32. Rather than use the Weierstrass Approximation Theorem in the proof of the Stone-Weierstrass Theorem, show that there are natural numbers m and n for which the polynomial $p(x) = 1 - (1 - x^n)^m$ satisfies (14). (Hint: Since $p(0) = 0$, $p(1) = 1$ and $p' > 0$ on $(0, 1)$, it suffices to choose m and n such that $p(c/2) < \epsilon$ and $p(c) > 1 - \epsilon$.)

33. Let $\mathcal{A}$ be a collection of continuous real-valued functions on a compact Hausdorff space X that separates the points of X. Show that every continuous real-valued function on X can be uniformly approximated arbitrarily closely by a polynomial in a finite number of functions of $\mathcal{A}$.

34. Let $\mathcal{A}$ be an algebra of continuous real-valued functions on a compact Hausdorff space X. Show that the closure of $\mathcal{A}$, $\overline{\mathcal{A}}$, also is an algebra.

35. Let $\mathcal{A}$ be an algebra of continuous real-valued functions on a compact Hausdorff space X that separates points. Show that either $\overline{\mathcal{A}} = C(X)$ or there is a point $x_0 \in X$ for which $\overline{\mathcal{A}} = \{f \in C(X) \mid f(x_0) = 0\}$. (Hint: If $1 \in \overline{\mathcal{A}}$, we are done. Moreover, if for each $x \in X$ there is an $f \in \mathcal{A}$ with $f(x) \neq 0$, then there is a $g \in \mathcal{A}$ that is positive on X and this implies that $1 \in \overline{\mathcal{A}}$.)

36. Let X be a compact Hausdorff space and $\mathcal{A}$ an algebra of continuous functions on X that separates points and contains the constant functions.

    (i) Given any two numbers a and b and points $u, v \in X$, show that there is a function f in $\mathcal{A}$ for which $f(u) = a$ and $f(v) = b$.

    (ii) Is it the case that given any two numbers a and b and disjoint closed subsets A and B of X, there is a function f in $\mathcal{A}$ for which $f = a$ on A and $f = b$ on B?

CHAPTER 13

Continuous Linear Operators Between Banach Spaces

Contents

We have already examined important specific classes of normed linear spaces. The most prominent of these are: (i) for a natural number n, Euclidean space $\mathbf{R}^n$; (ii) for a Lebesgue measurable subset E of real numbers and $1 \leq p < \infty$, the $L^p(E)$ space of Lebesgue measurable functions for which the pth power is integrable over E; (iii) for X a compact topological space, the linear space $C(X)$ of continuous real-valued functions on X, normed by the maximum norm. In this and the following three chapters we study general normed linear spaces and the continuous linear operators between such spaces. The most interesting results are obtained for complete normed linear spaces, which we call Banach spaces. The results we have established in the preceding four chapters for metric and topological spaces are our basic tools.

13.1 NORMED LINEAR SPACES

A linear space X is an abelian group with the group operation of addition denoted by $+$, for which, given a real number α and $u \in X$, there is defined the scalar product $\alpha \cdot u \in X$ for which the following three properties hold: for real numbers α and β and members u and v in X,

$$(\alpha + \beta) \cdot u = \alpha \cdot u + \beta \cdot u,$$

$$\alpha \cdot (u + v) = \alpha \cdot u + \alpha \cdot v,$$

$$(\alpha\beta) \cdot u = \alpha \cdot (\beta \cdot u) \text{ and } 1 \cdot u = u.$$

A linear space is also called a vector space and, paying respect to $\mathbf{R}^n$, members of a linear space are often called vectors. The quintessential example of a linear space is the collection of real-valued functions on an arbitrary nonempty set D where, for two functions $f, g: D \to \mathbf{R}$ and real number λ, addition $f + g$ and scalar multiplication $\lambda \cdot f$ are defined pointwise on D by

$$(f + g)(x) = f(x) + g(x) \text{ and } (\lambda \cdot f)(x) = \lambda f(x) \text{ for all } x \in D.$$

Recall the concept of norm on a linear space X, which we first studied in Chapter 7; a nonnegative real-valued function $\| \cdot \|$ defined on a linear space X is called a **norm** provided for all $u, v \in X$ and $\alpha \in \mathbf{R}$:

$$\|u\| = 0 \text{ if and only if } u = 0;$$

$$\|u + v\| \leq \|u\| + \|v\|;$$

$$\|\alpha u\| = |\alpha| \|u\|.$$

As we observed in Chapter 9, a norm on a linear space induces a metric on the space, where the distance between u and v is defined to be $\|u - v\|$. When we refer to metric properties of a normed space, such as boundedness and completeness, we mean with respect to the metric induced by the norm. Similarly, when we refer to topological properties, such as a sequence converging or a set being open, closed, or compact, we are referring to the topology induced by the above metric.[1]

Definition   *Two norms* $\| \cdot \|_1$ *and* $\| \cdot \|_2$ *on a linear space* X *are said to be* **equivalent** *provided there are constants* $c_1 \geq 0$ *and* $c_2 \geq 0$ *for which*

$$c_1 \cdot \|x\|_1 \leq \|x\|_2 \leq c_2 \cdot \|x\|_1 \text{ for all } x \in X.$$

We immediately see that two norms are equivalent if and only if their induced metrics are equivalent. Therefore, if a norm on a linear space is replaced by an equivalent norm, the topological and metric properties remain unchanged.

Concepts from linear algebra in finite dimensional spaces are also important for general linear spaces.[2] Given vectors $x_1, \ldots, x_n$ in a linear space X and real numbers $\lambda_1, \ldots, \lambda_n$, the vector

$$x = \sum_{k=1}^{n} \lambda_k x_k$$

is called a **linear combination** of the x_i's. A nonempty subset Y of X is called a **linear subspace**, or simply a subspace, provided every linear combination of vectors in Y also belongs to Y.

For a nonempty subset S of X, by the **span** of S we mean the set of all linear combinations of vectors in S: we denote the span of S by span$[S]$. We leave it as an exercise to show that span$[S]$ is a linear subspace of X, which is the smallest subspace of X that contains S in the sense that it is contained in any linear subspace that contains S. If $Y = \text{span}[S]$ we say that S spans Y. It will also be useful to consider the closure of the span of S, which we denote by $\overline{\text{span}}[S]$. We leave it as an exercise to show that the closure of a linear subspace of X is a linear subspace. Thus $\overline{\text{span}}[S]$ is a linear subspace of X which is the smallest closed linear subspace of X that contains S in the sense that it is contained in any closed linear subspace that contains S. We call $\overline{\text{span}}[S]$ the **closed linear span** of S.

---

[1] In the following chapters we consider topologies on a normed linear space X other than that induced by the norm and are explicit when we refer to topological properties with respect to these other topologies.

[2] We later refer to a few results from linear algebra but require nothing more than knowing that any two bases of a finite dimensional linear space have the same number of vectors, so dimension is properly defined, and that any linearly independent set of vectors in a finite dimensional linear space is a subset of a basis: see Peter Lax's *Linear Algebra* [Lax97].

For any two nonempty subsets A and B of a linear space X, we define the **sum** of A with B, written $A + B$, by

$$A + B = \{x + y \mid x \in A, y \in B\}.$$

In the case B is the singleton set $\{x_0\}$, we denote $A + \{x_0\}$ by $A + x_0$ and call this set a **translate** of A. For $\lambda \in \mathbf{R}$, we define λA to be the set of all elements of the form λx with $x \in A$. Observe that if Y and Z are subspaces of X, then the sum $Y + Z$ is also a subspace of X. In the case $Y \cap Z = \{0\}$ we denote $Y + Z$ by $Y \oplus Z$ and call this subspace of X the **direct sum** of Y and Z.

For a normed linear space X, the open ball of radius 1 centered at the origin, $\{x \in X \mid \|x\| < 1\}$, is called the **open unit ball** in X and $\{x \in X \mid \|x\| \le 1\}$ is called the **closed unit ball** in X. We call a vector $x \in X$ for which $\|x\| = 1$ a **unit vector**.

Almost all the important theorems for metric spaces require completeness. Therefore it is not surprising that among normed linear spaces those that are complete with respect to the metric induced by the norm will be the most important.

Definition *A normed linear space is called a* **Banach space** *provided it is complete as a metric space with the metric induced by the norm.*

The Riesz-Fischer Theorem tells us that for E a measurable set of real numbers and $1 \le p \le \infty$, $L^p(E)$ is a Banach space. We also proved that for X a compact topological space, $C(X)$, with the maximum norm, is a Banach space. Of course, we infer from the Completeness Axiom for $\mathbf{R}$ that each Euclidean space $\mathbf{R}^n$ is a Banach space.

PROBLEMS

1. Show that a nonempty subset S of a linear space X is a subspace if and only if $S + S = S$ and $\lambda \cdot S = S$ for each $\lambda \in \mathbf{R}, \lambda \ne 0$.

2. If Y and Z are subspaces of the linear space X, show that $Y + Z$ also is a subspace and $Y + Z = \text{span}[Y \cup Z]$.

3. Let S be a subset of a normed linear space X.
   (i) Show that the intersection of a collection of linear subspaces of X also is a linear subspace of X.

   (ii) Show that span$[S]$ is the intersection of all the linear subspaces of X that contain S and therefore is a linear subspace of X.

   (iii) Show that $\overline{\text{span}}[S]$ is the intersection of all the closed linear subspaces of X that contain S and therefore is a closed linear subspace of X.

4. For a normed linear space X, show that the function $\|\cdot\|\colon X \to \mathbf{R}$ is continuous.

5. For two normed linear spaces $(X, \|\cdot\|_1)$ and $(Y, \|\cdot\|_2)$, define a linear structure on the Cartesian product $X \times Y$ by $\lambda \cdot (x, y) = (\lambda x, \lambda y)$ and $(x_1, y_1) + (x_2, y_2) = (x_1 + x_2, y_1 + y_2)$. Define the product norm $\|\cdot\|$ by $\|(x, y)\| = \|x\|_1 + \|y\|_2$, for $x \in X$ and $y \in Y$. Show that this is a norm with respect to which a sequence converges if and only if each of the two component sequences converges. Furthermore, show that if X and Y are Banach spaces, then so is $X \times Y$.

6. Let X be a normed linear space.

   (i)   Let $\{x_n\}$ and $\{y_n\}$ be sequences in X such that $\{x_n\} \to x$ and $\{y_n\} \to y$. Show that for any real numbers α and β, $\{\alpha x_n + \beta y_n\} \to \alpha x + \beta y$.

   (ii) Use (i) to show that if Y is a subspace of X, then its closure $\overline{Y}$ also is a linear subspace of X.

   (iii) Use (i) to show that the vector sum is continuous from $X \times X$ to X and scalar multiplication is continuous from $\mathbf{R} \times X$ to X.

7. Show that the set $\mathcal{P}$ of all polynomials on $[a, b]$ is a linear space. For $\mathcal{P}$ considered as a subset of the normed linear space $C[a, b]$, show that $\mathcal{P}$ fails to be closed. For $\mathcal{P}$ considered as a subset of the normed linear space $L^1[a, b]$, show that $\mathcal{P}$ fails to be closed.

8. A nonnegative real-valued function $\| \cdot \|$ defined on a vector space X is called a **pseudonorm** if $\|x + y\| \le \|x\| + \|y\|$ and $\|\alpha x\| = |\alpha| \, \|x\|$. Define $x \cong y$, provided $\|x - y\| = 0$. Show that this is an equivalence relation. Define $X/_{\cong}$ to be the set of equivalence classes of X under $\cong$ and for $x \in X$ define $[x]$ to be the equivalence class of x. Show that $X/_{\cong}$ is a normed vector space if we define $\alpha[x] + \beta[y]$ to be the equivalence class of $\alpha x + \beta y$ and define $\|[x]\| = \|x\|$. Illustrate this procedure with $X = L^p[a, b], 1 \le p < \infty$.

13.2   LINEAR OPERATORS

Definition *Let X and Y be linear spaces. A mapping $T \colon X \to Y$ is said to be* **linear** *provided for each $u, v \in X$, and real numbers α and β,*

$$T(\alpha u + \beta v) = \alpha T(u) + \beta T(v).$$

Linear mappings are often called **linear operators** or linear transformations. In linear algebra one studies linear operators between finite dimensional linear spaces, which, with respect to a choice of bases for the domain and range, are all given by matrix multiplication. In our study of the $L^p(\mathrm{E})$ spaces for $1 \le p < \infty$, we considered continuous linear operators from L^p to $\mathbf{R}$. We called these operators functionals and proved the Riesz Representation Theorem that characterized them.

Definition *Let X and Y be normed linear spaces. A linear operator $T \colon X \to Y$ is said to be* **bounded** *provided there is a constant $M \ge 0$ for which*

$$\|T(u)\| \le M\|u\| \text{ for all } u \in X. \tag{1}$$

The infimum of all such M is called the **operator norm** *of T and denoted by $\|T\|$. The collection of bounded linear operators from X to Y is denoted by $\mathcal{L}(X, Y)$.*

Let X and Y be normed linear spaces and T belong to $\mathcal{L}(X, Y)$. It is easy to see that (1) holds for $M = \|T\|$. Hence, by the linearity of T,

$$\|T(u) - T(v)\| \le \|T\| \cdot \|u - v\| \text{ for all } u, v \in X. \tag{2}$$

From this we infer the following continuity property of a bounded linear operator T:

$$\text{if } \{u_n\} \to u \text{ in } X, \text{ then } \{T(u_n)\} \to T(u) \text{ in } Y. \tag{3}$$

Indeed, we have the following basic result for linear operators.

Theorem 1 *A linear operator between normed linear spaces is continuous if and only if it is bounded.*

Proof Let X and Y be normed linear spaces and $T: X \to Y$ be linear. If T is bounded, (3) tells us that T is continuous. Now suppose $T: X \to Y$ is continuous. Since T is linear, $T(0) = 0$. Therefore, by the $\epsilon - \delta$ criterion for continuity at $u = 0$, with $\epsilon = 1$, we may choose $\delta > 0$ such that $\|T(u) - T(0)\| < 1$ if $\|u - 0\| < \delta$, that is, $\|T(u)\| < 1$ if $\|u\| < \delta$. For any $u \in X, u \neq 0$, set $\lambda = \delta/\|u\|$ and observe by the positive homogeneity of the norm, $\|\lambda u\| \leq \delta$. Thus $\|T(\lambda u)\| \leq 1$. Since $\|T(\lambda u)\| = \lambda \|T(u)\|$, we conclude that (1) holds for $M = 1/\delta$. $\quad\square$

Definition *Let X and Y be linear spaces. For $T: X \to Y$ and $S: X \to Y$ linear operators and real numbers α, β we define $\alpha T + \beta S: X \to Y$ pointwise by*

$$(\alpha T + \beta S)(u) = \alpha T(u) + \beta S(u) \text{ for all } u \in X. \tag{4}$$

Under pointwise scalar multiplication and addition the collection of linear operators between two linear spaces is a linear space.

Proposition 2 *Let X and Y be normed linear space. Then the collection of bounded linear operators from X to Y, $\mathcal{L}(X, Y)$, is a normed linear space.*

Proof Let T and S belong to $\mathcal{L}(X, Y)$. We infer from the triangle inequality for the norm on Y and (2) that

$$\|(T + S)(u)\| \leq \|T(u)\| + \|S(u)\| \leq \|T\|\|u\| + \|S\|\|u\| = (\|T\| + \|S\|)\|u\| \text{ for all } u \in X.$$

Therefore $T + S$ is bounded and $\|T + S\| \leq \|T\| + \|S\|$. It is clear that for a real number α, αT is bounded and $\|\alpha T\| = |\alpha|\|T\|$ and $\|T\| = 0$ if and only if $T(u) = 0$ for all $u \in X$. $\quad\square$

Theorem 3 *Let X and Y be normed linear spaces. If Y is a Banach space, then so is $\mathcal{L}(X, Y)$.*

Proof Let $\{T_n\}$ be a Cauchy sequence in $\mathcal{L}(X, Y)$. Let u belong to X. Then, by (2), for all indices n and m,

$$\|T_n(u) - T_m(u)\| = \|(T_n - T_m)u\| \leq \|T_n - T_m\| \cdot \|u\|.$$

Thus $\{T_n(u)\}$ is a Cauchy sequence in Y. Since, by assumption, Y is complete, the sequence $\{T_n(u)\}$ converges to a member of Y, which we denote by $T(u)$. This defines a mapping $T: X \to Y$. We must show T belongs to $\mathcal{L}(X, Y)$ and $\{T_n\} \to T$ in $\mathcal{L}(X, Y)$. To establish linearity observe that for each u_1, u_2 in X, since each T_n is linear,

$$T(u_1) + T(u_2) = \lim_{n \to \infty} T_n(u_1) + \lim_{n \to \infty} T_n(u_2) = \lim_{n \to \infty} T_n(u_1 + u_2) = T(u_1 + u_2),$$

and similarly $T(\lambda u) = \lambda T(u)$.

We establish the boundedness of T and the convergence of $\{T_n\}$ to T in $\mathcal{L}(X, Y)$ simultaneously. Let $\epsilon > 0$. Choose an index N such that for all $n \geq N, k \geq 1$, $\|T_n - T_{n+k}\| < \epsilon/2$. Thus, by (2), for all $u \in X$,

$$\|T_n(u) - T_{n+k}(u)\| = \|(T_n - T_{n+k})u\| \leq \|T_n - T_{n+k}\| \cdot \|u\| < \epsilon/2\|u\|.$$

Fix $n \geq N$ and $u \in X$. Since $\lim_{k \to \infty} T_{n+k}(u) = T(u)$ and the norm is continuous we conclude that

$$\|T_n(u) - T(u)\| \leq \epsilon/2\|u\|.$$

In particular, the linear operator $T_N - T$ is bounded and therefore, since T_N also is bounded, so is T. Moreover, $\|T_n - T\| < \epsilon$ for $n \geq N$. Thus $\{T_n\} \to T$ in $\mathcal{L}(X, Y)$. $\qquad\square$

For two normed linear spaces X and Y, an operator $T \in \mathcal{L}(X, Y)$ is called an **isomorphism** provided it is one-to-one, onto, and has a continuous inverse. For T in $\mathcal{L}(X, Y)$, if it is one-to-one and onto, its inverse is linear. To be an isomorphism requires that the inverse be bounded, that is, the inverse belong to $\mathcal{L}(Y, X)$. Two normed linear spaces are said to be **isomorphic** provided there is an isomorphism between them. This is an equivalence relation that plays the same role for normed linear spaces that homeomorphism plays for topological spaces. An isomorphism that also preserves the norm is called an **isometric isomorphism**: it is an isomorphism that is also an isometry of the metric structures associated with the norms.

For a linear operator $T: X \to Y$, the subspace of X, $\{x \in X \,|\, T(x) = 0\}$, is called the **kernel** of T and denoted by $\ker T$. Observe that T is one-to-one if and only if $\ker T = \{0\}$. We denote the **image** of T, $T(X)$, by $\operatorname{Im} T$.

PROBLEMS

9. Let X and Y be normed linear spaces and $T: X \to Y$ be linear.

   (i)   Show that T is continuous if and only if it is continuous at a single point u_0 in X.

   (ii) Show that T is Lipschitz if and only if it is continuous.

   (iii) Show that neither (i) nor (ii) hold in the absense of the linearity assumption on T.

10. For X and Y normed linear spaces and $T \in \mathcal{L}(X, Y)$, show that $\|T\|$ is the smallest Lipschitz constant for the mapping T, that is, the smallest number $c \geq 0$ for which

$$\|T(u) - T(v)\| \leq c \cdot \|u - v\| \text{ for all } u, v \in X.$$

11. For X and Y normed linear spaces and $T \in \mathcal{L}(X, Y)$, show that

$$\|T\| = \sup \left\{ \|T(u)\| \;\middle|\; u \in X, \; \|u\| \leq 1 \right\}.$$

12. For X and Y normed linear spaces, let $\{T_n\} \to T$ in $\mathcal{L}(X, Y)$ and $\{u_n\} \to u$ in X. Show that $\{T_n(u_n)\} \to T(u)$ in Y.

13. Let X be a Banach space and $T \in \mathcal{L}(X, X)$ have $\|T\| < 1$.

   (i) Use the Contraction Mapping Principle to show that $I - T \in \mathcal{L}(X, X)$ is one-to-one and onto.

   (ii) Show that $I - T$ is an isomorphism.

14. (Neumann Series) Let X be a Banach space and $T \in \mathcal{L}(X, X)$ have $\|T\| < 1$. Define $T^0 = \text{Id}$.

   (i) Use the completeness of $\mathcal{L}(X, X)$ to show that $\sum_{n=0}^{\infty} T^n$ converges in $\mathcal{L}(X, X)$.

   (ii) Show that $(I - T)^{-1} = \sum_{n=0}^{\infty} T^n$.

15. For X and Y normed linear spaces and $T \in \mathcal{L}(X, Y)$, show that T is an isomporphism if and only if there is an operator $S \in \mathcal{L}(Y, X)$ such that for each $u \in X$ and $v \in Y$,

$$S(T(u)) = u \text{ and } T(S(v)) = v.$$

16. For X and Y normed linear spaces and $T \in \mathcal{L}(X, Y)$, show that $\ker T$ is a closed subspace of X and that T is one-to-one if and only if $\ker T = \{0\}$.

17. Let (X, ρ) be a metric space containing the point x_0. Define $\text{Lip}_0(X)$ to be the set of real-valued Lipschitz functions f on X that vanish at x_0. Show that $\text{Lip}_0(X)$ is a linear space that is normed by defining, for $f \in \text{Lip}_0(X)$,

$$\|f\| = \sup_{x \neq y} \frac{|f(x) - f(y)|}{\rho(x, y)}.$$

Show that $\text{Lip}_0(X)$ is a Banach space. For each $x \in X$, define the linear functional F_x on $\text{Lip}_0(X)$ by setting $F_x(f) = f(x)$. Show that F_x belongs to $\mathcal{L}(\text{Lip}_0(X), \mathbf{R})$ and that for $x, y \in X$, $\|F_x - F_y\| = \rho(x, y)$. Thus X is isometric to a subset of the Banach space $\mathcal{L}(\text{Lip}_0(X), \mathbf{R})$. Since any closed subset of a complete metric space is complete, this provides another proof of the existence of a completion for any metric space X. It also shows that any metric space is isometric to a subset of a normed linear space.

18. Use the preceding problem to show that every normed linear space is a dense subspace of a Banach space.

19. For X a normed linear space and $T, S \in \mathcal{L}(X, X)$, show that the composition $S \circ T$ also belongs to $\mathcal{L}(X, X)$ and $\|S \circ T\| \leq \|S\| \cdot \|T\|$.

20. Let X be a normed linear space and Y a closed linear subspace of X. Show that $\|x\|_1 = \inf_{y \in Y} \|x - y\|$ defines a pseudonorm on X. The normed linear space induced by the pseudonorm $\| \cdot \|_1$ (see Problem 8) is denoted by X/Y and called the **quotient space** of X modulo Y. Show that the natural map φ of X onto X/Y takes open sets into open sets.

21. Show that if X is a Banach space and Y a closed linear subspace of X, then the quotient X/Y also is a Banach space and the natural map $\varphi : X \to X/Y$ has norm 1.

22. Let X and Y be normed linear spaces, $T \in \mathcal{L}(X, Y)$ and $\ker T = Z$. Show that there is a unique bounded linear operator S from X/Z into Y such that $T = S \circ \varphi$ where $\varphi : X \to X/Z$ is the natural map. Moreover, show that $\|T\| = \|S\|$.

13.3   COMPACTNESS LOST: INFINITE DIMENSIONAL NORMED LINEAR SPACES

A linear space X is said to be finite dimensional provided there is a subset $\{e_1, \ldots, e_n\}$ of X that spans X. If no proper subset also spans X, we call the set $\{e_1, \ldots, e_n\}$ a basis for X and call n the dimension of X. If X is not spanned by a finite collection of vectors it is said to be infinite dimensional. Observe that a basis $\{e_1, \ldots, e_n\}$ for X is linearly independent in the sense that

$$\text{if } \sum_{i=1}^{n} x_i e_i = 0, \text{ then } x_i = 0 \text{ for all } 1 \leq i \leq n,$$

for otherwise a proper subset of $\{e_1, \ldots, e_n\}$ would span X.

Theorem 4 *Any two norms on a finite dimensional linear space are equivalent.*

Proof Since equivalence of norms is an equivalence relation on the set of norms on X, it suffices to select a particular norm $\| \cdot \|_*$ on X and show that any norm on X is equivalent to $\| \cdot \|_*$. Let dim $X = n$ and $\{e_1, \ldots, e_n\}$ be a basis for X. For any $x = x_1 e_1 + \ldots + x_n e_n \in X$, define

$$\|x\|_* = \sqrt{x_1^2 + \ldots + x_n^2}.$$

Since the Euclidean norm is a norm on $\mathbf{R}^n$, $\| \cdot \|_*$ is a norm on X.

Let $\| \cdot \|$ be any norm on X. We claim it is equivalent to $\| \cdot \|_*$. First we find a $c_1 \geq 0$ for which

$$\|x\| \leq c_1 \cdot \|x\|_* \text{ for all } x \in X. \tag{5}$$

Indeed, for $x = x_1 e_i + \ldots + x_n e_n \in X$, by the subadditivity and positive homogeneity of the norm $\| \cdot \|$, together with the Cauchy-Schwarz inequality on $\mathbf{R}^n$,

$$\|x\| \leq \sum_{i=1}^{n} |x_i| \|e_i\| \leq M \cdot \sum_{i=1}^{n} |x_i| = M \sqrt{n} \|x\|_*, \text{ where } M = \max_{1 \leq i \leq n} \|e_i\|.$$

Therefore (5) holds for $c_1 = M \sqrt{n}$. We now find a $c_2 > 0$ for which

$$\|x\|_* \leq c_2 \cdot \|x\| \text{ for all } x \in X. \tag{6}$$

Define the real-valued function $f \colon \mathbf{R}^n \to \mathbf{R}$ by

$$f(x_1, \ldots, x_n) = \left\| \sum_{i=1}^{n} x_i e_i \right\|.$$

This function is continuous since it is Lipschitz with Lipschitz constant c_1 if $\mathbf{R}^n$ is considered as a metric space with the Euclidean metric. Since $\{e_1, \ldots, e_n\}$ is linearly independent, f takes positive values on the boundary of the unit ball, $S = \{x \in \mathbf{R}^n \mid \sum_{i=1}^{n} x_i^2 = 1\}$, which is compact since it is both closed and bounded. A continuous real-valued function on a compact topological space takes a minimum value. Let $m > 0$ be the minimum value of f on S. By the homogeneity of the norm $\| \cdot \|$, we conclude that

$$\|x\| \geq m \cdot \|x\|_* \text{ for all } x \in X.$$

Thus (6) holds for $c_2 = 1/m$. $\qquad \square$

Corollary 5 *Any two normed linear spaces of the same finite dimension are isomorphic.*

Proof Since being isomorphic is an equivalence relation among normed linear spaces, it suffices to show that if X is a normed linear space of dimension n, then it is isomorphic to the

Euclidean space $\mathbf{R}^n$. Let $\{e_1, \ldots, e_n\}$ be a basis for X. Define the linear mapping $T: \mathbf{R}^n \to X$ by setting, for $x = (x_1, \ldots, x_n) \in \mathbf{R}^n$,

$$T(x) = \sum_{i=1}^{n} x_i e_i.$$

Since $\{e_1, \ldots, e_n\}$ is a basis, T is one-to-one and onto. Clearly T is linear. It remains to show that T and its inverse are continuous. Since a linear operator is continuous if and only if it is bounded, this amounts to showing that there are constants c_1 and c_2 such that for each $x \in \mathbf{R}^n$,

$$\|T(x)\| \leq c_1 \cdot \|x\|_* \text{ and } \|T(x)\| \geq c_2 \cdot \|x\|_*,$$

where $\|\cdot\|_*$ denotes the Euclidean norm on $\mathbf{R}^n$. The existence of these two constants follows from the observation that $x \mapsto \|T(x)\|$ defines a norm on $\mathbf{R}^n$, which, since all norms on $\mathbf{R}^n$ are equivalent, is equivalent to the Euclidean norm. $\qquad\square$

Corollary 6 *Any finite dimensional normed linear space is complete and therefore any finite dimensional subspace of a normed linear space is closed.*

Proof A finite dimensional space of dimension n is isomorphic to the Euclidean space $\mathbf{R}^n$, which is complete since $\mathbf{R}$ is complete. Since completeness is preserved under isomorphisms, every finite dimensional normed linear space is complete. For a finite dimensional subspace Y of a normed linear space X, since Y, with the metric induced by the inherited norm, is complete, Y is a closed subset of the metric space X, where X is considered as a metric space with the metric induced by the norm. $\qquad\square$

Corollary 7 *The closed unit ball in a finite dimensional normed linear space is compact.*

Proof Let X be a normed linear space of dimension n and B be its closed unit ball. Let $T: X \to \mathbf{R}^n$ be an isomorphism. Then the set $T(B)$ is bounded since the operator T is bounded and $T(B)$ is closed since T^{-1} is continuous. Therefore, $T(B)$, being a closed bounded subset of $\mathbf{R}^n$, is compact. Since compactness is preserved by continuous mappings and T^{-1} is continuous, B is compact. $\qquad\square$

Riesz's Theorem *The closed unit ball of a normed linear space X is compact if and only if X is finite dimensional.*

The heart of the proof of this theorem lies in the following lemma.

Riesz's Lemma *Let Y be a closed proper linear subspace of a normed linear space X. Then for each $\epsilon > 0$, there is a unit vector $x_0 \in X$ for which*

$$\|x_0 - y\| > 1 - \epsilon \text{ for all } y \in Y.$$

Proof We consider the case $\epsilon = 1/2$ and leave the general case as an exercise. Since Y is a proper subset of X, we may choose $x \in X \sim Y$. Since Y is a closed subset of X, its complement in X is open and therefore there is a ball centered at x that is disjoint from Y, that is,

$$\inf \{\|x - y'\| \mid y' \in Y\} = d > 0. \tag{7}$$

Choose a vector $y_1 \in Y$ for which

$$\|x - y_1\| < 2d. \tag{8}$$

Define

$$x_0 = \frac{x - y_1}{\|x - y_1\|}.$$

Then x_0 is a unit vector. Moreover, observe that for any $y \in Y$,

$$x_0 - y = \frac{x - y_1}{\|x - y_1\|} - y = \frac{1}{\|x - y_1\|}\{x - y_1 - \|x - y_1\| y\} = \frac{1}{\|x - y_1\|}\{x - y'\},$$

where $y' = y_1 + \|x - y_1\| y$ belongs to Y. Therefore, by (7) and (8),

$$\|x_0 - y\| > \frac{1}{2d}\|x_0 - y'\| \geq \frac{1}{2} \text{ for all } y \in Y. \qquad \square$$

Proof of Riesz's Theorem We have already shown that the closed unit ball B in a finite dimensional normed linear space is compact. It remains to show that B fails to be compact if X is infinite dimensional. Assume $\dim X = \infty$. We will inductively choose a sequence $\{x_n\}$ in B such that $\|x_n - x_m\| > 1/2$ for $n \neq m$. This sequence has no Cauchy subsequence and therefore no convergent subsequence. Thus B is not sequentially compact, and therefore, since B is a metric space, not compact.

It remains to choose this sequence. Choose any vector $x_1 \in B$. For a natural number n, suppose we have chosen n vectors in B, $\{x_1, \ldots, x_n\}$, each pair of which are more than a distance $1/2$ apart. Let X_n be the linear space spanned by these n vectors. Then X_n is a finite dimensional subspace of X and so it is closed. Moreover, X_n is a proper subspace of X since $\dim X = \infty$. By the preceding lemma we may choose x_{n+1} in B such that $\|x_i - x_{n+1}\| > 1/2$ for $1 \leq i \leq n$. Thus we have inductively chosen a sequence in B any two terms of which are more than a distance $1/2$ apart. $\qquad \square$

PROBLEMS

23. Show that a subset of a finite dimensional normed linear space X is compact if and only if it is closed and bounded.

24. Complete the proof of Riesz's Lemma for $\epsilon \neq 1/2$.

25. Exhibit an open cover of the closed unit ball of $X = \ell^2$ that has no finite subcover. Then do the same for $X = C[0, 1]$ and $X = L^2[0, 1]$.

26. For normed linear spaces X and Y, let $T: X \to Y$ be linear. If X is finite dimensional, show that T is continuous. If Y is finite dimensional, show that T is continuous if and only if $\ker T$ is closed.

27. (Another proof of Riesz's Theorem) Let X be an infinite dimensional normed linear space, B the closed unit ball in X, and B_0 the unit open ball in X. Suppose B is compact. Then the open cover $\{x + (1/3)B_0\}_{x \in B}$ of B has a finite subcover $\{x_i + (1/3)B_0\}_{1 \leq i \leq n}$. Use Riesz's Lemma with $Y = \text{span}[\{x_1, \ldots, x_n\}]$ to derive a contradiction.

28. Let X be a normed linear space. Show that X is separable if and only if there is a compact subset K of X for which $\overline{\text{span}}[K] = X$.

13.4   THE OPEN MAPPING AND CLOSED GRAPH THEOREMS

In this section, we use the Baire Category Theorem to establish two essential tools, the Open Mapping Theorem and the Closed Graph Theorem, for the analysis of linear operators between infinite dimensional Banach spaces. The Baire Category Theorem is used to prove the following theorem.

Theorem 8 *Let X and Y be Banach spaces and the linear operator $T: X \to Y$ be continuous. Then $T(X)$ is a closed subspace of Y if and only if there is a constant $M > 0$ for which given $y \in T(X)$, there is an $x \in X$ such that*

$$T(x) = y, \ \|x\| \leq M\|y\|. \tag{9}$$

Proof First suppose there is a constant $M > 0$ for which (9) holds. Let $\{y_n\}$ be a sequence in $T(X)$ that converges to $y_* \in Y$. We must show y_* belongs to $T(X)$. By selecting a subsequence if necessary, we may assume

$$\|y_n - y_{n-1}\| \leq 1/2^n \text{ for all } n \geq 2.$$

By the choice of M, for each natural number $n \geq 2$, there is a vector $u_n \in X$ for which

$$T(u_n) = y_n - y_{n-1} \text{ and } \|u_n\| \leq M/2^n.$$

Therefore, for $n \geq 2$, if we define $x_n = \sum_{j=2}^n u_j$, then

$$T(x_n) = y_n - y_1 \tag{10}$$

and

$$\|x_{n+k} - x_n\| \leq M \cdot \sum_{j=n}^{\infty} 1/2^j \text{ for all } k \geq 1. \tag{11}$$

But X is a Banach space and therefore the Cauchy sequence $\{x_n\}$ converges to a vector $x_* \in X$. Take the limit as $n \to \infty$ in (10) and use the continuity of T to infer that $y_* = T(x_*) - y_1$. Since y_1 belongs to $T(X)$ so does y_*. Thus $T(X)$ is closed.

To prove the converse, assume $T(X)$ is a closed subspace of Y. For notational convenience, assume $Y = T(X)$. Let B_X and B_Y denote the open unit balls in X and Y, respectively. Since $T(X) = Y$,

$$Y = \bigcup_{n=1}^{\infty} n \cdot T(B_X) = \bigcup_{n=1}^{\infty} n \cdot \overline{T(B_X)}.$$

The Banach space Y has nonempty interior and therefore we infer from the Baire Category Theorem that there is a natural number n such that the closed set $n \cdot \overline{T(B_X)}$ contains an open ball, which we write as $y_0 + [r_1 \cdot B_Y]$. Thus

$$r_1 B_Y \subseteq n\overline{T(B_X)} - y_0 \subseteq 2n\overline{T(B_X)}.$$

Hence, if we set $r = 2n/r_1$, since $\overline{T(B_X)}$ is closed, we obtain $\overline{B}_Y \subseteq r \cdot \overline{T(B_X)}$. Therefore, since $\overline{B}_Y$ is the closed unit ball in Y, for each $y \in Y$ and $\epsilon > 0$, there is an $x \in X$ for which

$$\|y - T(x)\| < \epsilon \text{ and } \|x\| \leq r \cdot \|y\|. \tag{12}$$

We claim that (9) holds for $M = 2r$. Indeed, let y_* belong to Y, $y_* \neq 0$. According to (12) with $\epsilon = 1/2 \cdot \|y_*\|$ and $y = y_*$, there is a vector $u_1 \in X$ for which

$$\|y_* - T(u_1)\| < 1/2 \cdot \|y_*\| \text{ and } \|u_1\| \le r \cdot \|y_*\|.$$

Now use (12) again, this time with $\epsilon = 1/2^2 \cdot \|y_*\|$ and $y = y_* - T(u_1)$. There is a vector u_2 in X for which

$$\|y_* - T(u_1) - T(u_2)\| < 1/2^2 \cdot \|y_*\| \text{ and } \|u_2\| \le r/2 \cdot \|y_*\|.$$

We continue this selection process and inductively choose a sequence $\{u_k\}$ in X such that for each k,

$$\|y - T(u_1) - T(u_2) - \ldots - T(u_k)\| < 1/2^k \cdot \|y_*\| \text{ and } \|u_k\| \le r/2^{k-1} \cdot \|y_*\|.$$

For each natural number n, define $x_n = \sum_{k=1}^{n} u_k$. Then, by the linearity of T, for each n,

$$\|y - T(x_n)\| \le 1/2^n \cdot \|y_*\|,$$

$$\|x_{n+k} - x_n\| \le r \cdot \|y_*\| \cdot \sum_{j=n}^{\infty} 1/2^j \text{ and } \|x_n\| \le 2 \cdot r \cdot \|y_*\|.$$

By assumption, X is complete. Therefore the Cauchy sequence $\{x_n\}$ converges to a vector x_* in X. Since T is continuous and the norm is continuous,

$$T(x_*) = y_* \text{ and } \|x_*\| \le 2 \cdot r \cdot \|y_*\|.$$

Thus (9) holds for $M = 2 \cdot r$. The proof is complete.   □

A mapping $f: X \to Y$ from the topological space X to the topological space Y is said to be **open** provided the image of each open set in X is open in the topological space $f(X)$, where $f(X)$ has the subspace topology inherited from Y. Therefore a continuous one-to-one mapping f of X into Y is open if and only if f is a topological homeomorphism between X and $f(X)$.

The Open Mapping Theorem *Let X and Y be Banach spaces and the linear operator $T: X \to Y$ be continuous. Then its image $T(X)$ is a closed subspace of Y if and only if the operator T is open.*

Proof The preceding theorem tells us that it suffices to show that T is open if and only if there is a constant $M > 0$ for which (9) holds. Let B_X and B_Y denote the open unit balls in X and Y, respectively. We infer from the homogeneity of T and of the norms that (9) is equivalent to the inclusion

$$\overline{B_Y} \cap T(X) \subseteq M \cdot T(\overline{B_X}).$$

By homogeneity, this inclusion is equivalent to the existence of a constant M' for which $B_Y \cap T(X) \subseteq M' \cdot T(B_X)$. Therefore, we must show that T is open if and only if there is an $r > 0$ for which

$$[r \cdot B_Y] \cap T(X) \subseteq T(B_X). \tag{13}$$

First assume the operator T is open. Then $T(B_X) \cap T(X)$ is an open subset of $T(X)$ which contains 0. Thus there is an $r > 0$ for which $r \cdot B_Y \cap T(X) \subseteq T(B_X) \cap T(X) \subseteq T(B_X)$. Therefore, (13) holds for this choice of r. To prove the converse, assume (13) holds. Let $\mathcal{O}$ be an open subset of X and x_0 belong to $\mathcal{O}$. We must show that $T(x_0)$ is an interior point of $T(\mathcal{O})$. Since x_0 is an interior point of $\mathcal{O}$, there is an $R > 0$ for which $x_0 + R \cdot B_X \subseteq \mathcal{O}$. We infer from (13) that the the open ball of radius $r \cdot R$ about $T(x_0)$ in $T(X)$ is contained in $T(\mathcal{O})$. Thus $T(x_0)$ is an interior point of $T(\mathcal{O})$. $\qquad\square$

Corollary 9 *Let X and Y be Banach spaces and $T \in \mathcal{L}(X, Y)$ be one-to-one and onto. Then T^{-1} is continuous.*

Proof The operator T^{-1} is continuous if and only if the operator T is open. $\qquad\square$

Corollary 10 *Let $\| \cdot \|_1$ and $\| \cdot \|_2$ be norms on a linear space X for which both $(X, \| \cdot \|_1)$ and $(X, \| \cdot \|_2)$ are Banach spaces. Suppose there is a $c \geq 0$ for which*

$$\| \cdot \|_2 \leq c \cdot \| \cdot \|_1 \text{ on } X.$$

Then these two norms are equivalent.

Proof Define the identity map Id: $X \to X$ by $\mathrm{Id}(x) = x$ for all $x \in X$. By assumption,

$$\mathrm{Id}: (X, \| \cdot \|_1) \to (X, \| \cdot \|_2)$$

is a bounded, and therefore continuous, operator between Banach spaces and, of course, it is both one-to-one and onto. By the Open Mapping Theorem, the inverse of the identity, Id: $(X, \| \cdot \|_2) \to (X, \| \cdot \|_1)$, also is continuous, that is, it is bounded: there is an $M \geq 0$ for which

$$\| \cdot \|_1 \leq M \cdot \| \cdot \|_2 \text{ on } X.$$

Therefore the two norms are equivalent. $\qquad\square$

Definition *A linear operator $T: X \to Y$ between normed linear spaces X and Y is said to be* **closed** *provided whenever $\{x_n\}$ is a sequence in X*

$$\text{if } \{x_n\} \to x_0 \text{ and } \{T(x_n)\} \to y_0, \text{ then } T(x_0) = y_0.$$

The **graph** of a mapping of $T: X \to Y$ is the set $\{(x, T(x)) \in X \times Y \mid x \in X\}$. Therefore an operator is closed if and only if its graph is a closed subspace of the product space $X \times Y$.

The Closed Graph Theorem *Let $T: X \to Y$ be a linear operator between the Banach spaces X and Y. Then T is continuous if and only if it is closed.*

Proof It is clear that T is closed if it is continuous. To prove the converse, assume T is closed. Introduce a new norm $\| \cdot \|_*$ on X by

$$\|x\|_* = \|x\| + \|T(x)\| \text{ for all } x \in X.$$

The closedness of the operator T is equivalent to the completeness of the normed linear space $(X, \| \cdot \|_*)$. On the other hand, we clearly have

$$\| \cdot \| \leq \| \cdot \|_* \text{ on } X.$$

Since both $(X, \|\cdot\|_*)$ and $(X, \|\cdot\|)$ are Banach spaces it follows from the preceding corollary that there is a $c \geq 0$ for which

$$\|\cdot\|_* \leq c \cdot \|\cdot\| \text{ on } X.$$

Thus for all $x \in X$,

$$\|T(x)\| \leq \|x\| + \|T(x)\| \leq c\|x\|.$$

Therefore T is bounded and hence is continuous. $\qquad\square$

Remark *Let X and Y be Banach spaces and the operator $T: X \to Y$ be linear. To establish continuity of T it is necessary to show that $\{T(x_n)\} \to T(x_0)$ in Y if $\{x_n\} \to x_0$ in X. The Closed Mapping Theorem provides a drastic simplification in this criterion. It tells us that to establish continuity of T it suffices to check that $\{T(x_n)\} \to T(x_0)$ in Y for sequences $\{x_n\}$ such that $\{x_n\} \to x_0$ in X and $\{T(x_n)\}$ is Cauchy in Y. The usefulness of this simplification will be evident in the proof the forthcoming Theorem 11.*

Let V be a linear subspace of a linear space X. An argument using Zorn's Lemma (see Problem 35) shows that there is a subspace W of X for which there is the direct sum decomposition

$$X = V \oplus W. \tag{14}$$

We call W a **linear complement** of V in X. If a subspace of X has a finite dimensional linear complement in X, then it is said to have **finite codimension** in X. For $x \in X$ and the decomposition (14), let $x = u + v$, for $v \in V$ and $w \in W$. Define $P(x) = v$. We leave it as an algebraic exercise to show that $P: X \to X$ is linear,

$$P^2 = P \text{ on } X, \ P(X) = V \text{ and } (\mathrm{Id} - P)(X) = W. \tag{15}$$

We call P the **projection** of X onto V along W. We leave it as a second algebraic exercise to show that if $P: X \to X$ is any linear operator for which $P^2 = P$, then

$$X = P(X) \oplus (\mathrm{Id} - P)(X). \tag{16}$$

We therefore call a linear operator $P: X \to X$ for which $P^2 = P$ a projection. If P is a projection, then $(\mathrm{Id} - P)^2 = \mathrm{Id} - P$ and therefore $\mathrm{Id} - P$ also is a projection.

Now assume the linear space X is normed. A closed subspace W of X for which (14) holds is called a **closed linear complement** of V in X. In general, it is very difficult to determine if a subspace has a closed linear complement. Corollary 8 of the next chapter tells us that every finite dimensional subspace of a normed linear space has a closed linear complement. Theorem 3 of Chapter 16 tells us that every closed subspace of a Hilbert space has a closed linear complement. For now we have the following criterion, in terms of the continuity of projections, for the existence of closed linear complements.

Theorem 11 *Let V be a closed subspace of a Banach space X. Then V has a closed linear complement in X if and only if there is a continuous projection of X onto V.*

Proof First assume there is a continuous projection P of X onto V. There is the direct sum decomposition $X = V \oplus (\mathrm{Id} - P)(X)$. We claim that $(\mathrm{Id} - P)(X)$ is closed. This is a consequence of the continuity of the projection $\mathrm{Id} - P$. To prove the converse, assume there is a closed subspace W of X for which there is the direct sum decomposition (14). Define P to be the projection of X onto V along W. We claim that P is continuous. The Closed Graph Theorem tells us that to verify this claim it is sufficient to show that the operator P is closed. Let $\{x_n\}$ be a sequence in X for which $\{x_n\} \to x_0$ and $\{P(x_n)\} \to y_0$. Since $\{P(x_n)\}$ is a sequence in the closed set V that converges to y_0, the vector y_0 belongs to V. Since $(\mathrm{Id} - P)(x_n)\}$ is a sequence in the closed set W that converges to $x_0 - y_0$, the vector $x_0 - y_0$ belongs to W. Therefore $P(y_0) = y_0$ and $P(x_0 - y_0) = 0$. Hence $y_0 = P(x_0)$. Thus the operator P is closed.   □

In view of Theorem 8 and its corollary, the Open Mapping Theorem, it is interesting to provide criteria to determine when the image of a continuous linear operator is closed. The following theorem provides one such criterion.

Theorem 12 *Let X and Y be Banach spaces and the linear operator $T: X \to Y$ be continuous. If $T(X)$ has a closed linear complement in Y, then $T(X)$ is closed in Y. In particular, if $T(X)$ has finite codimension in Y, then $T(X)$ is closed in Y.*

Proof Let Y_0 be a closed subspace of Y for which

$$T(X) \oplus Y_0 = Y. \tag{17}$$

Since Y is a Banach space, so is Y_0. Consider the Banach space $X \times Y_0$, where the linear structure on the Cartesian product is defined componentwise and the norm is defined by

$$\|(x, y)\| = \|x\| + \|y\| \text{ for all } (x, y) \in X \times Y_0.$$

Then $X \times Y_0$ is a Banach space. Define the linear operator $S: X \times Y_0 \to Y$ by

$$S(x, y) = T(x) + y \text{ for all } (x, y) \in X \times Y_0.$$

Then S is a continuous linear mapping of the Banach space $X \times Y_0$ onto the Banach space Y. It follows from Theorem 8 that there is an $M > 0$ such that for each $y \in Y$ there is an $(x', y') \in X \times Y_0$ for which

$$T(x') + y' = y \text{ and } \|x'\| + \|y'\| \le M \cdot \|y\|.$$

Thus, since $T(X) \cap Y_0 = \{0\}$, for each $y \in T(X)$, there is an $x \in X$ for which

$$T(x) = y \text{ and } \|x\| \le M \cdot \|y\|.$$

Once more we use Theorem 8 to conclude that $T(X)$ is a closed subspace of Y. Finally, since every finite dimensional subspace of a normed linear space is closed, if $T(X)$ has finite codimension, it is closed.   □

Remark *All linear operators on a finite dimensional normed linear space are continuous, open, and have closed images. The results in the section are only significant for linear operators defined on infinite dimensional Banach spaces, in which case continuity of the operator does not imply that the image is closed. We leave it as an exercise to verify that the operator $T: \ell^2 \to \ell^2$ defined by*

$$T(\{x_n\}) = \{x_n/n\} \text{ for } \{x_n\} \in \ell^2$$

is continuous but does not have closed image and is not open.   □

PROBLEMS

29. Let X be a finite dimensional normed linear space and Y a normed linear space. Show that every linear operator $T: X \to Y$ is continuous and open.

30. Let X be a Banach space and $P \in \mathcal{L}(X, X)$ be a projection. Show that P is open.

31. Let $T: X \to Y$ be a continuous linear operator between the Banach spaces X and Y. Show that T is open if and only if the image under T of the open unit ball in X is dense in a neighborhood of the origin in Y.

32. Let $\{u_n\}$ be a sequence in a Banach space X. Suppose that $\sum_{k=1}^{\infty} \|u_k\| < \infty$. Show that there is an $x \in X$ for which

$$\lim_{n \to \infty} \sum_{k=1}^{n} u_k = x.$$

33. Let X be a linear subspace of $C[0, 1]$ that is closed as a subset of $L^2[0, 1]$. Verify the following assertions to show that X has finite dimension. The sequence $\{f_n\}$ belongs to X.

   (i) Show that X is a closed subspace of $C[0, 1]$.

   (ii) Show that there is a constant $M \geq 0$ such that for all $f \in X$ we have $\|f\|_2 \leq \|f\|_\infty$ and $\|f\|_\infty \leq M \cdot \|f\|_2$.

   (iii) Show that for each $y \in [0, 1]$, there is a function k_y in L^2 such that for each $f \in X$ we have $f(y) = \int_0^1 k_y(x) f(x)\, dx$.

   (iv) Show that if $\{f_n\} \to f$ weakly in L^2, then $\{f_n\} \to f$ pointwise on $[0, 1]$.

   (v) Show $\{f_n\} \to f$ weakly in L^2, then $\{f_n\}$ is bounded (in what sense?), and hence $\{f_n\} \to f$ strongly in L^2 by the Lebesgue Dominated Convergence Theorem.

   (vi) Conclude that X, when normed by $\|\cdot\|_2$, has a compact closed unit ball and therefore, by Riesz's Theorem, is finite dimensional.

34. Let T be a linear operator from a normed linear space X to a finite-dimensional normed linear space Y. Show that T is continuous if and only if $\ker T$ is a closed subspace of X.

35. Suppose X be a Banach space, the operator $T \in \mathcal{L}(X, X)$ be open and X_0 be a closed subspace of X. The restriction T_0 of T to X_0 is continuous. Is T_0 necessarily open?

36. Let V be a linear subspace of a linear space X. Argue as follows to show that V has a linear complement in X.

   (i) If $\dim X < \infty$, let $\{e_i\}_{i=1}^{n}$ be a basis for V. Extend this basis for V to a basis $\{e_i\}_{i=1}^{n+k}$ for X. Then define $W = \text{span}[\{e_{n+1}, \ldots, e_{n+k}\}]$.

   (ii) If $\dim X = \infty$, apply Zorn's Lemma to the collection $\mathcal{F}$ of all subspaces Z of X for which $V \cap Z = \{0\}$, ordered by set inclusion.

37. Verify (15) and (16).

38. Let Y be a normed linear space. Show that Y is a Banach space if and only if there is a Banach space X and a continuous, linear, open mapping of X onto Y.

13.5   THE UNIFORM BOUNDEDNESS PRINCIPLE

As a consequence of the Baire Category Theorem we proved that if a family of continuous functions on a complete metric space is pointwise bounded, then there is an open set on which the family is uniformly bounded. This has the following fruitful consequences for families of linear operators.

The Uniform Boundedness Principle *For X a Banach space and Y a normed linear space, consider a family $\mathcal{F} \subseteq \mathcal{L}(X, Y)$. Suppose the family $\mathcal{F}$ is pointwise bounded in the sense that for each x in X there is a constant $M_x \geq 0$ for which*

$$\|T(x)\| \leq M_x \text{ for all } T \in \mathcal{F}.$$

Then the family $\mathcal{F}$ is uniformly bounded in the sense that there is a constant $M \geq 0$ for which $\|T\| \leq M$ for all T in $\mathcal{F}$.

Proof For each $T \in \mathcal{F}$, the real-valued function $f_T: X \to \mathbf{R}$ defined by $f_T(x) = \|Tx\|$ is a real-valued continuous function on X. Since this family of continuous functions is pointwise bounded on X and the metric space X is complete, by Theorem 6 of Chapter 10, there is an open ball $B(x_0, r)$ in X and a constant $C \geq 0$ for which

$$\|T(x)\| \leq C \text{ for all } x \in B(x_0, r) \text{ and } T \in \mathcal{F}.$$

Thus, for each $T \in \mathcal{F}$,

$$\|T(x)\| = \|T([x + x_0] - x_0)\| \leq \|T(x + x_0)\| + \|T(x_0)\| \leq C + M_{x_0} \text{ for all } x \in B(0, r).$$

Therefore, setting $M = (1/r)(C + M_{x_0})$, we have $\|T\| \leq M$ for all T in $\mathcal{F}$. □

The Banach–Saks–Steinhaus Theorem *Let X be a Banach space, Y a normed linear space, and $\{T_n: X \to Y\}$ a sequence of continuous linear operators. Suppose that for each $x \in X$,*

$$\lim_{n \to \infty} T_n(x) \text{ exists in } Y. \tag{18}$$

Then the sequence of operators $\{T_n: X \to Y\}$ is uniformly bounded. Furthermore, the operator $T: X \to Y$ defined by

$$T(x) = \lim_{n \to \infty} T_n(x) \text{ for all for all } x \in X$$

is linear, continuous, and

$$\|T\| \leq \liminf \|T_n\|.$$

Proof The pointwise limit of a sequence of linear operators is linear. Thus T is linear. We infer from the Uniform Boundedness Principle that the sequence $\{T_n\}$ is uniformly bounded. Therefore $\liminf \|T_n\|$ is finite. Let x belong to X. By the continuity of the norm on Y, $\lim_{n \to \infty} \|T_n(x)\| \to \|T(x)\|$. Since, for all n, $\|T_n(x)\| \leq \|T_n\| \cdot \|x\|$, we also have $\|T(x)\| \leq \liminf \|T_n\| \cdot \|x\|$. Therefore T is bounded and $\|T\| \leq \liminf \|T_n\|$. A bounded linear operator is continuous. □

In the case that Y is a Banach space, (18) is equivalent to the assertion that for each $x \in X$, $\{T_n(x)\}$ is a Cauchy sequence in Y.

PROBLEMS

39. As a consequence of the Baire Category Theorem we showed that a mapping that is the pointwise limit of a sequence of continuous mappings on a complete metric space must be continuous at some point. Use this to prove that the pointwise limit of a sequence of linear operators on a Banach space has a limit that is continuous at some point and hence, by linearity, is continuous.

40. Let $\{f_n\}$ be a sequence in $L^1[a, b]$. Suppose that for each $g \in L^\infty[a, b]$, $\lim_{n \to \infty} \int_E g \cdot f_n$ exists. Show that there is a function in $f \in L^1[a, b]$ such that $\lim_{n \to \infty} \int_E g \cdot f_n = \int_E g \cdot f$ for all $g \in L^\infty[a, b]$.

41. Let X be the linear space of all polynomials defined on $\mathbf{R}$. For $p \in X$, define $\|p\|$ to be the sum of the absolute values of the coefficients of p. Show that this is a norm on X. For each n, define $\psi_n: X \to \mathbf{R}$ by $\psi_n(p) = p^{(n)}(0)$. Use the properties of the sequence $\{\psi_n\}$ in $\mathcal{L}(X, \mathbf{R})$ to show that X is not a Banach space.

42. (i)   Use Zorn's Lemma to show that every linear space has a Hamel basis.

   (ii) Show that any Hamel basis for an infinite dimensional Banach space must be uncountable.

   (iii) Let X be the linear space of all polynomials defined on $\mathbf{R}$. Show that there is not a norm on X with respect to which X is a Banach space.

CHAPTER 14

Duality for Normed Linear Spaces

Contents

For a normed linear space X, we denoted the normed linear space of continuous linear real-valued functions of X by X^* and called it the **dual space** of X. In this and the following chapter, we explore properties of the mapping from $X \times X^*$ to $\mathbf{R}$ defined by

$$(x, \psi) \mapsto \psi(x) \text{ for all } x \in X, \psi \in X^*$$

to uncover analytic, geometric, and topological properties of Banach spaces. The departure point for this exploration is the Hahn-Banach Theorem. This is a theorem regarding the extension of certain linear functionals on subspaces of an unnormed linear space to linear functionals on the whole space. The elementary nature of this theorem provides it with such flexibility that in this chapter we deduce from it the following three properties of linear functionals: (i) for a normed linear space X, any bounded linear functional on a subspace of X may be extended to a bounded linear functional on all of X, without increasing its norm; (ii) for a locally convex topological vector space X, any two disjoint closed convex sets of X may be separated by a closed hyperplane; and (iii) for a reflexive Banach space X, any bounded sequence in X has a weakly convergent subsequence.

14.1 LINEAR FUNCTIONALS, BOUNDED LINEAR FUNCTIONALS, AND WEAK TOPOLOGIES

Let X be a linear space. We denote by $X^{\sharp}$ the linear space of linear real-valued functions on X. For $\psi \in X^{\sharp}, \psi \neq 0$, and $x_0 \in X$ for which $\psi(x_0) \neq 0$, we claim that X may be expressed as the direct sum

$$X = [\ker \psi] \oplus \operatorname{span} [x_0], \tag{1}$$

where the kernel of ψ, $\ker \psi$, is the subspace $\{x \in X \mid \psi(x) = 0\}$. Indeed, clearly $[\ker \psi] \cap \operatorname{span} [x_0] = \{0\}$. On the other hand, we may write each $x \in X$ as

$$x = \left[x - \frac{\psi(x)}{\psi(x_0)} \cdot x_0 \right] + \frac{\psi(x)}{\psi(x_0)} \cdot x_0 \text{ and } \psi\left(x - \frac{\psi(x)}{\psi(x_0)} \cdot x_0 \right) = 0.$$

Observe that for a real number c, if x_0 belongs to X and $\psi(x_0) = c$, then

$$\psi^{-1}(c) = \{x \in X \mid \psi(x) = c\} = \ker \psi + x_0.$$

Therefore, by (1), if X is finite dimensional of dimension n and ψ is nonzero, then for each $c \in \mathbf{R}$, the level set $\psi^{-1}(c)$ is the translate of an $(n-1)$ dimensional subspace of X.

If a linear subspace X_0 of X has the property that there is some $x_0 \in X$, $x_0 \neq 0$ for which $X = X_0 \oplus \text{span}\,[x_0]$, then X_0 is said to be of **codimension** 1 in X. A translate of a subspace of codimension 1 is called a **hyperplane**.

Proposition 1 *A linear subspace X_0 of a linear space X is of codimension 1 if and only if $X_0 = \ker \psi$, for some nonzero $\psi \in X^\sharp$.*

Proof We already observed that the kernel of a nonzero linear functional is of codimension 1. Conversely, suppose X_0 is a subspace of codimension 1. Then there is a vector $x_0 \neq 0$ for which $X = X_0 \oplus \text{span}\,[x_0]$. For $\lambda \in \mathbf{R}$ and $x \in X_0$, define $\psi(x + \lambda x_0) = \lambda$. Then $\psi \neq 0$, ψ is linear and $\ker \psi = X_0$. $\square$

The following proposition tells us that the linear functionals on a linear space are plentiful.

Proposition 2 *Let Y be a linear subspace of a linear space X. Then each linear functional on Y has an extension to a linear functional on all of X. In particular, for each $x \in X$, there is a $\psi \in X^\sharp$ for which $\psi(x) \neq 0$.*

Proof As we observed in the preceding chapter (see Problem 36 of that chapter), Y has a linear complement in X, that is, there is a linear subspace X_0 of X for which there is the direct sum decomposition

$$X = Y \oplus X_0.$$

Let η belong to $Y^\sharp$. For $x \in X$, we have $x = y + x_0$, where $y \in Y$ and $x_0 \in X_0$. Define $\eta(x) = \eta(y)$. This defines an extension of η to a linear functional on all of X.

Now let x belong to X. Define $\eta \colon \text{span}\,[x] \to \mathbf{R}$ by $\eta(\lambda x) = \lambda \cdot \|x\|$. By the first part of the proof, the linear functional η has an extension to a linear functional on all of X. $\square$

We are particularly interested in linear spaces X that are normed and subspaces of $X^\sharp$ that are contained in the dual space of X, X^*, that is, linear spaces of linear functionals that are continuous with respect to the topology induced by the norm. If X is a finite dimensional normed linear space, then every linear functional on X belongs to X^* (see Problem 3). This property characterizes finite dimensional normed linear spaces.

A subset B of a linear space X is called a **Hamel basis** for X provided each vector in X is expressible as a unique finite linear combination of vectors in B. We leave it as an exercise to infer from Zorn's Lemma that every linear space possesses a Hamel basis (see Problem 16).

Proposition 3 *Let X be a normed linear space. Then X is finite dimensional if and only if $X^\sharp = X^*$.*

Proof We leave it as an exercise to show that since all norms on a finite dimensional linear space are equivalent, all linear functionals on such spaces are bounded. Assume X is infinite dimensional. Let $\mathcal{B}$ be a Hamel basis for X. Without loss of generality we assume the vectors in $\mathcal{B}$ are unit vectors. Since X is infinite dimensional, we may choose a countably infinite subset of $\mathcal{B}$, which we enumerate as $\{x_k\}_{k=1}^\infty$. For each natural number k and vector $x \in X$, define $\psi_k(x)$ to be the coefficient of x_k with respect to the expansion of x in the Hamel basis $\mathcal{B}$. Then each ψ_k belongs to $X^\sharp$ and therefore the functional $\psi \colon X \to \mathbf{R}$ defined by

$$\psi(x) = \sum_{k=1}^\infty k \cdot \psi_k(x) \text{ for all } x \in X$$

also belongs to $X^\sharp$. This linear functional is not bounded since each x_k is a unit vector for which $\psi_k(x) = k$. $\qquad\square$

The following algebraic property of linear functionals is useful in establishing properties of weak topologies.

Proposition 4 *Let X be a linear space, the functional ψ belong to $X^\sharp$, and $\{\psi_i\}_{i=1}^n$ be contained in $X^\sharp$. Then ψ is a linear combination of $\{\psi_i\}_{i=1}^n$ if and only if*

$$\bigcap_{i=1}^n \ker \psi_i \subseteq \ker \psi. \tag{2}$$

Proof It is clear that if ψ is a linear combination of $\{\psi_i\}_{i=1}^n$, then the inclusion (2) holds. We argue inductively to prove the converse. For $n = 1$, suppose (2) holds. We assume $\psi \neq 0$, for otherwise there is nothing to prove. Choose $x_0 \neq 0$ for which $\psi(x_0) = 1$. Then $\psi_1(x_0) \neq 0$ also since $\ker \psi_1 \subseteq \ker \psi$. However, $X = \ker \psi_1 \oplus \mathrm{span}\,[x_0]$. Therefore, if we define $\lambda_1 = 1/\psi_1(x_0)$ we see, by direct substitution, that $\psi = \lambda_1 \psi_1$. Now assume that for linear functionals on any linear space, if (2) holds for $n = k-1$, then ψ is a linear combination of $\psi_1, \ldots, \psi_{k-1}$. Suppose (2) holds for $n = k$. If $\psi_k = 0$, there is nothing to prove. So choose $x_0 \in X$ with $\psi_k(x_0) = 1$. Then $X = Y \oplus \mathrm{span}\,[x_0]$, where $Y = \ker \psi_k$, and therefore

$$\bigcap_{i=1}^{k-1} [\ker \psi_i \cap Y] \subseteq \ker \psi \cap Y.$$

By the induction assumption, there are real numbers $\lambda_1, \ldots, \lambda_{k-1}$ for which

$$\psi = \sum_{i=1}^{k-1} \lambda_i \cdot \psi_i \text{ on } Y.$$

A direct substitution shows that if we define $\lambda_k = \psi(x_0) - \sum_{i=1}^{k-1} \lambda_i \cdot \psi_i(x_0)$, then

$$\psi = \sum_{i=1}^k \lambda_i \cdot \psi_i \text{ on } X.$$

$\qquad\square$

Recall that for two topologies $\mathcal{T}_1$ and $\mathcal{T}_2$ on a set X, we say that $\mathcal{T}_1$ is weaker than $\mathcal{T}_2$, or $\mathcal{T}_2$ is stronger than $\mathcal{T}_1$, provided $\mathcal{T}_1 \subseteq \mathcal{T}_2$. Observe that a function on X that is continuous with respect to a topology on X, then it is also continuous with respect to any stronger topology on X but may not be continuous with respect to a weaker topology. If $\mathcal{F}$ is any collection of real-valued functions on a set X, the weak topology on X induced by $\mathcal{F}$, or the $\mathcal{F}$-weak topology on X, is defined to be the weakest topology on X (that is, the topology with the fewest number of sets) for which each function in $\mathcal{F}$ is continuous. A base at $x \in X$ for the $\mathcal{F}$-weak topology on X comprises sets of the form

$$\mathcal{N}_{\epsilon, f_1, \ldots, f_n}(x) = \left\{ x' \in X \mid |f_k(x') - f_k(x)| < \epsilon \text{ for } 1 \le k \le n \right\}, \tag{3}$$

where $\epsilon > 0$ and $\{f_k\}_{k=1}^n$ is a finite subcollection of $\mathcal{F}$. For a topology on a set, we know what it means for a sequence in the set to converge, with respect to the topology, to a point in the set. It is easy to see that a sequence $\{x_n\}$ in X converges to $x \in X$ with respect to the $\mathcal{F}$-weak topology if and only if

$$\lim_{n \to \infty} f(x_n) = f(x) \text{ for all } f \in \mathcal{F}. \tag{4}$$

A function on X that is continuous with respect to the $\mathcal{F}$-weak topology is called $\mathcal{F}$-weakly continuous. Similarly, we have $\mathcal{F}$-weakly open sets, $\mathcal{F}$-weakly closed sets, and $\mathcal{F}$-weakly compact sets.

For a linear space X, it is natural and very useful to consider weak topologies induced on X by linear subspaces W of $X^\sharp$.

Proposition 5 *Let X be a linear space and W a subspace of $X^\sharp$. Then a linear functional $\psi: X \to \mathbf{R}$ is W-weakly continuous if and only if it belongs to W.*

Proof By the definition of the W-weak topology, each linear functional in W is W-weakly continuous. It remains to prove the converse. Suppose the linear functional $\psi: X \to \mathbf{R}$ is W-weakly continuous. By the continuity of ψ at 0, there is a neighborhood $\mathcal{N}$ of 0 for which $|\psi(x)| = |\psi(x) - \psi(0)| < 1$ if $x \in \mathcal{N}$. There is a neighborhood in the base for the W-topology at 0 that is contained in $\mathcal{N}$. Choose $\epsilon > 0$ and $\psi_1, \ldots, \psi_n$ in W for which $\mathcal{N}_{\epsilon, \psi_1, \ldots, \psi_n} \subseteq \mathcal{N}$. Thus

$$|\psi(x)| < 1 \text{ if } |\psi_k(x)| < \epsilon \text{ for all } 1 \le k \le n.$$

By the linearity of ψ and the ψ_k's, we have the inclusion $\bigcap_{k=1}^n \ker \psi_k \subseteq \ker \psi$. According to Proposition 4, ψ is a linear combination of $\psi_1, \ldots, \psi_n$. Therefore, since W is a linear space, ψ belongs to W. $\qquad\square$

The above proposition establishes a one-to-one correspondence between linear subspaces of $X^\sharp$ and weak topologies on X induced by such subspaces.

Definition *Let X be a normed linear space. The weak topology induced on X by the dual space X^* is called the **weak topology** on X.*

A base at $x \in X$ for the weak topology on X comprises sets of the form

$$\mathcal{N}_{\epsilon, \psi_1, \ldots, \psi_n}(x) = \left\{ x' \in X \mid |\psi_k(x' - x)| < \epsilon \text{ for } 1 \le k \le n \right\}, \tag{5}$$

where $\epsilon > 0$ and $\{\psi_k\}_{k=1}^n$ is a finite subcollection of X^*. For topological concepts with respect to the weak topology, we use the adjective "weakly": so we have weakly compact sets, weakly open sets, etc. Thus a sequence $\{x_n\}$ in X converges weakly to $x \in X$ if and only if

$$\lim_{n\to\infty} \psi(x_n) = \psi(x) \text{ for all } \psi \in X^*. \tag{6}$$

It is convenient to write $\{x_n\} \rightharpoonup x$ in X to mean that $\{x_n\}$ is a sequence in X that converges weakly to the point $x \in X$.

For X a normed linear space and W a subspace of X^*, there is the following inclusion among topologies on X:

W-weak topology on $X \subseteq$ weak topology on $X \subseteq$ strong topology on X.

We infer from Proposition 5 that the W-weak topology coincides with the weak topology if and only if $W = X^*$. Furthermore, the weak topology coincides with the strong topology if and only if X is finite dimensional (see Problem 6). Frequently, for a normed linear space, we call the topology induced by the norm the **strong topology** on X. If no adjective is attached to a topological concept associated with a normed linear space, it is implicitly assumed that the reference topology is the strong topology.

For normed linear spaces that are dual spaces, there is a third important topology on the space besides the weak and the strong topologies. Indeed, for a normed linear space X and $x \in X$ we define the functional $J(x): X^* \to \mathbf{R}$ by

$$J(x)[\psi] = \psi(x) \text{ for all } \psi \in X^*.$$

It is clear that the evaluation functional $J(x)$ is linear and is bounded on X^* with $\|J(x)\| \le \|x\|$. Moreover, the operator $J: X \to (X^*)^*$ is linear and therefore $J(X)$ is a linear subspace of $(X^*)^*$.

Definition *Let X be a normed linear space. The weak topology on X^* induced by $J(X) \subseteq (X^*)^*$ is called the* **weak-∗ topology** *on X^*.*

A base at $\psi \in X^*$ for the weak-∗ topology on X^* comprises sets of the form

$$\mathcal{N}_{\epsilon, x_1, \ldots, x_n}(\psi) = \{\psi' \in X^* \mid |(\psi' - \psi)(x_k)| < \epsilon \text{ for } 1 \le k \le n\}, \tag{7}$$

where $\epsilon > 0$ and $\{x_k\}_{k=1}^n$ is a finite subset of X. A subset of X^{**} that is open with respect to the weak-∗ topology is said to be weak-∗ open, similarly for other topological concepts. Thus a sequence $\{\psi_n\}$ in X^* is weak-∗ convergent to $\psi \in X^*$ if and only if

$$\lim_{n\to\infty} \psi(x_n) = \psi(x) \text{ for all } x \in X. \tag{8}$$

Therefore weak-∗ convergence in X^* is simply pointwise convergence. For a normed linear space X, the strong, weak, and weak-∗ topologies on X^* are related by the following inclusions:

weak-∗ topology on $X^* \subseteq$ weak topology on $X^* \subseteq$ strong topology on X^*.

Definition *Let X be a normed linear space. The linear operator* $J: X \to (X^*)^*$ *defined by*

$$J(x)[\psi] = \psi(x) \text{ for all } x \in X, \psi \in X^*$$

is called the **natural embedding** *of X into* $(X^*)^*$. *The space X is said to be* **reflexive** *provided* $J(X) = (X^*)^*$.

It is customary to denote $(X^*)^*$ by X^{**} and call X^{**} the **bidual** of X.

Proposition 6 *A normed linear space X is reflexive if and only if the weak and weak-* topologies on X^* are the same.*

Proof Clearly if X is reflexive, then the weak and weak-* topologies on X^* are the same. Conversely, suppose these two topologies are the same. Let $\Psi: X^* \to \mathbf{R}$ be a continuous linear functional. By definition of the weak topology, Ψ is continuous with respect to the weak topology on X^*. Therefore it is continuous with respect to the weak-* topology. We infer from Proposition 5 that Ψ belongs to $J(X)$. Therefore $J(X) = X^{**}$. $\square$

At present, we are not justified in calling $J: X \to X^{**}$ an "embedding" since we have not shown that J is one-to-one. In fact, we have not even shown that on a general normed linear space X there are any nonzero bounded linear functionals. We need a variation of Proposition 2 for linear functionals that are bounded. The forthcoming Hahn-Banach Theorem will provide this variation and, moreover, show that J is an isometry. Of course, we have already studied the dual spaces of some particular normed linear spaces. For instance, if E is a Lebesgue measurable set of real numbers and $1 \leq p < \infty$, the Riesz Representation Theorem characterizes the dual of $L^p(E)$.

PROBLEMS

1. Verify the two direct substitution assertions in the proof of Proposition 4.

2. Let X_0 be a codimension 1 subspace of a normed linear space X. Show that X_0 is closed with respect to the strong topology if and only if the $X_0 = \ker \psi$ for some $\psi \in X^*$.

3. Show that if X is a finite dimensional normed linear space, then every linear functional on X is continuous.

4. Let X be a finite dimensional normed linear space of dimension n. Let $\{e_1, \ldots, e_n\}$ be a basis for X. For $1 \leq i \leq n$, define $\psi_i \in X^*$ by $\psi_i(x) = x_i$ for $x = x_1 e_1 + \cdots + x_n e_n \in X$. Show that $\{\psi_1, \ldots, \psi_n\}$ is a basis for X^*. Thus dim $X^* = n$.

5. Let X be a finite dimensional linear space. Show that the weak and strong topologies on X are the same.

6. Show that every nonempty weakly open subset of an infinite dimensional normed linear space is unbounded with respect to the norm.

7. Let X be a finite dimensional space. Show that the natural embedding $J: X \to X^{**}$ is one-to-one. Then use Problem 4 to show that $J: X \to X^{**}$ is onto, so X is reflexive.

8. For a vector $v \neq 0$ in Euclidean space $\mathbf{R}^n$, explicitly exhibit a linear functional $\psi: \mathbf{R}^n \to \mathbf{R}$ for which $\psi(v) = 1$.

9. For a sequence $\{x_n\} \neq 0$ in ℓ^2, explicitly exhibit a continuous linear functional $\psi \colon \ell^2 \to \mathbf{R}$ for which $\psi(\{x_n\}) = 1$.

10. For a function $f \neq 0$ in $L^p[a, b], 1 \leq p \leq \infty$, explicitly exhibit a continuous linear functional $\psi \colon L^p[a, b] \to \mathbf{R}$ for which $\psi(f) = 1$.

11. Consider $C[a, b]$ with the maximum norm. For a function $f \neq 0$ in $C[a, b]$, explicitly exhibit a continuous linear functional $\psi \colon C[a, b] \to \mathbf{R}$ for which $\psi(f) = 1$.

12. For $1 < p < \infty$, let Y be a closed subspace of $L^p[a, b]$ of codimension 1. Show that there is function $g \in L^q[a, b]$, where q is the conjugate of p, for which

$$Y = \left\{ f \in L^p[a, b] \;\middle|\; \int_{[a, b]} f \cdot g\, dm = 0 \right\}.$$

13. Let X be a normed linear space and ψ belong to $X^\sharp \sim X^*$. Show that $\ker \psi$ is dense, with respect to the strong topology, in X.

14. Let X be the normed linear space of polynomials restricted to $[a, b]$. For $p \in X$, define $\psi(p)$ to be the sum of the coefficients of p. Show that ψ is linear. Is ψ continuous if X has the topology induced by the maximum norm?

15. Let X be the normed linear space of sequences of real numbers that have only a finite number of nonzero terms. For $x = \{x_n\} \in X$, define $\psi(x) = \sum_{n=1}^{\infty} x_n$. Show that ψ is linear. Is ψ continuous if X has the topology induced by the ℓ^∞ norm?

16. Let X be a linear space. A subset E of X is said to be linearly independent provided each $x \in E$ fails to be a finite linear combination of points in $E \sim \{x\}$. Define $\mathcal{F}$ to be the collection of nonempty subsets of X that are linearly independent. Order $\mathcal{F}$ by set inclusion. Apply Zorn's Lemma to conclude that X has a Hamel basis.

17. Provide an example of a discontinuous linear operator T from a normed linear space X to a normed linear space Y for which T has a closed graph. (Hint: Let ψ be a discontinuous linear functional on a normed linear space X and $Y = \{y \in X \times \mathbf{R} \mid y = \langle x, \psi(x) \rangle\}$, the graph of ψ). Does this contradict the Closed Graph Theorem?

14.2 THE HAHN-BANACH THEOREM

Definition *A functional* $p \colon X \to [0, \infty)$ *on a linear space* X *is said to be* **positively homogeneous** *provided*

$$p(\lambda x) = \lambda p(x) \text{ for all } x \in X, \lambda > 0,$$

and said to be **subadditive** *provided*

$$p(x + y) \leq p(x) + p(y) \text{ for all } x, y \in X.$$

Any norm on a linear space is both subadditive (the triangle inequality) and positively homogeneous.

The Hahn-Banach Lemma *Let* p *be a positively homogeneous, subadditive functional on the linear space* X *and* Y *a subspace of* X *on which there is defined a linear functional* ψ *for which*

$$\psi \leq p \text{ on } Y.$$

Let z belong to X~Y. Then ψ can be extended to a linear functional ψ on span $[Y + z]$ for which

$$\psi \le p \text{ on } \text{span} [Y + z].$$

Proof Since every vector in span $[Y + z]$ may be written uniquely as $y + \lambda z$, for $y \in Y$ and $\lambda \in \mathbf{R}$, it is sufficient to find a number $\psi(z)$ with the property that

$$\psi(y) + \lambda\psi(z) \le p(y + \lambda z) \text{ for all } y \in Y \text{ and } \lambda \in \mathbf{R}. \tag{9}$$

Indeed, for such a number $\psi(z)$, define $\psi(y + \lambda z) = \psi(y) + \lambda\psi(z)$ for all y in Y and $\lambda \in \mathbf{R}$ to obtain the required extension.

For any vectors $y_1, y_2 \in Y$, since ψ is linear, $\psi \le p$ on Y and p is subadditive,

$$\psi(y_1) + \psi(y_2) = \psi(y_1 + y_2) \le p(y_1 + y_2) = p((y_1 - z) + (y_2 + z)) \le p(y_1 - z) + p(y_2 + z),$$

and therefore

$$\psi(y_1) - p(y_1 - z) \le -\psi(y_2) + p(y_2 + z).$$

As we vary y_1 and y_2 among all vectors in Y, any number on the left-hand side of this inequality is no greater than any number on the right. By the completeness of $\mathbf{R}$, if we define $\psi(z)$ to be the supremum of the numbers on the left-hand side of this inequality, then $\psi(z) \in \mathbf{R}$. Furthermore, for any $y \in Y$, $\psi(y) - p(y - z) \le \psi(z)$, by the choice of $\psi(z)$ as an upper bound and $\psi(z) \le -\psi(y) + p(y + z)$ by the choice of $\psi(z)$ as the least upper bound. Therefore

$$\psi(y) - p(y - z) \le \psi(z) \le -\psi(y) + p(y + z) \text{ for all } y \in Y. \tag{10}$$

Let y belong to Y. For $\lambda > 0$, in the inequality $\psi(z) \le -\psi(y) + p(y + z)$, replace y by y/λ, multiply each side by λ, and use the positive homogeneity of both p and ψ to obtain the desired inequality (9). For $\lambda < 0$, in the inequality $\psi(y) - p(y - z) \le \psi(z)$, replace y by $-y/\lambda$, multiply each side by $-\lambda$, and once more use positive homogeneity to obtain the desired inequality (9). Therefore (9) holds if the number $\psi(z)$ is chosen so that (10) holds. $\square$

The Hahn-Banach Theorem *Let p be a positively homogeneous, subadditive functional on a linear space X and Y a subspace of X on which there is defined a linear functional ψ for which*

$$\psi \le p \text{ on } Y.$$

Then ψ may be extended to a linear functional ψ on all of X for which $\psi \le p$ on all of X.

Proof Consider the family $\mathcal{F}$ of all linear functionals η defined on a subspace Y_η of X for which $Y \subseteq Y_\eta$, $\eta = \psi$ on Y, and $\eta \le p$ on Y_η. This particular family $\mathcal{F}$ of extensions of ψ is partially ordered by defining $\eta_1 \prec \eta_2$ provided $Y_{\eta_1} \subseteq Y_{\eta_2}$ and $\eta_1 = \eta_2$ on Y_{η_1}.

Let $\mathcal{F}_0$ be a totally ordered subfamily of $\mathcal{F}$. Define Z to be the union of the domains of the functionals in $\mathcal{F}_0$. Since $\mathcal{F}_0$ is totally ordered, any two such domains are contained in just one of them and therefore, since each domain is a linear subspace of X, so is Z. For $z \in Y$, choose $\eta \in \mathcal{F}_0$ such that $z \in Y_\eta$: define $\eta^*(z) = \eta(z)$. Then, again by the total ordering of $\mathcal{F}_0$, η^* is a properly defined linear functional on Z. Observe that $\eta^* \le p$ on Z, $Y \subseteq Z$ and $\eta^* = \psi$ on Y, since each functional in $\mathcal{F}_0$ has these three properties. Thus $\eta \prec \eta^*$ for all $\eta \in \mathcal{F}_0$. Therefore every totally ordered subfamily of $\mathcal{F}$ has an upper bound. Hence, by Zorn's Lemma, $\mathcal{F}$ has a maximal member ψ_0. Let the domain of ψ_0 be Y_0. By definition, $Y \subseteq Y_0$ and $\psi_0 \le p$ on Y_0. We infer from the Hahn-Banach Lemma that this maximal extension ψ_0 is defined on all of X. $\square$

Theorem 7 *Let X_0 be a linear subspace of a normed linear space X. Then each bounded linear functional ψ on X_0 has an extension to a bounded linear functional on all of X that has the same norm as ψ. In particular, for each $x \in X$, there is a $\psi \in X^*$ for which*

$$\psi(x) = \|x\| \text{ and } \|\psi\| = 1. \tag{11}$$

Proof Let $\psi \colon X_0 \to \mathbf{R}$ be linear and bounded. Define

$$M = \|\psi\| = \sup \left\{ |\psi(x)| \mid x \in X_0, \|x\| \leq 1 \right\}.$$

Define $p \colon X \to \mathbf{R}$ by

$$p(x) = M \cdot \|x\| \text{ for all } x \in X.$$

The functional p is subadditive and positively homogeneous. By the definition of M,

$$\psi \leq p \text{ on } X_0.$$

By the Hahn-Banach Theorem, ψ may be extended to a continuous linear functional ψ on all of X and $\psi(x) \leq p(x) = M\|x\|$ for all $x \in X$. Replacing x by $-x$ we infer that $|\psi(x)| \leq p(x) = M\|x\|$ for all $x \in X$ and therefore the extension of ψ to all of X has the same norm as $\psi \colon X_0 \to \mathbf{R}$.

Now let x belong to X. Define $\eta \colon \operatorname{span}[x] \to \mathbf{R}$ by $\eta(\lambda x) = \lambda \cdot \|x\|$. Observe that $\|\eta\| = 1$. By the first part of the proof, the functional η has an extension to a bounded linear functional on all of X that also has norm 1. $\qquad\square$

Example Let x_0 belong to the closed, bounded interval $[a, b]$. Define

$$\psi(f) = \psi(x_0) \text{ for all } f \in C[a, b].$$

We consider $C[a, b]$ as a subspace of $L^\infty[a, b]$ (see Problem 27). We infer from the preceding theorem that ψ has an extension to a bounded linear functional $\psi \colon L^\infty[a, b] \to \mathbf{R}$.

Example Define the positively homogeneous, subadditive functional p on ℓ^∞ by

$$p(\{x_n\}) = \limsup\{x_n\} \text{ for all } \{x_n\} \in \ell^\infty.$$

Let $c_0 \subseteq \ell^\infty$ be the subspace of convergent sequences. Define L on c_0 by

$$L(\{x_n\}) = \lim_{n \to \infty} x_n \text{ for all } \{x_n\} \in c_0.$$

Since L is linear and $L \leq p$ on c_0, L has an extension to a linear functional L on ℓ^∞ for which $L \leq p$ on ℓ^∞. Any such extension is called a **Banach limit**.

In the preceding chapter we considered whether a closed subspace X_0 of a Banach space X has a closed linear complement in X. The following corollary tells us it does if X_0 is finite dimensional.

Corollary 8 *Let X be a normed linear space. If X_0 is a finite dimensional subspace of X, then there is a closed linear subspace X_1 of X for which $X = X_0 \oplus X_1$.*

Proof Let $e_1, \ldots, e_n$ be a basis for X_0. For $1 \leq k \leq n$, define $\psi_k \colon X_0 \to \mathbf{R}$ by $\psi_k \left(\sum_{i=1}^{n} \lambda_i \cdot e_i \right)$ $= \lambda_k$. Since X_0 is finite dimensional, the ψ_k's are continuous. According to Theorem 7, each ψ_k has an extension to a continuous functional ψ'_k on all of X. Therefore each ψ'_k has a closed kernel so that the subspace $X_1 = \cap_{k=1}^{n} \ker \psi'_k$ also is closed. It is easy to check that $X = X_0 \oplus X_1$. $\qquad \square$

Corollary 9 *Let X be a normed linear space. Then the natural embedding $J \colon X \to X^{**}$ is an isometry.*

Proof Let x belong to X. Observe that by the definition of the norm on the dual space

$$|\psi(x)| \leq \|\psi\| \cdot \|x\| \text{ for all } \psi \in X^*.$$

Thus

$$|J(x)(\psi)| \leq \|x\| \cdot \|\psi\| \text{ for all } \psi \in X^*.$$

Therefore $J(x)$ is bounded and $\|J(x)\| \leq \|x\|$. On the other hand, according to Theorem 7, there is a $\psi \in X^*$ for which $\|\psi\| = 1$ and $J(x)(\psi) = \|x\|$. Therefore $\|x\| \leq \|J(x)\|$. We conclude that J is an isometry. $\qquad \square$

Theorem 10 *Let X_0 be a subspace of the normed linear space X. Then a point x in X belongs to the closure of X_0 if and only if whenever a functional $\psi \in X^*$ vanishes on X_0, it also vanishes at x.*

Proof It is clear by continuity that if a continuous functional vanishes on X_0 it also vanishes on the closure of X_0. To prove the converse, let x_0 belong to $X \sim \overline{X_0}$. We must show that there is a $\psi \in X^*$ that vanishes on X_0 but $\psi(x_0) \neq 0$. Define $Z = \overline{X_0} \oplus [x_0]$ and $\psi \colon Z \to \mathbf{R}$ by

$$\psi(x + \lambda x_0) = \lambda \text{ for all } x \in \overline{X_0} \text{ and } \lambda \in \mathbf{R}.$$

We claim that ψ is bounded. Indeed, since $\overline{X_0}$ is closed, its complement is open. Thus there is an $r > 0$ for which $\|u - x_0\| \geq r$ for all $u \in \overline{X_0}$. Thus, for $x \in \overline{X_0}$ and $\lambda \in \mathbf{R}$,

$$\|x + \lambda x_0\| = |\lambda| \|(-1/\lambda \cdot x) - x_0\| \geq |\lambda| \cdot r.$$

From this we infer that $\psi \colon Z \to \mathbf{R}$ is bounded with $\|\psi\| \leq 1/r$. Theorem 7 tells us that ψ has an extension to a bounded linear functional on all of X. This extension belongs to X^*, vanishes on X_0, and yet $\psi(x_0) \neq 0$. $\qquad \square$

We leave the proof of the following corollary as an exercise.

Corollary 11 *Let S be a subset of the normed linear space X. Then the linear span of S is dense in X if and only if whenever $\psi \in X^*$ vanishes on S, then $\psi = 0$.*

Theorem 12 *Let X be a normed linear space. Then every weakly convergent sequence in X is bounded. Moreover, if $\{x_n\} \rightharpoonup x$ in X, then*

$$\|x\| \leq \liminf \|x_n\|. \tag{12}$$

Proof Let $\{x_n\} \to x$ in X. Then $\{J(x_n): X^* \to \mathbf{R}\}$ is a sequence of functionals that converges pointwise to $J(x): X^* \to \mathbf{R}$. The Uniform Boundedness Theorem tells us that $\{J(x_n)\}$ is a bounded sequence of linear functionals on X^*. Since the natural embedding J is an isometry, the sequence $\{x_n\}$ is bounded. To verify (12), according to Theorem 7, there is a functional $\psi \in X^*$ for which $\|\psi\| = 1$ and $\psi(x) = \|x\|$. Now

$$|\psi(x_n)| \le \|\psi\| \cdot \|x_n\| = \|x_n\| \text{ for all } n.$$

Moreover, $|\{\psi(x_n)\}|$ converges to $|\psi(x)| = \|x\|$. Therefore

$$\|x\| = \lim_{n\to\infty} |\psi(x_n)| \le \liminf \|x_n\|.$$

$\square$

Remark *The Hahn-Banach Theorem has a rather humble nature. The only mathematical concepts needed for its statement are linear spaces and linear, subadditive, and positively homogeneous functionals. Besides Zorn's Lemma, its proof relies on nothing more than the rudimentary properties of the real numbers. Nevertheless, often by making a clever choice of the functional p, this theorem permits us to create basic analytical, geometric, and topological tools for functional analysis. We established Theorem 7 by applying the Hahn-Banach Theorem with the functional p chosen to be a multiple of the norm. In Section 4 of this chapter, we use the Hahn-Banach Theorem with p the so-called gauge functional associated with a convex set to separate disjoint convex subsets of a linear space by a hyperplane. In the next chapter, we use the natural embedding J of a normed linear space into its bidual to prove that the closed unit ball of a Banach space X is weakly sequentially compact if and only if X is reflexive.* [1]

PROBLEMS

18. Let X be a normed linear space, ψ belong to X^*, and $\{\psi_n\}$ be in X^*. Show that if $\{\psi_n\}$ converges weak-$*$ to ψ, then

$$\|\psi\| \le \limsup \|\psi_n\|.$$

19. Let $X = \mathbf{R}^n$ be normed with the Euclidean norm, Y a subspace of X, and $\psi: Y \to \mathbf{R}$ a linear functional. Define $Y^\perp$ to be the linear subspace of $\mathbf{R}^n$ consisting of vectors orthogonal to Y. Then $\mathbf{R}^n = Y \oplus Y^\perp$. For $x = y + y'$, $y \in Y$, $y' \in Y^\perp$, define $\bar\psi(x) = \psi(y)$. Show that this properly defines $\bar\psi \in (\mathbf{R}^n)^*$, is an extension of ψ on Y, and has the same norm as $\psi|_Y$.

20. Let $X = L^p = L^p[a, b]$, $1 < p < \infty$ and m be Lebesgue measure. For $f \neq 0$ in L^p, define

$$\psi(h) = \frac{1}{\|f\|_p^{p-1}} \int_{[a,b]} \operatorname{sgn}(f) \cdot |f|^{p-1} \cdot h \, dm \text{ for all } h \in L^p.$$

Use Hölder's Inequality to show that $\psi \in (L^p)^*$, $\|\psi\| = 1$ and $\psi(f) = \|f\|_p$.

21. For each point x in a normed linear space X, show that

$$\|x\| = \sup \{\psi(x) \mid \psi \in X^*, \|\psi\| \le 1\}.$$

---

[1]An interesting extension of the Hahn-Banach Theorem due to Agnew and Morse and a variety of applications of the Hahn-Banach Theorem may be found in Peter Lax's *Functional Analysis* [Lax02].

22. Let X be a normed linear space and Y a closed subspace of X. Show that for each $x_0 \in X \sim Y$, there is a $\psi \in X^*$ such that

$$\|\psi\| = 1, \psi = 0 \text{ on } Y \text{ and } \psi(x_0) = d, \text{ where } d = \text{dist}(x_0, Y) = \inf \{\|x_0 - y\| \mid y \in Y\}.$$

23. Let Y be a linear subspace of a normed linear space X and z be a vector in X. Show that

$$\text{dist}(z, Y) = \sup \{\psi(z) \mid \|\psi\| = 1, \psi = 0 \text{ on } Y\}.$$

24. Let X be a vector space. A subset C of X is called a **cone** provided $x + y \in C$ and $\lambda x \in C$ whenever x, y belong to C and $\lambda > 0$. Define a partial order in X by defining $x \prec y$ to mean $y - x \in C$. A linear functional f on X is said to be positive (with respect to the cone C) provided $f \geq 0$ on C. Let Y be any subspace of X with the property that for each $x \in X$ there is a $y \in Y$ with $x \leq y$. Show that each positive linear functional on Y may be extended to a positive linear functional on X. (Hint: Adapt the Hahn-Banach Lemma and use Zorn's Lemma with respect to the relation $\prec$ to find a maximal extension.)

25. Let X_0 be a subset of a metric space X. Use the Tietze Extension Theorem to show that every continuous real-valued function on X_0 has a continuous extension to all of X if and only if X_0 is closed. Does this contradict Theorem 7?

26. Let (X, ρ) be a metric space that contains the closed set F. Show that a point $x \in X$ belongs to F if and only if every continuous functional on X that vanishes on F also vanishes at x. Can this be used to prove Theorem 10?

27. Let $[a, b]$ be a closed, bounded interval of real numbers and consider $L^\infty[a, b]$, now formally considered as the collection of equivalence classes for the relation of pointwise equality almost everywhere among essentially bounded functions. Let X be the subspace of $L^\infty[a, b]$ comprising those equivalence classes that contain a continuous function. Show that such an equivalence class contains exactly one continuous function. Thus X is linearly isomorphic to $C[a, b]$ and therefore, modulo this identification, we may consider $C[a, b]$ to be a linear subspace $L^\infty[a, b]$. Show that $C[a, b]$ is a closed subspace of the Banach space $L^\infty[a, b]$.

28. Define $\psi \colon C[a, b] \to \mathbf{R}$ by $\psi(f) = f(a)$ for all $f \in C[a, b]$. Use Theorem 7 to extend ψ to a continuous linear functional on all of $L^\infty[a, b]$ (see the preceding problem). Show that there is no functional $h \in L^1[a, b]$ for which

$$\psi(f) = \int_a^b h \cdot f \text{ for all } f \in L^\infty[a, b].$$

14.3 REFLEXIVE BANACH SPACES AND WEAK SEQUENTIAL CONVERGENCE

Theorem 13 *Let X be a normed linear space. If its dual space X^* is separable, then X also is separable.*

Proof Since X^* is separable, so is its closed unit sphere $S^* = \{\psi \in X^* \mid \|\psi\| = 1\}$. Let $\{\psi_n\}_{n=1}^\infty$ be a countable dense subset of S^*. For each index n, choose $x_n \in X$ for which

$$\|x_n\| = 1 \text{ and } \psi_n(x_n) > 1/2.$$

Define X_0 to be the closed linear span of the set $\{x_n \mid 1 \leq n < \infty\}$. Then X_0 is separable since finite linear combinations, with rational coefficients, of the x_n's is a countable set that is dense in X_0. We claim $X_0 = X$. Indeed, otherwise, by Theorem 10, we may choose $\psi^* \in X^*$ for which

$$\|\psi^*\| = 1 \text{ and } \psi^* = 0 \text{ on } X_0.$$

Since $\{\psi_n\}_{n=1}^{\infty}$ is dense in S^*, there is a natural number n_0 for which $\|\psi^* - \psi_{n_0}\| < 1/2$. Therefore

$$|(\psi_{n_0} - \psi^*)(x_{n_0})| \le \|\psi_{n_0} - \psi^*\| \cdot \|x_{n_0}\| < 1/2 \text{ and yet } (\psi_{n_0} - \psi^*)(x_{n_0}) = \psi_{n_0}(x_{n_0}) > 1/2.$$

From this contradiction we infer that X is separable. $\qquad\square$

Corollary 14 *A reflexive Banach space is separable if and only if its dual is separable.*

Proof Let X be a Banach space. The preceding theorem tells us that if X^* is separable so is X, irrespective of any reflexivity assumption. Now assume that X is reflexive and separable. Thus $J(X) = X^{**} = (X^*)^*$ is separable since J is an isometry. According to the preceding theorem, with X replaced by X^*, X^* is separable. $\qquad\square$

Proposition 15 *A closed subspace of a reflexive Banach space is reflexive.*

Proof Let X_0 be a closed subspace of reflexive Banach space X. Define J to be the natural embedding of X in its bidual X^{**}. Let J_0 be the natural embedding of X_0 in its bidual X_0^{**}. To show that J_0 is onto, let S belong to X_0^{**}. Define $S' \in X^{**}$ by

$$S'(\psi) = S(\psi|_{X_0}) \text{ for all } \psi \in X^*.$$

Then $S' \colon X_0^* \to \mathbf{R}$ is linear and it is bounded with $\|S'\| \le \|S\|$. By the reflexivity of X, there is an $x_0 \in X$ for which $S' = J(x_0)$. But if $\psi \in X^*$ vanishes on X_0, then $S'(\psi) = 0$, so that

$$\psi(x_0) = J(x_0)[\psi] = S'(\psi) = 0.$$

Theorem 10 tells us that x_0 belongs to X_0. Therefore $S = J_0(x_0)$. $\qquad\square$

We record again Helley's Theorem, which we proved in Chapter 8.

Theorem 16 (Helley's Theorem) *Let X be a separable normed linear space. Then every bounded sequence $\{\psi_n\}$ in X^* has a subsequence that converges pointwise on X to $\psi \in X^*$, that is, $\{\psi_n\}$ has a subsequence that converges to ψ with respect to the weak-$*$ topology.*

Theorem 17 *Let X be a reflexive Banach space. Then every bounded sequence in X has a weakly convergent subsequence.*

Proof Let $\{x_n\}$ be a bounded sequence in X. Define X_0 to be the closure of the linear span of the set $\{x_n \mid n \in \mathbf{N}\}$. Then X_0 is separable since finite linear combinations of the x_n's, with rational coefficients, is a countable set that is dense in X_0. Of course X_0 is closed. Proposition 15 tells us that X_0 is reflexive. Let J_0 be the natural embedding of X_0 in its bidual X_0^{**}. It follows from Proposition 15 that X_0^* also is separable. Then $\{J_0(x_n)\}$ is a bounded sequence of bounded linear functionals on a separable Banach space X_0^*. According to Helley's Theorem, a subsequence $\{J_0(x_{n_k})\}$ converges weak-$*$ to $S \in (X_0^*)^*$. Since X_0 is reflexive, there is some

$x_0 \in X_0$ for which $S = J_0(x_0)$. Since every functional in X^* restricts to a functional in X_0^*, the weak-$*$ convergence of $\{J_0(x_{n_k})\}$ to $J_0(x_0)$ means precisely that $\{x_{n_k}\}$ converges weakly to x_0. □

Corollary 18 *Let X be a reflexive Banach space. Then every continuous real-valued linear functional on X takes a maximum value on the closed unit ball B of X.*

Proof Let ψ belong to X^*. The supremum of the functional values of ψ on B is $\|\psi\|$. Choose a sequence $\{x_n\}$ in B for which $\lim_{n\to\infty} \psi(x_n) = \|\psi\|$. In view of Theorem 17, we may assume that $\{x_n\}$ converges weakly to x_0. According to (12), x_0 belongs to B. Since

$$\lim_{n\to\infty} \psi(x_n) = \psi(x_0),$$

ψ takes a maximum value on B at x_0. □

Theorem 17 makes it interesting to identify which of the classical Banach spaces are reflexive.

Proposition 19 *Let $[a, b]$ be a closed, bounded interval of real numbers. Then $C[a, b]$, normed with the maximum norm, is not reflexive.*

Proof Assume $[a, b] = [0, 1]$. For $x \in [0, 1]$, define the evaluation functional $\psi_x \colon C[0, 1] \to \mathbf{R}$ by $\psi_x(f) = f(x)$. Then ψ_x is a bounded linear functional on $C[0, 1]$. Therefore, if $\{f_n\}$ converges weakly to f in $C[0, 1]$, then $\{f_n\} \to f$ pointwise on $[0, 1]$. For a natural number n, define $f_n(x) = x^n$ for $x \in [0, 1]$. Then $\{f_n\}$ converges pointwise to a function f that is not continuous. Therefore no subsequence can converge pointwise to a continuous function and hence no subsequence can converge weakly to a function in $C[0, 1]$. We infer from Theorem 17 that $C[0, 1]$ fails to be reflexive. □

Proposition 20 *For $1 < p < \infty$ and E a Lebesgue measurable set of real numbers, $L^p(E)$ is reflexive.*

Proof Let q be conjugate to p. Define the Riesz representation mapping $\mathcal{R}$ from $L^q(E)$ to $(L^p(E))^*$ by

$$\mathcal{R}(g)[f] = \int_W g \cdot f \text{ for all } g \in L^q(E),\, f \in L^p(E).$$

The Riesz Representation Theorem tells us that $\mathcal{R}$ is an isomorphism of $L^q(E)$ onto $(L^p(E))^*$. Let T be a bounded linear functional on $(L^p(E))^*$. We must show that there is a function $f \in L^p(E)$ for which $T = J(f)$, that is, since $\mathcal{R}$ is onto,

$$T(\mathcal{R}(g)) = J(f)[\mathcal{R}(g)] = \mathcal{R}(g)[f] = \int_E g \cdot f \text{ for all } g \in L^q(E). \tag{13}$$

However, the composition $T \circ \mathcal{R}$ is a bounded linear functional on $L^q(E)$. The Riesz Representation Theorem, with p and q interchanged, tells us that there is a function $f \in L^p(E)$ for which

$$(T \circ \mathcal{R})[g] = \int_E f \cdot g \text{ for all } g \in L^q(E).$$

Thus

$$T(\mathcal{R}(g)) = (T \circ \mathcal{R})[g] = \int_E f \cdot g = \int_E g \cdot f \text{ for all } g \in L^q(E),$$

that is, (13) holds.   □

In general, neither $L^1(E)$ nor $L^\infty(E)$ is reflexive. Consider $E = [0, 1]$. Observe that $L^1[0, 1]$ is separable while $(L^1[0, 1])^*$ is not separable since it is isomorphic to $L^\infty[0, 1]$, which is not separable. We infer from Corollary 14 that $L^1[0, 1]$ is not reflexive. Observe that $C[0, 1]$ is a closed subspace of $L^\infty[0, 1]$ (see Problem 27). By the preceding proposition, $C[0, 1]$ is not reflexive and therefore Proposition 15 tells us that neither is $L^\infty[0, 1]$.

Remark *Some care is needed when establishing reflexivity. R.C. James has given an example of a Banach space X that is isomorphic to X^{**} but fails to be reflexive.[2] Reflexivity requires not just that X is isomorphic to X^{**}: it requires that the natural embedding J of X into X^{**} is an isomorphism.*

Remark *The contrast between reflexivity for spaces of integrable functions and spaces of continuous functions is striking. The forthcoming Theorem 8 of Chapter 19 tells us that for $1 < p < \infty$, the most general L^p spaces are reflexive. On the other hand, if K is any compact Hausdorff space and $C(K)$ is normed by the maximum norm, then $C(K)$ is reflexive if and only if K is a finite set (see Problem 11 of Chapter 15).*

PROBLEMS

29. Show that a collection of bounded linear functions is equicontinuous if and only if it is uniformly bounded.

30. Let X be a separable normed linear space. Show that its closed unit sphere $S = \{x \in X \mid \|x\| = 1\}$ also is separable.

31. Find a compact metric space X for which $C(X)$, normed by the the maximum norm, is reflexive.

32. Let c_0 be the subspace of ℓ^∞ consisting of sequences that converge to 0. Show that c_0 is a closed subspace of ℓ^∞ whose dual space is isomorphic to ℓ^1. Conclude that c_0 is not reflexive and therefore neither is ℓ^∞.

33. For $1 \leq p \leq \infty$, show that the sequence space ℓ^p is reflexive if and only if $1 < p < \infty$. (For $p = \infty$, see the preceding problem.)

34. Consider the functional $\psi \in (C[-1, 1])^*$ defined by

$$\psi(h) = \int_{-1}^0 h - \int_0^1 h \text{ for all } h \in C[-1, 1].$$

Show that ψ fails to take a maximum on the closed unit ball of $C[-1, 1]$. Use this to provide another proof that $C[-1, 1]$ fails to be reflexive.

35. For $1 \leq p < \infty$, show that a bounded sequence in ℓ^p converges weakly if and only if it converges componentwise.

---

[2] "A non-reflexive Banach space isomorphic to its second dual," *Proc. Nat. Acad. Sci.,* 37, 1951.

36. For $1 \le p < \infty$ and $[a, b]$ a closed, bounded interval of real numbers, show that a bounded sequence $\{f_n\}$ in $L^p[a, b]$ converges weakly to f if and only if $\{\int_E f_n\} \to \int_E f$ for every Lebesgue measurable subset E of $[a, b]$.

37. For $[a, b]$ a closed, bounded interval of real numbers, show that if a sequence $\{f_n\}$ in $C[a, b]$ converges weakly, then it converges pointwise.

38. For X and Y normed linear spaces and an operator $S \in \mathcal{L}(X, Y)$, define the adjoint of S, $S^* \in \mathcal{L}(Y^*, X^*)$ by

$$[S^*(\psi)](x) = \psi(S(x)) \text{ for all } \psi \in Y^*, x \in X.$$

(i) Show that $\|S^*\| = \|S\|$ and that S^* is an isomorphism if S is an isomorphism.

(ii) For $1 < p < \infty$ and $X = L^p(E)$, where E is a measurable set of real numbers, show that the natural embedding $J: X \to X^{**}$ may be expressed as the composition

$$J = [\mathcal{R}_q^*]^{-1} \circ \mathcal{R}_p,$$

where $\mathcal{R}_p$ and $\mathcal{R}_q$ are the Riesz representing operators.

39. Let X be a reflexive Banach space and $T: X \to X$ a linear operator. Show that T belongs to $\mathcal{L}(X, X)$ if and only if whenever $\{x_n\}$ converges weakly to x, $\{T(x_n)\}$ converges weakly to $T(x)$.

14.4 LOCALLY CONVEX TOPOLOGICAL VECTOR SPACES

There is a very nice class of topologies on a vector space X, topologies for which X is said to be a locally convex topological vector space, which, for our purposes, has two virtues: This class is large enough so that, for a normed linear space X, it includes both the strong topology on X induced by a norm and the weak topologies on X induced by any subspace W of X^* that separates points. On the other hand, this class of topologies is small enough so that for linear spaces with these topologies, if K is a closed convex set that does not contain the point x_0, there is a closed hyperplane passing through x_0 that contains no point of K.

For two vectors u, v in a linear space X, a vector x that can be expressed as

$$x = \lambda u + (1 - \lambda)v \text{ for } 0 \le \lambda \le 1$$

is called a **convex combination** of u and v. A subset K of X is said to be **convex** provided it contains all convex combinations of vectors in K. Every linear subspace of a linear space is convex, and the open and closed balls in a normed space also are convex.

Definition *A **locally convex topological vector space** is a linear space X together with a Hausdorff topology that possesses the following properties:*

(i) *Vector addition is continuous, that is, the map $(x, y) \mapsto x + y$ is continuous from $X \times X$ to X;*

(ii) *Scalar multiplication is continuous, that is, the map $(\lambda, x) \mapsto \lambda \cdot x$ is continuous from $\mathbf{R} \times X$ to X;*

(iii) *There is a base at the origin for the topology consisting of convex sets.*

For a normed linear space X, a subspace W of X^* is said to **separate points** in X provided for each $u, v \in X$, there is a $\psi \in W$ for which $\psi(u) \neq \psi(v)$. Recall that for a subspace

W of X^* and point $x \in X$, a neighborhood base of x with respect to the W-weak topology comprises sets of the form

$$\mathcal{N}_{\epsilon, \psi_1, \ldots, \psi_n}(x) = \{x' \in X \mid |\psi_i(x - x')| < \epsilon \text{ for } 1 \leq i \leq n\},$$

where $\epsilon > 0$ and each ψ_i belongs to W.

Proposition 21 *Let X be a normed linear space. Then the linear space X is a locally convex topological vector space with respect to the topology induced by the norm and also with respect to the W-weak topology induced by any subspace W of X^* that separates points in X.*

Proof First consider X with the topology induced by the norm. Since the topology is induced by a metric, it is Hausdorff. From the subadditivity and homogeneity of the norm we infer that vector addition and scalar multiplication are continuous. Finally, each open ball centered at the origin is convex and the collection of such balls is a base at the origin for the topology induced by the norm.

Now let W be a subspace of X^* that separates points. To show that the W-weak topology is Hausdorff, let u and v be distinct vectors in X. Since W separates points there is a $\psi \in W$ such that $|\psi(u) - \psi(v)| = r > 0$. Then $\{x \in X \mid |\psi(u) - \psi(x)| < r/2\}$ and $\{x \in X \mid |\psi(v) - \psi(x)| < r/2\}$ are disjoint W-weak neighborhoods of u and v, respectively. To show that vector addition is continuous, let x_1 and x_2 belong to X. Consider a W-weak neighborhood $\mathcal{N}_{\epsilon, \psi_1, \ldots, \psi_n}(x_1 + x_2)$ of $x_1 + x_2$. Then the W-weak neighborhoods $\mathcal{N}_{\epsilon/2, \psi_1, \ldots, \psi_n}(x_1)$ and $\mathcal{N}_{\epsilon/2, \psi_1, \ldots, \psi_n}(x_2)$ of x_1 and x_2, respectively, have the property that

$$\text{if } (u, v) \in \mathcal{N}_{\epsilon/2, \psi_1, \ldots, \psi_n}(x_1) \times \mathcal{N}_{\epsilon/2, \psi_1, \ldots, \psi_n}(x_2), \text{ then } u + v \in \mathcal{N}_{\epsilon, \psi_1, \ldots, \psi_n}(x_1 + x_2).$$

Thus vector addition is continuous at $(x_1, x_2) \in X \times X$. A similar argument shows that scalar multiplication is continuous. Finally, a basic neighborhood of the origin is of the form $\mathcal{N}_{\epsilon, \psi_1, \ldots, \psi_n}(0)$ and this set is convex since each ψ_k is linear. $\qquad\square$

Definition *Let E be a subset of a linear space X. A point $x_0 \in E$ is said to be an **internal point** of E provided for each $x \in X$, there is some $\lambda_0 > 0$ for which $x_0 + \lambda \cdot x$ belongs to E if $|\lambda| \leq \lambda_0$.*

Proposition 22 *Let X be a locally convex topological vector space.*

   (i) *A subset $\mathcal{N}$ of X is open if and only if for each $x_0 \in X$ and $\lambda \neq 0$, $x_0 + \mathcal{N}$ and $\lambda \cdot \mathcal{N}$ are open.*

   (ii) *The closure of a convex subset of X is convex.*

   (iii) *Every point in an open subset $\mathcal{O}$ of X is an internal point of $\mathcal{O}$.*

Proof We first verify (i). For $x_0 \in X$, define the translation map $T_{x_0} \colon X \to X$ by $T_{x_0}(x) = x + x_0$. Then T_{x_0} is continuous since vector addition is continuous. The map T_{-x_0} also is continuous and is the inverse of T_{x_0}. Therefore T_{x_0} is a homeomorphism of X onto X. Thus $\mathcal{N}$ is open if and only if $\mathcal{N} + x_0$ is open. The proof of invariance of the topology under nonzero scalar multiplication is similar.

To verify (ii), let K be a convex subset of X. Fix $\lambda \in [0, 1]$. Define the mapping $\Psi \colon X \times X \to X$ by

$$\Psi(u, v) = \lambda u + (1 - \lambda)v \text{ for all } u, v \in X.$$

Since scalar multiplication and vector addition are continuous, $\Psi: X \times X \to X$ is continuous, where $X \times X$ has the product topology. A continuous mapping maps the closure of a set into the closure of the image of the set. Thus $\Psi(\overline{K \times K}) \subseteq \overline{\Psi(K \times K)}$. However, $\overline{K \times K} = \overline{K} \times \overline{K}$. Moreover, since K is convex, $\Psi(K \times K) \subseteq K$. Therefore $\Psi(\overline{K} \times \overline{K}) \subseteq \overline{K}$. Since this holds for all $\lambda \in [0, 1]$, the closure of K is convex.

To verify (iii), let x_0 belong to $\mathcal{O}$. Define $g: \mathbf{R} \times X \to X$ by $g(\lambda, x) = \lambda \cdot x + x_0$. Since scalar multiplication is continuous, the mapping g is continuous. But $g(0, 0) = x_0$ and $\mathcal{O}$ is a neighborhood of $g(0, 0)$. Thus there is a neighborhood $\mathcal{N}_1$ of $0 \in \mathbf{R}$ and a neighborhood $\mathcal{N}_0$ of $0 \in X$ for which $g(\mathcal{N}_1 \times \mathcal{N}_2) \subseteq \mathcal{O}$. Choose $\lambda_0 > 0$ for which $[-\lambda_0, \lambda_0] \subseteq \mathcal{N}_1$. Then $x_0 + \lambda \cdot x$ belongs to E if $|\lambda| \leq \lambda_0$. $\quad\square$

Proposition 23 *Let X be a locally convex topological vector space and $\psi: X \to \mathbf{R}$ be linear. Then ψ is continuous if and only if there is a neighborhood of the origin on which $|\psi|$ is bounded, that is, there is a neighborhood of the origin, $\mathcal{N}_0$, and an $M > 0$ for which*

$$|\psi| \leq M \text{ on } \mathcal{N}_0. \tag{14}$$

Proof First suppose ψ is continuous. Then it is continuous at $x = 0$ and so, since $\psi(0) = 0$, there is a neighborhood $\mathcal{N}_0$ of 0 such that $|\psi(x)| = |\psi(x) - \psi(0)| < 1$ for $x \in \mathcal{N}_0$. Thus $|\psi|$ is bounded on $\mathcal{N}_0$. To prove the converse, let $\mathcal{N}_0$ be a neighborhood 0 and $M > 0$ be such that (14) holds. For each $\lambda > 0$, $\lambda \cdot \mathcal{N}_0$ is also a neighborhood of 0 and $|\psi| \leq \lambda \cdot M$ on $\lambda \cdot \mathcal{N}_0$. To verify continuity of $\psi: X \to \mathbf{R}$, let x_0 belong to X and $\epsilon > 0$. Choose λ so that $\lambda \cdot M < \epsilon$. Then $x_0 + \lambda \cdot \mathcal{N}_0$ is a neighborhood of x_0 and if x belongs to $x_0 + \lambda \cdot \mathcal{N}_0$, then $x - x_0$ belongs to $\lambda \cdot \mathcal{N}_0$ so that

$$|\psi(x) - \psi(x_0)| = |\psi(x - x_0)| \leq \lambda \cdot M < \epsilon. \qquad\qquad\square$$

For an infinite dimensional normed linear space X, Theorem 9 of the following chapter tells us that the weak topology on X is not metrizable. Therefore in an infinite dimensional space, care is needed in using weak sequential convergence arguments to establish weak topological properties.

Example (von Neumann) For each natural number n, let e_n denote the sequence in ℓ^2 whose nth component is 1 and other components vanish. Define

$$E = \left\{ e_n + n \cdot e_m \mid n \text{ and } m \text{ any natural numbers}, m > n \right\}.$$

We leave it as an exercise to show that 0 is a point of closure, with respect to the weak topology, of E but there is no sequence in E that converges weakly to 0.

Remark *Two metrics on a set X induce the same topology if and only if a sequence that is convergent with respect to one of the metrics is convergent with respect to the other. Things are quite different for locally convex topological vector spaces. There are linear spaces X that have distinct locally convex topologies with respect to which the convergence of sequences is the same. A classic example of this is the sequence space $X = \ell^1$. The space X is a locally convex topological vector space with respect to the strong topology and with respect to the weak topology and these topologies are distinct (see Problem 6). However, a lemma of Schur asserts that a sequence converges weakly in ℓ^1 if and only if it converges strongly in ℓ^1.[3]*

---

[3]See Robert E. Megginson's *An Introduction to Banach Space Theory* [Meg98].

Remark *A topological vector space is defined to be a linear space with a Hausdorff topology with respect to which vector addition and scalar multiplication are continuous. In the absence of local convexity, such spaces can be rather pathological. For instance, if $0 < p < 1$, let X be the linear space of all Lebesgue measurable extended real-valued functions on $[0, 1]$ for which $|f|^p$ is integrable over $[0, 1]$ with respect to Lebesgue measure. Define*

$$\rho(f, g) = \int_{[0, 1]} |f - g|^p \, dm \text{ for all } f, g \in X.$$

Then, after identifying functions that are equal almost everywhere, ρ is a metric that induces a Hausdorff topology on X with respect to which vector addition and scalar multiplication are continuous. But there are no continuous linear functionals on X besides the zero functional (see Problem 50). In the next section we show that there are lots of continuous linear functionals on a topological vector space that is locally convex.

PROBLEMS

40. Let X be a normed linear space and W be a subspace of X^*. Show that the W-weak topology on X is Hausdorff if and only if W separates points in X.

41. Let X be a normed linear space and $\psi: X \to \mathbf{R}$ be linear. Show that ψ is continuous with respect to the weak topology if and only if it is continuous with respect to the strong topology.

42. Let X be a locally convex topological vector space and $\psi: X \to \mathbf{R}$ be linear. Show that ψ is continuous if and only if it is continuous at the origin.

43. Let X be a locally convex topological vector space and $\psi: X \to \mathbf{R}$ be linear. Show that ψ is continuous if and only if there is a neighborhood $\mathcal{O}$ of the origin for which $f(\mathcal{O}) \neq \mathbf{R}$.

44. Let X be a normed linear space and W a subspace of X^* that separates points. For any topological space Z, show that a mapping $f: Z \to X$ is continuous, where X has the W-weak topology, if and only if $\psi \circ f: Z \to \mathbf{R}$ is continuous for all $\psi \in W$.

45. Show that the topology on a finite dimensional locally convex topological vector space is induced by a norm.

46. Let X be a locally convex topological space. Show that the linear space X' of all linear continuous functionals $\psi: X \to \mathbf{R}$ also has a topology with respect to which it is a locally convex topological space on which, for each $x \in X$, the linear functional $\psi \longmapsto \psi(x)$ is continuous.

47. Let X and Y be locally convex topological vector spaces and $T: X \to Y$ be linear, one-to one, and onto. Show that T is a topological homeomorphism if and only if it maps base at the origin for the topology on X to a base at the origin for the topology on Y.

48. Let X be a linear space and the function $\sigma: X \to [0, \infty)$ have the following properties: for all $u, v \in X$, (i) $\sigma(u + v) \leq \sigma(u) + \sigma(v)$; (ii) $\sigma(u) = 0$ if and only if $u = 0$; (iii) $\sigma(u) = \sigma(-u)$. Define $\rho(u, v) = \sigma(u - v)$. Show that ρ is a metric on X.

49. (Nikodym) Let X be the linear space of all measurable real-valued functions on $[0, 1]$. Define

$$\sigma(f) = \int_{[0, 1]} \frac{|f|}{1 + |f|} \text{ for all } f \in X.$$

(i)   Use Problem 48 to show that $\rho(u, v) = \sigma(u - v)$ defines a metric on X.

(ii) Show that $\{f_n\} \to f$ with respect to the metric ρ if and only if $\{f_n\} \to f$ in measure.

(iii) Show that (X, ρ) is a complete metric space.

(iv) Show that the mapping $(f, g) \mapsto f + g$ is a continuous mapping of $X \times X$ into X.

(v)   Show that the mapping $(\lambda, f) \mapsto \lambda \cdot g$ is a continuous mapping of $\mathbf{R} \times X$ into X.

(vi) Show that there are no nonzero continuous linear functionals ψ on X. (Hint: Let $\psi \colon X \to \mathbf{R}$ be linear and continuous. Show that there is an n such that $\psi(f) = 0$ whenever f is the characteristic function of an interval of length less than $1/n$. Hence $\psi(f) = 0$ for all step functions f.)

50. (Day) For $0 < p < 1$, let X be the linear space of all measurable (with respect to the Lebesgue measure m) real-valued functions on $[0, 1]$ for which $|f|^p$ is integrable. Define

$$\sigma(f) = \int_{[0, 1]} |f|^p \, dm \text{ for all } f \in X.$$

(i)   Use Problem 48 to show that $\rho(u, v) = \sigma(u - v)$ defines a metric on X.

(ii) Show that the linear space X, with the topology determined by ρ, is a topological vector space.

(iii) For a nonzero function f in X and natural number n, show that there is a partition $0 = x_0 < x_1 < \ldots x_n = 1$ of $[0, 1]$ for which $\int_{x_{k-1}}^{x_k} f = 1/n \cdot \int_0^1 f$, for all $1 \leq k \leq n$.

(iv) For a nonzero function f in X and natural number n, show that there are functions $f_1, \ldots, f_n$ for which $\rho(f_k, 0) < 1/n$ for $1 \leq k \leq n$ and

$$f = \sum_{k=1}^{n} 1/n \cdot f_n.$$

(v)   Show that there are no continuous nonzero linear functionals on X.

51. Let S be the space of all sequences of real numbers, and define

$$\sigma(x) = \sum \frac{|x_n|}{2^n[1 + |x_n|]} \text{ for all } x = \{x_n\} \in S.$$

Prove the analogues of (i), (iii), (iv), and (v) of the preceding problem. What is the most general continuous linear functional on S?

14.5   THE SEPARATION OF CONVEX SETS AND MAZUR'S THEOREM

In the first section of this chapter we showed that a hyperplane in a linear space X is the level set of a nonzero linear functional on X. We therefore say that two nonempty subsets A and B of X may be **separated by a hyperplane** provided there is a linear functional $\psi \colon X \to \mathbf{R}$ and $c \in \mathbf{R}$ for which

$$\psi < c \text{ on } A \text{ and } \psi > c \text{ on } B.$$

Observe that if A is the singleton set $\{x_0\}$, then this means precisely that

$$\psi(x_0) < \inf_{x \in B} \psi(x).$$

Definition *Let K be a convex subset of a linear space X for which the origin is an internal point. The* **gauge functional**[4] *for K, $p_K : X \to [0, \infty)$, is defined by*

$$p_K(x) = \inf \{\lambda > 0 \mid x \in \lambda \cdot K\} \text{ for all } x \in X.$$

Note it is precisely because the origin is an internal point of the convex set K that its gauge functional is finite. Also note that the gauge functional associated with the unit ball of a normed linear space is the norm itself.

Proposition 24 *Let K be a convex subset of a linear space X that contains the origin as an internal point and p_K the gauge functional for K. Then p_K is subadditive and positively homogeneous.*

Proof We establish subadditivity and leave the proof of positive homogeneity as an exercise. Let $u, v \in X$ and suppose, for $\lambda > 0$ and $\mu > 0$, that $x \in \lambda K$ and $y \in \mu K$. Then, since K is convex,

$$\frac{1}{\lambda + \mu} \cdot (x + y) = \frac{\lambda}{\lambda + \mu} \cdot \frac{x}{\lambda} + \frac{\mu}{\lambda + \mu} \cdot \frac{y}{\mu} \in K.$$

Therefore, $x + y \in (\lambda + \mu)K$ so that $p_K(x + y) \le \lambda + \mu$. Taking infima, first over all such λ and then over all such μ, we conclude that $p_K(x + y) \le p_K(x) + p_K(y)$.   □

The Hyperplane Separation Lemma *Let K_1 and K_2 be two nonempty disjoint convex subsets of a linear space X, one of which has an internal point. Then there is a nonzero linear functional $\psi : X \to \mathbf{R}$ for which*

$$\sup_{x \in K_1} \psi(x) \le \inf_{x \in K_2} \psi(x). \tag{15}$$

Proof Let x_1 be an internal point of K_1 and x_2 any point of K_2. Define

$$z = x_2 - x_1 \text{ and } K = K_1 + [-K_2] + z.$$

Then K is a convex set that contains the origin as an internal point and does not contain z. Let $p = p_K : X \to \mathbf{R}$ be the gauge functional for K. Define $Y = \text{span}\,[z]$ and the linear functional $\psi : Y \to \mathbf{R}$ by $\psi(\lambda z) = \lambda$. Thus $\psi(z) = 1$, and since $1 \le p(z)$ because $z \notin K$, we conclude that $\psi \le p$ on Y. According to the preceding proposition, p is subadditive and positively homogeneous. Thus the Hahn-Banach Theorem tells us that ψ may be extended to a linear functional on all of X so that $\psi \le p$ on all of X. Let $x \in K_1$ and $y \in K_2$. Then $x - y + z \in K$ so that $p(x - y + z) \le 1$ and thus, since ψ is linear and $\psi \le p$ on all of X,

$$\psi(x) - \psi(y) + \psi(z) = \psi(x - y + z) \le p(x - y + z) \le 1.$$

Since $\psi(z) = 1$, we have $\psi(x) \le \psi(y)$. This holds for each $x \in K_1$ and y in K_2, so

$$\sup_{x \in K_1} \psi(x) \le \inf_{y \in K_2} \psi(y).$$

Of course, $\psi \ne 0$ since $\psi(z) = 1$.   □

---

[4] A gauge functional is often called a Minkowski functional.

The Hyperplane Separation Theorem *Let X be a locally convex topological vector space, K a nonempty closed convex subset of X, and x_0 a point in X that lies outside of K. Then K and x_0 may be separated by a closed hyperplane, that is, there is a continuous linear functional $\psi: X \to \mathbf{R}$ for which*

$$\psi(x_0) < \inf_{x \in K} \psi(x). \tag{16}$$

Proof Since K is closed, $X \sim K$ is open. Choose a convex neighborhood $\mathcal{N}_0$ of 0 for which

$$K \cap [\mathcal{N}_0 + x_0] = \emptyset.$$

We may, possibly by replacing $\mathcal{N}_0$ with $\mathcal{N}_0 \cap [-\mathcal{N}_0]$, suppose $\mathcal{N}_0$ is symmetric with respect to the origin, that is, $\mathcal{N}_0 = -\mathcal{N}_0$. By the Hyperplane Separation Lemma, there is a nonzero linear functional $\psi: X \to \mathbf{R}$ for which

$$\sup_{x \in \mathcal{N}_0 + x_0} \psi(x) \leq \inf_{x \in K} \psi(x). \tag{17}$$

Since $\psi \neq 0$, we may choose $z \in X$ such that $\psi(z) > 0$. According to Proposition 22, an interior point of a set is an internal point. Choose $\lambda > 0$ such that $\lambda \cdot z \in \mathcal{N}_0$. Since $\lambda \psi(z) > 0$ and $\lambda z + x_0 \in \mathcal{N}_0 + x_0$, we infer from the linearity of ψ and inequality (17) that

$$\psi(x_0) < \lambda \psi(z) + \psi(x_0) = \psi(\lambda z + x_0) \leq \sup_{x \in \mathcal{N}_0 + x_0} \psi(x) \leq \inf_{x \in K} \psi(x).$$

It remains to show that ψ is continuous. Define $M = [\inf_{x \in K} \psi(x)] - \psi(x_0)$. We infer from (17) that $\psi \leq M$ on $\mathcal{N}_0$. Since $\mathcal{N}_0$ is symmetric, $|\psi| \leq M$ on $\mathcal{N}_0$. By Proposition 23, ψ is continuous. $\qquad\square$

Corollary 25 *Let X be a normed linear space, K a nonempty strongly closed convex subset of X, and x_0 a point in X that lies outside of K. Then there is a functional $\psi \in X^*$ for which*

$$\psi(x_0) < \inf_{x \in K} \psi(x). \tag{18}$$

Proof According to Theorem 21, the linear space X is a locally convex topological vector space with respect to the strong topology. The conclusion now follows from the Hyperplane Separation Theorem. $\qquad\square$

Corollary 26 *Let X be a normed linear space and W a subspace of its dual space X^* that separates points in X. Furthermore, let K be a nonempty W-weakly closed convex subset of X and x_0 a point in X that lies outside of K. Then there is a functional $\psi \in W$ for which*

$$\psi(x_0) < \inf_{x \in K} \psi(x). \tag{19}$$

Proof According to Theorem 21, the linear space X is a locally convex topological vector space with respect to the W-weak topology. Corollary 5 tells us that the W-weakly continuous linear functionals on X belong to W. The conclusion now follows from the Hyperplane Separation Theorem. $\qquad\square$

Mazur's Theorem *Let K be a convex subset of a normed linear space X. Then K is strongly closed if and only if it is weakly closed.*

Proof Since each $\psi \in X^*$ is continuous with respect to the strong topology, each weakly open set is strongly open and therefore each weakly closed set is strongly closed, irrespective of any convexity assumption. Now suppose K is nonempty, strongly closed, and convex. Let x_0 belong to $X \sim K$. By Corollary 25, there is a $\psi \in X^*$ for which

$$\psi(x_0) < \alpha = \inf_{x \in K} \psi(x).$$

Then $\{x \in X \mid \psi(x) < \alpha\}$ is a weak neighborhood of x_0 that is disjoint from K. Thus $X \sim K$ is weakly open and therefore its complement in X, K, is weakly closed. $\square$

Corollary 27 Let K be a strongly closed convex subset of a normed linear space X. Suppose $\{x_n\}$ is a sequence in K that converges weakly to $x \in X$. Then x belongs to K.

Proof The weak limit of a sequence in K is a point of closure of K with respect to the weak topology. Therefore x belongs to the weak closure of K. But Mazur's Theorem tells us that the weak closure of K is K itself. $\square$

Theorem 28 Let X be a reflexive Banach space. Then each strongly closed bounded convex subset of X is weakly sequentially compact.

Proof Theorem 17 tells us that every bounded sequence in X has a weakly convergent subsequence. Therefore, by the preceding corollary, every sequence in K has a subsequence that converges weakly to a point in K. $\square$

The following is a variation of the Banach-Saks Theorem; the conclusion is weaker, but it holds for general normed linear spaces.

Theorem 29 Let X be a normed linear space and $\{x_n\}$ a sequence X that converges weakly to $x \in X$. Then there is a sequence $\{z_n\}$ that converges strongly to x and each z_n is a convex combination of $\{x_n, x_{n+1}, \ldots\}$.

Proof We argue by contradiction. If the conclusion is false, then there is a natural number n and an $\epsilon > 0$ for which, if we define K_0 to be the set of all convex combinations of $\{x_n, x_{n+1}, \ldots\}$, then

$$\|x - z\| \geq \epsilon \text{ for all } z \in K_0.$$

Define K to be the strong closure of K_0. Then x does not belong to K. The strong closure of a convex set is convex. Moreover, K is convex since K_0 is convex. Therefore, by Mazur's Theorem, K is weakly closed. Since $\{x_n\}$ converges to x with respect to the weak topology, x is a point of closure of K with respect to the weak topology. But a point of closure of a closed set belongs to the set. This contradiction concludes the proof. $\square$

The following theorem is a generalization of Corollary 18.

Theorem 30 Let K be a strongly closed bounded convex subset of a reflexive Banach space X. Let the function $f: K \to \mathbf{R}$ be continuous with respect to the strong topology on K and convex in the sense that for $u, v \in K$ and $0 \leq \lambda \leq 1$.

$$f(\lambda u + (1 - \lambda)v) \leq \lambda f(u) + (1 - \lambda)f(v).$$

If f is bounded below on K, then f takes a minimum value on K.

Proof Define m to be the infimum of $f(K)$. Choose a sequence $\{x_n\}$ in K such that $\{f(x_n)\}$ converges to m. According to Theorem 28, K is weakly sequentially compact. We may assume that $\{x_n\}$ converges weakly to $x \in K$. Let $\epsilon > 0$. Choose a natural number N such that

$$m \le f(x_k) < m + \epsilon \text{ for all } k \ge N. \tag{20}$$

Theorem 29 tells us that there is a sequence $\{z_n\}$ that converges strongly to x and each z_n is a convex combination of $\{x_n, x_{n+1}, \ldots\}$. By the continuity of f with respect to the strong topology on K, $\{f(z_n)\} \to f(x)$. On the other hand, from the convexity of f and (20),

$$m \le f(z_n) < m + \epsilon \text{ for all } n \ge N.$$

Therefore $m \le f(x) \le m + \epsilon$. This holds for all $\epsilon > 0$ and hence f takes its minimum value on K at the point x. $\square$

PROBLEMS

52. For each natural number n, let e_n denote the sequence in ℓ^2 whose nth component is 1 and other components vanish. Define $E = \{e_n + n \cdot e_m \mid n \text{ and } m \text{ any natural numbers}, m > n\}$. Show that 0 is a point of closure of E but no sequence in E converges weakly to 0. Consider the topological space $X = E \cup \{0\}$ with the weak topology. Find a function $f \colon X \to \mathbf{R}$ that fails to be continuous at 0 and yet has the property that whenever a sequence $\{x_n\}$ in E converges weakly to 0, its image sequence $\{f(x_n)\}$ converges to $f(0)$.

53. Find a subset of the plane $\mathbf{R}^2$ for which the origin is an internal point but not an interior point.

54. Let X be a locally convex topological vector space and V a convex, symmetric with respect to the origin (that is, $V = -V$) neighborhood of the origin. If p_V is the gauge functional for V and ψ is a linear real-valued functional on X such that $\psi \le p_V$ on X, show that ψ is continuous.

55. Let X be a locally convex topological vector space, Y a closed subspace of X, and x_0 belong to $X \sim Y$. Show that there is a continuous functional $\psi \colon X \to \mathbf{R}$ such that

$$\psi(x_0) \ne 0 \text{ and } \psi = 0 \text{ on } Y.$$

56. Let X be a normed linear space and W a proper subspace of X^* that separates points. Let ψ belong to $X^* \sim W$. Show that $\ker \psi$ is strongly closed and convex but not W-weakly closed. (Hint: Otherwise, apply Corollary 26 with $K = \ker \psi$.)

57. Let X be a normed linear space. Show that the closed unit ball B^* of X^* is weak-$*$ closed.

58. Show that the Hyperplane Separation Theorem may be amended as follows: the point x_0 may be replaced by a convex set K_0 that is disjoint from K and the conclusion is that K and K_0 can be separated by a closed hyperplane if K_0 is either compact or open.

59. Show that the weak topology on an infinite dimensional normed linear space is not first countable.

60. Show that every weakly compact subset of a normed linear space is bounded with respect to the norm.

61. Let Y be a closed subspace of a reflexive Banach space X. For $x_0 \in X \sim Y$, show that there is a point in Y that is closest to x_0.

62. Let X be normed linear space, W a finite dimensional subspace of X^* and ψ a functional in $X^* \sim W$. Show that there is a vector $x \in X$ such that $\psi(x) \neq 0$ while $\varphi(x) = 0$ for all φ in W. (Hint: First show this is true if X is finite dimensional.)

63. Let X be a normed linear space. Show that any dense subset of $B^* = \{\psi \in X^* \mid \|\psi\| \leq 1\}$ separates points in X.

64. Complete the final part of the proof of Theorem 11.

65. Find an example of a bounded subset A of a normed linear space X, $\mathcal{F}$ a set of functionals in X^* containing $\mathcal{F}_0$ as a dense subset of $\mathcal{F}$ (dense in the sense of the norm topology on X^*) such that $\mathcal{F}$ and $\mathcal{F}_0$ generate different weak topologies for X, but the same weak topology for A.

14.6   THE KREIN-MILMAN THEOREM

Definition *Let K be a nonempty convex subset of a locally convex topological vector space X. A nonempty subset E of K is called an **extreme subset**[5] of K provided it is both convex and closed and whenever a vector $x \in E$ is a convex combination of vectors u and v in K, then both u and v belong to E. A point $x \in K$ is called an **extreme point** of K provided the singleton set $\{x\}$ is an extreme subset of K.*

We leave it as two exercises to show that if the intersection of a collection of extreme subsets of K is nonempty, then the intersection is an extreme subset of K and, moreover, if A is an extreme subset of B and B is an extreme subset of K, then A is an extreme subset of K.

Lemma 31 *Let K be a nonempty, compact, convex subset of a locally convex topological vector space X and $\psi \colon X \to \mathbf{R}$ be linear and continuous. Then the set of points in K at which ψ takes its maximum value on K is an extreme subset of K.*

Proof Since K is compact and ψ is continuous, ψ takes a maximum value, m, on K. The subset M of K on which ψ takes its maximum value is closed, since ψ is continuous, and is convex since ψ is linear. Let $x \in M$ be a convex combination of vectors u, v in K. Choose $0 \leq \lambda \leq 1$ for which $x = \lambda u + (1 - \lambda)v$. Since

$$\psi(u) \leq m, \psi(v) \leq m \text{ and } m = \psi(x) = \lambda\psi(u) + (1 - \lambda)\psi(v),$$

we must have $\psi(u) = \psi(v) = m$, that is, $u, v \in M$. $\qquad\square$

The Krein-Milman Lemma *Let K be a nonempty, compact, convex subset of a locally convex topological vector space X. Then K has an extreme point.*

Proof The strategy of the proof is first to apply Zorn's Lemma to find an extreme subset E of K that contains no proper subset which also is an extreme subset of K. We then infer from the Hyperplane Separation Theorem and the preceding lemma that E is a singleton set.

Consider the collection $\mathcal{F}$ of extreme subsets of K. Then $\mathcal{F}$ is nonempty since it contains K. We order $\mathcal{F}$ by containment. Let $\mathcal{F}_0 \subseteq \mathcal{F}$ be totally ordered. Then $\mathcal{F}_0$ has the

---

[5] An extreme subset of K is also often called a supporting set for K.

finite intersection property since for any finite subcollection of $\mathcal{F}_0$, because $\mathcal{F}_0$ is totally ordered, one of the subsets of this finite subcollection is contained in all the others and therefore the intersection is nonempty. Thus $\mathcal{F}_0$ is a collection of nonempty closed subsets of the compact set K which has the finite intersection property. Hence if we let E_0 be the intersection of the sets in $\mathcal{F}_0$, E_0 is nonempty. As already observed, E_0 is an extreme subset of K since it is the nonempty intersection of such sets. Thus E_0 is a lower bound for $\mathcal{F}_0$. Therefore every totally ordered subcollection of $\mathcal{F}$ has a lower bound and hence, by Zorn's Lemma, $\mathcal{F}$ has a minimal member, that is, there is an extreme subset E of K which contains no proper extreme subset.

We claim that E is a singleton set. Indeed, otherwise we may select two points u and v in K. It follows from the Hahn-Banach Theorem that there is a $\psi \in X^*$ for which $\psi(u) < \psi(v)$. According to Lemma 31, the subset M of E on which ψ takes its maximum value on E is an extreme subset of E. Since E is an extreme subset of K, M is also an extreme subset of K. Clearly $u \notin M$, and therefore M is a proper subset of E. This contradicts the minimality of E. Thus E is a singleton set and therefore K has an extreme point.   ☐

Definition *Let K be a subset of a locally convex topological vector space X. Then the* **closed convex hull** *of K is defined to be the intersection of all closed convex subsets of X that contain K.*

We infer from Mazur's Theorem that in a normed linear space, the weakly closed convex hull of a set equals its strongly closed convex hull. It is clear that the closed convex hull of a set K is a closed convex set that contains K and that is contained in any other closed convex set that contains K.

The Krein-Milman Theorem *Let K be a nonempty, compact, convex subset of a locally convex topological vector space X. Then K is the closed convex hull of its extreme points.*

Proof By the Krein-Milman Lemma, the set E of extreme points of K is nonempty. Let C be the closed convex hull of E. If $K \neq C$, choose $x_0 \in K \sim C$. By the Hyperplane Separation Theorem, since C is convex and closed, there is a continuous linear functional $\psi: X \to \mathbf{R}$ such that

$$\psi(x_0) > \max_{x \in C} \psi(x) \geq \max_{x \in E} \psi(x). \tag{21}$$

By Lemma 31, if m is the maximum value taken by ψ on K, then $M = \{x \in K \mid \psi(x) = m\}$ is an extreme subset of K. By the Krein-Milman Lemma, applied now with K replaced by the nonempty compact convex set M, there is a point $z \in M$ that is an extreme point of M. As we already observed, an extreme point of an extreme subset of K is also an extreme point of K. We infer from (21) that $\psi(z) \geq \psi(x_0) > \psi(z)$. This contradiction shows that $K = C$.   ☐

There are many interesting applications of the Krein-Milman Theorem.[6] In Chapter 22, this theorem is used to prove the existence of ergodic measure preserving transformations. Louis de Branges has used this theorem to provide an elegant proof of the Stone-Weirstrass Theorem (see Problem 53 of Chapter 21).

---

[6] See Peter Lax's *Functional Analysis* [Lax97].

Remark *To apply the Krein-Milman Theorem it is necessary to establish criteria for identifying which subsets of a locally convex topological space are compact. In particular, to identify which convex subsets of a normed linear space X are weakly compact and which convex subsets of its dual space X* are weak-* compact. In the next chapter we prove a theorem of Alaoglu, which tells us that the closed unit ball of the dual of a normed linear space X is weak-* compact. Therefore every bounded convex subset of X* that is weak-* closed is weak-* compact. From Alaoglu's Theorem and Mazur's Theorem we then infer that any strongly closed bounded convex subset of a reflexive Banach space is weakly compact.*

PROBLEMS

66. Find the extreme points of each of the following subsets of the plane $\mathbf{R}^2$:
    (i) $\{(x, y) \mid x^2 + y^2 = 1\}$; (ii) $\{(x, y) \mid |x| + |y| = 1\}$; (iii) $\{(x, y) \mid \max\{x, y\} = 1\}$.

67. In each of the following, B denotes the closed unit ball of a normed linear space X.
    (i)   Show that the only possible extreme points of B have norm 1.
    (ii) If $X = L^p[a, b], 1 < p < \infty$, show that every unit vector in B is an extreme point of B.
    (iii) If $X = L^\infty[a, b]$, show that the extreme points of B are those functions $f \in B$ such that $|f| = 1$ a.e. on $[a, b]$.
    (iv) If $X = L^1[a, b]$, show that B fails to have any extreme points.
    (v)   If $X = l^p, 1 \le p \le \infty$, what are the extreme points of B?
    (vi) If $X = C(K)$, where K is a compact Hausdorff topological space and X is normed by the maximum norm, what are the extreme points of B?

68. A norm on a linear space is said to be **strictly convex** provided whenever u and v are distinct unit vectors and $0 < \lambda < 1$, then $\|\lambda u + (1 - \lambda)v\| < 1$. Show that the Euclidean norm on $\mathbf{R}^n$ and the usual norm on $L^p[a, b], 1 < p < \infty$ are strictly convex.

69. Let X be a reflexive Banach space with a strictly convex norm and K a nonempty closed convex subset of X. For $z \in X \sim K$, use the reflexivity of X to show that there is a point $x_0 \in K$ that is closest to z in the sense that

$$\|z - x_0\| \le \|x - z\| \text{ for all } x \in K.$$

Then use the strict convexity of the norm to show that x_0 is unique and is an extreme point of K.

CHAPTER 15

Compactness Regained:
The Weak Topology

Contents

We proved a theorem of Riesz which asserts that the closed unit ball of an infinite dimensional normed linear space fails to be compact with respect to the strong topology induced by the norm. In this chapter we prove a precise theorem regarding the manner in which, for an infinite dimensional Banach space, compactness of the closed unit ball is regained with respect to the weak topology. We prove that if B is the closed unit ball of a Banach space X, then the following are equivalent:

  (i) X is reflexive;

  (ii) B is weakly compact;

  (iii) B is weakly sequentially compact.

The first compactness result we establish is Alaoglu's Theorem, an extension of Helley's Theorem to non-separable spaces, which tells us that for a normed linear space X, the closed unit ball of the dual space X^* is compact with respect to the weak-$*$ topology. This direct consequence of the Tychonoff Product Theorem enables us to use the natural embedding of a Banach space in its bidual, $J: X \rightarrow X^{**}$, to prove the equivalences (i)–(ii). What is rather surprising is that, for the weak topology on B, sequential compactness is equivalent to compactness despite the fact that in general the weak topology on B is not metrizable.

15.1 ALAOGLU'S EXTENSION OF HELLEY'S THEOREM

Let X be a normed linear space, B its closed unit ball and B^* the closed unit ball of its dual space X^*. Assume X is separable. Choose $\{x_n\}$ to be a dense subset of B and define

$$\rho(\psi, \eta) = \sum_{n=1}^{\infty} \frac{1}{2^n} \cdot |(\psi - \eta)(x_n)| \text{ for all } \psi, \eta \in B^*.$$

Then ρ is a metric that induces the weak-$*$ topology on B^* (see Corollary 11). For a metric space, compactness is the same as sequential compactness. Therefore Helley's Theorem may be restated as follows: If X is a separable normed linear space, then the closed unit ball B^* of its dual space X^* is weak-$*$ compact. We now use the Tychonoff Product Theorem to show that the separability assumption is not needed.

Recall a special case of the Tychonoff Product Theorem: Let Λ be any set. Consider the collection $\mathcal{F}(\Lambda)$ of all real-valued functions on Λ that take values in the closed, bounded interval $[-1, 1]$. Consider $\mathcal{F}(\Lambda)$ as a topological space with the product topology. A base at $f \in \mathcal{F}(\Lambda)$ for the product topology on $\mathcal{F}(\Lambda)$ comprise sets of the form

$$\mathcal{N}_{\epsilon, \lambda_1, \ldots, \lambda_n}(f) = \{f' \in \mathcal{F}(\Lambda) \mid |f'(\lambda_k) - f(\lambda_k)| < \epsilon \text{ for } 1 \le k \le n\},$$

where $\epsilon > 0$ and the λ_k's belong to Λ. The Tychonoff Product Theorem implies that the topological space consisting of $\mathcal{F}(\Lambda)$ with the product topology is compact. Therefore every closed subset $\mathcal{F}_0(\Lambda)$ of $\mathcal{F}(\Lambda)$, with the topology induced by the product topology, also is compact.

Alaoglu's Theorem *Let X be a normed linear space. Then the closed unit ball B^* of its dual space X^* is compact with respect to the weak-$*$ topology.*

Proof Denote the closed unit balls in X and X^* by B and B^*, respectively. By the preceding discussion, the topological space $\mathcal{F}(B)$ consisting of functions from B to $[-1, 1]$, with the product topology, is compact.

Define the restriction map $R: B^* \to \mathcal{F}(B)$ by $R(\psi) = \psi|_B$ for $\psi \in B^*$. We claim that (i) $R(B^*)$ is a closed subset of $\mathcal{F}(B)$ and (ii) the restriction map R is a topological homeomorphism from B^*, with the weak-$*$ topology, onto $R(B^*)$, with the product topology. Suppose, for the moment, that (i) and (ii) have been established. By the preceding discussion, the Tychonoff Product Theorem tells us that $R(B^*)$ is compact. Therefore any space topologically homeomorphic to $R(B^*)$ is compact. In particular, by (ii), B^* is weak-$*$ compact.

It remains to verify (i) and (ii). First observe that R is one-to-one since for $\psi, \eta \in B^*$, with $\psi \neq \eta$, there is some $x \in B$ for which $\psi(x) \neq \eta(x)$ and thus $R(\psi) \neq R(\eta)$. A direct comparison of the basic open sets in the weak-$*$ topology with basic open sets in the product topology reveals that R is a homeomorphism of B^* onto $R(B^*)$. It remains to show that $R(B^*)$ is closed with respect to the product topology. Let $f: B \to [-1, 1]$ be a point of closure, with respect to the product topology, of $R(B^*)$. To show that $f \in R(B^*)$ it suffices (see Problem 1) to show that for all $u, v \in B$ and $\lambda \in \mathbf{R}$ for which $u+v$ and λu also belong to B,

$$f(u + v) = f(u) + f(v) \text{ and } f(\lambda u) = \lambda f(u). \tag{1}$$

However, for any $\epsilon > 0$, the weak-$*$ neighborhood of f, $\mathcal{N}_{\epsilon, u, v, u+v}(f)$, contains some $R(\psi_\epsilon)$ and since ψ_ϵ is linear, we have $|f(u + v) - f(u) - f(v)| < 3\epsilon$. Therefore, the first equality in (1) holds. The proof of the second is similar. $\square$

Corollary 1 *Let X be a normed linear space. Then there is a compact Hausdorff space K for which X is linearly isomorphic to a linear subspace of $C(K)$, normed by the maximum norm.*

Proof Let K be the closed unit ball of the dual space, with the weak-$*$ topology. Alaoglu's Theorem tells us that K is compact and it certainly is Hausdorff. Define $\Phi: X \to C(K)$ by $\Phi(x) = J(x)|_K$. Since the natural embedding $J: X \to X^{**}$ is an isometry, so is Φ. $\square$

Corollary 2 *Let X be a normed linear space. Then the closed unit ball B^* of its dual space X^* possesses an extreme point.*

Proof We consider X^* as a locally convex topological space with its weak-$*$ topology. According to Alaoglu's Theorem, B^* is convex and compact. The Krein-Milman Lemma tells us that B^* possesses an extreme point. $\qquad\square$

Remark *Alaoglu's Theorem does not tell us that the closed unit ball of the dual of a normed linear space is sequentially compact with respect to the weak-$*$ topology. For instance, for $X = \ell^\infty$, B^*, the closed unit ball of X^*, is not weak-$*$ sequentially compact. Indeed, the sequence $\{\psi_n\} \subseteq B^*$ defined for each n by*

$$\psi_n(\{x_k\}) = x_n \text{ for all } \{x_k\} \in \ell^\infty,$$

fails to have a weak-$*$ convergent subsequence. Alaoglu's Theorem is a generalization of Helley's Theorem from the viewpoint of compactness, not sequential compactness. By Helley's Theorem, B^* is weak-$*$ sequentially compact if X is separable, and the forthcoming Corollary 6 tells us that B^* also is weak-$*$ sequentially compact if X is reflexive.

PROBLEMS

1. For X a normed linear space with closed unit ball B, suppose the function $f: B \to [-1, 1]$ has the property that whenever $u, v, u + v$, and λu belong to B, $f(u + v) = f(u) + f(v)$ and $f(\lambda u) = \lambda f(u)$. Show that f is the restriction to B of a linear functional on all of X which belongs to the closed unit ball of X^*.

2. Let X be a normed linear space and K be a bounded convex weak-$*$ closed subset of X^*. Show that K possesses an extreme point.

3. Show that any nonempty weakly open set in an infinite dimensional normed linear space is unbounded with respect to the norm.

4. Use the Baire Category Theorem and the preceding problem to show that the weak topology on an infinite dimensional Banach space is not metrizable by a complete metric.

5. Is every Banach space isomorphic to the dual of a Banach space?

15.2   REFLEXIVITY AND WEAK COMPACTNESS: KAKUTANI'S THEOREM

Proposition 3 *Let X be a normed linear space. Then the natural embedding $J: X \to X^{**}$ is a topological homeomorphism between the locally convex topological vector spaces X and $J(X)$, where X has the weak topology and $J(X)$ has the weak-$*$ topology.*

Proof Let x_0 belong to X. A neighborhood base for the weak topology at $x_0 \in X$ is defined by sets of the form, for $\epsilon > 0$ and $\psi_1, \ldots, \psi_n \in X^*$,

$$\mathcal{N}_{\epsilon, \psi_1, \ldots, \psi_n}(x_0) = \{x \in X \mid |\psi_i(x - x_0)| < \epsilon \text{ for } 1 \le i \le n\}.$$

Now $[J(x) - J(x_0)]\psi_i = \psi_i(x - x_0)$ for each $x \in X$ and $1 \le i \le n$, and therefore

$$J(\mathcal{N}_{\epsilon, \psi_1, \ldots, \psi_n}(x_0)) = J(X) \cap \mathcal{N}_{\epsilon, \psi_1, \ldots, \psi_n}(J(x_0)).$$

Therefore J maps a base for the weak topology at the origin in X onto a base for the weak-∗ topology at the origin in $J(X)$. Thus J is a homeomorphism from X, with the weak topology, onto $J(X)$, with the weak-∗ topology.   □

Kakutani's Theorem   *A Banach space is reflexive if and only if its closed unit ball is weakly compact.*

Proof   Let X be a Banach space. Denote the closed unit balls in X and X^{**} by B and B^{**}, respectively. Assume X is reflexive. The natural embedding is an isomorphism and therefore J is a one-to-one map of B onto B^{**}. On the other hand, according to Proposition 3, J is a homeomorphism from B, with the weak topology, onto B^{**}, with the weak-∗ topology. But by Alaoglu's Theorem, applied with X replaced by X^*, B^{**} is weak-∗ compact, so any topological space homeomorphic to it also is compact. In particular, B is weakly compact.

Now assume B is weakly compact. The continuous image of compact topological spaces is compact. We infer from Proposition 3 that $J(B)$ is compact with respect to the weak-∗ topology. Of course, $J(B)$ is convex. To establish the reflexivity of X, we argue by contradiction. Assume X is not reflexive. Let T belong to $B^{**} \sim J(B)$. Apply Corollary 26 of the Hyperplane Separation Theorem in the case that X is replaced by X^* and $W = J(X^*)$. Thus there is a functonal $\psi \in X^*$ for which $\|\psi\| = 1$ and

$$T(\psi) < \inf{}_{S \in J(B)} S(\psi) = \inf{}_{x \in B} \psi(x).$$

The right-hand infimum equals -1, since $\|\psi\| = 1$. Therefore $T(\psi) < -1$. This is a contradiction since $\|T\| \le 1$ and $\|\psi\| = 1$. Therefore X is reflexive.   □

Corollary 4   *Every closed, bounded, convex subset of a reflexive Banach space is weakly compact.*

Proof   Let X be a Banach space. According to Kakutani's Theorem, the closed unit ball of X is weakly compact. Hence so is any closed ball. According to Mazur's Theorem, every closed, convex subset of X is weakly closed. Therefore any closed, convex, bounded subset of X is a weakly closed subset of a weakly compact set and hence must be weakly compact.   □

Corollary 5   *Let X be a reflexive Banach space. Then the closed unit ball of its dual space, B^*, is sequentially compact with respect to the weak-∗ topology.*

Proof   Since X is reflexive, the weak topology on B^* is the same as the weak-∗ topology. Therefore, by Alaoglu's Theorem, B^* is weakly compact. We infer from Kakutani's Theorem that X^* is reflexive. We therefore infer from Theorem 17 of the preceding chapter that every bounded sequence in X^* has a weak-∗ convergent subsequence. But B^* is weak-∗ closed. Thus B^* is sequentially compact with respect to the weak-∗ topology.   □

PROBLEMS

6. Show that every weakly compact subset of a normed linear space is bounded with respect to the norm.

7. Show that the closed unit ball B^* of the dual X^* of a Banach space X has an extreme point.

8. Let T_1 and T_2 be two compact, Hausdorff topologies on a set S for which $T_1 \subseteq T_2$. Show that $T_1 = T_2$.

9. Let X be a normed linear space containing the subspace Y. For $A \subseteq Y$, show that the weak topology on A induced by Y^* is the same as the topology A inherits as a subspace of X with its weak topology.

10. Argue as follows to show that a Banach space X is reflexive if and only if its dual space X^* is reflexive.

    (i) If X is reflexive, show that the weak and weak-$*$ topologies on B^* are the same, and infer from this that X^* is reflexive.

    (ii) If X^* is reflexive, use Problem 8 to show that the weak and weak-$*$ topologies on B^* are the same, and infer from this and Proposition 6 of Chapter 14 that $J(X) = X^{**}$.

11. For X a Banach space, by the preceding problem, if X is reflexive, then so in X^*. Conclude that X is not reflexive if there is a closed subspace of X^* that is not reflexive. Let K be an infinite compact Hausdorff space and $\{x_n\}$ an enumeration of a countably infinite subset of K. Define the operator $T : l^1 \rightarrow [C(K)]^*$ by

$$[T(\{\eta_k\})](f) = \sum_{k=1}^{\infty} \eta_k \cdot f(x_k) \text{ for all } \{\eta_k\} \in l^1 \text{ and } f \in C(k).$$

    Show that T is an isometry and therefore, since l^1 is not reflexive, neither is $T(l^1)$ and therefore neither is $C(K)$. Use a dimension counting argument to show that $C(K)$ is reflexive if K is a finite set.

12. If Y is a linear subspace of a Banach space X, we define the *annihilator* $Y^{\perp}$ to be the subspace of X^* consisting of those $\psi \in X^*$ for which $\psi = 0$ on Y. If Y is a subspace of X^*, we define Y^0 to be the subspace of vectors in X for which $\psi(x) = 0$ for all $\psi \in Y$.

    (i) Show that $Y^{\perp}$ is a closed linear subspace of X^*.

    (ii) Show that $(Y^{\perp})^0 = \overline{Y}$.

    (iii) If X is reflexive and Y is subspace of X^*, show that $Y^{\perp} = J(Y^0)$.

15.3 COMPACTNESS AND WEAK SEQUENTIAL COMPACTNESS: THE EBERLEIN-ŠMULIAN THEOREM

Theorem 6 (Goldstine's Theorem) *Let X be a normed linear space, B the closed unit ball of X, and B^{**} the closed unit ball of X^{**}. Then the the weak-$*$ closure of $J(B)$ is B^{**}.*

Proof According to Corollary 9 of the preceding chapter, J is an isometry. Thus $J(B) \subseteq B^{**}$. Let C be the weak-$*$ closure of $J(B)$. We leave it as an exercise to show that B^{**} is weak-$*$ closed. Thus $C \subseteq B^{**}$. Since B is convex and J is linear, $J(B)$ is convex. Proposition 22 of the preceding chapter tells us that, in a locally convex topological vector space, the closure of a convex set is convex. Thus C is a convex set that is closed with respect to the weak-$*$ topology. Suppose $C \neq B^{**}$. Let T belong to $B^{**} \sim C$. We now invoke the Hyperplane Separation Theorem in the case that X is replaced by $(X^*)^*$ and $(X^*)^*$ is considered as a locally convex topological vector space with the weak-$*$ topology; see Corollary 26 of the preceding chapter. Thus there is some $\psi \in X^*$ for which $\|\psi\| = 1$ and

$$T(\psi) < \inf{}_{S \in C} S(\psi). \tag{2}$$

Observe that since C contains $J(B)$,

$$\inf_{S \in C} S(\psi) \le \inf_{x \in B} \psi(x) = -1.$$

Therefore $T(\psi) < -1$. This is a contradiction since $\|T\| \le 1$ and $\|\psi\| = 1$. Therefore $C = J(B)$ and the proof of is complete. $\square$

Lemma 7 *Let X be a normed linear space and W a finite dimensional subspace of X^*. Then there is a finite subset F of X for which*

$$\|\psi\|/2 \le \max_{x \in F} \psi(x) \text{ for all } \psi \in W. \tag{3}$$

Proof Since W is finite dimensional, its closed unit sphere $S^* = \{\psi \in W \mid \|\psi\| = 1\}$ is compact and therefore is totally bounded. Choose a finite subset $\{\psi_1, \ldots, \psi_n\}$ of S^* for which $S^* \subseteq \cup_{k=1}^n B(\psi_k, 1/4)$. For $1 \le k \le n$, choose a unit vector x_k in X for which $\psi_k(x_k) > 3/4$. Let ψ belong to S^*. Observe that

$$\psi(x_k) = \psi_k(x_k) + [\psi - \psi_k]x_k \ge 3/4 + [\psi - \psi_k]x_k \text{ for } 1 \le k \le n.$$

If we choose k such that $\|\psi - \psi_k\| < 1/4$, then since $\|x_k\| = 1$, $\psi(x_k) \ge 1/2 = 1/2\|\psi\|$. Thus (3) holds if $F = \{x_1, \ldots, x_k\}$ and $\psi \in W$ has $\|\psi\| = 1$. It therefore holds for all $\psi \in W$. $\square$

Theorem 8 (the Eberlein-Šmulian Theorem) *Let B be the closed unit ball of a Banach space X. Then B is weakly compact if and only if it is weakly sequentially compact.*

Proof We first assume B is compact. Kakutani's Theorem tells us that X is reflexive. According to Theorem 17 of the preceding chapter, every bounded sequence in X has a weakly convergent subsequence. Since B is weakly closed, B is weakly sequentially compact.

To prove the converse, assume B is weakly sequentially compact. To show that B is compact it suffices, by Kakutani's Theorem, to show that X is reflexive.[1] Let T belong to B^{**}. Goldstine's Theorem tells us that T belongs to the weak-$*$ closure of $J(B)$. We will use the preceding lemma to show that T belongs to $J(B)$.

Choose $\psi_1 \in B^*$. Since T belongs to the weak-$*$ closure of $J(B)$, we may choose $x_1 \in B$ for which $J(x_1)$ belongs to $\mathcal{N}_{1,\psi_1}(T)$. Define $N(1) = 1$ and $W_1 = \text{span}[\{T, J(x_1)\}] \subseteq X^{**}$. Let n be a natural number for which there has been defined a natural number $N(n)$, a subset $\{x_k\}_{1 \le k \le n}$ of B, a subset $\{\psi_k\}_{1 \le k \le N(n)}$ of X^* and we have defined $W_n = \text{span}[\{T, J(x_1), \ldots, J(x_n)\}]$. Since T belongs to the weak-$*$ closure of $J(B)$, we may choose $x_{n+1} \in B$ for which

$$J(x_{n+1}) \in \mathcal{N}_{1/(n+1),\psi_1,\ldots,\psi_{N(n)}}(T). \tag{4}$$

Define

$$W_{n+1} = \text{span}[\{T, J(x_1), \ldots, J(x_{n+1})\}]. \tag{5}$$

---

[1] This elegant proof that sequential compactness of the closed unit ball implies reflexivity is due to R. J. Whitley, "An elementary proof of the Eberlein-Šmulian Theorem," *Mathematische Annalen*, 1967.

We infer from the preceding lemma, in the case X is replaced by X^*, that there is a natural number $N(n+1) > N(n)$ and a finite subset $\{\psi_k\}_{N(n)<k\leq N(n+1)}$ of X^* for which

$$\|S\|/2 < \max_{N(n)<k\leq N(n+1)} S(\psi_k) \text{ for all } S \in W_{n+1}. \tag{6}$$

We have therefore inductively defined a strictly increasing sequence of natural numbers $\{N(n)\}$, a sequence $\{x_n\}$ in B, a sequence $\{\psi_n\}$ in X^*, and a sequence $\{W_n\}$ of subspaces of X^{**} for which (4) and (6) hold. Since $\{W_n\}$ is an ascending sequence for which (6) holds for every index n,

$$\|S\|/2 \leq \sup_{1\leq k<\infty} S(\psi_k) \text{ for all } S \in W \equiv \overline{\text{span}}[\{T, J(x_1), \ldots, J(x_n), \ldots\}]. \tag{7}$$

Since (4) holds for all n,

$$|(T - J(x_m))[\psi_n]| < 1/m \text{ if } n < N(m). \tag{8}$$

Since B is sequentially compact, there is a subsequence $\{x_{n_k}\}$ of $\{x_n\}$ that converges weakly to $x \in B$. Mazur's Theorem tells us that a sequence of convex combinations of the terms of the sequence $\{x_{n_k}\}$ converges strongly to x. The image under J of this sequence of convex combinations converges strongly to $J(x)$ in X^{**}. Thus $J(x)$ belongs to W. But T also belongs to W. Therefore $T - J(x)$ belongs to W. We claim that $T = J(x)$. In view of (7) to verify this claim it is necessary and sufficient to show that

$$(T - J(x))[\psi_n] = 0 \text{ for all } n. \tag{9}$$

Fix a natural number n. Observe that for each index k,

$$(T - J(x))[\psi_n] = (T - J(x_{n_k}))[\psi_n] + (J(x_{n_k}) - J(x))[\psi_n].$$

We infer from (8) that if $N(n_k) > n$, then $|(T - J(x_{n_k}))[\psi_n]| < 1/n_k$. On the other hand,

$$(J(x_{n_k}) - J(x))[\psi_n] = \psi_n(x_{n_k} - x) \text{ for all } k$$

and $\{x_{n_k}\}$ converges weakly to x. Thus

$$(T - J(x))[\psi_n] = \lim_{k\to\infty}(T - J(x_{n_k}))[\psi_n] + \lim_{k\to\infty}(J(x_{n_k}) - J(x))[\psi_n] = 0. \qquad \square$$

We gather Kakutani's Theorem and the Eberlein-Šmulian Theorem into the following statement.

Characterization of Weak Compactness *Let B be the closed unit ball of a Banach space X. Then the following three assertions are equivalent:*

(i) *X is reflexive;*

(ii) *B is weakly compact;*

(iii) *B is weakly sequentially compact.*

PROBLEMS

13. In a general topological space that is not metrizable a sequence may converge to more than one point. Show that this cannot occur for the W-weak topology on a normed linear space X, where W is a subspace of X^* that separates points in X.

14. Show that there is a bounded sequence in $L^\infty[0, 1]$ that fails to have a weakly convergent subsequence. Show that the closed unit ball of $C[a, b]$ is not weakly compact.

15. Let K be a compact, metric space with infinitely many points. Show that there is a bounded sequence in $C(K)$ that fails to have a weakly convergent subsequence (see Problem 11), but every bounded sequence of continuous linear functionals on $C(K)$ has a subsequence that converges pointwise to a continuous linear functional on $C(K)$.

15.4 METRIZABILITY OF WEAK TOPOLOGIES

If the weak topology on the closed unit ball of a Banach space is metrizable, then the Eberlein-Šmulian Theorem is an immediate consequence of the equivalence of compactness and sequential compactness for a metric space. To better appreciate this theorem, we now establish some metrizable properties of weak topologies. The first theorem presents a good reason why analysts should not just stick with metric spaces.

Theorem 9 *Let X be an infinite dimensional normed linear space. Then neither the weak topology on X nor the weak-$*$ topology on X^* is metrizable.*

Proof To show that the weak topology on X is not metrizable, we argue by contradiction. Otherwise, there is a metric $\rho: X \times X \to [0, \infty)$ that induces the weak topology on X. Fix a natural number n. Consider the weak neighborhood $\{x \in X \mid \rho(x, 0) < 1/n\}$ of 0. We may choose a finite subset F_n of X^* and $\epsilon_n > 0$ for which

$$\{x \in X \mid |\psi(x)| < \epsilon_n \text{ for all } \psi \in F_n\} \subseteq \{x \in X \mid \rho(x, 0) < 1/n\}.$$

Define W_n to be the linear span of F_n. Then

$$\cap_{\psi \in W_n} \ker \psi \subseteq \{x \in X \mid \rho(x, 0) < 1/n\}. \tag{10}$$

Since X is infinite dimensional, it follows from the Hahn-Banach Theorem that X^* also is infinite dimensional. Choose $\psi_n \in X^* \sim W_n$. We infer from Proposition 4 of the preceding chapter that there is an $x_n \in X$ for which $\psi_n(x_n) \neq 0$ while $\psi(x_n) = 0$ for all $\psi \in F_n$. Define $u_n = n \cdot u_n / \|u_n\|$. Observe that $\|u_n\| = n$ and, by (10), that $\rho(u_n, 0) < 1/n$. Therefore $\{u_n\}$ is an unbounded sequence in X that converges weakly to 0. This contradicts Theorem 12 of the preceding chapter. Therefore the weak topology is not metrizable.

To prove that the weak-$*$ topology on X^* is not metrizable, we once more argue by contradiction. Otherwise, there is a metric $\rho^*: X^* \times X^* \to [0, \infty)$ that induces the weak-$*$ topology on X^*. Fix a natural number n. Consider the weak-$*$ neighborhood $\{\psi \in X^* \mid \rho^*(\psi, 0) < 1/n\}$ of 0. We may choose a finite subset A_n of X and $\epsilon_n > 0$ for which

$$\{\psi \in X^* \mid |\psi(x)| < \epsilon_n \text{ for all } x \in A_n\} \subseteq \{\psi \in X^* \mid \rho^*(\psi, 0) < 1/n\}.$$

Define X_n to be the linear span of A_n. Then

$$\{\psi \in X^* \mid \psi(x) = 0 \text{ for all } x \in X_n\} \subseteq \{\psi \in X^* \mid \rho^*(\psi, 0) < 1/n\}. \tag{11}$$

Since X_n is finite dimensional, it is closed and is a proper subspace of X since X is infinite dimensional. It follows from Corollary 11 of the preceding chapter that there is a nonzero functional $\psi_n \in X^*$ which vanishes on X_n. Define $\varphi_n = n \cdot \psi_n / \|\psi_n\|$. Observe that $\|\varphi_n\| = n$ and, by (11), that $\rho^*(\varphi_n, 0) < 1/n$. Therefore $\{\varphi_n\}$ is an unbounded sequence in X^* that converges pointwise to 0. This contradicts the Uniform Boundedness Theorem. Thus the weak-$*$ topology on X^* is not metrizable. $\qquad \square$

Theorem 10 *Let X be a normed linear space and W a separable subspace of X^* that separates points in X. Then the W-weak topology on the closed unit ball B of X is metrizable.*

Proof Since W is separable, $B^* \cap W$ also is separable, where B^* is the closed unit ball of X^*. Choose a countable dense subset $\{\psi_k\}_{k=1}^\infty$ of $B^* \cap W$. Define $\rho: B \times B \to \mathbf{R}$ by

$$\rho(u, v) = \sum_{k=1}^\infty \frac{1}{2^k} \cdot |\psi_k(u - v)| \text{ for all } u, v \in B.$$

This is properly defined since each ψ_k belongs to B^*. We first claim that ρ is a metric on B. The symmetry and triangle inequality are inherited by ρ from the linearity of ψ_k's. On the other hand, since W separates points in X, any dense subset of $S^* \cap W$ also separates points in X. Therefore, for $u, v \in B$ with $u \neq v$, there is a natural number k for which $\psi_k(u - v) \neq 0$ and therefore $\rho(u, v) > 0$. Thus ρ is a metric on B. Observe that for each natural number n, since each ψ_k belongs to B^*,

$$\frac{1}{2^n} \left[\sum_{k=1}^n |\psi_k(x)| \right] \leq \rho(x, 0) \leq \sum_{k=1}^n |\psi_k(x)| + 1/2^n \text{ for all } x \in B. \tag{12}$$

We leave it as an exercise to infer from these inequalities and the denseness of $\{\psi_k\}_{k=1}^\infty$ in $B^* \cap W$ that $\{x \in B \mid \rho(x, 0) < 1/n\}_{n=1}^\infty$ is a base at the origin for the W-weak topology on B. Therefore the topology induced by the metric ρ is the W-weak topology on B. $\qquad \square$

Corollary 11 *Let X be a normed linear space.*

(i) *The weak topology on the closed unit ball B of X is metrizable if X^* is separable.*

(ii) *The weak-$*$ topology on the closed unit ball B^* of X^* is metrizable if X is separable.*

Theorem 12 *Let X be a reflexive Banach space. Then the weak topology on the closed unit ball B is metrizable if and only if X is separable.*

Proof Since X is reflexive, Theorem 14 of the preceding chapter tells us that if X is separable, so is X^*. Therefore, by the preceding corollary, if X is separable, then the weak topology on B is metrizable. Conversely, suppose the weak topology on B is metrizable. Let $\rho: B \times B \to [0, \infty)$ be a metric that induces the weak topology on B. Let n be a natural number. We may choose a finite subset F_n of X^* and $\epsilon_n > 0$ for which

$$\{x \in B \mid |\psi(x)| < \epsilon_n \text{ for all } \psi \in F_n\} \subseteq \{x \in B \mid \rho(x, 0) < 1/n\}.$$

Therefore

$$\left[\bigcap_{\psi \in F_n} \ker \psi \right] \cap B \subseteq \{x \in B \mid \rho(x, 0) < 1/n\}. \tag{13}$$

Define Z to be the closed linear span of $\bigcup_{n=1}^{\infty} F_n$. Then Z is separable since finite linear combinations, with rational coefficients, of functionals in $\bigcup_{n=1}^{\infty} F_n$ is a countable dense subset of Z. We claim that $Z = X^*$. Otherwise, Corollary 11 of the preceding chapter tells us that there is a nonzero $S \in (X^*)^*$, which vanishes of Z. Since X is reflexive, there is some $x_0 \in X$ for which $S = J(x_0)$. Thus $x_0 \neq 0$ and $\psi_k(x_0) = 0$ for all k. According to (13), $\rho(x_0, 0) < 1/n$ for all n. Hence $x_0 \neq 0$ but $\rho(x_0, 0) = 0$. This is a contradiction. Therefore X^* is separable. Theorem 13 of the preceding chapter tells us that X also is separable. $\qquad\square$

PROBLEMS

16. Show that the dual of an infinite dimensional normed linear space also is infinite dimensional.

17. Complete the last step of the proof of Theorem 10 by showing that the inequalities (12) imply that the metric ρ induces the W-weak topology.

18. Let X be a Banach space, W a closed subspace of its dual X^*, and ψ_0 belong to $X^* \sim W$. Show that if either W is finite dimensional or X is reflexive, then there is a vector x_0 in X for which $\psi_0(x_0) \neq 0$ but $\psi(x_0) = 0$ for all $\psi \in W$. Exhibit an example of an infinite dimensional closed subspace W of X^* for which this separation property fails.

CHAPTER 16

Continuous Linear Operators on Hilbert Spaces

Contents

The inner product $\langle u, v \rangle$ of two vectors $u = (u_1, \ldots, u_n)$ and $v \in (v_1, \ldots, v_n)$ in Euclidean space $\mathbf{R}^n$ is defined by

$$\langle u, v \rangle = \sum_{k=1}^{n} u_k v_k.$$

We call this the Euclidean inner product. The Euclidean norm $\| \cdot \|$ is determined by the relation

$$\|u\| = \sqrt{\langle u, u \rangle} \text{ for all } u \in \mathbf{R}^n.$$

With respect to the Euclidean inner product there is the important notion of orthogonality, which brings a geometric viewpoint to the study of problems in finite dimensional spaces: subspaces have orthogonal complements and the solvability of systems of equations can be determined by orthogonality relations. The inner product also brings to light interesting classes of linear operators that have quite special structure: prominent among these are the symmetric operators for which there is a beautiful eigenvector representation. In this chapter we study Banach spaces H that have an inner product that is related to the norm as it is in the Euclidean spaces. These spaces are called Hilbert spaces. We show that if V is a closed subspace of a Hilbert space H, then H is the direct sum of V and its orthogonal complement. Based on this structural property, we prove the Riesz-Fréchet Representation Theorem, which characterizes the dual space of a Hilbert space. From this we infer, using Helley's Theorem, that every bounded sequence in a Hilbert space has a weakly convergent subsequence. We prove Bessel's Inequality from which we infer that a countable orthonormal set is an orthonormal basis if and only if its linear span is dense. The chapter concludes with an examination of bounded symmetric operators and compact operators on a Hilbert space, in preparation for the proof of two theorems: the Hilbert-Schmidt Theorem regarding an eigenvalue expansion for compact symmetric operators and the Riesz-Schauder Theorem regarding the Fredholm properties of compact perturbations of the identity operator.

16.1   THE INNER PRODUCT AND ORTHOGONALITY

Definition *Let H be a linear space. A function $\langle \cdot, \cdot \rangle \colon H \times H \to \mathbf{R}$ is called an **inner product** on H provided for all x_1, x_2, x and $y \in H$ and real numbers α and β,*

(i) $\langle \alpha x_1 + \beta x_2, y \rangle = \alpha \langle x_1, y \rangle + \beta \langle x_2, y \rangle$,

(ii) $\langle x, y \rangle = \langle y, x \rangle$,

(iii) $\langle x, x \rangle > 0$ if $x \neq 0$.

*A linear space H together with an inner product on H is called an **inner product space**.*

Property (ii) is called **symmetry**. From (i) and (ii) it follows that $\langle x, \alpha y_1 + \beta y_2 \rangle = \alpha \langle x, y_1 \rangle + \beta \langle x, y_2 \rangle$: this property, together with (i), is called **bilinearity**.

Among infinite dimensional linear spaces two examples of inner product spaces come to mind. For two sequences $x = \{x_k\}$ and $y = \{y_k\} \in \ell^2$, the ℓ^2 inner product, $\langle x, y \rangle$, is defined by

$$\langle x, y \rangle = \sum_{k=1}^{\infty} x_k y_k.$$

For E a measurable set of real numbers and two functions f and $g \in L^2(E)$, the L^2 inner product, $\langle f, g \rangle$, is defined by

$$\langle f, g \rangle = \int_E f \cdot g,$$

where the integral is with respect to Lebesgue measure.

In Chapter 7 we obtained the Cauchy-Schwartz Inequality for $L^2(E)$ as a special case of Hölder's Inequality. This inequality holds for any inner product space.

The Cauchy-Schwarz Inequality *For any two vectors u, v in an inner product space H,*

$$|\langle u, v \rangle| \leq \|u\| \cdot \|v\|.$$

To verify this, observe that

$$0 \leq \|u + tv\|^2 = \|u\|^2 + 2t \langle u, v \rangle + t^2 \|v\|^2 \text{ for all } t \in \mathbf{R}.$$

The quadratic polynomial in t defined by the right-hand side fails to have distinct real roots and therefore its discriminant is not positive, that is, the Cauchy-Schwarz Inequality holds.

Proposition 1 *For a vector h in an inner product space H, define*

$$\|h\| = \sqrt{\langle h, h \rangle}.$$

Then $\| \cdot \|$ is a norm on H called the norm induced by the inner product $\langle \cdot, \cdot \rangle$.

Proof The only property of a norm that is not evident for $\| \cdot \|$ is the triangle inequality. This, however, is a consequence of the Cauchy-Schwarz Inequality since, for two vectors $u, v \in H$,

$$\|u + v\|^2 = \langle u + v, \ u + v \rangle = \|u\|^2 + 2\langle u, \ v \rangle + \|v\|^2 \leq \|u\|^2 + 2\|u\|\|v\| + \|v\|^2 = (\|u\| + \|v\|)^2.$$

$\square$

The following identity characterizes norms that are induced by an inner product; see Problem 7.

The Parallelogram Identity *For any two vectors u, v in an inner product space H,*

$$\|u - v\|^2 + \|u + v\|^2 = 2\|u\|^2 + 2\|v\|^2.$$

To verify this identity just add the following two equalities:

$$\|u - v\|^2 = \|u\|^2 - 2\langle u, \ v \rangle + \|v\|^2;$$

$$\|u + v\|^2 = \|u\|^2 + 2\langle u, \ v \rangle + \|v\|^2.$$

Definition *An inner product space H is called a **Hilbert space** provided it is a Banach space with respect to the norm induced by the inner product.*

The Riesz-Fischer Theorem tells us that for E a measurable set of real numbers, $L^2(E)$ is a Hilbert space and, as a consequence, so is ℓ^2.

Proposition 2 *Let K be a nonempty closed convex subset of a Hilbert space H and h_0 belong to $H \sim K$. Then there is exactly one vector $h_* \in K$ that is closest to h_0 in the sense that*

$$\|h_0 - h_*\| = \text{dist}(h_0, \ K) = \inf_{h \in K} \|h_0 - h\|.$$

Proof By replacing K by $K - h_0$, we may assume that $h_0 = 0$. Let $\{h_n\}$ be a sequence in K for which

$$\lim_{n \to \infty} \|h_n\| = \inf_{h \in K} \|h\|. \tag{1}$$

We infer from the parallelogram identity and the convexity of K that for each m and n,

$$\|h_n\|^2 + \|h_m\|^2 = 2\left\|\frac{h_n + h_m}{2}\right\|^2 + 2\left\|\frac{h_n - h_m}{2}\right\|^2 \geq 2 \cdot \inf_{h \in K} \|h\| + 2 \cdot \left\|\frac{h_n - h_m}{2}\right\|^2. \tag{2}$$

From (1) and (2) we infer that $\{h_n\}$ is a Cauchy sequence. Since H is complete and K is closed, $\{h_n\}$ converges strongly to $h^* \in K$. By the continuity of the norm, $\|h^*\| = \inf_{h \in K} \|h\|$. This point in K that is closest to the origin is unique. Indeed, if h^* is another vector in K that is closest to the origin, then, if we substitute h^* for h_n and h_* for h_m in inequality (2), we have

$$0 \geq \|h^*\|^2 + \|h_*\|^2 - 2 \cdot \inf_{h \in K} \|h\| \geq 2 \cdot \left\|\frac{h^* - h_*}{2}\right\|.$$

Thus $h^* = h_*$.

$\square$

Definition *Two vectors u, v in the inner product space H are said to be* **orthogonal** *provided $\langle u, v \rangle = 0$. A vector u is said to be* **orthogonal** *to a subset S of H provided it is orthogonal to each vector in S. We denote by $S^\perp$ the collection of vectors in H that are orthogonal to S.*

We leave it as an exercise to infer from the Cauchy-Schwarz Inequality that if S is a subset of an inner product space H, then $S^\perp$ is a closed subspace of H. The following theorem is fundamental.

Theorem 3 *Let V be a closed subspace of a Hilbert space H. Then H has the orthogonal direct sum decomposition*

$$H = V \oplus V^\perp. \tag{3}$$

Proof Let h_0 belong to $H \sim V$. The preceding proposition tells us there is a unique vector $h^* \in V$ that is closest to h_0. Let h be any vector in V. For a real number t, since V is a linear space, the vector $h^* - th$ belongs to V and therefore

$$\langle h_0 - h^*, h_0 - h^* \rangle = \|h_0 - h^*\|^2 \le \|h_0 - (h^* - th)\|^2 = \langle h_0 - h^*, h_0 - h^* \rangle + 2t \cdot \langle h_0 - h^*, h \rangle + t^2 \langle h, h \rangle.$$

Hence

$$0 \le 2t \cdot \langle h_0 - h^*, h \rangle + t^2 \langle h, h \rangle \text{ for all } t \in R,$$

and therefore $\langle h_0 - h^*, h \rangle = 0$. Thus the vector $h_0 - h^*$ is orthogonal to V. Observe that $h_0 = h^* + [h_0 - h^*]$. We conclude that $H = V + V^\perp$ and since $V \cap V^\perp = \{0\}$, $H = V \oplus V^\perp$. $\square$

We leave the proof of the following corollary as an exercise.

Corollary 4 *Let S be a subset of a Hilbert space H. Then the closed linear span of S is all of H if and only if $S^\perp = \{0\}$.*

In view of (3), for a closed subspace V of H, we call $V^\perp$ the **orthogonal complement** of V in H and refer to (3) as an orthogonal decomposition of H. The operator $P \in \mathcal{L}(H)$ that is the projection of H onto V along $V^\perp$ is called the **orthogonal projection** of H onto V.

Proposition 5 *Let P be the orthogonal projection of a Hilbert space H onto a nontrivial closed subspace V of H. Then $\|P\| = 1$ and*

$$\langle Pu, v \rangle = \langle u, Pv \rangle \text{ for all } u, v \in H. \tag{4}$$

Proof Let the vector u belong to H. Then

$$\|u\|^2 = \langle P(u) + (\text{Id} - P)(u), P(v) + (\text{Id} - P)(v) \rangle = \|P(u)\|^2 + \|(\text{Id} - P)(u)\|^2 \ge \|P(u)\|^2,$$

and hence $\|P(u)\| \le \|u\|$. We therefore have $\|P\| \le 1$ and conclude that $\|P\| = 1$ since $P(v) = v$ for each nonzero vector in V. If the vector v also belongs to H, then

$$\langle P(u), (\text{Id} - P)(v) \rangle = \langle (\text{Id} - P)(u), P(v) \rangle = 0,$$

so that

$$\langle P(u), v \rangle = \langle P(u), P(v) \rangle = \langle u, P(v) \rangle. \qquad \square$$

The proofs of many results we established for general Banach spaces are much simpler for the special case of Hilbert spaces; see Problems 11–15.

Remark *A Banach space X is said to be* **complemented** *provided every closed subspace of X has a closed linear complement. A Banach space X is said to be* **Hilbertable** *provided there is an inner product on X whose induced norm is equivalent to the given norm. We infer from Theorem 3 that a Hilbertable Banach space is complemented. A remarkable theorem of Joram Lindenstrauss and Lior Tzafriri asserts that the converse is true: If a Banach space is complemented, then it is Hilbertable.* [1]   □

PROBLEMS

In the following problems, H is a Hilbert space.

1. Let $[a, b]$ be a closed, bounded interval of real numbers. Show that the $L^2[a, b]$ inner product is also an inner product on $C[a, b]$. Is $C[a, b]$, considered as an inner product space with the $L^2[a, b]$ inner product, a Hilbert space?

2. Show that the maximum norm on $C[a, b]$ is not induced by an inner product and neither is the usual norm on ℓ^1.

3. Let H_1 and H_2 be Hilbert spaces. Show that the Cartesian product $H_1 \times H_2$ also is a Hilbert space with an inner product with respect to which $H_1 \times \{0\} = [\{0\} \times H_2]^\perp$.

4. Show that if S is a subset of an inner product space H, then $S^\perp$ is a closed subspace of H.

5. Let S be a subset of H. Show that $S = (S^\perp)^\perp$ if and only if S is a closed subspace of H.

6. (Polarization Identity) Show that for any two vectors $u, v \in H$,

$$\langle u, v \rangle = \frac{1}{4}[\|u + v\|^2 - \|u - v\|^2].$$

7. (Jordan-von Neumann) Let X be a linear space normed by $\| \cdot \|$. Use the polarization identity to show that $\| \cdot \|$ is induced by an inner product if and only if the parallelogram identity holds.

8. Let V be a closed subspace of H and P a projection of H onto V. Show that P is the orthogonal projection of H onto V if and only if (4) holds.

9. Let T belong to $\mathcal{L}(H)$. Show that T is an isometry if and only if

$$\langle T(u), T(v) \rangle = \langle u, v \rangle \text{ for all } u, v \in H.$$

10. Let V be a finite dimensional subspace of H and $\varphi_1, \ldots, \varphi_n$ a basis for V consisting of unit vectors, each pair of which is orthogonal. Show that the orthogonal projection P of H onto V is given by

$$P(h) = \sum_{k=1}^{n} \langle h, \varphi_k \rangle \varphi_k \text{ for all } h \in V.$$

11. For h a vector in H, show that the function $u \mapsto \langle h, u \rangle$ belongs to H^*.

---

[1]"On the complemented subspace problem," *Israel Journal of Math*, 9, 1971.

12. For any vector $h \in H$, show that there is a bounded linear functional $\psi \in H^*$ for which

$$\|\psi\| = 1 \text{ and } \psi(h) = \|h\|.$$

13. Let V be a closed subspace of H and P the orthogonal projection of H onto V. For any normed linear space X and $T \in \mathcal{L}(V, X)$, show that $T \circ P$ belongs to $\mathcal{L}(H, X)$, and is an extension of $T: V \to X$ for which $\|T \circ P\| = \|T\|$.

14. Prove the Hyperplane Separation Theorem for H, considered as a locally convex topological vector space with respect to the strong topology, by directly using Proposition 2.

15. Use Proposition 2 to prove the Krein-Milman Lemma in a Hilbert space.

16.2 THE DUAL SPACE AND WEAK SEQUENTIAL CONVERGENCE

For E a measurable set of real numbers, $1 \leq p < \infty$, and q the conjugate to p, the Riesz Representation Theorem for $L^p(E)$ explicitly describes a linear isometry of $L^q(E)$ onto $[L^p(E)]^*$. The $p = 2$ case of this theorem extends to general Hilbert spaces.

The Riesz-Fréchet Representation Theorem *Let H be a Hilbert space. Define the operator $T: H \to H^*$ by assigning to each $h \in H$ the linear functional $T(h): H \to \mathbf{R}$ defined by*

$$T(h)[u] = \langle h, u \rangle \text{ for all } u \in H. \tag{5}$$

Then T is a linear isometry of H onto H^*.

Proof Let h belong to H. Then $T(h)$ is linear. We infer from the Cauchy-Schwarz Inequality that the functional $T(h): H \to \mathbf{R}$ is bounded and $\|T(h)\| \leq \|h\|$. But if $h \neq 0$, then $T(h)[h/\|h\|] = \|h\|$. Therefore $\|T(h)\| = \|h\|$. Thus T is an isometry. It is clear that T is linear. It remains to show that $T(H) = H^*$. Let $\psi_0 \neq 0$ belong to H^*. Since ψ_0 is continuous, its kernel is a closed proper subspace of H. By Theorem 3, since $\ker \psi \neq H$, we may choose a unit vector $h_* \in H$ that is orthogonal to $\ker \psi_0$. Define $h_0 = \psi_0(h_*)h_*$. We claim that $T(h_0) = \psi_0$. Indeed, for $h \in H$,

$$h - \frac{\psi_0(h)}{\psi_0(h_*)}h_* \in \ker \psi_0, \text{ so that } \langle h - \frac{\psi_0(h)}{\psi_0(h_*)}h_*, h_* \rangle = 0$$

and therefore $\psi_0(h) = \langle h_0, h \rangle = T(h_0)[h]$. $\qquad\square$

As in the case of a general Banach space, for a sequence in a Hilbert space H, we write $\{u_n\} \rightharpoonup u$ in H to mean that the sequence $\{u_n\}$ is a sequence in H that converges weakly to $u \in H$. In view of the Riesz-Fréchet Representation Theorem,

$$\{u_n\} \rightharpoonup u \text{ in } H \text{ if and only if } \lim_{n \to \infty} \langle h, u_n \rangle = \langle h, u \rangle \text{ for all } h \in H.$$

Theorem 6 *Every bounded sequence in a Hilbert space H has a weakly convergent subsequence.*

Proof Let $\{h_n\}$ be a bounded sequence in H. Define H_0 to be the closed linear span of $\{h_n\}$. Then H_0 is separable. For each natural number n, define $\psi_n \in [H_0]^*$ by

$$\psi_n(h) = \langle h_n, h \rangle \text{ for all } h \in H_0.$$

Since $\{h_n\}$ is bounded, we infer from the Cauchy-Schwarz Inequality that $\{\psi_n\}$ also is bounded. Then $\{\psi_n\}$ is a bounded sequence of bounded linear functionals on the separable normed linear space H_0. Helley's Theorem tells us that there is a subsequence $\{\psi_{n_k}\}$ of $\{\psi_n\}$ that converges pointwise to $\psi_0 \in [H_0]^*$. According to the Riesz-Fréchet Representation Theorem, there is a vector $h_0 \in H_0$ for which $\psi_0 = T(h_0)$. Thus

$$\lim_{k \to \infty} \langle h_{n_k}, h \rangle = \langle h_0, h \rangle \text{ for all } h \in H_0.$$

Let P be the orthogonal projection on H onto H_0. For each index k, since $(\text{Id} - P)[H] = P(H)^\perp$,

$$\langle h_{n_k}, (\text{Id} - P)[h] \rangle = \langle h_0, (\text{Id} - P)[h] \rangle = 0 \text{ for all } h \in H.$$

Therefore

$$\lim_{k \to \infty} \langle h_{n_k}, h \rangle = \langle h_0, h \rangle \text{ for all } h \in H.$$

Thus $\{h_{n_k}\}$ converges weakly to h_0 in H. $\qquad\square$

We gather in the following proposition some properties regarding weakly convergent sequences which we established earlier for general Banach spaces but which, because of the Riesz-Fréchet Representation Theorem, have much simpler proofs in the case of Hilbert spaces (see Problem 17).

Proposition 7 *Let $\{u_n\} \to u$ weakly in the Hilbert space H. Then $\{u_n\}$ is bounded and*

$$\|u\| \leq \liminf \|u_n\|.$$

Moreover, if $\{v_n\} \to v$ strongly in H, then

$$\lim_{n \to \infty} \langle u_n, v_n \rangle = \langle u, v \rangle. \tag{6}$$

The following two propositions describe properties of weakly convergent sequences in a Hilbert space, which in Chapter 8 we already noted hold in the $L^p(E)$ spaces, for E a measurable set of real numbers and $1 < p < \infty$, but do not hold in general Banach spaces.

The Banach-Saks Theorem *Let $\{u_n\} \to u$ weakly in the Hilbert space H. Then there is a subsequence $\{u_{n_k}\}$ of $\{u_n\}$ for which*

$$\lim_{k \to \infty} \frac{u_{n_1} + \cdots + u_{n_k}}{k} = u \text{ strongly in } H. \tag{7}$$

Proof Replacing each u_n with $u_n - u$ we may suppose that $u = 0$. Since a weakly convergent sequence is bounded, we may choose $M > 0$ such that

$$\|u_n\|^2 \leq M \text{ for all } n.$$

We will inductively choose a subsequence $\{u_{n_k}\}$ of $\{u_n\}$ with the property that for all k,

$$\left\| u_{n_1} + \cdots + u_{n_k} \right\|^2 \leq (2 + M)k. \tag{8}$$

For such a sequence,

$$\left\| \frac{u_{n_1} + \cdots + u_{n_k}}{k} \right\|^2 \le \frac{(2+M)}{k} \text{ for all } k \tag{9}$$

and the proof is complete.

Define $n_1 = 1$. Since $\{u_n\} \to 0$ and u_{n_1} belongs to H, we can choose an index n_2 such that $|\langle u_{n_1}, u_{n_2}\rangle| < 1$. Suppose we have chosen natural numbers $n_1 < n_2 < \cdots < n_k$ such that

$$\|u_{n_1} + \cdots + u_{n_j}\|^2 \le (2+M)j \text{ for } j = 1, \ldots, k.$$

Since $\{u_n\} \to 0$ and $u_{n_1} + \cdots + u_{n_k}$ belongs to H, we may choose $n_{k+1} > n_k$ such that

$$|\langle u_{n_1} + \cdots + u_{n_k}, u_{n_{k+1}}\rangle| \le 1.$$

However,

$$\|u_{n_1} + \cdots + u_{n_k} + u_{n_{k+1}}\|^2 = \|u_{n_1} + \cdots + u_{n_k}\|^2 + 2\langle u_{n_1} + \cdots + u_{n_k}, u_{n_{k+1}}\rangle + \|u_{n_{k+1}}\|^2$$

Therefore,

$$\|u_{n_1} + \cdots + u_{n_{k+1}}\|^2 \le (2+M)k + 2 + M = (2+M)(k+1).$$

We have chosen a subsequence so that (8) holds. $\qquad\square$

The Radon-Riesz Theorem *Let $\{u_n\} \to u$ weakly in the Hilbert space H. Then*

$$\{u_n\} \to u \text{ strongly in } H \text{ if and only if } \lim_{n\to\infty} \|u_n\| = \|u\|.$$

Proof Since the norm is continuous on H, with respect to the strong topology, if $\{u_n\} \to u$ strongly, then $\lim_{n\to\infty} \|u_n\| = \|u\|$. On the other hand, if $\lim_{n\to\infty} \|u_n\| = \|u\|$, then since

$$\|u_n - u\|^2 = \|u_n\|^2 - 2\langle u_n, u\rangle + \|u\|^2 \text{ for all } n,$$

the weakly convergent sequence $\{u_n\}$ is strongly convergent. $\qquad\square$

Theorem 8 *Let H be a Hilbert space. Then H is reflexive. Therefore every nonempty strongly closed bounded convex subset K of H is weakly compact and hence is the strongly closed convex hull of its extreme points.*

Proof To establish reflexivity it is necessary to show that the natural embedding $J: H \to [H^*]^*$ is onto. Let $\Psi: H^* \to \mathbf{R}$ be a bounded linear functional. Let $T: H \to [H]^*$ be the isomorphism described by the Riesz-Fréchet Representation Theorem. Then $\Psi \circ T: H \to \mathbf{R}$, being the composition of bounded linear operators, is bounded. The Riesz-Fréchet Representation Theorem tells us that there is a vector $h_0 \in H$ for which $\Psi \circ T = T(h_0)$. Therefore

$$\Psi(T(h)) = T(h_0)[h] = T(h)[h_0] = J(h_0)[T(h)] \text{ for all } h \in H.$$

Since $T(H) = H^*$, $\Psi = J(h_0)$. Thus H is reflexive. We infer from Kakutani's Theorem and Mazur's Theorem that every strongly closed bounded convex subset K of H is weakly compact. Therefore, by the Krein-Milman Theorem and another application of Mazur's Theorem, such a set K is the strongly closed convex hull of its extreme points. $\qquad\square$

PROBLEMS

16. Show that neither ℓ^1, ℓ^∞, $L^1[a, b]$ nor $L^\infty[a, b]$ is Hilbertable.

17. Prove Proposition 7.

18. Let H be an inner product space. Show that since H is a dense subset of a Banach space X whose norm restricts to the norm induced by the inner product on H, the inner product on H extends to X and induces the norm on X. Thus inner product spaces have Hilbert space completions.

16.3 BESSEL'S INEQUALITY AND ORTHONORMAL BASES

Throughout this section H is an inner product space.

Definition *A subset S of H is said to be* **orthogonal** *provided every two vectors in S are orthogonal. If such a set has the further property that each vector in S is a unit vector, then S is said to be* **orthonormal.**

The General Pythagorean Identity *If $u_1, u_2, \ldots, u_n$ are n orthonormal vectors in H, and $\alpha_1, \ldots, \alpha_n$ are real numbers, then*

$$\|\alpha_1 u_1 + \cdots + \alpha_n u_n\|^2 = \|\alpha_1\|^2 + \cdots + \|\alpha_n\|^2.$$

This identity follows from an expansion of the right-hand side of the following identity

$$\|\alpha_1 u_1 + \cdots + \alpha_n u_n\|^2 = \langle \alpha_1 u_1 + \cdots + \alpha_n u_n, \, \alpha_1 u_1 + \cdots + \alpha_n u_n \rangle.$$

Bessel's Inequality *For $\{\varphi_k\}$ an orthonormal sequence in H and h a vector in H,*

$$\sum_{k=1}^{\infty} \langle \varphi_k, h \rangle^2 \le \|h\|^2.$$

To verify this inequality, fix a natural number n and define $h_n = \sum_{k=1}^{n} \langle \varphi_k, h \rangle \varphi_k$. Then, by the General Pythagorean Identity,

$$
\begin{aligned}
0 \le \|h - h_n\|^2 &= \|h\|^2 - 2\langle h, h_n \rangle + \|h_n\|^2 \\
&= \|h\|^2 - 2\sum_{k=1}^{n} \langle h, \varphi_k \rangle \langle h, \varphi_k \rangle + \sum_{k=1}^{n} \langle h, \varphi_k \rangle^2 \\
&= \|h\|^2 - \sum_{k=1}^{n} \langle h, \varphi_k \rangle^2.
\end{aligned}
$$

Therefore

$$\sum_{k=1}^{n} \langle \varphi_k, h \rangle^2 \le \|h\|^2.$$

Take the limit as n $\to \infty$ to obtain Bessel's Inequality.

Proposition 9 *Let $\{\varphi_k\}$ be an orthonormal sequence in a Hilbert space H and the vector h belong to H. Then the series $\sum_{k=1}^{\infty} \langle \varphi_k, h \rangle \varphi_k$ converges strongly in H and the vector $h - \sum_{k=1}^{\infty} \langle \varphi_k, h \rangle \varphi_k$ is orthogonal to each φ_k.*

Proof For a natural number n, define $h_n = \sum_{k=1}^{n} \langle \varphi_k, h \rangle \varphi_k$. By the General Pythagorean Identity, for each pair of natural numbers n and k,

$$\|h_{n+k} - h_n\|^2 = \sum_{i=n+1}^{n+k} \langle \varphi_i, h \rangle^2.$$

However, by Bessel's Inequality, the series $\sum_{i=1}^{\infty} \langle \varphi_i, h \rangle^2$ converges and hence $\{h_n\}$ is a Cauchy sequence in H. Since H is complete, $\sum_{k=1}^{\infty} \langle \varphi_k, h \rangle \varphi_k$ converges strongly to a vector $h_* \in H$. Fix a natural number m. Observe that if $n > m$, then $h - h_n$ is orthogonal to φ_m. By the continuity of the inner product, $h - h_*$ is orthogonal to φ_m. $\qquad \square$

Definition *An orthonormal sequence* $\{\varphi_k\}$ *in a Hilbert space H is said to be* **complete** *provided the only vector $h \in H$ that is orthogonal to every φ_k is $h = 0$.*

We infer from Corollary 4 that an orthonormal sequence $\{\varphi_k\}$ in a Hilbert space H is complete if and only if the closed linear span of $\{\varphi_k\}$ is H.

Definition *An orthonormal sequence* $\{\varphi_k\}$ *in a Hilbert space H is called an* **orthonormal basis** *for H provided*

$$h = \sum_{k=1}^{\infty} \langle \varphi_k, h \rangle \varphi_k \text{ for all } h \in H. \tag{10}$$

Proposition 10 *An orthonormal sequence* $\{\varphi_k\}$ *in a Hilbert space H is complete if and only if it is an orthonormal basis.*

Proof First assume $\{\varphi_k\}$ is complete. According to the preceding proposition, $h - \sum_{k=1}^{\infty} \langle \varphi_k, h \rangle \varphi_k$ is orthogonal to each φ_k. Therefore, by the completeness of $\{\varphi_k\}$, (10) holds. Conversely, suppose (10) holds. Then if $h \in H$ is orthogonal to all φ_k, then

$$h = \sum_{k=1}^{\infty} \langle \varphi_k, h \rangle \varphi_k = \sum_{k=1}^{\infty} 0 \cdot \varphi_k = 0.$$

$\qquad \square$

Example The countable collection of functions in $L^2[0, 2\pi]$ consisting of the constant function that takes the value $1/\sqrt{2\pi}$ and the functions $\{1/\sqrt{2\pi} \cdot \sin kt, \ 1/\sqrt{2\pi} \cdot \cos kt\}_{k=1}^{\infty}$ are a complete orthonormal sequence for the Hilbert space $L^2[0, 2\pi]$. Indeed, we infer from the elementrary trigonometric identities that this sequence is orthonormal. We infer from the Stone-Weierstrass Theorem that the linear span of this sequence is dense, with respect to the maximum norm, in the Banach space $C[a, b]$. Thus, by the density of $C[a, b]$ in $L^2[0, 2\pi]$, the linear span of this sequence is dense in $L^2[0, 2\pi]$.

If a Hilbert space H possesses an orthonormal basis $\{\varphi_k\}$, then, since finite rational linear combinations of the φ_k's are a countable dense subset of H, H must be separable. It turns out that separability is also a sufficient condition for a Hilbert space to possess an orthonormal basis.

Theorem 11 *Every infinite dimensional separable Hilbert space posesses an orthonormal basis.*

Proof Let $\mathcal{F}$ be the collection of subsets of H that are orthonormal. Order $\mathcal{F}$ by inclusion. For every linearly ordered subcollection of $\mathcal{F}$, the union of the sets in the subcollection is an upper bound for the subcollection. By Zorn's Lemma, we may select a maximal subset S_0 of $\mathcal{F}$. Since H is separable, S_0 is countable. Let $\{\varphi_k\}_{k=1}^{\infty}$ be an enumeration of S_0. If $h \in H, h \neq 0$, then, by Proposition 9, $h - \sum_{k=1}^{\infty}\langle\varphi_k, h\rangle\varphi_k$ is orthogonal to each φ_k. Therefore $h - \sum_{k=1}^{\infty}\langle\varphi_k, h\rangle\varphi_k = 0$, for otherwise the union of S_0 and the normalization of $h - \sum_{k=1}^{\infty}\langle\varphi_k, h\rangle\varphi_k$ would be an orthonormal set that properly contains S_0. Therefore $\{\varphi_k\}_{k=1}^{\infty}$ is an orthonormal basis for H. □

PROBLEMS

19. Show that an orthonormal subset of a separable Hilbert space H must be countable.

20. Let $\{\varphi_k\}$ be an orthonormal sequence in a Hilbert space H. Show that $\{\varphi_k\}$ converges weakly to 0 in H.

21. Let $\{\varphi_k\}$ be an orthonormal basis for the separable Hilbert space H. Show that $\{u_n\} \to u$ in H if and only if for each k, $\lim_{n\to\infty}\langle u_n, \varphi_k\rangle = \langle u, \varphi_k\rangle$.

22. Show that any two infinite dimensional separable Hilbert spaces are isometrically isomorphic and that any such isomorphism preserves the inner product.

23. Let H be a Hilbert space and V a closed separable subspace of H for which $\{\varphi_k\}$ is an orthonormal basis. Show that the orthogonal projection of H onto V, P, is given by

$$P(h) = \sum_{k=1}^{\infty}\langle\varphi_k, h\rangle\varphi_k \text{ for all } h \in H.$$

24. (Parseval's Identities) Let $\{\varphi_k\}$ be an orthonormal basis for a Hilbert space H. Verify that

$$\|h\|^2 = \sum_{k=1}^{\infty}\langle\varphi_k, h\rangle^2 \text{ for all } h \in H.$$

Also verify that

$$\langle u, v\rangle = \sum_{k=1}^{\infty} a_k \cdot b_k \text{ for all } u, v \in H,$$

where, for each natural number k, $a_k = \langle u, \varphi_k\rangle$ and $b_k = \langle v, \varphi_k\rangle$.

25. Verify the assertions in the example of the orthonormal basis for $L^2[0, 2\pi]$.

26. Use Proposition 10 and the Stone-Weierstrass Theorem to show that for each $f \in L^2[-\pi, \pi]$,

$$f(x) = a_0/2 + \sum_{k=1}^{\infty}[a_k \cdot \cos kx + b_k \cdot \sin kx],$$

where the convergence is in $L^2[-\pi, \pi]$ and each

$$a_k = \frac{1}{\pi}\int_{-\pi}^{\pi} f(x)\cos kx\, dx \text{ and } b_k = \frac{1}{\pi}\int_{-\pi}^{\pi} f(x)\sin kx\, dx$$

16.4   ADJOINTS AND SYMMETRY FOR LINEAR OPERATORS

Throughout this section, H denotes a Hilbert space. We denote $\mathcal{L}(H, H)$ by $\mathcal{L}(H)$. Let T belong to $\mathcal{L}(H)$. For a fixed vector v in H, the mapping

$$u \mapsto \langle T(u), v \rangle \text{ for } u \in H,$$

belongs to H^* since it is linear and, by the Cauchy-Schwarz Inequality, $|\langle T(u), v \rangle| \leq c \cdot \|u\|$ for all $u \in H$, where $c = \|T\| \cdot \|v\|$. According to the Riesz-Fréchet Representation Theorem, there is a unique vector $h \in H$ such that $\langle T(u), v \rangle = \langle h, u \rangle = \langle u, h \rangle$ for all $u \in H$. We denote this vector h by $T^*(v)$. This defines a mapping $T^*: H \to H$ that is determined by the relation

$$\langle T(u), v \rangle = \langle u, T^*(v) \rangle \text{ for all } u, v \in H. \tag{11}$$

We call T^* the **adjoint** of T.

Proposition 12 *Let H be a Hilbert space. If T belongs to $\mathcal{L}(H)$, so does T^* and $\|T\| = \|T^*\|$.*

Proof Clearly T^* is linear. Let h be a unit vector in H. Then, by the Cauchy-Schwarz Inequality,

$$\|T^*(h)\|^2 = \langle T^*(h), T^*(h) \rangle = \langle T(T^*(h)), h \rangle \leq \|T\| \|T^*(h)\|.$$

Thus T^* belongs to $\mathcal{L}(H)$ and $\|T^*\| \leq \|T\|$. But also observe that

$$\|T(h)\|^2 = \langle T(h), T(h) \rangle = \langle T^*(T(h)), h \rangle \leq \|T^*\| \|T(h)\|.$$

Therefore $\|T\| \leq \|T^*\|$. $\square$

We leave it as an exercise to verify the following structural properties of adjoints: for $T, S \in \mathcal{L}(H)$,

$$(T^*)^* = T, \ (T + S)^* = T^* + S^* \text{ and } (T \circ S)^* = S^* \circ T^*. \tag{12}$$

Proposition 13 *Let H be a Hilbert space. Suppose T belongs to $\mathcal{L}(H)$ and has a closed image. Then*

$$\text{Im } T \oplus \ker T^* = H. \tag{13}$$

Proof Since Im T is closed, it suffices, by Theorem 3, to show that $\ker T^* = [\text{Im } T]^\perp$. But this is an immediate consequence of the relation (11). $\square$

Proposition 14 *Let H be a Hilbert space. Suppose T belongs to $\mathcal{L}(H)$ and there is a $c > 0$ for which* [2]

$$\langle T(h), h \rangle \geq \|h\|^2 \text{ for all } h \in H. \tag{14}$$

Then T is invertible.

---

[2] An operator T for which (14) holds is called **positive definite**.

Proof The inequality (14) implies that $\ker T = \{0\}$. We infer from (14) and the Cauchy-Schwarz Inequality that

$$\|T(u) - T(v)\| \geq c\|u - v\| \text{ for all } u, v \in H.$$

We claim that T has closed range. Indeed, let $\{T(h_n)\} \to h$ strongly in H. Then $\{T(h_n)\}$ is Cauchy. The above inequality implies that $\{h_n\}$ is Cauchy. But H is complete and therefore there is a vector h_* to which $\{h_n\}$ converges strongly. By the continuity of T, $T(h_*) = h$. Therefore $T(H)$ is closed. We also claim that $\ker T^* = \{0\}$. Indeed, by (14), the symmetry of the inner product and the definition of the adjoint,

$$\langle T^*(h), h \rangle = \langle T(h), h \rangle \geq \|h\|^2 \text{ for all } h \in H.$$

Therefore $\ker T^* = \{0\}$. We infer from the preceding proposition that $T(H) = H$. $\square$

An examination of the proof of the Riesz-Fréchet Representation Theorem reveals that the symmetry of the inner product was not used. The following important generalization of this theorem has many applications in the study of partial differential equations.

Theorem 15 (the Lax-Milgram Lemma) *Let H be a Hilbert space. Suppose the function $B: H \times H \to \mathbf{R}$ has the following three properties:*

(i) For each $u \in H$, the following two functionals are linear on H;

$$v \mapsto B(u, v) \text{ and } v \mapsto B(v, u).$$

(ii) There is a $c_1 > 0$ for which

$$|B(u, v)| \leq c_1 \cdot \|u\| \cdot \|v\| \text{ for all } u, v \in H.$$

(iii) There is a $c_2 > 0$ for which

$$B(h, h) \geq c_2 \cdot \|h\|^2 \text{ for all } h \in H.$$

Then for each $\psi \in H^*$, there is a unique $h \in H$ for which

$$\psi(u) = B(h, u) \text{ for all } u \in H.$$

Proof Let $T: H \to H^*$ be the isomorphism defined by the Riesz-Fréchet Representation Theorem, that is, for each $h \in H$,

$$T(h)[u] = \langle h, u \rangle \text{ for all } u \in H. \tag{15}$$

For each $h \in H$, define the functional $S(h): H \to \mathbf{R}$ by

$$S(h)[u] = B(h, u) \text{ for all } u \in H. \tag{16}$$

We infer from assumptions (i) and (ii) that each $S(h)$ is a bounded linear functional on H and that the operator $S: H \to H^*$ is linear and continuous. Since T is an isomorphism of H

onto H^*, to show that S is an isomorphism of H onto H^* is equivalent to showing that the operator $T^{-1} \circ S \in \mathcal{L}(H)$ is invertible. However, by assumption (iii),

$$\langle (T^{-1} \circ S)(h), h \rangle = S(h)[h] = B(h, h) \geq c_2 \cdot \|h\|^2 \text{ for all } h \in H.$$

The preceding proposition tells us that $T^{-1} \circ S \in \mathcal{L}(H)$ is invertible.   □

Definition *An operator $T \in \mathcal{L}(H)$ is said to be* **symmetric** *or* **self-adjoint** *provided $T = T^*$, that is,*

$$\langle T(u), v \rangle = \langle u, T(v) \rangle \text{ for all } u, v \in H.$$

Example Let $\{\varphi_k\}$ be an orthonormal basis for the separable Hilbert space H and T belong to $\mathcal{L}(H)$. Then, by the continuity of the inner product, T is symmetric if and only if

$$\langle T(\varphi_i), \varphi_j \rangle = \langle T(\varphi_j), \varphi_i \rangle \text{ for all } 1 \leq i, j < \infty.$$

In particular, if H is Euclidean space $\mathbf{R}^n$, then T is symmetric if and only if the $n \times n$ matrix that represents T with respect to an orthonormal basis is a symmetric matrix.

A symmetric operator $T \in \mathcal{L}(H)$ is said to be **nonnegative**, written $T \geq 0$, provided $\langle T(h), h \rangle \geq 0$ for all $h \in H$. Moreover, for two symmetric operators $A, B \in \mathcal{L}(H)$, we write $A \geq B$ provided $A - B \geq 0$. The sum of nonnegative, symmetric operators is nonnegative and symmetric. Moreover,

if $T \in \mathcal{L}(H)$ is symmetric and nonnegative, then so is S^*TS for any $S \in \mathcal{L}(H)$,   (17)

since for each $h \in H$, $\langle S^*TS(h), h \rangle = \langle T(S(h)), S(h) \rangle \geq 0$. In Problems 37–43 we explore a few of the many interesting consequences of this order relation among symmetric operators.

The Polarization Identity *For a symmetric operator $T \in \mathcal{L}(H)$,*

$$\langle T(u), v \rangle = \frac{1}{4} \left[\langle T(u+v), u+v \rangle - \langle T(u-v), u-v \rangle \right] \text{ for all } u, v \in H.   (18)$$

To verify this identity, simply expand the two inner products on the right-hand side. If we associate with a symmetric operator $T \in \mathcal{L}(H)$ the **quadratic form** $Q_T: H \to \mathbf{R}$ defined by

$$Q_T(u) = \langle T(u), u \rangle \text{ for all } u \in H,$$

the Polarization Identity tells us that T is completely determined by Q_T. In particular, $T = 0$ on H if and only if $Q_T = 0$ on H. In fact, the following much sharper result holds. It is useful, for $T \in \mathcal{L}(H)$ and $\lambda \in \mathbf{R}$, to denote $\lambda \operatorname{Id} - T$ by $\lambda - T$, where the identity mapping Id: $H \to H$ is defined by $\operatorname{Id}(h) = h$ for all $h \in H$.

Proposition 16 *Let H be a Hilbert space and the operator $T \in \mathcal{L}(H)$ be symmetric. Then*

$$\|T\| = \sup_{\|u\|=1} |\langle T(u), u \rangle|.   (19)$$

Proof Denote $\sup_{\|u\|=1}|\langle T(u), u\rangle|$ by η. If $\eta = 0$, we infer from the Polarization Identity that $T = 0$. So consider the case $\eta > 0$. Observe that, by the Cauchy-Schwarz Inequality, for a unit vector $u \in H$,

$$|\langle T(u), u\rangle| \le \|T(u)\|\|u\| \le \|T\|.$$

Thus, $\eta \le \|T\|$. To prove the inequality in the opposite direction, observe that the two symmetric operators $\eta - T$ and $\eta + T$ are nonnegative and therefore, by (17), the two operators

$$(\eta + T)^*(\eta - T)(\eta + T) = (\eta + T)(\eta - T)(\eta + T)$$

and

$$(\eta - T)^*(\eta + T)(\eta - T) = (\eta - T)(\eta + T)(\eta - T)$$

also are nonnegative and hence so is their sum $2\eta(\eta^2 - T^2)$. Since $2\eta > 0$, $\eta^2 - T^2$ is nonnegative, that is,

$$\|T(u)\|^2 = \langle T(u), T(u)\rangle = \langle T^2(u), u\rangle \le \eta^2 \langle u, u\rangle = \eta^2\|u\|^2 \text{ for all } u \in H.$$

Hence $\|T\| \le \eta$. $\qquad\square$

A general strategy in the study of a linear operator $T \in \mathcal{L}(H)$ is to express H as a direct sum $H_1 \oplus H_2$ for which $T(H_1) \subseteq H_1$ and $T(H_2) \subseteq H_2$. When this occurs we say the decomposition $H = H_1 \oplus H_2$ **reduces** the operator T. In general, if $T(H_1) \subseteq H_1$ we cannot infer that $T(H_2) \subseteq H_2$. However, for symmetric operators on H and an orthogonal direct sum decomposition of H, we have the following simple but very useful result.

Proposition 17 *Let H be a Hilbert space. Suppose the operator $T \in \mathcal{L}(H)$ is symmetric and V is a subspace of H for which $T(V) \subseteq V$. Then $T(V^\perp) \subseteq V^\perp$.*

Proof Let u belong to $V^\perp$. Then for any $v \in V$, $\langle T(u), v\rangle = \langle u, T(v)\rangle$ and $\langle u, T(v)\rangle = 0$ since $T(V) \subseteq V$ and $u \in V^\perp$. Thus $T(u) \in V^\perp$. $\qquad\square$

PROBLEMS

27. Verify (12).

28. Let T and S belong to $\mathcal{L}(H)$ and be symmetric. Show that $T = S$ if and only if $Q_T = Q_S$.

29. Show the symmetric operators are a closed subspace of $\mathcal{L}(H)$. Also show that if T and S are symmetric, then so is the composition $S \circ T$ if and only if T commutes with S with respect to composition, that is, $S \circ T = T \circ S$.

30. (Hellinger-Toplitz) Let H be a Hilbert space and the linear operator $T: H \to H$ have the property that the $\langle T(u), v\rangle = \langle u, T(v)\rangle$ for all $u, v \in h$. Show that T belongs to $\mathcal{L}(H)$.

31. Exhibit an operator $T \in \mathcal{L}(\mathbf{R}^2)$ for which $\|T\| > \sup_{\|u\|=1}|\langle T(u), u\rangle|$.

32. Let S and T in $\mathcal{L}(H)$ be symmetric. Assume $S \ge T$ and $T \ge S$. Prove that $T = S$.

33. Let V be a closed nontrivial subspace of a Hilbert space H and P the orthogonal projection of H onto V. Show that $P = P^*$, $P \ge 0$, and $\|P\| = 1$.

34. Let $P \in \mathcal{L}(H)$ be a projection. Show that P is the orthogonal projection of H onto $P(H)$ if and only if $P = P^*$.

35. Let $\{\varphi_k\}$ be an orthonormal basis for a Hilbert space H and for each natural number n, define P_n to be the orthogonal projection of H onto the linear span of $\{\varphi_1, \ldots, \varphi_n\}$. Show that P_n is symmetric and

$$0 \leq P_n \leq P_{n+1} \leq \text{Id for all } n.$$

Show that $\{P_n\}$ converges pointwise on H to Id but does not converge unformly on the unit ball.

36. Show that if $T \in \mathcal{L}(H)$ is invertible, so is $T^* \circ T$ and therefore so is T^*.

37. (a General Cauchy-Schwarz Inequality) Let $T \in \mathcal{L}(H)$ be symmetric and nonnegative. Show that for all $u, v \in H$,

$$|\langle T(u), v \rangle|^2 \leq \langle T(u), u \rangle \cdot \langle T(v), v \rangle.$$

38. Use the preceding problem to show that if $S, T \in \mathcal{L}(H)$ are symmetric and $S \geq T$, then for each $u \in H$,

$$\|S(u) - T(u)\|^4 = \langle (S-T)(u), (S-T)(u) \rangle^2 \leq |\langle (S-T)(u), u \rangle| |\langle (S-T)^2(u), (S-T)(u) \rangle|$$

and thereby conclude that

$$\|S(u) - T(u)\|^4 \leq |\langle S(u), u \rangle - \langle T(u), u \rangle| \cdot \|S - T\|^3 \cdot \|u\|^2.$$

39. (a Monotone Convergence Theorem for Symmetric Operators) A sequence $\{T_n\}$ of symmetric operators in $\mathcal{L}(H)$ is said to be monotone increasing provided $T_{n+1} \geq T_n$ for each n, and said to be bounded above provided there is a symmetric operator S in $\mathcal{L}(H)$ such that $T_n \leq S$ for all n.

    (i) Use the preceding problem to show that a monotone increasing sequence $\{T_n\}$ of symmetric operators in $\mathcal{L}(H)$ converges pointwise to a symmetric operator in $\mathcal{L}(H)$ if and only if it is bounded above.

    (ii) Show that a monotone increasing sequence $\{T_n\}$ of symmetric operators in $\mathcal{L}(H)$ is bounded above if and only if it is pointwise bounded, that is, for each $h \in H$, the sequence $\{T_n(h)\}$ is bounded.

40. Let $S \in \mathcal{L}(H)$ be a symmetric operator for which $0 \leq S \leq \text{Id}$. Define a sequence $\{T_n\}$ in $\mathcal{L}(H)$ by letting $T_1 = 1/2(\text{Id} - S)$ and if n is a natural number for which $T_n \in \mathcal{L}(H)$ has been defined, defining $T_{n+1} = 1/2(\text{Id} - S + T_n^2)$.

    (i)   Show that for each natural number n, T_n and $T_{n+1} - T_n$ are polynomials in $\text{Id} - S$ with nonnegative coefficients.

    (ii) Show that $\{T_n\}$ is a monotone increasing sequence of symmetric operators that is bounded above by Id.

    (iii) Use the preceding problem to show that $\{T_n\}$ converges pointwise to a symmetric operator T for which $0 \leq T \leq \text{Id}$ and $T = 1/2(\text{Id} - S + T^2)$.

    (iv) Define $A = (\text{Id} - T)$. Show that $A^2 = S$.

41. (Square Roots of Nonnegative Symmetric Operators) Let $T \in \mathcal{L}(H)$ be a nonnegative symmetric operator. A nonnegative symmetric operator $A \in \mathcal{L}(H)$ is called a square root of T provided $A^2 = T$. Use the inductive construction in the preceding problem to show that T has a square root A which commutes with each operator in $\mathcal{L}(H)$ that commutes with T. Show that the square root is unique: it is denoted by $\sqrt{T}$. Finally, show that T is invertible if and only if $\sqrt{T}$ is invertible.

42. An invertible operator $T \in \mathcal{L}(H)$ is said to be **orthogonal** provided $T^{-1} = T^*$. Show that an invertible operator is orthogonal if and only if it is an isometry.

43. (Polar Decompositions) Let $T \in \mathcal{L}(H)$ be invertible. Show that there is an orthogonal invertible operator $A \in \mathcal{L}(H)$ and a nonnegative symmetric invertible operator $B \in \mathcal{L}(H)$ such that $T = B \circ A$. (Hint: Show that T^*T is invertible and symmetric and let $B = \sqrt{T \circ T^*}$.)

16.5   COMPACT OPERATORS

Definition *An operator $T \in \mathcal{L}(H)$ is said to be **compact** provided $T(B)$ has compact closure, with respect to the strong topology, where B is the closed unit ball in H.*

Any operator $T \in \mathcal{L}(H)$ maps bounded sets to bounded sets. An operator $T \in \mathcal{L}(H)$ is said to be of **finite rank** provided its image is finite dimensional. Since a bounded subset of a finite dimensional space has compact closure, every operator of finite rank is compact. In particular, if H is finite dimensional, then every operator in $\mathcal{L}(H)$ is compact. On the other hand, according to Riesz's Theorem, or by Theorem 11, the identity operator $\mathrm{Id}\colon H \to H$ fails to be compact if H is infinite dimensional. For the same reason, an invertible operator in $\mathcal{L}(H)$ fails to be compact if H is infinite dimensional.

In any metric space, compactness of a set is the same as sequential compactness. Furthermore, since a metric space is compact if and only if it is complete and totally bounded, a subset of a complete metric space has compact closure if and only if it is totally bounded. We therefore have the following useful characterizations of compactness for a bounded linear operator.

Proposition 18 *Let H be a Hilbert space and K belong to $\mathcal{L}(H)$. Then the following are equivalent:*

(i) *K is compact;*

(ii) *$K(B)$ is totally bounded, where B is the closed unit ball in H;*

(iii) *If $\{h_n\}$ is a bounded sequence in H, then $\{K(h_n)\}$ has a strongly convergent subsequence.*

Example Let $\{\varphi_k\}$ be an orthonormal basis for the separable Hilbert space H and $\{\lambda_k\}$ a sequence of real numbers that converges to 0. Define

$$T(h) = \sum_{k=1}^{\infty} \lambda_k \langle h, \varphi_k \rangle \varphi_k \text{ for } h \in H.$$

We infer from Bessel's Inequality and the boundedness of $\{\lambda_k\}$ that T belongs to $\mathcal{L}(H)$ and we claim that T is compact. According to the preceding proposition, to show that K is compact it suffices to show that $T(B)$ is totally bounded. Let $\epsilon > 0$. Choose N such that $|\lambda_k| < \epsilon/2$ for $k \geq N$. Define $T_N \in \mathcal{L}(H)$ by

$$T_N(h) = \sum_{k=1}^{N} \lambda_k \langle h, \varphi_k \rangle \varphi_k \text{ for } h \in H.$$

We infer from Bessel's Inequality that $\|T(h) - T_N(h)\| < \epsilon/2\|h\|$ for $h \in H$. But $T_N(B)$ is a bounded subset of a finite dimensional space, so it is totally bounded. Let $\epsilon > 0$. There is a finite $\epsilon/2$-net for $T_N(B)$ and by doubling the radius of each of the balls in this net we get a finite ϵ-net for $T(B)$.

A linear operator $T: H \to H$ belongs to $\mathcal{L}(H)$ if and only if it maps weakly convergent sequences to weakly convergent sequences (see Problem 47).

Proposition 19 *Let H be a Hilbert space. Then an operator T in $\mathcal{L}(H)$ is compact if and only if it maps weakly convergent sequences to strongly convergent sequences, that is,*

$$\text{if } \{h_n\} \rightharpoonup h, \text{ then } \{T(h_n)\} \to T(h).$$

Proof According to the preceding proposition, an operator is compact if and only if it maps bounded sequences to sequences that have a strongly convergent subsequence. First assume that T is compact. Observe that for any operator $T \in \mathcal{L}(H)$, if $\{u_k\} \rightharpoonup u$, then $\{T(u_n)\} \rightharpoonup T(u)$, since for each $v \in H$,

$$\lim_{k \to \infty} \langle T(u_k), v \rangle = \lim_{k \to \infty} \langle u_k, T^*(v) \rangle = \langle u, T^*(v) \rangle = \langle T(u), v \rangle.$$

Let $\{h_n\} \rightharpoonup h$ in H. By the compactness of T, every subsequence of $\{T(h_n)\}$ has a further subsequence that converges strongly and, by the preceding observation, its strong limit must be $T(h)$. Therefore the entire sequence $\{T(h_n)\}$ converges strongly to $T(h)$. To prove the converse, assume T maps weakly convergent sequences to strongly convergent subsequences. Let $\{h_n\}$ be a bounded sequence. Theorem 6 tells us that $\{h_n\}$ has a weakly convergent subsequence. The image of this weakly convergent subsequence converges strongly. $\qquad \square$

Schauder's Theorem *A compact linear operator on a Hilbert space has a compact adjoint.*

Proof Let $K \in \mathcal{L}(H)$ be compact. According to the preceding proposition, it suffices to show that K^* maps weakly convergent sequences to strongly convergent sequences. Let $\{h_n\} \rightharpoonup h$ in H. For each n,

$$\|K^*(h_n) - K^*(h)\|^2 = \langle KK^*(h_n) - KK^*(h), h_n - h \rangle. \tag{20}$$

Since K^* is continuous, $\{K^*(h_n)\}$ converges weakly to $K^*(h)$. The preceding proposition tells us that $\{KK^*(h_n)\} \to KK^*(h)$ strongly in H. Therefore, by Proposition 7,

$$\lim_{k \to \infty} \langle KK^*(h_n) - KK^*(h), h_n - h \rangle = 0.$$

We infer from (20) that $\{K^*(h_n)\}$ converges strongly to $K^*(h)$. $\qquad \square$

PROBLEMS

44. Show that if H is infinite dimensional and $T \in \mathcal{L}(H)$ is invertible, then T is not compact.

45. Prove Proposition 18.

46. Let $\mathcal{K}(H)$ denote the set of compact operators in $\mathcal{L}(H)$. Show that $\mathcal{K}(H)$ is a linear subspace of $\mathcal{L}(H)$. Moreover, show that for $K \in \mathcal{K}(H)$ and $T \in \mathcal{L}(H)$, both $K \circ T$ and $T \circ K$ belong to $\mathcal{K}(H)$.

47. Show that a linear operator $T: H \to H$ is continuous if and only if it maps weakly convergent sequences to weakly convergent sequences.

48. Show that $K \in \mathcal{L}(H)$ is compact if and only if whenever $\{u_n\} \rightharpoonup u$ in H and $\{v_n\} \rightharpoonup v$ in H, then $\langle K(u_n), v_n \rangle \to \langle K(u), v \rangle$.

49. Let $\{P_n\}$ be a sequence of orthogonal projections in $\mathcal{L}(H)$ with the property that for natural numbers n and m, $P_n(H)$ and $P_m(H)$ are orthogonal finite dimensional subspaces of H. Let $\{\lambda_n\}$ be a bounded sequence of real numbers. Show that

$$K = \sum_{n=1}^{\infty} \lambda_n \cdot P_n$$

is a properly defined symmetric operator in $\mathcal{L}(H)$ that is compact if and only if $\{\lambda_n\}$ converges to 0.

50. For X a Banach space, define an operator $T \in \mathcal{L}(X)$ be be compact provided $T(B)$ has compact closure. Show that Proposition 18 holds for a general Banach space and Proposition 19 holds for a reflexive Banach space.

16.6 THE HILBERT-SCHMIDT THEOREM

A nonzero vector $u \in H$ is said to be an **eigenvector** of the operator $T \in \mathcal{L}(H)$ provided there is some $\lambda \in \mathbf{R}$ for which $T(u) = \lambda u$. We call λ the **eigenvalue** of T associated with the eigenvector u. One of the centerpieces of linear algebra is the following assertion: If H is a finite dimensional Hilbert space and $T \in \mathcal{L}(H)$ is symmetric, then there is an orthonormal basis for H consisting of eigenvectors of T, that is, if H has dimension n, there is an orthonormal basis $\{\varphi_1, \ldots, \varphi_n\}$ for H and numbers $\{\lambda_1, \ldots, \lambda_n\}$ such that $T(\varphi_k) = \lambda_k \varphi_k$ for $1 \le k \le n$. Thus

$$T(h) = \sum_{k=1}^{n} \lambda_k \langle h, \varphi_k \rangle \varphi_k \text{ for all } h \in H. \tag{21}$$

Of course, in the absence of symmetry, a bounded linear operator, even on a finite dimensional space, may fail to have any eigenvectors. As the following example shows, even a symmetric operator on an infinite dimensional Hilbert space may fail to have any eigenvectors.

Example Define $T \in \mathcal{L}(L^2[a, b])$ by $[T(f)](x) = xf(x)$ for $f \in L^2[a, b]$. For $u, v \in L^2[a, b]$,

$$\langle T(u), v \rangle = \int_a^b xu(x)v(x)\,dx = \langle u, T(v) \rangle.$$

Thus T is symmetric and one easily checks that it has no eigenvectors.

We associated with a symmetric operator $T \in \mathcal{L}(H)$, the quadratic form $Q_T : H \to \mathbf{R}$ defined by

$$Q_T(h) = \langle T(h), h \rangle \text{ for all } h \in H.$$

It is useful to define the Raleigh quotient for T, $R_T : H \sim \{0\} \to \mathbf{R}$, by

$$R_T(h) = \frac{\langle T(h), h \rangle}{\langle h, h \rangle} \text{ for all } h \in H \sim \{0\}.$$

Observe that a maximizer h_* for the quadratic form Q_T on the unit sphere $S = \{h \in H \mid \|h\| = 1\}$ is a maximizer for the Raleigh quotient R_T on $H \sim \{0\}$.

The Hilbert-Schmidt Lemma *Let H be a Hilbert space and $T \in \mathcal{L}(H)$ be compact and symmetric. Then T has an eigenvalue λ for which*

$$|\lambda| = \|T\| = \sup_{\|h\|=1} |\langle T(h), h \rangle|. \tag{22}$$

Proof If $T = 0$ on H, then every nonzero vector in H is an eigenvector of T with corresponding eigenvalue $\lambda = 0$. So consider the case $T \neq 0$. Proposition 16 tells us that

$$\|T\| = \sup_{\|h\|=1} |\langle T(h), h \rangle|.$$

By possibly replacing T by $-T$ we may suppose that $\|T\| = \sup_{\|h\|=1} \langle T(h), h \rangle$. Denote $\sup_{\|h\|=1} \langle T(h), h \rangle$ by η. Let $S = \{h \in H \mid \|h\| = 1\}$ be the unit sphere in H.

Let $\{h_k\}$ be a sequence of unit vectors for which $\lim_{k \to \infty} \langle T(h_k), h_k \rangle = \eta$. By Theorem 6, by possibly passing to a subsequence, we may suppose that $\{h_k\}$ converges weakly to h_*. We have $\|h_*\| \leq \liminf \|h_n\| = 1$. According to Proposition 19, since T is compact, $\{T(h_n)\}$ converges strongly to $T(h_*)$. Therefore, by Proposition 7,

$$\lim_{k \to \infty} \langle T(h_k), h_k \rangle = \langle T(h_*), h_* \rangle.$$

Thus $\eta = \langle T(h_*), h_* \rangle$. Now $h_* \neq 0$ since $\eta \neq 0$. Moreover, h_* must be a unit vector. Indeed, otherwise $0 < \|h_*\| < 1$, in which case the quadratic form Q_T takes a value greater than η at $h_*/\|h_*\| \in S$, contradicting the choice of η as being an upper bound for Q_T on S. Thus $h_* \in S$ and $Q_T(h) \leq Q_T(h_*)$ for all $h \in S$. Therefore, for the Raleigh Quotient for T, R_T, we have

$$R_T(h) \leq R_T(h_*) \text{ for all } h \in H \sim \{0\}.$$

Let h_0 be any vector in H. Observe that the function $f \colon \mathbf{R} \to \mathbf{R}$, defined by $f(t) = R_T(h_* + th_0)$ for $t \in R$, has a maximum value at $t = 0$ and therefore $f'(0) = 0$. A direct calculation gives

$$0 = f'(0) = \frac{\langle T(h_0), h_* \rangle + \langle T(h_*), h_0 \rangle}{\|h_*\|^2} - \langle T(h_*), h_* \rangle \frac{\langle h_*, h_0 \rangle + \langle h_0, h_* \rangle}{\|h_*\|^4}.$$

But T is symmetric, h_* is a unit vector, and $\eta = \langle T(h_*), h_* \rangle$ so that

$$\langle T(h_*) - \eta h_*, h_0 \rangle = 0.$$

Since this holds for all $h_0 \in H$, $T(h_*) = \eta h_*$.   □

The Hilbert-Schmidt Theorem *Let H be a Hilbert space. Suppose $K \in \mathcal{L}(H)$ is a compact symmetric operator that is not of finite rank. Then there is an orthonormal basis $\{\psi_k\}$ for $[\ker K]^\perp$ together with a sequence of real nonzero numbers $\{\lambda_k\}$ such that $\lim_{k \to \infty} \lambda_k = 0$ and $K(\psi_k) = \lambda_k \psi_k$ for each k. Thus*

$$K(h) = \sum_{k=1}^{\infty} \lambda_k \langle h, \psi_k \rangle \psi_k \text{ for all } h \in H. \tag{23}$$

Proof Let S be the unit sphere in H. According to the Hilbert-Schmidt Lemma, we may choose a vector $\psi_1 \in S$ and $\mu_1 \in \mathbf{R}$ for which

$$K(\psi_1) = \mu_1\psi_1 \text{ and } |\mu_1| = \sup_{h\in S} |\langle K(h), h\rangle|.$$

Since $K \neq 0$, we infer from Proposition 16 that $\mu_1 \neq 0$. Define $H_1 = [\text{span}\{\psi_1\}]^\perp$. Since $K(\text{span}\{\psi_1\}) \subseteq \text{span}\{\psi_1\}$, it follows from Proposition 17 that $K(H_1) \subseteq H_1$. Thus if we define K_1 to be the restriction of K to H_1, then $K_1 \in \mathcal{L}(H_1)$ is compact and symmetric. We again apply the Hilbert-Schmidt Lemma to choose a vector $\psi_2 \in S \cap H_1$ and $\mu_2 \in \mathbf{R}$ for which

$$K(\psi_2) = \mu_2\psi_2 \text{ and } |\mu_2| = \sup\left\{|\langle K(h), h\rangle| \mid h \in S \cap H_1\right\}.$$

Observe that $|\mu_2| \leq |\mu_1|$. Moreover, since K does not have finite rank, we again use Proposition 16 to conclude that $\mu_2 \neq 0$. We argue inductively to choose an orthogonal sequence of unit vectors in H, $\{\psi_k\}$, and a sequence of nonzero real numbers $\{\mu_k\}$ such that for each index k,

$$K(\psi_k) = \mu_k\psi_k \text{ and } |\mu_k| = \sup\left\{|\langle K(h), h\rangle| \mid h \in S \cap [\text{span}\{\psi_1, \ldots, \psi_{k-1}\}]^\perp\right\}. \tag{24}$$

Observe that $\{|\mu_k|\}$ is decreasing. We claim that $\{\mu_k\} \to 0$. Indeed, otherwise, since this sequence is decreasing, there is some $\epsilon > 0$ such that $|\mu_k| \geq \epsilon$ for all k. Therefore, for natural numbers m and n, since ψ_n is orthogonal to ψ_m,

$$\|K(\psi_n) - K(\psi_m)\|^2 = \mu_n^2\|\psi_n\|^2 + \mu_m^2\|\psi_m\|^2 \geq 2\epsilon^2.$$

Thus $\{K(\psi_k)\}$ has no strongly convergent subsequence and this contradicts the compactness of the operator K. Therefore $\{\mu_k\} \to 0$. Define H_0 to be the closed linear span of $\{\psi_k\}_{k=1}^\infty$. Then, by Proposition 10, $\{\psi_k\}_{k=1}^\infty$ is an orthonormal basis for H_0. Since $K(H_0) \subseteq H_0$, it follows from Proposition 17 that $K(H_0^\perp) \subseteq H_0^\perp$. But observe that if $h \in H_0^\perp$ is a unit vector, then, for each k, $h \in S \cap [\text{span}\{\psi_1, \ldots, \psi_{k-1}\}]^\perp$ and therefore $|\langle K(h), h\rangle| \leq |\mu_k|$. Since $\{\mu_k\} \to 0$, $\langle K(h), h\rangle = 0$. Thus $Q_T = 0$ on $H_0^\perp$ and hence, by the polarization identity, $\ker K = H_0^\perp$. Thus $H_0 = [\ker K]^\perp$. $\square$

In case a symmetric operator $T \in \mathcal{L}(H)$ has finite rank, define H_0 to be the image of T. Then $\ker T = H_0^\perp$. The above argument establishes a finite orthonormal basis for H_0 consisting of eigenvectors of T, thereby recovered a basic result of linear algebra that was mentioned at the beginning of this section.

PROBLEMS

51. Let H be a Hilbert space and $T \in \mathcal{L}(H)$ be compact and symmetric. Define

$$\alpha = \inf_{\|h\|=1} \langle T(h), h\rangle \text{ and } \beta = \sup_{\|h\|=1} \langle T(h), h\rangle.$$

Show that if $\alpha < 0$, then α is an eigenvalue of T and if $\beta > 0$, then β is an eigenvalue of T. Exhibit an example where $\alpha = 0$ and yet α is not an eigenvalue of T, that is, T is one-to-one.

52. Let H be a Hilbert space and $K \in \mathcal{L}(H)$ be compact and symmetric. Suppose

$$\sup_{\|h\|=1} \langle K(h), h \rangle = \beta > 0.$$

Let $\{h_n\}$ be a sequence of unit vectors for which $\lim_{n \to \infty} \langle K(h_n), h_n \rangle = \beta$. Show that a subsequence of $\{h_n\}$ converges strongly to an eigenvector of T with corresponding eigenvalue β.

16.7   THE RIESZ-SCHAUDER THEOREM: CHARACTERIZATION OF FREDHOLM OPERATORS

A subspace X_0 of the Banach space X is said to be of **finite codimension** in X provided X_0 has a finite dimensional linear complement in X, that is, there is a finite dimensional subspace X_1 of X for which $X = X_0 \oplus X_1$. The codimension of X_0, denoted by codim X_0, is properly defined to be the dimension of a linear complement of X_0; all linear complements have the same dimension (see Problem 66). A cornerstone of linear algebra is the assertion that if X is a finite dimensional linear space and $T: X \to X$ is linear, then the sum of the rank of T and the nullity of T equals the dimension of X, that is, if dim $X = n$,

$$\dim \operatorname{Im} T + \dim \ker T = n,$$

and therefore, since codim Im $T = n - \dim \operatorname{Im} T$,

$$\dim \ker T = \operatorname{codim} \operatorname{Im} T. \tag{25}$$

Our principal goal in this section is to prove that if H is a Hilbert space and the operator $T \in \mathcal{L}(H)$ is a compact perturbation of the identity operator, then T has a finite dimensional kernel and a finite codimensional image for which (25) holds.

Proposition 20   *Let H be a Hilbert space and $K \in \mathcal{L}(H)$ be compact. Then $\operatorname{Id} + K$ has finite dimensional kernel and a closed image.*

Proof   Suppose $\ker(\operatorname{Id} + K)$ is infinite dimensional. We infer from Proposition 11 that there is an orthogonal sequence of unit vectors $\{u_k\}$ contained in $\ker(\operatorname{Id} + K)$. Since $\|K(u_n) - K(u_m)\| = \|u_n - u_m\| = \sqrt{2}$, if $m \neq n$, the sequence $\{K(u_n)\}$ has no convergent subsequence. This contradicts the compactness of the operator K. Thus $\dim[\ker(\operatorname{Id} + K)] < \infty$. Let $H_0 = [\ker(\operatorname{Id} + K)]^\perp$. We claim that there is a $c > 0$ for which

$$\|u + K(u)\| \geq c\|u\| \text{ for all } u \in H_0. \tag{26}$$

Indeed, if there is no such c, then we can choose a sequence $\{h_n\}$ of unit vectors in H_0 such that $\{u_n + K(u_n)\} \to 0$ strongly in H. Since K is compact, by passing to a subsequence if necessary, we may suppose that $\{K(u_n)\} \to h_0$ strongly. Therefore $\{u_n\} \to -h_0$ strongly. By the continuity of K, $h_0 + K(h_0) = 0$. Thus h_0 is a unit vector that belongs to both $[\ker(\operatorname{Id} + K)]^\perp$ and $\ker(\operatorname{Id} + K)$. This contradiction confirms the existence of a $c > 0$ for which (26) holds. We infer from (26) and the completeness of H_0 that $(\operatorname{Id} + K)(H_0)$ is closed. Since $(\operatorname{Id} + K)(H_0) = (\operatorname{Id} + K)(H)$, $\operatorname{Im}(\operatorname{Id} + K)$ is closed. $\qquad \square$

Definition *Let $\{\varphi_n\}$ be an orthonormal basis for the separable Hilbert space H. For each n, define $P_n \in \mathcal{L}(H)$ by*

$$P_n(h) = \sum_{k=1}^{n} \langle \varphi_k, h \rangle \varphi_k \text{ for all } h \in H.$$

We call $\{P_n\}$ the **orthogonal projection sequence** *induced by $\{\varphi_n\}$.*

For an orthogonal projection sequence $\{P_n\}$ induced by an orthonormal basis $\{\varphi_n\}$, each P_n is the orthogonal projection of H into span $\{\varphi_1, \ldots, \varphi_n\}$ and therefore $\|P_n\| = 1$. Moreover, by the very definition of an orthonormal basis, $\{P_n\} \to$ Id pointwise on H. Therefore, for any $T \in \mathcal{L}(H)$, $\{P_n \circ T\}$ is a sequence of operators of finite rank that converges pointwise to T on H.

Proposition 21 *Let $\{P_n\}$ be the orthogonal projection sequence induced by the orthonormal basis $\{\varphi_n\}$ for the separable Hilbert space H. Then an operator $T \in \mathcal{L}(H)$ is compact if and only if $\{P_n \circ T\} \to T$ in $\mathcal{L}(H)$.*

Proof First assume $\{P_n \circ T\} \to T$ in $\mathcal{L}(H)$. For each natural number n, $P_n \circ T$ has finite dimensional range and therefore $(P_n \circ T)(B)$ is totally bounded, where B is the unit ball in H. Since $\{P_n \circ T\} \to T \in \mathcal{L}(H)$, $\{P_n \circ T\}$ converges uniformly on B to T. Therefore $T(B)$ also is totally bounded. We infer from Proposition 18 that the operator T is compact. To prove the converse, assume T is compact. Then the set $\overline{T(B)}$ is compact with respect to the strong topology. For each natural number n, define $\psi_n \colon \overline{T(B)} \to \mathbf{R}$ by

$$\psi_n(h) = \|P_n(h) - h\| \text{ for all } h \in \overline{T(B)}.$$

Since each P_n has norm 1, the sequence of real-valued functions $\{\psi_n \colon \overline{T(B)} \to \mathbf{R}\}$ is equicontinuous, bounded, and converges pointwise to 0 on the compact set $\overline{T(B)}$. We infer from the Arzelà-Ascoli Theorem that $\{\psi_n \colon \overline{T(B)} \to \mathbf{R}\}$ converges uniformly to 0. This means precisely that $\{P_n \circ T\} \to T$ in $\mathcal{L}(H)$. $\qquad\square$

Proposition 22 *Let H be a Hilbert space and $K \in \mathcal{L}(H)$ be compact. If Id $+K$ is one-to-one, then it is onto.*

Proof We leave it as an exercise (Problem 53) to show that there is a closed separable subspace H_0 of H for which $K(H_0) \subseteq H_0$ and $K = 0$ on $H_0^{\perp}$. Therefore, by replacing H by H_0 we may suppose H is separable. We argue as we did in the proof of Proposition 20 to show that there is a $c > 0$ for which

$$\|h + K(h)\| \geq c\|h\| \text{ for all } h \in H. \tag{27}$$

According to Theorem 11, H has an orthonormal basis $\{\varphi_n\}$. Let $\{P_n\}$ be the orthogonal projection sequence induced by $\{\varphi_n\}$. For each natural number n, let H_n be the linear span of $\{\varphi_1, \ldots, \varphi_n\}$. Since the operator K is compact, according to the preceding proposition, $\{P_n \circ K\} \to K$ in $\mathcal{L}(H)$. Choose a natural number N for which $\|P_n \circ K - K\| < c/2$ for all $n \geq N$. We infer from (27) that

$$\|u + P_n \circ K(u)\| \geq c/2\|u\| \text{ for all } u \in H \text{ and all } n \geq N. \tag{28}$$

To show that $(Id + K)(H) = H$, let h_* belong to H. Let $n \geq N$. It follows from (28) that the restriction to H_n of $Id + P_n \circ K$ is a one-to-one linear operator that maps the finite dimensional space H_n into itself. A one-to-one linear operator on a finite dimensional space is onto. Therefore this restriction maps H_n onto H_n. Thus, there is a vector $u_n \in H_n$ for which

$$u_n + (P_n \circ K)(u_n) = P_n(h_*). \tag{29}$$

Take the inner product of each side of this equality with $v \in H$ and use the symmetry of the projection P_n to conclude that

$$\langle u_n + K(u_n), P_n(v) \rangle = \langle h_*, P_n(v) \rangle \text{ for all } n \geq N, v \in H. \tag{30}$$

We infer from (29) and the estimate (28) that

$$\|h_*\| \geq \|P_n(h_*)\| = \|u_n + (P_n \circ K)u_n\| \geq c/2\|u_n\| \text{ for all } n \geq N.$$

Therefore the sequence $\{u_n\}$ is bounded. Theorem 6 tells us that there is a subsequence $\{h_{n_k}\}$ that converges weakly to $h \in H$. Therefore $\{h_{n_k} + K(h_{n_k})\}$ converges weakly to $h + K(h)$. Take the limit as $k \to \infty$ in (30) with $n = n_k$ to conclude, by Proposition 7, that

$$\langle u + K(u), v \rangle = \langle h_*, v \rangle \text{ for all } v \in H.$$

Therefore $u + K(u) = h_*$. Thus $(Id + K)(H) = H$. $\qquad\square$

The Riesz-Schauder Theorem *Let H be a Hilbert space and $K \in \mathcal{L}(H)$ be compact. Then $Im(Id + K)$ is closed and*

$$\dim \ker (Id + K) = \dim \ker (Id + K^*) < \infty. \tag{31}$$

In particular, $Id + K$ is one-to-one if and only if it is onto.

Proof According to Proposition 20, a compact perturbation of the identity has finite dimensional kernel and a closed image. We will show that

$$\dim \ker (Id + K) \geq \dim \ker (Id + K^*). \tag{32}$$

Once this is established, we replace K by K^* and use the observation that $(K^*)^* = K$, together with Schauder's Theorem regarding the compactness of K^*, to obtain the inequality in the opposite direction. We argue by contradiction to verify (32). Otherwise, $\dim \ker (Id + K) < \dim \ker (Id + K^*)$. Let P be the orthogonal projection of H onto $\ker (Id + K)$ and A a linear mapping of $\ker (Id + K)$ into $\ker (Id + K^*)$ that is one-to-one but not onto. Define $K' = K + A \circ P$. Since $Id + K$ has closed image, Proposition 13 tells us that

$$H = Im(Id + K) + \ker (Id + K^*)$$

and therefore $Id + K'$ is one-to-one but not onto. On the other hand, since $A \circ P$ is of finite rank, it is compact and therefore so is K'. These two assertions contradict the preceding proposition. Therefore (32) is established. Since $Id + K$ has closed image, we infer from (14) and (32) that $Id + K$ is one-to-one if and only if it is onto. $\qquad\square$

Corollary 23 (the Fredholm Alternative) *Let H be a Hilbert space, $K \in \mathcal{L}(H)$ compact, and μ a nonzero real number. Then exactly one of the following holds:*

(i) *There is a nonzero solution of the following equation*

$$\mu h - K(h) = 0, h \in H.$$

(ii) *For every $h_0 \in H$, there is a unique solution of the equation*

$$\mu h - K(h) = h_0, h \in H.$$

Definition   *Let H be a Hilbert space and T belong to $\mathcal{L}(H)$. Then T is said to be **Fredholm** provided the kernel of T is finite dimensional and the image of T has finite codimension. For such an operator, its index, ind T, is defined by*

$$\text{ind } T = \dim \ker T - \text{codim } \text{Im } T.$$

In the proof of the Riesz-Schauder Theorem, we first established that Im T is closed and used this, together with (14), to show that Im T has finite codimension equal to dim ker T^*. However, Theorem 12 of Chapter 13 tells us that if H is a Hilbert space and the operator $T \in \mathcal{L}(H)$ has a finite codimensional image, then its image is closed. Therefore each Fredholm operator has a closed image and hence, again by (14), codim Im $T = $ dim ker T^*.

We say that an operator $T \in \mathcal{L}(H)$ is **invertible** provided it is one-to-one and onto. The Open Mapping Theorem tells us that the inverse of an invertible operator is continuous and therefore an invertible operator is an isomorphism.

Theorem 24   *Let H be a Hilbert space and T belong to $\mathcal{L}(H)$. Then T is Fredholm of index 0 if and only if $T = S + K$, where $S \in \mathcal{L}(H)$ is invertible and $K \in \mathcal{L}(H)$ is compact.*

Proof   First assume T is Fredholm of index 0. Since Im T is closed, Proposition 13 tells us that

$$H = \text{Im } T \oplus \ker T^*. \tag{33}$$

Since dim ker $T = $ dim ker $T^* < \infty$, we may choose a one-to-one linear operator A of ker T onto ker T^*. Let P be the orthogonal projection of H onto ker T. Define $K = A \circ P \in \mathcal{L}(H)$ and $S = T - K$. Then $T = S + K$. The operator K is compact since it is of finite rank, while the operator S is invertible by (33) and the choice of P and A. Hence T is a compact perturbation of a invertible operator.

To prove the converse, suppose $T = S + K$, where $S \in \mathcal{L}(H)$ is invertible and $K \in \mathcal{L}(H)$ is compact. Observe that

$$T = S \circ [\text{Id} + S^{-1} \circ K]. \tag{34}$$

Since S^{-1} is continuous and K is compact, $S^{-1} \circ K$ is compact. The Riesz-Schauder Theorem tells us that $\text{Id} + S^{-1} \circ K$ is Fredholm of index 0. The composition of a Fredholm operator with an invertible operator is also Fredholm of index 0 (see Problem 55). We therefore infer from (34) that T is Fredholm of index 0.   □

We leave it as an exercise to establish the following corollary.

Corollary 25 *Let H be a Hilbert space and T and S in $\mathcal{L}(H)$ be Fredholm of index 0. Then the composition $S \circ T$ is also Fredholm of index 0.*

Remark *The Riesz-Schauder Theorem and Theorem 24 are true for operators on a general Banach space. However, the general method of proof must be different. An essential ingredient in the proof of Proposition 22 is the approximation in $\mathcal{L}(H)$ of a compact operator by an operator of finite rank. Per Enflo has shown that there are linear compact operators on a separable Banach space that cannot be approximated in $\mathcal{L}(H)$ by linear operators of finite rank.*[3]

PROBLEMS

53. Let $K \in \mathcal{L}(H)$ be compact. Show that $T = K^* K$ is compact and symmetric. Then use the Hilbert-Schmidt Theorem to show that there is an orthonormal sequence $\{\varphi_k\}$ of H such that $T(\varphi_k) = \lambda_k \varphi_k$ for all k and $T(h) = 0$ if h is orthogonal to $\{\varphi_k\}_{k=0}^{\infty}$. Conclude that if h is orthogonal to $\{\varphi_k\}_{k=0}^{\infty}$, then

$$\|K(h)\|^2 = \langle K(h),\ K(h) \rangle = \langle T(h),\ h \rangle = 0.$$

Define H_0 to be the closed linear span of $\{K^m(\varphi_k) \mid m \geq 1, k \geq 1\}$. Show that H_0 is closed and separable, $K(H_0) \subseteq H_0$ and $K = 0$ on $H_0^{\perp}$.

54. Let $\mathcal{K}(H)$ denote the set of compact operators in $\mathcal{L}(H)$. Show that $\mathcal{K}(H)$ is a closed subspace of $\mathcal{L}(H)$ that has the set of operators of finite rank as a dense subspace. Is $\mathcal{K}(H)$ an open subset of $\mathcal{L}(H)$?

55. Show that the composition of a Fredholm operator of index 0 with an invertible operator is also Fredholm of index 0.

56. Show that the composition of two Fredholm operators of index 0 is also Fredholm of index 0.

57. Show that an operator $T \in \mathcal{L}(H)$ is Fredholm of index 0 if and only if it is the perturbation of an invertible operator by an operator of finite rank.

58. Argue as follows to show that the collection of invertible operators in $\mathcal{L}(H)$ is an open subset of $\mathcal{L}(H)$.

   (i) For $A \in \mathcal{L}(H)$ with $\|A\| < 1$, use the completeness of $\mathcal{L}(H)$ to show that the so-called Neumann series $\sum_{n=0}^{\infty} A^n$ converges to an operator in $\mathcal{L}(H)$ that is the inverse of $\mathrm{Id} - A$.

   (ii) For an invertible operator $S \in \mathcal{L}(H)$ show that for any $T \in \mathcal{L}(H)$, $T = S[\mathrm{Id} + S^{-1}(T - S)]$.

   (iii) Use (i) and (ii) to show that if $S \in \mathcal{L}(H)$ is invertible then so is any $T \in \mathcal{L}(H)$ for which $\|S - T\| < 1/\|S^{-1}\|$.

59. Show that the set of operators in $\mathcal{L}(H)$ that are Fredholm of index 0 is an open subset of $\mathcal{L}(H)$.

60. By following the orthogonal approximation sequence method used in the proof of Proposition 22, provide another proof of Proposition 14 in case H is separable.

61. For $T \in \mathcal{L}(H)$, suppose that $\langle T(h),\ h \rangle \geq \|h\|^2$ for all $h \in H$. Assume that $K \in \mathcal{L}(H)$ is compact and $T + K$ is one-to-one. Show that $T + K$ is onto.

---

[3] "A counterexample to the approximation problem in Banach spaces," *Acta Mathematica, 130,* 1973.

62. Let $K \in \mathcal{L}(H)$ be compact and $\mu \in \mathbf{R}$ have $|\mu| > \|K\|$. Show that $\mu - K$ is invertible.

63. Let $S \in \mathcal{L}(H)$ have $\|S\| < 1$, $K \in \mathcal{L}(H)$ be compact and $(\mathrm{Id} + S + K)(H) = H$. Show that $\mathrm{Id} + S + K$ is one-to-one.

64. Let $\mathcal{GL}(H)$ denote the set of invertible operators in $\mathcal{L}(H)$.

   (i) Show that under the operation of composition of operators, $\mathcal{GL}(H)$ is a group: it is called the general linear group of H.

   (ii) An operator T in $\mathcal{GL}(H)$ is said be orthogonal, provided that $T^* = T^{-1}$. Show that the set of orthogonal operators is a subgroup of $\mathcal{GL}(H)$: it is called the orthogonal group.

65. Let H be a Hilbert space, $T \in \mathcal{L}(H)$ be Fredholm of index zero, and $K \in \mathcal{L}(H)$ be compact. Show that $T + K$ is Fredholm of index zero.

66. Let X_0 be a finite codimensional subspace of a Banach space X. Show that all finite dimensional linear complements of X_0 in X have the same dimension.

PART THREE

MEASURE AND INTEGRATION: GENERAL THEORY

CHAPTER 17

General Measure Spaces: Their Properties and Construction

Contents

The first goal of the present chapter is to abstract the most important properties of Lebesgue measure on the real line in the absence of any topology. We shall do this by giving certain axioms that Lebesgue measure satisfies and base our theory on these axioms. As a consequence our theory will be valid for every system satisfying the given axioms.

To establish that Lebesgue measure on the real line is a countably additive set function on a σ-algebra we employed only the most rudimentary set-theoretic concepts. We defined a primitive set function by assigning length to each bounded interval, extended this set function to the set function outer measure defined for every subset of real numbers, and then distinguished a collection of measurable sets. We proved that the collection of measurable sets is a σ-algebra on which the restriction of outer measure is a measure. We call this the Carathéodory construction of Lebesgue measure. The second goal of this chapter is to show that the Carathéodory construction is feasible for a general abstract set X. Indeed, we show that any nonnegative set function μ defined on a collection S of subsets of X induces an outer measure μ^* with respect to which we can identify a σ-algebra $\mathcal{M}$ of measurable sets. The restriction of μ^* to $\mathcal{M}$ is a measure that we call the Carathéodory measure induced by μ. We conclude the chapter with a proof of the Carathéodory-Hahn Theorem, which tells us of very general conditions under which the Carathéodory measure induced by a set function μ is an extension of μ.

17.1 MEASURES AND MEASURABLE SETS

Recall that a σ-algebra of subsets of a set X is a collection of subsets of X that contains the empty-set and is closed with respect to the formation of complements in X and with respect to the formation of countable unions and therefore, by De Morgan's Identities, with respect to the formation of intersections. By a set function μ we mean a function that assigns an extended real number to certain sets.

Definition *By a* **measurable space** *we mean a couple* $(X, \mathcal{M})$ *consisting of a set X and a* σ-*algebra* $\mathcal{M}$ *of subsets of X. A subset E of X is called* **measurable** *(or measurable with respect to* $\mathcal{M}$*) provided E belongs to* $\mathcal{M}$.

Definition *By a* **measure** μ *on a measurable space* $(X, \mathcal{M})$ *we mean an extended real-valued nonnegative set function* $\mu: \mathcal{M} \to [0, \infty]$ *for which* $\mu(\emptyset) = 0$ *and which is* **countably additive** *in the sense that for any countable disjoint collection* $\{E_k\}_{k=1}^{\infty}$ *of measurable sets,*

$$\mu\left(\bigcup_{k=1}^{\infty} E_k\right) = \sum_{k=1}^{\infty} \mu(E_k).$$

By a **measure space** $(X, \mathcal{M}, \mu)$ *we mean a measurable space* $(X, \mathcal{M})$ *together with a measure* μ *defined on* $\mathcal{M}$.

One example of a measure space is $(\mathbf{R}, \mathcal{L}, m)$, where $\mathbf{R}$ is the set of real numbers, $\mathcal{L}$ the collection of Lebesgue measurable sets of real numbers, and m Lebesgue measure. A second example of a measure space is $(\mathbf{R}, \mathcal{B}, m)$, where $\mathcal{B}$ is the collection of Borel sets of real numbers and m is again Lebesgue measure. For any set X, we define $\mathcal{M} = 2^X$, the collection of all subsets of X, and define a measure η by defining the measure of a finite set to be the number of elements in the set and the measure of an infinite set to be ∞. We call η the **counting measure** on X. For any σ-algebra $\mathcal{M}$ of subsets of a set X and point x_0 belonging to X, the **Dirac measure** concentrated at x_0, denoted by δ_{x_0}, assigns 1 to a set in $\mathcal{M}$ that contains x_0 and 0 to a set that does not contain x_0: this defines the Dirac measure space $(X, \mathcal{M}, \delta_{x_0})$. A slightly bizarre example is the following: let X be any uncountable set and $\mathcal{C}$ the collection of those subsets of X that are either countable or the complement of a countable set. Then $\mathcal{C}$ is a σ-algebra and we can define a measure on it by setting $\mu(A) = 0$ for each countable subset of X and $\mu(B) = 1$ for each subset of X whose complement in X is countable. Then $(X, \mathcal{C}, \mu)$ is a measure space.

It is useful to observe that for any measure space $(X, \mathcal{M}, \mu)$, if X_0 belongs to $\mathcal{M}$, then $(X_0, \mathcal{M}_0, \mu_0)$ is also a measure space where $\mathcal{M}_0$ is the collection of subsets of $\mathcal{M}$ that are contained in X_0 and μ_0 is the restriction of μ to $\mathcal{M}_0$.

Proposition 1 *Let* $(X, \mathcal{M}, \mu)$ *be a measure space.*

(Finite Additivity) For any finite disjoint collection $\{E_k\}_{k=1}^{n}$ *of measurable sets,*

$$\mu\left(\bigcup_{k=1}^{n} E_k\right) = \sum_{k=1}^{n} \mu(E_k).$$

(Monotonicity) If A and B are measurable sets and $A \subseteq B$, *then*

$$\mu(A) \leq \mu(B).$$

(Excision) If, moreover, $A \subseteq B$ *and* $\mu(A) < \infty$, *then*

$$\mu(B \sim A) = \mu(B) - \mu(A),$$

so that if $\mu(A) = 0$, *then*

$$\mu(B \sim A) = \mu(B).$$

(Countable Monotonicity) For any countable collection $\{E_k\}_{k=1}^{\infty}$ of measurable sets that covers a measurable set E,

$$\mu(E) \le \sum_{k=1}^{\infty} \mu(E_k).$$

Proof Finite additivity follows from countable additivity by setting $E_k = \emptyset$, so that $\mu(E_k) = 0$, for $k > n$. By finite additivity,

$$\mu(B) = \mu(A) + \mu(B \sim A),$$

which immediately implies monotonicity and excision. To verify countable monotonicity, define $G_1 = E_1$ and then define

$$G_k = E_k \sim \left[\bigcup_{i=1}^{k-1} E_i \right] \text{ for all } k \ge 2.$$

Observe that

$$\{G_k\}_{k=1}^{\infty} \text{ is disjoint, } \bigcup_{k=1}^{\infty} G_k = \bigcup_{k=1}^{\infty} E_k \text{ and } G_k \subseteq E_k \text{ for all } k.$$

From the monotonicity and countable additivity of μ we infer that

$$\mu(E) \le \mu\left(\bigcup_{k=1}^{\infty} E_k \right) = \mu\left(\bigcup_{k=1}^{\infty} G_k \right) = \sum_{k=1}^{\infty} \mu(G_k) \le \sum_{k=1}^{\infty} \mu(E_k). \qquad \square$$

The countable monotonicity property is an amalgamation of countable additivity and monotonicity, which we name since it is invoked so frequently.

A sequence of sets $\{E_k\}_{k=1}^{\infty}$ is called **ascending** provided for each k, $E_k \subseteq E_{k+1}$, and said to be **descending** provided for each k, $E_{k+1} \subseteq E_k$.

Proposition 2 (Continuity of Measure) *Let $(X, \mathcal{M}, \mu)$ be a measure space.*

(i) If $\{A_k\}_{k=1}^{\infty}$ is an ascending sequence of measurable sets, then

$$\mu\left(\bigcup_{k=1}^{\infty} A_k \right) = \lim_{k \to \infty} \mu(A_k). \tag{1}$$

(ii) If $\{B_k\}_{k=1}^{\infty}$ is a descending sequence of measurable sets for which $\mu(B_1) < \infty$, then

$$\mu\left(\bigcap_{k=1}^{\infty} B_k \right) = \lim_{k \to \infty} \mu(B_k). \tag{2}$$

The proof of the continuity of measure is the same, word for word, as the proof of the continuity of Lebesgue measure on the real line; see page 44.

For a measure space $(X, \mathcal{M}, \mu)$ and a measurable subset E of X, we say that a property holds **almost everywhere** on E, or it holds **for almost all** x in E, provided it holds on $E \sim E_0$, where E_0 is a measurable subset of E for which $\mu(E_0) = 0$.

The Borel-Cantelli Lemma *Let $(X, \mathcal{M}, \mu)$ be a measure space and $\{E_k\}_{k=1}^{\infty}$ a countable collection of measurable sets for which $\sum_{k=1}^{\infty} \mu(E_k) < \infty$. Then almost all x in X belong to at most a finite number of the E_k's.*

Proof For each n, by the countable monotonicity of μ, $\mu(\bigcup_{k=n}^{\infty} E_k) \leq \sum_{k=n}^{\infty} \mu(E_k)$. Hence, by the continuity of μ,

$$\mu\left(\bigcap_{n=1}^{\infty}\left[\bigcup_{k=n}^{\infty} E_k\right]\right) = \lim_{n\to\infty} \mu(\bigcup_{k=n}^{\infty} E_k) \leq \lim_{n\to\infty} \sum_{k=n}^{\infty} \mu(E_k) = 0.$$

Observe that $\bigcap_{n=1}^{\infty}\left[\bigcup_{k=n}^{\infty} E_k\right]$ is the set of all points in X that belong to an infinite number of the E_k's. □

Definition *Let $(X, \mathcal{M}, \mu)$ be a measure space. The measure μ is called **finite** provided $\mu(X) < \infty$. It is called **σ-finite** provided X is the union of a countable collection of measurable sets, each of which has finite measure. A measurable set E is said to be of **finite measure** provided $\mu(E) < \infty$, and said to be **σ-finite** provided E is the union of a countable collection of measurable sets, each of which has finite measure.*

Regarding the criterion for σ-finiteness, the countable cover by sets of finite measure may be taken to be disjoint. Indeed, if $\{X_k\}_{k=1}^{\infty}$ is such a cover replace, for $k \geq 2$, each X_k by $X_k \sim \bigcup_{j=1}^{k-1} X_j$ to obtain a disjoint cover by sets of finite measure. Lebesgue measure on $[0, 1]$ is an example of a finite measure, while Lebesgue measure on $(-\infty, \infty)$ is an example of a σ-finite measure. The counting measure on an uncountable set is not σ-finite.

Many familiar properties of Lebesgue measure on the real line and Lebesgue integration for functions of a single real variable hold for arbitrary σ-finite measures, and many treatments of abstract measure theory limit themselves to σ-finite measures. However, many parts of the general theory do not require the assumption of σ-finiteness, and it seems undesirable to have a development that is unnecessarily restrictive.

Definition *A measure space $(X, \mathcal{M}, \mu)$ is said to be **complete** provided $\mathcal{M}$ contains all subsets of sets of measure zero, that is, if E belongs to $\mathcal{M}$ and $\mu(E) = 0$, then every subset of E also belongs to $\mathcal{M}$.*

We proved that Lebesgue measure on the real line is complete. Moreover, we also showed that the Cantor set, a Borel set of Lebesgue measure zero, contains a subset that is not Borel; see page 52. Thus Lebesgue measure on the real line, when restricted to the σ-algebra of Borel sets, is not complete. The following proposition, whose proof is left to the reader (Problem 9), tells us that each measure space can be completed. The measure space $(X, \mathcal{M}_0, \mu_0)$ described in this proposition is called the **completion** of $(X, \mathcal{M}, \mu)$.

Proposition 3 *Let $(X, \mathcal{M}, \mu)$ be a measure space. Define $\mathcal{M}_0$ to be the collection of subsets E of X of the form $E = A \cup B$ where $B \in \mathcal{M}$ and $A \subseteq C$ for some $C \in \mathcal{M}$ for which $\mu(C) = 0$.*

For such a set E define $\mu_0(E) = \mu(B)$. Then M_0 is a σ-algebra that contains M, μ_0 is a measure that extends μ, and (X, M_0, μ_0) is a complete measure space.

PROBLEMS

1. Let f be a nonnegative Lebesgue measurable function on $\mathbf{R}$. For each Lebesgue measurable subset E of $\mathbf{R}$, define $\mu(E) = \int_E f$, the Lebesgue integral of f over E. Show that μ is a measure on the σ-algebra of Lebesgue measurable subsets of $\mathbf{R}$.

2. Let M be a σ-algebra of subsets of a set X and the set function $\mu: M \to [0, \infty)$ be finitely additive. Prove that μ is a measure if and only if whenever $\{A_k\}_{k=1}^{\infty}$ is an ascending sequence of sets in M, then

$$\mu\left(\bigcup_{k=1}^{\infty} A_k\right) = \lim_{k \to \infty} \mu(A_k).$$

3. Let M be a σ-algebra of subsets of a set X. Formulate and establish a correspondent of the preceding problem for descending sequences of sets in M.

4. Let $\{(X_\lambda, M_\lambda, \mu_\lambda)\}_{\lambda \in \Lambda}$ be a collection of measure spaces parametrized by the set Λ. Assume the collection of sets $\{X_\lambda\}_{\lambda \in \Lambda}$ is disjoint. Then we can form a new measure space (called their union) (X, B, μ) by letting $X = \bigcup_{\lambda \in \Lambda} X_\lambda$, B be the collection of subsets B of X such that $B \cap X_\lambda \in M_\lambda$ for all $\lambda \in \Lambda$ and defining $\mu(B) = \sum_{\lambda \in \Lambda} \mu_\lambda[B \cap X_\lambda]$ for $B \in B$.

   (i) Show that M is a σ-algebra.

   (ii) Show that μ is a measure.

   (iii) Show that μ is σ-finite if and only if all but a countable number of the measures μ_λ have $\mu(X_\lambda) = 0$ and the remainder are σ-finite.

5. Let (X, M, μ) be a measure space. The symmetric difference, $E_1 \Delta E_2$, of two subsets E_1 and E_2 of X is defined by

$$E_1 \Delta E_2 = [E_1 \sim E_2] \cup [E_2 \sim E_1].$$

   (i) Show that if E_1 and E_2 are measurable and $\mu(E_1 \Delta E_2) = 0$, then $\mu(E_1) = \mu(E_2)$.

   (ii) Show that if μ is complete, $E_1 \in M$ and $E_2 \sim E_1 \in M$, then $E_2 \in M$ if $\mu(E_1 \Delta E_2) = 0$.

6. Let (X, M, μ) be a measure space and X_0 belong to M. Define M_0 to be the collection of sets in M that are subsets of X_0 and μ_0 the restriction of μ to M_0. Show that (X_0, M_0, μ_0) is a measure space.

7. Let (X, M) be a measurable space. Verify the following:

   (i) If μ and ν are measures defined on M, then the set function λ defined on M by $\lambda(E) = \mu(E) + \nu(E)$ also is a measure. We denote λ by $\mu + \nu$.

   (ii) If μ and ν are measures on M and $\mu \geq \nu$, then there is a measure λ on M for which $\mu = \nu + \lambda$.

   (iii) If ν is σ-finite, the measure λ in (ii) is unique.

   (iv) Show that in general the measure λ need not be unique but that there is always a smallest such λ.

8. Let $(X, \mathcal{M}, \mu)$ be a measure space. The measure μ is said to be **semifinite** provided each measurable set of infinite measure contains measurable sets of arbitrarily large finite measure.

   (i)   Show that each σ-finite measure is semifinite.

   (ii) For $E \in \mathcal{M}$, define $\mu_1(E) = \mu(E)$ if $\mu(E) < \infty$, and if $\mu(E) = \infty$ define $\mu_1(E) = \infty$ if E contains measurable sets of arbitrarily large finite measure and $\mu_1(E) = 0$ otherwise. Show that μ_1 is a semifinite measure: it is called the semifinite part of μ.

   (iii) Find a measure μ_2 on $\mathcal{M}$ that only takes the values 0 and ∞ and $\mu = \mu_1 + \mu_2$.

9. Prove Proposition 3, that is, show that $\mathcal{M}_0$ is a σ-algebra, μ_0 is properly defined, and $(X, \mathcal{M}_0, \mu_0)$ is complete. In what sense is $\mathcal{M}_0$ minimal?

10. If $(X, \mathcal{M}, \mu)$ is a measure space, we say that a subset E of X is **locally measurable** provided for each $B \in \mathcal{M}$ with $\mu(B) < \infty$, the intersection $E \cap B$ belongs to $\mathcal{M}$. The measure μ is called **saturated** provided every locally measurable set is measurable.

   (i)   Show that each σ-finite measure is saturated.

   (ii) Show that the collection $\mathcal{C}$ of locally measurable sets is a σ-algebra.

   (iii) Let $(X, \mathcal{M}, \mu)$ be a measure space and $\mathcal{C}$ the σ-algebra of locally measurable sets. For $E \in \mathcal{C}$, define $\overline{\mu}(E) = \mu(E)$ if $E \in \mathcal{M}$ and $\overline{\mu}(E) = \infty$ if $E \notin \mathcal{M}$. Show that $(X, \mathcal{C}, \overline{\mu})$ is a saturated measure space.

   (iv) If μ is semifinite and $E \in \mathcal{C}$, set $\mu(E) = \sup\{\mu(B) \mid B \in \mathcal{M}, \ B \subseteq E\}$. Show that $(X, \mathcal{C}, \mu)$ is a saturated measure space and that μ is an extension of μ. Give an example to show that $\overline{\mu}$ and μ may be different.

11. Let μ and η be measures on the measurable space $(X, \mathcal{M})$. For $E \in \mathcal{M}$, define $\nu(E) = \max\{\mu(E), \eta(E)\}$. Is ν a measure on $(X, \mathcal{M})$?

17.2   SIGNED MEASURES: THE HAHN AND JORDAN DECOMPOSITIONS

Observe that if μ_1 and μ_2 are two measures defined on the same measurable space $(X, \mathcal{M})$, then, for positive numbers α and β, we may define a new measure μ_3 on X by setting

$$\mu_3(E) = \alpha \cdot \mu_1(E) + \beta \cdot \mu_2(E) \text{ for all } E \text{ in } \mathcal{M}.$$

It turns out to be important to consider set functions that are linear combinations of measures but with coefficients that may be negative. What happens if we try to define a set function ν on $\mathcal{M}$ by

$$\nu(E) = \mu_1(E) - \mu_2(E) \text{ for all } E \text{ in } \mathcal{M}?$$

The first thing that may occur is that ν is not always nonnegative. Moreover, $\nu(E)$ is not even defined for $E \in \mathcal{M}$ such that $\mu_1(E) = \mu_2(E) = \infty$. With these considerations in mind we make the following definition.

Definition By a **signed measure** ν on the measurable space $(X, \mathcal{M})$ we mean an extended real-valued set function $\nu: \mathcal{M} \to [-\infty, \infty]$ that possesses the following properties:

   (i) ν assumes at most one of the values $+\infty$, $-\infty$.

   (ii) $\nu(\emptyset) = 0$.

(iii) *For any countable collection $\{E_k\}_{k=1}^{\infty}$ of disjoint measurable sets,*

$$\nu(\bigcup_{k=1}^{\infty} E_k) = \sum_{k=1}^{\infty} \nu(E_k),$$

where the series $\sum_{k=1}^{\infty} \nu(E_k)$ converges absolutely if $\nu(\bigcup_{k=1}^{\infty} E_k)$ is finite.

A measure is a special case of a signed measure. It is not difficult to see that the difference of two measures, one of which is finite, is a signed measure. In fact, the forthcoming Jordan Decomposition Theorem will tell us that every signed measure is the difference of two such measures.

Let ν be a signed measure. We say that a set A is **positive** (with respect to ν) provided A is measurable and for every measurable subset E of A we have $\nu(E) \geq 0$. The restriction of ν to the measurable subsets of a positive set is a measure. Similarly, a set B is called **negative** (with respect to ν) provided it is measurable and every measurable subset of B has nonpositive ν measure. The restriction of $-\nu$ to the measurable subsets of a negative set also is a measure. A measurable set is called **null** with respect to ν provided every measurable subset of it has ν measure zero. The reader should carefully note the distinction between a null set and a set of measure zero: While every null set must have measure zero, a set of measure zero may well be a union of two sets whose measures are not zero but are negatives of each other. By the monotonicity property of measures, a set is null with respect to a measure if and only if it has measure zero. Since a signed measure ν does not take the values ∞ and $-\infty$, for A and B measurable sets,

$$\text{if } A \subseteq B \text{ and } |\nu(B)| < \infty, \text{ then } |\nu(A)| < \infty. \tag{3}$$

Proposition 4 *Let ν be a signed measure on the measurable space $(X, \mathcal{M})$. Then every measurable subset of a positive set is itself positive and the union of a countable collection of positive sets is positive.*

Proof The first statement is trivially true by the definition of a positive set. To prove the second statement, let A be the union of a countable collection $\{A_k\}_{k=1}^{\infty}$ of positive sets. Let E be a measurable subset of A. Define $E_1 = E \cap A_1$. For $k \geq 2$, define

$$E_k = [E \cap A_k] \sim [A_1 \cup \ldots \cup A_{k-1}].$$

Then each E_k is a measurable subset of the positive set A_k and therefore $\nu(E_k) \geq 0$. Since E is the union of the countable disjoint collection $\{E_k\}_{k=1}^{\infty}$,

$$\nu(E) = \sum_{k=1}^{\infty} \nu(E_k) \geq 0.$$

Thus A is a positive set. $\square$

Hahn's Lemma   *Let ν be a signed measure on the measurable space $(X, \mathcal{M})$ and E a measurable set for which $0 < \nu(E) < \infty$. Then there is a measurable subset A of E that is positive and of positive measure.*

Proof If E itself is a positive set, then the proof is complete. Otherwise, E contains sets of negative measure. Let m_1 be the smallest natural number for which there is a measurable set of measure less than $-1/m_1$. Choose a measurable set $E_1 \subseteq E$ with $\nu(E_1) < -1/m_1$. Let n be a natural number for which natural numbers $m_1, \ldots, m_n$ and measurable sets $E_1, \ldots, E_n$ have been chosen such that, for $1 \le k \le n$, m_k is the smallest natural number for which there is a measurable subset of $E \sim \bigcup_{j=1}^{k-1} E_j$ of measure less than $-1/m_k$ and E_k is a subset of $[E \sim \bigcup_{j=1}^{k-1} E_j]$ for which $\nu(E_k) < -1/m_k$.

If this selection process terminates, then the proof is complete. Otherwise, define

$$A = E \sim \bigcup_{k=1}^{\infty} E_k, \text{ so that } E = A \cup \left[\bigcup_{k=1}^{\infty} E_k \right] \text{ is a disjoint decomposition of } E.$$

Since $\bigcup_{k=1}^{\infty} E_k$ is a measurable subset of E and $|\nu(E)| < \infty$, by (3) and the countable additivity of ν,

$$-\infty < \nu\left(\bigcup_{k=1}^{\infty} E_k \right) = \sum_{k=1}^{\infty} \nu(E_k) \le \sum_{k=1}^{\infty} -1/m_k.$$

Thus $\lim_{k \to \infty} m_k = \infty$. We claim that A is a positive set. Indeed, if B is a measurable subset of A, then, for each k,

$$B \subseteq A \subseteq E \sim \left[\bigcup_{j=1}^{k-1} E_j \right],$$

and so, by the minimal choice of m_k, $\nu(B) \ge -1/(m_k - 1)$. Since $\lim_{k \to \infty} m_k = \infty$, we have $\nu(B) \ge 0$. Thus A is a positive set. It remains only to show that $\nu(A) > 0$. But this follows from the finite additivity of ν since $\nu(E) > 0$ and $\nu(E \sim A) = \nu(\bigcup_{k=1}^{\infty} E_k) = \sum_{k=1}^{\infty} \nu(E_k) < 0$. $\square$

The Hahn Decomposition Theorem *Let ν be a signed measure on the measurable space $(X, \mathcal{M})$. Then there is a positive set A for ν and a negative set B for ν for which*

$$X = A \cup B \text{ and } A \cap B = \emptyset.$$

Proof Without loss of generality we assume $+\infty$ is the infinite value omitted by ν. Let $\mathcal{P}$ be the collection of positive subsets of X and define $\lambda = \sup \{\nu(E) \mid E \in \mathcal{P}\}$. Then $\lambda \ge 0$ since $\mathcal{P}$ contains the empty set. Let $\{A_k\}_{k=1}^{\infty}$ be a countable collection of positive sets for which $\lambda = \lim_{k \to \infty} \nu(A_k)$. Define $A = \bigcup_{k=1}^{\infty} A_k$. By Proposition 4, the set A is itself a positive set, and so $\lambda \ge \nu(A)$. On the other hand, for each k, $A \sim A_k \subseteq A$ and so $\nu(A \sim A_k) \ge 0$. Thus

$$\nu(A) = \nu(A_k) + \nu(A \sim A_k) \ge \nu(A_k).$$

Hence $\nu(A) \ge \lambda$. Therefore $\nu(A) = \lambda$, and $\lambda < \infty$ since ν does not take the value ∞.

Let $B = X \sim A$. We argue by contradiction to show that B is negative. Assume B is not negative. Then there is a subset E of B with positive measure and therefore, by Hahn's Lemma, a subset E_0 of B that is both positive and of positive measure. Then $A \cup E_0$ is a positive set and

$$\nu(A \cup E_0) = \nu(A) + \nu(E_0) > \lambda,$$

a contradiction to the choice of λ. $\square$

A decomposition of X into the union of two disjoint sets A and B for which A is positive for v and B negative is called a **Hahn decomposition** for v. The preceding theorem tells us of the existence of a Hahn decomposition for each signed measure. Such a decomposition may not be unique. Indeed, if $\{A, B\}$ is a Hahn decomposition for v, then by excising from A a null set E and grafting this subset onto B we obtain another Hahn decomposition $\{A \sim E, B \cup E\}$.

If $\{A, B\}$ is a Hahn decomposition for v, then we define two measures v^+ and v^- with $v = v^+ - v^-$ by setting

$$v^+(E) = v(E \cap A) \text{ and } v^-(E) = -v(E \cap B).$$

Two measures v_1 and v_2 on $(X, \mathcal{M})$ are said to be **mutually singular** (in symbols $v_1 \perp v_2$) if there are disjoint measurable sets A and B with $X = A \cup B$ for which $v_1(A) = v_2(B) = 0$. The measures v^+ and v^- defined above are mutually singular. We have thus established the existence part of the following proposition. The uniqueness part is left to the reader (see Problem 13).

The Jordan Decomposition Theorem   *Let v be a signed measure on the measurable space $(X, \mathcal{M})$. Then there are two mutually singular measures v^+ and v^- on $(X, \mathcal{M})$ for which $v = v^+ - v^-$. Moreover, there is only one such pair of mutually singular measures.*

The decomposition of a signed measure v given by this theorem is called the **Jordan decomposition** of v. The measures v^+ and v^- are called the positive and negative parts (or variations) of v. Since v assumes at most one of the values $+\infty$ and $-\infty$, either v^+ or v^- must be finite. If they are both finite, we call v a finite signed measure. The measure $|v|$ is defined on $\mathcal{M}$ by

$$|v|(E) = v^+(E) + v^-(E) \text{ for all } E \in \mathcal{M}.$$

We leave it as an exercise to show that

$$|v|(X) = \sup \sum_{k=1}^{n} |v(E_k)|, \tag{4}$$

where the supremum is taken over all finite disjoint collections $\{E_k\}_{k=1}^{n}$ of measurable subsets of X. For this reason $|v|(X)$ is called the **total variation** of v and denoted by $\|v\|_{var}$.

Example   Let $f: \mathbf{R} \to \mathbf{R}$ be a function that is Lebesgue integrable over $\mathbf{R}$. For a Lebesgue measurable set E, define $v(E) = \int_E f \, dm$. We infer from the countable additivity of integration (see page 90) that v is a signed measure on the measurable space $(\mathbf{R}, \mathcal{L})$. Define $A = \{x \in \mathbf{R} \mid f(x) \geq 0\}$ and $B = \{x \in \mathbf{R} \mid f(x) < 0\}$ and define, for each Lebesgue measurable set E,

$$v^+(E) = \int_{A \cap E} f \, dm \text{ and } v^-(E) = -\int_{B \cap E} f \, dm.$$

Then $\{A, B\}$ is a Hahn decomposition of $\mathbf{R}$ with respect to the signed measure v. Moreover, $v = v^+ - v^-$ is a Jordan decomposition of v.

PROBLEMS

12. In the above example, let E be a Lebesgue measurable set such that $0 < v(E) < \infty$. Find a positive set A contained in E for which $v(A) > 0$.

13. Let μ be a measure and μ_1 and μ_2 be mutually singular measures on a measurable space (X, μ) for which $\mu = \mu_1 - \mu_2$. Show that $\mu_2 = 0$. Use this to establish the uniqueness assertion of the Jordan Decomposition Theorem.

14. Show that if E is any measurable set, then

$$-\nu^-(E) \le \nu(E) \le \nu^+(E) \text{ and } |\nu(E)| \le |\nu|(E).$$

15. Show that if ν_1 and ν_2 are any two finite signed measures, then so is $\alpha\nu_1 + \beta\nu_2$, where α and β are real numbers. Show that

$$|\alpha\nu| = |\alpha||\nu| \text{ and } |\nu_1 + \nu_2| \le |\nu_1| + |\nu_2|,$$

where $\nu \le \mu$ means $\nu(E) \le \mu(E)$ for all measurable sets E.

16. Prove (4).

17. Let μ and ν be finite signed measures. Define $\mu \wedge \nu = \frac{1}{2}(\mu + \nu - |\mu - \nu|)$ and $\mu \vee \nu = \mu + \nu - \mu \wedge \nu$.

   (i) Show that the signed measure $\mu \wedge \nu$ is smaller than μ and ν but larger than any other signed measure that is smaller than μ and ν.

   (ii) Show that the signed measure $\mu \vee \nu$ is larger than μ and ν but smaller than any other measure that is larger than μ and ν.

   (iii) If μ and ν are positive measures, show that they are mutually singular if and only if $\mu \wedge \nu = 0$.

17.3   THE CARATHÉODORY MEASURE INDUCED BY AN OUTER MEASURE

We now define the general concept of an outer measure and of measurability of a set with respect to an outer measure, and show that the Carathéodory strategy for the construction of Lebesgue measure on the real line is feasible in general.

Definition *A set function $\mu: S \to [0, \infty]$ defined on a collection S of subsets of a set X is called* **countably monotone** *provided whenever a set $E \in S$ is covered by a countable collection $\{E_k\}_{k=1}^\infty$ of sets in S, then*

$$\mu(E) \le \sum_{k=1}^\infty \mu(E_k).$$

As we already observed, the monotonicity and countable additivity properties of a measure tell us that a measure is countably monotone. If the countably monotone set function $\mu: S \to [0, \infty]$ has the property that $\emptyset$ belongs to S and $\mu(\emptyset) = 0$, then μ is **finitely monotone** in the sense that whenever a set $E \in S$ is covered by a finite collection $\{E_k\}_{k=1}^n$ of sets in S, then

$$\mu(E) \le \sum_{k=1}^n \mu(E_k).$$

To see this, set $E_k = \emptyset$ for $k > n$. In particular, such a set function μ is **monotone** in the sense that if A and B belong to S and $A \subseteq B$, then $\mu(A) \le \mu(B)$.

Definition *A set function $\mu^*: 2^X \to [0, \infty]$ is called an* **outer measure** *provided $\mu^*(\emptyset) = 0$ and μ^* is countably monotone.*

Guided by our experience in the construction of Lebesgue measure from Lebesgue outer measure on the real line, we follow Constantine Carathéodory and define the measurability of a set as follows.

Definition *For an outer measure* $\mu^*: 2^X \to [0, \infty]$, *we call a subset E of X* **measurable** *(with respect to μ^*) provided for every subset A of X,*

$$\mu^*(A) = \mu^*(A \cap E) + \mu^*(A \cap E^C).$$

Since μ^* is finitely monotone, to show that $E \subseteq X$ is measurable it is only necessary to show that

$$\mu^*(A) \geq \mu^*(A \cap E) + \mu^*(A \cap E^C) \text{ for all } A \subseteq X \text{ such that } \mu^*(A) < \infty.$$

Directly from the definition we see that a subset E of X is measurable if and only if its complement in X is measurable and, by the monotonicity of μ^*, that every set of outer measure zero is measurable. Hereafter in this section, $\mu^*: 2^X \to [0, \infty]$ is a reference outer measure and measurable means measurable with respect to μ^*.

Proposition 5 *The union of a finite collection of measurable sets is measurable.*

Proof We first show that the union of two measurable sets is measurable. Let E_1 and E_2 be measurable. Let A be any subset of X. First using the measurability of E_1, then the measurability of E_2, we have

$$\mu^*(A) = \mu^*(A \cap E_1) + \mu^*(A \cap E_1^C)$$

$$= \mu^*(A \cap E_1) + \mu^*([A \cap E_1^C] \cap E_2) + \mu^*([A \cap E_1^C] \cap E_2^C).$$

Now use the set identities

$$[A \cap E_1^C] \cap E_2^C = A \cap [E_1 \cup E_2]^C$$

and

$$[A \cap E_1] \cup [A \cap E_2 \cap E_1^C] = A \cap [E_1 \cup E_2],$$

together with the finite monotonicity of outer measure, to obtain

$$\mu^*(A) = \mu^*(A \cap E_1) + \mu^*(A \cap E_1^C)$$

$$= \mu^*(A \cap E_1) + \mu^*([A \cap E_1^C] \cap E_2) + \mu^*([A \cap E_1^C] \cap E_2^C)$$

$$= \mu^*(A \cap E_1) + \mu^*([A \cap E_1^C] \cap E_2) + \mu^*(A \cap [E_1 \cup E_2]^C)$$

$$\geq \mu^*(A \cap [E_1 \cup E_2]) + \mu^*(A \cap [E_1 \cup E_2]^C).$$

Thus $E_1 \cup E_2$ is measurable. Now let $\{E_k\}_{k=1}^n$ be any finite collection of measurable sets. We prove the measurability of the union $\bigcup_{k=1}^n E_k$, for general n, by induction. This is trivial for $n = 1$. Suppose it is true for $n - 1$. Thus, since

$$\bigcup_{k=1}^n E_k = \left[\bigcup_{k=1}^{n-1} E_k\right] \cup E_n$$

and the union of two measurable sets is measurable, the set $\bigcup_{k=1}^n E_k$ is measurable. $\square$

Proposition 6 *Let $A \subseteq X$ and $\{E_k\}_{k=1}^n$ be a finite disjoint collection of measurable sets. Then*

$$\mu^*\left(A \cap \left[\bigcup_{k=1}^n E_k\right]\right) = \sum_{k=1}^n \mu^*(A \cap E_k).$$

In particular, the restriction of μ^* to the collection of measurable sets is finitely additive.

Proof The proof proceeds by induction on n. It is clearly true for $n = 1$, and we assume it is true for $n - 1$. Since the collection $\{E_k\}_{k=1}^n$ is disjoint,

$$A \cap \left[\bigcup_{k=1}^n E_k\right] \cap E_n = A \cap E_n$$

and

$$A \cap \left[\bigcup_{k=1}^n E_k\right] \cap E_n^C = A \cap \left[\bigcup_{k=1}^{n-1} E_k\right].$$

Hence by the measurability of E_n and the induction assumption, we have

$$\mu^*\left(A \cap \left[\bigcup_{k=1}^n E_k\right]\right) = \mu^*(A \cap E_n) + \mu^*\left(A \cap \left[\bigcup_{k=1}^{n-1} E_k\right]\right)$$

$$= \mu^*(A \cap E_n) + \sum_{k=1}^{n-1} \mu^*(A \cap E_k)$$

$$= \sum_{k=1}^n \mu^*(A \cap E_k).$$ $\square$

Proposition 7 *The union of a countable collection of measurable sets is measurable.*

Proof Let $E = \bigcup_{k=1}^\infty E_k$, where each E_k is measurable. Since the complement in X of a measurable set is measurable and, by Proposition 5, the union of a finite collection of measurable sets is measurable, by possibly replacing each E_k with $E_k \sim \bigcup_{i=1}^{k-1} E_i$, we may suppose that $\{E_k\}_{k=1}^\infty$ is disjoint. Let A be any subset of X. Fix an index n. Define $F_n = \bigcup_{k=1}^n E_k$. Since F_n is measurable and $F_n^C \supseteq E^C$, we have

$$\mu^*(A) = \mu^*(A \cap F_n) + \mu^*(A \cap F_n^C) \geq \mu^*(A \cap F_n) + \mu^*(A \cap E^C).$$

By Proposition 6,

$$\mu^*(A \cap F_n) = \sum_{k=1}^{n} \mu^*(A \cap E_k).$$

Thus

$$\mu^*(A) \geq \sum_{k=1}^{n} \mu^*(A \cap E_k) + \mu^*(A \cap E^C).$$

The left-hand side of this inequality is independent of n and therefore

$$\mu^*(A) \geq \sum_{k=1}^{\infty} \mu^*(A \cap E_k) + \mu^*(A \cap E^C).$$

By the countable monotonicity of outer measure we infer that

$$\mu^*(A) \geq \mu^*(A \cap E) + \mu^*(A \cap E^C).$$

Thus E is measurable. $\qquad\square$

Theorem 8 *Let μ^* be an outer measure on 2^X. Then the collection $\mathcal{M}$ of sets that are measurable with respect to μ^* is a σ-algebra. If $\overline{\mu}$ is the restriction of μ^* to $\mathcal{M}$, then $(X, \mathcal{M}, \overline{\mu})$ is a complete measure space.*

Proof We already observed that the complement in X of a measurable subset of X also is measurable. According to Proposition 7, the union of a countable collection of measurable sets is measurable. Therefore $\mathcal{M}$ is a σ-algebra. By the definition of an outer measure, $\mu^*(\emptyset) = 0$ and therefore $\emptyset$ is measurable and $\overline{\mu}(\emptyset) = 0$. To verify that $\overline{\mu}$ is a measure on $\mathcal{M}$, it remains to show it is countably additive. Since μ^* is countably monotone and μ^* is an extension of $\overline{\mu}$, the set function $\overline{\mu}$ is countably monotone. Therefore we only need show that if $\{E_k\}_{k=1}^{\infty}$ is a disjoint collection of measurable sets, then

$$\mu^*\left(\bigcup_{k=1}^{\infty} E_k\right) \geq \sum_{k=1}^{\infty} \mu^*(E_k). \tag{5}$$

However, μ^* is monotone and, by taking $A = X$ in Proposition 7, we see that μ^* is additive over finite disjoint unions of measurable sets. Therefore, for each n,

$$\mu^*\left(\bigcup_{k=1}^{\infty} E_k\right) \geq \mu^*\left(\bigcup_{k=1}^{n} E_k\right) = \sum_{k=1}^{n} \mu^*(E_k).$$

The left-hand side of this inequality is independent of n and therefore (5) holds. $\qquad\square$

17.4 THE CONSTRUCTION OF OUTER MEASURES

We constructed Lebesgue outer measure on subsets of the real line by first defining the primitive set function that assigns length to a bounded interval. We then defined the outer measure of a set to be the infimum of sums of lengths of countable collections of bounded intervals that cover the set. This method of construction of outer measure works in general.

Theorem 9 *Let S be a collection of subsets of a set X and $\mu: S \to [0, \infty]$ a set function. Define $\mu^*(\emptyset) = 0$ and for $E \subseteq X$, $E \neq \emptyset$, define*

$$\mu^*(E) = \inf \sum_{k=1}^{\infty} \mu(E_k), \tag{6}$$

where the infimum is taken over all countable collections $\{E_k\}_{k=1}^{\infty}$ of sets in S that cover E.[1] Then the set function $\mu^*: 2^X \to [0, \infty]$ is an outer measure called the **outer measure induced by** μ.

Proof To verify countable monotonicity, let $\{E_k\}_{k=1}^{\infty}$ be a collection of subsets of X that covers a set E. If $\mu^*(E_k) = \infty$ for some k, then $\mu^*(E) \leq \sum_{k=1}^{\infty} \mu^*(E_k) = \infty$. Therefore we may assume each E_k has finite outer measure. Let $\epsilon > 0$. For each k, there is a countable collection $\{E_{ik}\}_{i=1}^{\infty}$ of sets in S that covers E_k and

$$\sum_{i=1}^{\infty} \mu(E_{ik}) < \mu^*(E_k) + \frac{\epsilon}{2^k}.$$

Then $\{E_{ik}\}_{1 \leq k, i < \infty}$ is a countable collection of sets in S that covers $\bigcup_{k=1}^{\infty} E_k$ and therefore also covers E. By the definition of outer measure,

$$\mu^*(E) \leq \sum_{1 \leq k, i < \infty} \mu(E_{ik}) = \sum_{k=1}^{\infty} \left[\sum_{i=1}^{\infty} \mu(E_{ik}) \right]$$

$$\leq \sum_{k=1}^{\infty} \mu^*(E_k) + \sum_{k=1}^{\infty} \epsilon/2^k$$

$$= \sum_{k=1}^{\infty} \mu^*(E_k) + \epsilon.$$

Since this holds for all $\epsilon > 0$, it also holds for $\epsilon = 0$.   □

Definition *Let S be a collection of subsets of X, $\mu: S \to [0, \infty]$ a set function, and μ^* the outer measure induced by μ. The measure $\overline{\mu}$ that is the restriction of μ^* to the σ-algebra $\mathcal{M}$ of μ^*-measurable sets is called the* **Carathéodory measure induced by** μ.

$$\mu^*: 2^X \to [0, \infty]$$
(the induced outer measure)

$$\mu: S \to [0, \infty]$$
(a general set function)

$$\overline{\mu}: \mathcal{M} \to [0, \infty]$$
(the induced Carathéodory measure)

The Carathéodory Construction

[1] We follow the convention that the infimum of the empty-set is ∞. Therefore a subset E of X that cannot be covered by a countable collection of sets in S has outer measure equal to ∞.

For a collection S of subsets of X, we use S_σ to denote those sets that are countable unions of sets of S and use $S_{\sigma\delta}$ to denote those sets that are countable intersections of sets in S_σ. Observe that if S is the collection of open integrals of real numbers, then S_σ is the collection of open subsets of $\mathbf{R}$ and $S_{\sigma\delta}$ is the collection of G_δ subsets of $\mathbf{R}$.

We proved that a set E of real numbers is Lebesgue measurable if and only if it is a subset of a G_δ set G for which $G{\sim}E$ has Lebesgue measure zero: see page 40. The following proposition tells us of a related property of the Carathéodory measure induced by a general set function. This property is a key ingredient in the proof of a number of important theorems, among which are the proofs of the Carathéodory-Hahn Theorem, which we prove in the following section, and the forthcoming theorems of Fubini and Tonelli.

Proposition 10 *Let $\mu\colon S \to [0, \infty]$ be a set function defined on a collection S of subsets of a set X and $\overline{\mu}\colon M \to [0, \infty]$ the Carathéodory measure induced by μ. Let E be a subset of X for which $\mu^*(E) < \infty$. Then there is a subset A of X for which*

$$A \in S_{\sigma\delta},\ E \subseteq A \text{ and } \mu^*(E) = \mu^*(A).$$

Furthermore, if E and each set in S is measurable with respect to μ^*, then so is A and

$$\overline{\mu}(A \sim E) = 0.$$

Proof Let $\epsilon > 0$. We claim that there is a set A_ϵ for which

$$A_\epsilon \in S_\sigma,\ E \subseteq A_\epsilon \text{ and } \mu^*(A_\epsilon) < \mu^*(E) + \epsilon. \tag{7}$$

Indeed, since $\mu^*(E) < \infty$, there is a cover of E by a collection $\{E_k\}_{k=1}^\infty$ of sets in S for which

$$\sum_{k=1}^\infty \mu(E_k) < \mu^*(E) + \epsilon.$$

Define $A_\epsilon = \bigcup_{k=1}^\infty E_k$. Then A_ϵ belongs to S_σ and $E \subseteq A_\epsilon$. Furthermore, since $\{E_k\}_{k=1}^\infty$ is a countable collection of sets in S that covers A_ϵ, by the definition of the outer measure μ^*,

$$\mu^*(A_\epsilon) \le \sum_{k=1}^\infty \mu(E_k) < \mu^*(E) + \epsilon.$$

Thus (7) holds for this choice of A_ϵ.

Define $A = \bigcap_{k=1}^\infty A_{1/k}$. Then A belongs to $S_{\sigma\delta}$ and E is a subset of A since E is a subset of each $A_{1/k}$. Moreover, by the monotonicity of μ^* and the estimate (7),

$$\mu^*(E) \le \mu^*(A) \le \mu^*(A_{1/k}) \le \mu^*(E) + \frac{1}{k} \text{ for all } k.$$

Thus $\mu^*(E) = \mu^*(A)$.

Now assume that E is μ^*-measurable and each set in S is μ^*-measurable. Since the measurable sets are a σ-algebra, the set A is measurable. But μ^* is an extension of the measure $\overline{\mu}$. Therefore, by the excision property of measure,

$$\overline{\mu}(A \sim E) = \overline{\mu}(A) - \overline{\mu}(E) = \mu^*(A) - \mu^*(E) = 0. \qquad \square$$

PROBLEMS

18. Let $\mu^*: 2^X \to [0, \infty]$ be an outer measure. Let $A \subseteq X$, $\{E_k\}_{k=1}^\infty$ be a disjoint countable collection of measurable sets and $E = \bigcup_{k=1}^\infty E_k$. Show that

$$\mu^*(A \cap E) = \sum_{k=1}^\infty \mu^*(A \cap E_k).$$

19. Show that any measure that is induced by an outer measure is complete.

20. Let X be any set. Define $\eta: 2^X \to [0, \infty]$ by defining $\eta(\emptyset) = 0$ and for $E \subseteq X$, $E \neq \emptyset$, defining $\eta(E) = \infty$. Show that η is an outer measure. Also show that the set function that assigns 0 to every subset of X is an outer measure.

21. Let X be a set, $S = \{\emptyset, X\}$ and define $\mu(\emptyset) = 0$, $\mu(X) = 1$. Determine the outer measure μ^* induced by the set function $\mu: S \to [0, \infty)$ and the σ-algebra of measurable sets.

22. On the collection $S = \{\emptyset, [1, 2]\}$ of subsets of $\mathbf{R}$, define the set function $\mu: S \to [0, \infty)$ as follows: $\mu(\emptyset) = 0$, $\mu([1, 2]) = 1$. Determine the outer measure μ^* induced by μ and the σ-algebra of measurable sets.

23. On the collection S of all subsets of $\mathbf{R}$, define the set function $\mu: S \to \mathbf{R}$ by setting $\mu(A)$ to be the number of integers in A. Determine the outer measure μ^* induced by μ and the σ-algebra of measurable sets.

24. Let S be a collection of subsets of X and $\mu: S \to [0, \infty]$ a set function. Is every set in S measurable with respect to the outer measure induced by μ?

17.5 THE CARATHÉODORY-HAHN THEOREM: THE EXTENSION OF A PREMEASURE TO A MEASURE

Let $\mu: S \to [0, \infty]$ be a set function that is defined on a nonempty collection S of subsets of a set X. We ask the following question: What properties must the collection S and set function μ possess in order that the Carathéodory measure $\bar{\mu}$ induced by μ be an extension of μ: that is, every set E in S is measurable with respect to the outer measure μ^* induced by μ and, moreover, $\mu(E) = \mu^*(E)$? We will identify necessary properties that the set function μ must possess for this to be so and show that these same properties are sufficient, provided the collection S has finer set-theoretic structure.

We call a set function $\mu: S \to [0, \infty]$ **finitely additive** provided whenever $\{E_k\}_{k=1}^n$ is a finite disjoint collection of sets in S and $\bigcup_{k=1}^n E_k$ also belongs to S, then

$$\mu\left(\bigcup_{k=1}^n E_k\right) = \sum_{k=1}^n \mu(E_k).$$

Proposition 11 *Let S be a collection of subsets of a set X and $\mu: S \to [0, \infty]$ a set function. In order that the Carathéodory measure induced by μ be an extension of μ it is necessary that μ be both finitely additive and countably monotone and, if $\emptyset$ belongs to S, that $\mu(\emptyset) = 0$.*

Proof Let $(X, \mathcal{M}, \bar{\mu})$ denote the Carathéodory measure space induced by μ and suppose $\bar{\mu}: \mathcal{M} \to [0, \infty]$ extends $\mu: S \to [0, \infty]$. First of all, observe that if $\emptyset$ belongs to S, then $\mu(\emptyset) = \bar{\mu}(\emptyset) = 0$ since $\bar{\mu}$ is a measure that extends μ. Now let $\{E_k\}_{k=1}^n$ be a disjoint collection of sets in S such that $\bigcup_{k=1}^{n} E_k$ also belongs to S. A measure is finitely additive since it is countably additive and the empty-set has measure zero. Therefore, since $\overline{\mu}$ extends μ,

$$\mu\left(\bigcup_{k=1}^{n} E_k\right) = \overline{\mu}\left(\bigcup_{k=1}^{n} E_k\right) = \sum_{k=1}^{n} \overline{\mu}(E_k) = \sum_{k=1}^{n} \mu(E_k).$$

Thus μ is finitely additive. To establish countable monotonicity observe that $\mu(E) = \mu^*(E)$ for all $E \in S$ if and only if μ is countably monotone. Thus if $\overline{\mu}$ extends μ, $\mu^*(E) = \overline{\mu}(E) = \mu(E)$ for all $E \in S$ and hence μ is countably monotone. $\square$

This proposition suggests that it is useful to single out and name the following class of set functions.

Definition *Let S be a collection of subsets of a set X and $\mu \colon S \to [0, \infty]$ a set function. Then μ is called a* **premeasure** *provided μ is both finitely additive and countably monotone and, if $\emptyset$ belongs to S, then $\mu(\emptyset) = 0$.*

Being a premeasure is a necessary but not sufficient condition for the Carathéodory measure induced by μ to be an extension of μ (examine the premeasures defined in Problems 25 and 26). However, if we impose on S finer set-theoretic structure, this necessary condition is also sufficient.

Definition *A collection S of subsets of X is said to be closed with respect to the formation of relative complements provided whenever A and B belong to S, the relative complement $A \sim B$ belongs to S. The collection S is said to be closed with respect to the formation of finite intersections provided whenever A and B belong to S, the intersection $A \cap B$ belongs to S.*

Observe that if a collection of sets S is closed with respect to the formation of relative complements, then it is also closed with respect to the formation of finite intersections since if A and B belong to S so does

$$A \cap B = A \sim [A \sim B].$$

Also observe that if a nonempty collection of sets S is closed with respect to the formation of relative complements, then it contains $\emptyset$. Indeed, $\emptyset = A \sim A$, where A belongs to S.

Theorem 12 *Let $\mu \colon S \to [0, \infty]$ be a premeasure on a nonempty collection S of subsets of X that is closed with respect to the formation of relative complements. Then the Carathéodory measure $\overline{\mu} \colon \mathcal{M} \to [0, \infty]$ induced by μ is an extension of μ: it is called the* **Carathéodory extension** *of μ.*

Proof Let A belong to S. To show that A is measurable with respect to the outer measure induced by μ it suffices to let E be any subset of X of finite outer measure, let $\epsilon > 0$ and verify that

$$\mu^*(E) + \epsilon \geq \mu^*(E \cap A) + \mu^*(E \cap A^C). \tag{8}$$

By the definition of outer measure, there is a collection $\{E_k\}_{k=1}^{\infty}$ of sets in S that covers E and

$$\mu^*(E) + \epsilon \geq \sum_{k=1}^{\infty} \mu(E_k). \tag{9}$$

However, for each k, since S is closed with respect to the formation of relative complements, $E_k \sim A$ belongs to S and so does $E_k \cap A = E_k \sim [E_k \sim A]$. A premeasure is finitely additive. Therefore

$$\mu(E_k) = \mu(E_k \cap A) + \mu(E_k \cap A^C).$$

Sum these inequalities to conclude that

$$\sum_{k=1}^{\infty} \mu(E_k) = \sum_{k=1}^{\infty} \mu(E_k \cap A) + \sum_{k=1}^{\infty} \mu(E_k \cap A^C). \tag{10}$$

Observe that $\{E_k \cap A\}_{k=1}^{\infty}$ and $\{E_k \cap A^C\}_{k=1}^{\infty}$ are countable collections of sets in S that cover $E \cap A$ and $E \cap A^C$, respectively. Therefore, by the very definition of outer measure,

$$\sum_{k=1}^{\infty} \mu(E_k \cap A) \geq \mu^*(E \cap A) \text{ and } \sum_{k=1}^{\infty} \mu(E_k \cap A^C) \geq \mu^*(E \cap A^C).$$

The desired inequality (8) follows from the these two inequalities together with (9) and (10).

Clearly $\mu(E) = \mu^*(E)$ for each set $E \in S$ if and only if μ is countable monotone. Hence for each $E \in S$, $\mu(E) = \mu^*(E)$ and therefore, since each set $E \in S$ is measurable, $\mu(E) = \overline{\mu}(E)$. $\qquad \square$

Remark *Observe the quite distinct roles played by the two properties of a premeasure in the proof of the above theorem. We used the finite additivity of μ to infer that every set in S is μ^*-measurable. The countable monotonicity of μ is equivalent to the equality $\mu(E) = \mu^*(E)$ for all $E \in S$.*

A number of natural premeasures, including the premeasure length defined on the collection of bounded intervals of real numbers, are defined on collections of sets that are not closed with respect to the formation of relative complements. However, we now introduce the notion of a semiring. We show that a semiring S has the property that every premeasure on S has a unique extension to a premeasure on a collection of sets that is closed with respect to the formation of relative complements. This purely set-theoretic result, together with Theorem 12, will be used to show that premeasures on semirings are extended by their induced Carathéodory measure.

Definition *A nonempty collection S of subsets of a set X is called a **semiring** provided whenever A and B belong to S, then $A \cap B$ also belongs to S and there is a finite disjoint collection $\{C_k\}_{k=1}^{n}$ of sets in S for which*

$$A \sim B = \bigcup_{k=1}^{n} C_k.$$

Proposition 13 *Let S be a semiring of subsets of a set X. Define S' to be the collection of unions of finite disjoint collections of sets in S. Then S' is closed with respect to the formation of relative complements. Furthermore, any premeasure on S has a unique extension to a premeasure on S'.*

Proof It is clear that S' is closed with respect to the formation of finite unions and finite intersections. Let $\{A_k\}_{k=1}^n$ and $\{B_j\}_{j=1}^m$ be two finite disjoint collections of sets in S. Observe that

$$\left[\bigcup_{k=1}^n A_k \right] \sim \left[\bigcup_{j=1}^m B_j \right] = \bigcup_{k=1}^n \left[\bigcap_{j=1}^m (A_k \sim B_j) \right]. \tag{11}$$

Since each $A_k \sim B_j$ belongs to S' and S' is closed with respect to the formation of finite unions and finite intersections, we infer from (11) that S' is closed with respect to the formation of relative complements.

Let $\mu: S \to [0, \infty]$ be a premeasure on S. For $E \subseteq X$ such that $E = \bigcup_{k=1}^n A_k$, where $\{A_k\}_{k=1}^n$ is a disjoint collection of sets in S, define $\mu'(E) = \sum_{k=1}^n \mu(A_k)$. To verify that $\mu'(E)$ is properly defined, let E also be the disjoint union of the finite collection $\{B_j\}_{j=1}^m$ of sets in S. We must show that

$$\sum_{j=1}^m \mu(B_j) = \sum_{k=1}^n \mu(A_k).$$

However, by finite additivity of a premeasure,

$$\mu(B_j) = \sum_{k=1}^n \mu(B_j \cap A_k) \text{ for } 1 \leq j \leq m$$

and

$$\mu(A_k) = \sum_{j=1}^m \mu(B_j \cap A_k) \text{ for } 1 \leq k \leq n.$$

Therefore

$$\sum_{j=1}^m \mu(B_j) = \sum_{j=1}^m \left[\sum_{k=1}^n \mu(B_j \cap A_k) \right] = \sum_{k=1}^n \left[\sum_{j=1}^m \mu(B_j \cap A_k) \right] = \sum_{k=1}^n \mu(A_k).$$

Thus μ' is properly defined on S.

It remains to show that μ' is a premeasure on S'. Since μ' is properly defined it inherits finite additivity from the finite additivity possessed by μ. To establish the countable monotonicity of μ', let $E \in S'$ be covered by the collection $\{E_k\}_{k=1}^\infty$ of sets in S'. Without loss of generality we may assume that $\{E_k\}_{k=1}^\infty$ is a disjoint collection of sets in S (see part (iii) of Problem 31). Let $E = \bigcup_{j=1}^m A_j$, where the union is disjoint and each A_j belongs to S. For each j, A_j is covered by $\bigcup_{k=1}^\infty (A_j \cap E_k)$, a countable collection of sets in S and therefore, by the countable monotonicity of μ,

$$\mu(A_j) \leq \sum_{k=1}^\infty \mu(A_j \cap E_k).$$

Thus, by the finite monotonicity of μ,

$$\mu'(E) = \sum_{j=1}^{m} \mu(A_j) \le \sum_{j=1}^{m} \left[\sum_{k=1}^{\infty} \mu(A_j \cap E_k) \right]$$

$$= \sum_{k=1}^{\infty} \left[\sum_{j=1}^{m} \mu(A_j \cap E_k) \right]$$

$$= \sum_{k=1}^{\infty} \mu(E \cap E_k)$$

$$\le \sum_{k=1}^{\infty} \mu'(E_k).$$

Therefore μ' is countably monotone. The proof is complete. □

For S a collection of subsets of X, a set function $\mu: S \to [0, \infty]$ is said to be σ-finite provided $X = \bigcup_{k=1}^{\infty} S_k$ where for each k, $S_k \in S$ and $\mu(S_k) < \infty$.

The Carathéodory-Hahn Theorem   *Let $\mu: S \to [0, \infty]$ be a premeasure on a semiring S of subsets of X. Then the Carathéodory measure $\overline{\mu}$ induced by μ is an extension of μ. Furthermore, if μ is σ-finite, then so is $\overline{\mu}$ and $\overline{\mu}$ is the unique measure on the σ-algebra of μ^*-measurable sets that extends μ.*

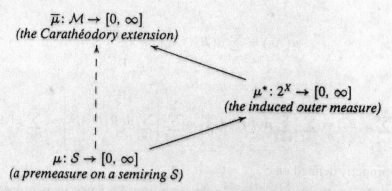

$$\overline{\mu}: \mathcal{M} \to [0, \infty]$$
(the Carathéodory extension)

$$\mu^*: 2^X \to [0, \infty]$$
(the induced outer measure)

$$\mu: S \to [0, \infty]$$
(a premeasure on a semiring S)

The Carathéodory Construction Extends a Premeasure on a Semiring to a Measure

Proof We infer from Theorem 12 and Proposition 13 that $\overline{\mu}$ extends μ. Now assume that μ is σ-finite. To prove uniqueness, let μ_1 be another measure on $\mathcal{M}$ that extends μ. We express $X = \bigcup_{k=1}^{\infty} X_k$, where the union is disjoint and for each k, X_k belongs to S and $\mu(X_k) < \infty$. By the countable additivity of a measure, to prove uniqueness it suffices to show that $\overline{\mu}$ and μ_1 agree on the measurable sets contained in each X_k. Let E be measurable with $E \subseteq E_0$, where $E_0 \in S$ and $\mu(E_0) < \infty$. We will show that

$$\overline{\mu}(E) = \mu_1(E). \tag{12}$$

According to Proposition 10, there is a set $A \in S_{\sigma\delta}$ for which $E \subseteq A$ and $\overline{\mu}(A \sim E) = 0$. We may assume that $A \subseteq E_0$. However, by the countable monotonicity of μ_1, if B is measurable and $\mu^*(B) = 0$, then $\mu_1(B) = 0$. Therefore $\mu_1(A \sim E) = 0$. On the other hand, by the countable additivity of μ_1 and $\overline{\mu}$, these measures agree on S_σ, and therefore by the continuity of measure they agree of the subsets of E_0 which belong to $S_{\sigma\delta}$. Therefore $\mu_1(A) = \overline{\mu}(A)$. Hence

$$\mu_1(A \sim E) = \overline{\mu}(A \sim E) \text{ and } \mu_1(A) = \overline{\mu}(A),$$

and so (12) is verified. $\square$

Corollary 14 *Let S be a semiring of subsets of a set X and B the smallest σ-algebra of subsets of X that contains S. Then two σ-finite measures on B are equal if and only if they agree on sets in S.*

The set-theoretic restrictions on the collection of sets S that are imposed in the Carathéodory-Hahn Theorem are satisfied in a number of important cases. For example, the collection of bounded intervals of real numbers and the collection of subsets of the plane $\mathbf{R}^2$ that are Cartesian products of bounded intervals of real numbers are semirings (see Problem 33). Moreover, the collection of bounded intervals in $\mathbf{R}^n$ is a semiring. This will permit us to construct Lebesgue measure on $\mathbf{R}^n$ by use of the Carathéodory construction.

We note that the uniqueness assertion in the Carathéodory-Hahn Theorem may fail if the premeasure is not assumed to be σ-finite (see Problem 32).

It is useful for the reader to be familiar with some of the vocabulary associated with properties of collections S of subsets of a set X. A collection S is called a **ring** of sets provided it is closed with respect to the formation of finite unions and relative complements and, therefore, with respect to the formation of finite intersections. A ring that contains X is called an **algebra** while a semiring that contains X is called a **semialgebra.**

PROBLEMS

25. Let X be any set containing more than one point and A a proper nonempty subset of X. Define $S = \{A, X\}$ and the set function $\mu : S \to [0, \infty]$ by $\mu(A) = 1$ and $\mu(X) = 2$. Show that $\mu : S \to [0, \infty]$ is a premeasure. Can μ be extended to a measure? What are the subsets of X that are measurable with respect to the outer measure μ^* induced by μ?

26. Consider the collection $S = \{\emptyset, [0, 1], [0, 3], [2, 3]\}$ of subsets of $\mathbf{R}$ and define $\mu(\emptyset) = 0$, $\mu([0, 1]) = 1$, $\mu([0, 3]) = 1$, $\mu([2, 3]) = 1$. Show that $\mu : S \to [0, \infty]$ is a premeasure. Can μ be extended to a measure? What are the subsets of $\mathbf{R}$ that are measurable with respect to the outer measure μ^* induced by μ?

27. Let S be a collection of subsets of a set X and $\mu : S \to [0, \infty]$ a set function. Show that μ is countably monotone if and only if μ^* is an extension of μ.

28. Show that a set function is a premeasure if it has an extension that is a measure.

29. Show that a set function on a σ-algebra is a measure if and only if it is a premeasure.

30. Let S be a collection of sets that is closed with respect to the formation of finite unions and finite intersections.

    (i) Show that S_σ is closed with respect to the formation of countable unions and finite intersections.

    (ii) Show that each set in $S_{\sigma\delta}$ is the intersection of a *decreasing* sequence of S_σ sets.

31. Let S be a semialgebra of subsets of a set X and S' the collection of unions of finite disjoint collections of sets in S.

    (i) Show that S' is an algebra.

    (ii) Show that $S_\sigma = S'_\sigma$ and therefore $S_{\sigma\delta} = S'_{\sigma\delta}$.

    (iii) Let $\{E'_k\}_{k=1}^\infty$ be a collection of sets in S'. Show that we can express $\bigcup_{k=1}^\infty E'_k$ as the disjoint union $\bigcup_{k=1}^\infty E_k$ of sets in S for which

$$\sum_{k=1}^\infty \mu'(E'_k) \geq \sum_{k=1}^\infty \mu(E_k).$$

    (iv) Let A belong to $S'_{\sigma\delta}$. Show that A is the intersection of a descending sequence $\{A_k\}_{k=1}^\infty$ of sets in S_σ.

32. Let $\mathbf{Q}$ be the set of rational numbers and S the collection of all finite unions of intervals of the form $(a, b] \cap \mathbf{Q}$, where $a, b \in \mathbf{Q}$ and $a \leq b$. Define $\mu(a, b] = \infty$ if $a < b$ and $\mu(\emptyset) = 0$. Show that S is closed with respect to the formation of relative complements and $\mu: S \to [0, \infty]$ is a premeasure. Then show that the extension of μ to the smallest σ-algebra containing S is not unique.

33. By a bounded interval of real numbers we mean a set of the form $[a, b]$, $[a, b)$, $(a, b]$ or (a, b) for real numbers $a \leq b$. Thus we consider the empty-set and a set consisting of a single point to be a bounded interval. Show that each of the following three collections of sets S is a semiring.

    (i) Let S be the collection of all bounded intervals of real numbers.

    (ii) Let S be the collection of all subsets of $\mathbf{R} \times \mathbf{R}$ that are products of bounded intervals of real numbers.

    (iii) Let n be a natural number and X be the n-fold Cartesian product of $\mathbf{R}$:

$$X = \overbrace{\mathbf{R} \times \cdots \times \mathbf{R}}^{n\text{ times}}.$$

    Let S be the collection of all subsets of X that are n-fold Cartesian products of bounded intervals of real numbers.

34. If we start with an outer measure μ^* on 2^X and form the induced measure $\bar\mu$ on the μ^*-measurable sets, we can view $\bar\mu$ as a set function and denote by μ^+ the outer measure induced by $\bar\mu$.

    (i) Show that for each set $E \subseteq X$ we have $\mu^+(E) \geq \mu^*(E)$.

    (ii) For a given set E, show that $\mu^+(E) = \mu^*(E)$ if and only if there is a μ^*-measurable set $A \supseteq E$ with $\mu^*(A) = \mu^*(E)$.

35. Let S be a σ-algebra of subsets of X and $\mu: S \to [0, \infty]$ a measure. Let $\bar\mu: \mathcal{M} \to [0, \infty]$ be the measure induced by μ via the Carathéodory construction. Show that S is a subcollection of $\mathcal{M}$ and it may be a proper subcollection.

36. Let μ be a finite premeasure on an algebra S, and μ^* the induced outer measure. Show that a subset E of X is μ^*-measurable if and only if for each $\epsilon > 0$ there is a set $A \in S_\delta$, $A \subseteq E$, such that $\mu^*(E \sim A) < \epsilon$.

CHAPTER 18

Integration Over General Measure Spaces

Contents

We begin the study of integration over general measure spaces by devoting the first section to the consideration of measurable functions. Much of this is quite similar to the study of Lebesgue measurable functions on a single real variable. Our approach to general integration differs from the one we pursued in Chapter 4 for integration with respect to Lebesgue measure for functions of a real variable. In Section 2, we first define the integral for a nonnegative simple function and then directly define the integral of a nonnegative measurable function f as the supremum of integrals of nonnegative simple functions ψ for which $0 \leq \psi \leq f$. At this early stage we establish the general Fatou's Lemma, which is the cornerstone of the full development of the integral, and its close relatives, the Monotone Convergence Theorem and Beppo Levi's Lemma. In the third section, we consider integration for general measurable functions and establish the linearity and monotonicity properties of the integral, the continuity, and countable additivity of integration, and the Integral Comparison Test and Vitali Convergence Theorem. In Section 4, we introduce the concept of absolute continuity of one measure with respect to another and prove the Radon-Nikodym Theorem, a far-reaching generalization of the representation of absolutely continuous functions of a real variable as indefinite integrals. We also establish the Lebesgue Decomposition Theorem for measures. The chapter concludes with an application of the Baire Category Theorem to prove the Vitali–Hahn–Nikodym Theorem, which tells us of very general assumptions under which the setwise limit of a sequence of measures is again a measure.

18.1 MEASURABLE FUNCTIONS

For a measurable space $(X, \mathcal{M})$, the concept of a measurable function on X is identical with that for functions of a real variable with respect to Lebesgue measure. The proof of the following proposition is exactly the same as the proof for Lebesgue measure on the real line; see page 54.

Proposition 1 *Let $(X, \mathcal{M})$ be a measurable space and f an extended real-valued function* *defined on X. Then the following statements are equivalent:*

   (i) *For each real number c, the set $\{x \in X \mid f(x) < c\}$ is measurable.*

  (ii) *For each real number c, the set $\{x \in X \mid f(x) \leq c\}$ is measurable.*

 (iii) *For each real number c, the set $\{x \in X \mid f(x) > c\}$ is measurable.*

 (iv) *For each real number c, the set $\{x \in X \mid f(x) \geq c\}$ is measurable.*

Each of these properties implies that for each extended real number c,

$$\text{the set } \{x \in X \mid f(x) = c\} \text{ is measurable.}$$

Definition   *Let $(X, \mathcal{M})$ be a measurable space. An extended real-valued function f on X is said to be* **measurable** *(or measurable with respect to $\mathcal{M}$) provided one, and hence all, of the four statements of Proposition 1 holds.*

For a set X and the σ-algebra $\mathcal{M} = 2^X$ of all subsets of X, every extended real-valued function on X is measurable with respect to $\mathcal{M}$. At the opposite extreme, consider the σ-algebra $\mathcal{M} = \{X, \emptyset\}$, with respect to which the only measurable functions are those that are constant. If X is a topological space and $\mathcal{M}$ is a σ-algebra of subsets of X that contains the topology on X, then every continuous real-valued function on X is measurable with respect to $\mathcal{M}$. In Part 1 we studied functions of a real variable that are measurable with respect to the σ-algebra of Lebesgue measurable sets.

Since a bounded, open interval of real numbers is the intersection of two unbounded, open intervals and each open set of real numbers is the countable union of a collection of open intervals, we have the following characterizaton of real-valued measurable functions (see also Problem 1).

Proposition 2 *Let $(X, \mathcal{M})$ be a measurable space and f a real-valued function on X. Then f is measurable if and only if for each open set $\mathcal{O}$ of real numbers, $f^{-1}(\mathcal{O})$ is measurable.*

For a measurable space $(X, \mathcal{M})$ and measurable subset E of X, we call an extended real-valued function f that is defined on E measurable provided it is measurable with respect to the measurable space $(E, \mathcal{M}_E)$, where $\mathcal{M}_E$ is the collection of sets in $\mathcal{M}$ that are contained in E. The restriction of a measurable function on X to a measurable set is measurable. Moreover, for an extended real-valued function f of X and measurable subset E of X, the restriction of f to both E and $X \sim E$ are measurable if and only if f is measurable on X.

Proposition 3 *Let $(X, \mathcal{M}, \mu)$ be a complete measure space and X_0 a measurable subset of X for which $\mu(X \sim X_0) = 0$. Then an extended real-valued function f on X is measurable if and only if its restriction to X_0 is measurable. In particular, if g and h are extended real-valued functions on X for which $g = h$ a.e. on X, then g is measurable if and only if h is measurable.*

Proof Define f_0 to be the restriction of f to X_0. Let c be a real number and $E = (c, \infty)$. If f is measurable, then $f^{-1}(E)$ is measurable and hence so is $f^{-1}(E) \cap X_0 = f_0^{-1}(E)$. Therefore f_0 is measurable. Now assume f_0 is measurable. Then

$$f^{-1}(E) = f_0^{-1}(E) \cup A,$$

where A is a subset of $X \sim X_0$. Since $(X, \mathcal{M}, \mu)$ is complete, A is measurable and hence so is $f^{-1}(E)$. Therefore the function f is measurable. The second assertion follows from the first.   □

This proposition is false if the measure space $(X, \mathcal{M}, \mu)$ fails to be complete (see Problem 2). The proof of the following theorem is exactly the same as the proof in the case of Lebesgue measure on the real line; see page 56.

Theorem 4 *Let $(X, \mathcal{M})$ be a measurable space and f and g measurable real-valued functions on X.*

(Linearity) For any real numbers α and β,

$$\alpha f + \beta g \text{ is measurable.}$$

(Products)

$$f \cdot g \text{ is measurable.}$$

(Maximum and Minimum) The functions $\max\{f, g\}$ and $\min\{f, g\}$ are measurable.

Remark *The sum of two extended real-valued functions is not defined at points where the functions take infinite values of opposite sign. Nevertheless, in the study of linear spaces of integrable functions it is necessary to consider linear combinations of extended real-valued measurable functions. For measurable functions that are finite almost everywhere, we proceed as we did for functions of a real variable. Indeed, for a measure space $(X, \mathcal{M}, \mu)$, consider two extended real-valued measurable functions f and g on X that are finite a.e. on X. Define X_0 to be the set of points in X at which both f and g are finite. Since f and g are measurable functions, X_0 is a measurable set. Moreover, $\mu(X \sim X_0) = 0$. For real numbers α and β, the linear combination $\alpha f + \beta g$ is a properly defined real-valued function on X_0. We say that $\alpha f + \beta g$ is measurable on X provided its restriction to X_0 is measurable with respect to the measurable space $(X_0, \mathcal{M}_0)$, where $\mathcal{M}_0$ is the σ-algebra consisting of all sets in $\mathcal{M}$ that are contained in X_0. If $(X, \mathcal{M}, \mu)$ is complete, Proposition 3 tells us that this definition is equivalent to the assertion that one, and hence any, extension of $\alpha f + \beta g$ on X_0 to an extended real-valued function on all of X is a measurable function on X. We regard the function $\alpha f + \beta g$ on X as being any measurable extended real-valued function on X that agrees with $\alpha f + \beta g$ on X_0. Similar considerations apply to the product of f and g and their maximum and minimum. With this convention, the preceding theorem holds if the extended real-valued measurable functions f and g are finite a.e. on X.*

We have already seen that the composition of Lebesgue measurable functions of a single real variable need not be measurable (see the example on page 58). However, the following composition criterion is very useful. It tells us, for instance, that if f is a measurable function and $0 < p < \infty$, then $|f|^p$ also is measurable.

Proposition 5 *Let $(X, \mathcal{M})$ be a measurable space, f a measurable real-valued function on X, and $\varphi: \mathbf{R} \to \mathbf{R}$ continuous. Then the composition $\varphi \circ f: X \to \mathbf{R}$ also is measurable.*

Proof Let $\mathcal{O}$ be an open set of real numbers. Since φ is continuous, $\varphi^{-1}(\mathcal{O})$ is open. Hence, by Proposition 2, $f^{-1}(\varphi^{-1}(\mathcal{O})) = (\varphi \circ f)^{-1}(\mathcal{O})$ is a measurable set and so $\varphi \circ f$ is a measurable function. $\qquad \square$

A fundamentally important property of measurable functions is that, just as in the special case of Lebesgue measurable functions of a real variable, measurability of functions is preserved under the formation of pointwise limits.

Theorem 6 *Let* $(X, \mathcal{M}, \mu)$ *be a measure space and* $\{f_n\}$ *a sequence of measurable functions on* X *for which* $\{f_n\} \to f$ *pointwise a.e. on* X. *If either the measure space* $(X, \mathcal{M}, \mu)$ *is complete or the convergence is pointwise on all of* X, *then* f *is measurable.*

Proof In view of Proposition 3, possibly by excising from X a set of measure 0, we suppose the sequence converges pointwise on all of X. Fix a real number c. We must show that the set $\{x \in X \mid f(x) < c\}$ is measurable. Observe that for a point $x \in X$, since $\lim_{n\to\infty} f_n(x) = f(x)$, $f(x) < c$ if and only if there are natural numbers n and k such that for all $j \geq k$, $f_j(x) < c - 1/n$. But for any natural numbers n and j, since the function f_j is measurable, the set $\{x \in X \mid f_j(x) < c - 1/n\}$ is measurable. Since $\mathcal{M}$ is closed with respect to the formation of countable intersections, for any k,

$$\bigcap_{j=k}^{\infty} \{x \in X \mid f_j(x) < c - 1/n\}$$

also is measurable. Consequently,

$$\{x \in X \mid f(x) < c\} = \bigcup_{1 \leq k, n < \infty} \left[\bigcap_{j=k}^{\infty} \{x \in X \mid f_j(x) < c - 1/n\} \right]$$

is measurable since $\mathcal{M}$ is closed with respect to the formation of countable unions. $\qquad \square$

This theorem is false if the measure space fails to be complete (see Problem 3).

Corollary 7 *Let* $(X, \mathcal{M}, \mu)$ *be a measure space and* $\{f_n\}$ *a sequence of measurable functions on* X. *Then the following functions are measurable:*

$$\sup\{f_n\}, \ \inf\{f_n\}, \ \limsup\{f_n\}, \ \liminf\{f_n\}.$$

Definition *Let* $(X, \mathcal{M})$ *be a measurable space. For a measurable set* E, *its* **characteristic function,** χ_E, *is the function on* X *that takes the value 1 on* E *and 0 on* $X \sim E$. *A real-valued function* ψ *on* X *is said to be* **simple** *provided there is a finite collection* $\{E_k\}_{k=1}^{n}$ *of measurable sets and a corresponding set of real numbers* $\{c_k\}_{k=1}^{n}$ *for which*

$$\psi = \sum_{k=1}^{n} c_k \cdot \chi_{E_k} \ on \ X.$$

Observe that a simple function on X is a measurable real-valued function on X that takes a finite number of real values.

The Simple Approximation Lemma   *Let* $(X, \mathcal{M})$ *be a measurable space and* f *a measurable function on* X *that is bounded on* X, *that is, there is an* $M \geq 0$ *for which* $|f| \leq M$ *on* X. *Then for each* $\epsilon > 0$, *there are simple functions* φ_ϵ *and* ψ_ϵ *defined on* X *that have the following approximation properties:*

$$\varphi_\epsilon \leq f \leq \psi_\epsilon \text{ and } 0 \leq \psi_\epsilon - \varphi_\epsilon < \epsilon \text{ on } X.$$

Proof   Let $[c, d)$ be a bounded interval that contains the image of X, $f(X)$, and

$$c = y_0 < y_1 < \ldots < y_{n-1} < y_n = d$$

a partition of the closed, bounded interval $[c, d]$ such that $y_k - y_{k-1} < \epsilon$ for $1 \leq k \leq n$. Define

$$I_k = [y_{k-1}, y_k) \text{ and } X_k = f^{-1}(I_k) \text{ for } 1 \leq k \leq n.$$

Since each I_k is an interval and the function f is measurable, each set X_k is measurable. Define the simple functions φ_ϵ and ψ_ϵ on X by

$$\varphi_\epsilon = \sum_{k=1}^{n} y_{k-1} \cdot \chi_{X_k} \text{ and } \psi_\epsilon = \sum_{k=1}^{n} y_k \cdot \chi_{X_k}.$$

Let x belong to X. Since $f(X) \subseteq [c, d)$, there is a unique $k, 1 \leq k \leq n$, for which $y_{k-1} \leq f(x) < y_k$ and therefore

$$\varphi_\epsilon(x) = y_{k-1} \leq f(x) < y_k = \psi_\epsilon(x).$$

But $y_k - y_{k-1} < \epsilon$, and therefore φ_ϵ and ψ_ϵ have the required approximation properties. $\square$

The Simple Approximation Theorem   *Let* $(X, \mathcal{M}, \mu)$ *be a measure space and* f *a measurable function on* X. *Then there is a sequence* $\{\psi_n\}$ *of simple functions on* X *that converges pointwise on* X *to* f *and has the property that*

$$|\psi_n| \leq |f| \text{ on } X \text{ for all } n.$$

(i) *If* X *is* σ-*finite, then we may choose the sequence* $\{\psi_n\}$ *so that each* ψ_n *vanishes outside a set of finite measure.*

(ii) *If* f *is nonnegative, we may choose the sequence* $\{\psi_n\}$ *to be increasing and each* $\psi_n \geq 0$ *on* X.

Proof   Fix a natural number n. Define $E_n = \{x \in X \mid |f(x)| \leq n\}$. Since $|f|$ is a measurable function, E_n is a measurable set and the restriction of f to E_n is a bounded measurable function. By the Simple Approximation Lemma, applied to the restriction of f to E_n and with the choice of $\epsilon = 1/n$, we may select simple functions h_n and g_n on E_n, which have the following approximation properties:

$$h_n \leq f \leq g_n \text{ and } 0 \leq g_n - h_n < 1/n \text{ on } E_n.$$

For x in E_n, define $\psi_n(x) = 0$ if $f(x) = 0$, $\psi_n(x) = \max\{h_n(x), 0\}$ if $f(x) > 0$ and $\psi_n(x) = \min\{g_n(x), 0\}$ if $f(x) < 0$. Extend ψ_n to all of X by setting $\psi_n(x) = n$ if $f(x) > n$

and $\psi_n(x) = -n$ if $f(x) < -n$. This defines a sequence $\{\psi_n\}$ of simple functions on X. It follows, as it did in the proof for the case of Lebesgue measurable functions of a real variable (see page 62), that, for each n, $|\psi_n| \le |f|$ on X and the sequence $\{\psi_n\}$ converges pointwise on X to f.

If X is σ-finite, express X as the union of a countable ascending collection $\{X_n\}_{n=1}^\infty$ of measurable subsets, each of which has finite measure. Replace each ψ_n by $\psi_n \cdot \chi_{X_n}$ and (i) is verified. If f is nonnegative, replace each ψ_n by $\max_{1 \le i \le n} |\psi_i|$ and (ii) is verified. $\square$

The proof of the following general form of Egoroff's Theorem follows from the continuity and countable additivity of measure, as did the proof in the case of Lebesgue measurable functions of a real variable; see page 65.

Egoroff's Theorem   Let $(X, \mathcal{M}, \mu)$ be a finite measure space and $\{f_n\}$ a sequence of measurable functions on X that converges pointwise a.e. on X to a function f that is finite a.e. on X. Then for each $\epsilon > 0$, there is a measurable subset X_ϵ of X for which

$$\{f_n\} \to f \text{ uniformly on } X_\epsilon \text{ and } \mu(X \sim X_\epsilon) < \epsilon.$$

PROBLEMS

In the following problems $(X, \mathcal{M}, \mu)$ is a reference measure space and measurable means with respect to $\mathcal{M}$.

1. Show that an extended real-valued function on X is measurable if and only if $f^{-1}\{\infty\}$ and $f^{-1}\{-\infty\}$ are measurable and so is $f^{-1}(E)$ for every Borel set of real numbers.

2. Suppose $(X, \mathcal{M}, \mu)$ is not complete. Let E be a subset of a set of measure zero that does not belong to $\mathcal{M}$. Let $f = 0$ on X and $g = \chi_E$. Show that $f = g$ a.e. on X while f is measurable and g is not.

3. Suppose $(X, \mathcal{M}, \mu)$ is not complete. Show that there is a sequence $\{f_n\}$ of measurable functions on X that converges pointwise a.e. on X to a function f that is not measurable.

4. Let E be a measurable subset of X and f an extended real-valued function on X. Show that f is measurable if and only if its restrictions to E and $X \sim E$ are measurable.

5. Show that an extended real-valued function f on X is measurable if and only if for each rational number c, $\{x \in X \mid f(x) < c\}$ is a measurable set.

6. Consider two extended real-valued measurable functions f and g on X that are finite a.e. on X. Define X_0 to be the set of points in X at which both f and g are finite. Show that X_0 is measurable and $\mu(X \sim X_0) = 0$.

7. Let X be a nonempty set. Show that every extended real-valued function on X is measurable with respect to the measurable space $(X, 2^X)$.

   (i) Let x_0 belong to X and δ_{x_0} be the Dirac measure at x_0 on 2^X. Show that two functions on X are equal a.e. $[\delta_{x_0}]$ if and only if they take the same value at x_0.

   (ii) Let η be the counting measure on 2^X. Show that two functions on X are equal a.e. $[\eta]$ if and only if they take the same value at every point in X.

8. Let X be a topological space and $\mathcal{B}(X)$ the smallest σ-algebra containing the topology on X. $\mathcal{B}(X)$ is called the Borel σ-algebra associated with the topological space X. Show that any continuous real-valued function on X is measurable with respect to the Borel measurable space $(X, \mathcal{B}(X))$.

9. If a real-valued function on **R** is measurable with respect to the σ-algebra of Lebesgue measurable sets, is it necessarily measurable with respect to the Borel measurable space $(\mathbf{R}, \mathcal{B}(\mathbf{R}))$?

10. Check that the proofs of Proposition 1 and Theorem 4 follow from the proofs of the corresponding results in the case of Lebesgue measure on the real line.

11. Complete the proof of the Simple Approximation Lemma.

12. Prove Egoroff's Theorem. Is Egoroff's Theorem true in the absence of the assumption that the limit function is finite a.e.?

13. Let $\{f_n\}$ be a sequence of real-valued measurable functions on X such that, for each natural number n, $\mu\{x \in X \mid |f_n(x) - f_{n+1}(x)| > 1/2^n\} 1/2^n$. Show that $\{f_n\}$ is pointwise convergent a.e. on X. (Hint: Use the Borel-Cantelli Lemma.)

14. Under the assumptions of Egoroff's Theorem, show that $X = \bigcup_{k=0}^{\infty} X_k$, where each X_k is measurable, $\mu(X_0) = 0$ and, for $k \geq 1$, $\{f_n\}$ converges uniformly to f on X_k.

15. A sequence $\langle f_n \rangle$ of measurable real-valued functions on X is said to **converge in measure** to a measurable function f provided that for each $\eta > 0$,

$$\lim_{n \to \infty} \mu\{x \in X \mid |f_n(x) - f(x)| > \eta\} = 0.$$

A sequence $\langle f_n \rangle$ of measurable functions is said to be **Cauchy in measure** provided that for each $\epsilon > 0$ and $\eta > 0$, there is an index N such that for each $m, n \geq N$,

$$\mu\{x \in X \mid |f_n(x) - f_m(x)| > \eta\} < \epsilon.$$

   (i) Show that if $\mu(X) < \infty$ and $\{f_n\}$ converges pointwise a.e. on X to a measurable function f, then $\{f_n\}$ converges to f in measure. (Hint: Use Egoroff's Theorem.)

   (ii) Show that if $\{f_n\}$ converges to f in measure, then there is a subsequence of $\{f_n\}$ that converges pointwise a.e. on X to f. (Hint: Use the Borel-Cantelli Lemma.)

   (iii) Show that if $\{f_n\}$ is Cauchy in measure, then there is a measurable function f to which $\{f_n\}$ converges in measure.

16. Assume $\mu(X) < \infty$. Show that $\{f_n\} \to f$ in measure if and only if each subsequence of $\{f_n\}$ has a further subsequence that converges pointwise a.e. on X to f. Use this to show that for two sequences that converge in measure, the product sequence also converges in measure to the product of the limits.

18.2 INTEGRATION OF NONNEGATIVE MEASURABLE FUNCTIONS

In Chapter 4 we developed integration for Lebesgue measurable functions of a real variable with respect to Lebesgue measure. We first defined the integral of a simple function over a set of finite Lebesgue measure. The second step was to define the concepts of integrability and integral for a bounded function on a set of finite measure and use the Simple Approximation Lemma to show that a bounded measurable function that vanished outside a set of finite Lebesgue measure is integrable and that the integral of such functions possessed the anticipated linearity, monotonicity, and additivity over domains properties. We then defined the Lebesgue integral of a nonnegative Lebesgue measurable function f over an arbitrary Lebesgue measurable set E to be the supremum of $\int_E g$ as g ranged over all bounded Lebesgue measurable functions g for which $0 \leq g \leq f$ on E and that vanish outside a set of finite Lebesgue measure. This approach is not appropriate in the case of a general measure space. Indeed, for a measure space $(X, \mathcal{M}, \mu)$, if $\mu(X) = \infty$, we certainly want $\int_X 1 \, d\mu = \infty$. However, if X is nonempty, $\mathcal{M} = \{X, \emptyset\}$ and the measure μ is defined by setting $\mu(\emptyset) = 0$ and $\mu(X) = \infty$, then the only measurable function g that vanishes outside of a set of finite measure is $g \equiv 0$, and hence the supremum of $\int_X g \, d\mu$ over such functions is zero. To circumvent this difficulty, for the general integral, we first define the integral of nonnegative *simple* functions and then define the integral of a nonnegative measurable function directly in terms of integrals of nonnegative simple functions. We almost immediately establish a general version of Fatou's Lemma and make this the cornerstone of further development. We devote this section to integration of nonnegative measurable functions.

Definition *Let $(X, \mathcal{M}, \mu)$ be a measure space and ψ a nonnegative simple function on X. Define the integral of ψ over X, $\int_X \psi \, d\mu$, as follows: if $\psi = 0$ on X, define $\int_E \psi \, d\mu = 0$. Otherwise, let $c_1, c_2, \ldots, c_n$ be the positive values taken by ψ on X and, for $1 \leq k \leq n$, define $E_k = \{x \in X \mid \psi(x) = c_k\}$. Define*

$$\int_X \psi \, d\mu = \sum_{k=1}^{n} c_k \cdot \mu(E_k), \tag{1}$$

using the convention that the right-hand side is ∞ if, for some k, $\mu(E_k) = \infty$. For a measurable subset E of X, the integral of ψ over E with respect to μ is defined to be $\int_X \psi \cdot \chi_E \, d\mu$ and denoted by $\int_E f \, d\mu$.

Proposition 8 *Let $(X, \mathcal{M}, \mu)$ be a measure space and φ and ψ nonnegative simple function on X. If α and β are positive real numbers, then*

$$\int_X [\alpha \cdot \psi + \beta \cdot \varphi] \, d\mu = \alpha \cdot \int_X \psi \, d\mu + \beta \cdot \int_X \psi \, d\mu. \tag{2}$$

If A and B are disjoint measurable subsets of X, then

$$\int_{A \cup B} \psi \, d\mu = \int_A \psi \, d\mu + \int_B \psi \, d\mu. \tag{3}$$

In particular, if $X_0 \subseteq X$ is measurable and $\mu(X \sim X_0) = 0$, then

$$\int_X \psi \, d\mu = \int_{X_0} \psi \, d\mu. \tag{4}$$

Furthermore, if $\psi \leq \varphi$ a.e. on X, then

$$\int_X \psi \, d\mu \leq \int_X \varphi \, d\mu. \tag{5}$$

Proof If either ψ or φ is positive on a set of infinite measure, then the linear combination $\alpha \cdot \psi + \beta \cdot \varphi$ has the same property and therefore each side of (2) is infinite. We therefore assume both ψ and φ vanish outside a set of finite measure and hence so does the linear combination $\alpha \cdot \psi + \beta \cdot \varphi$. In this case the proof of (2) is exactly the same as the proof for Lebesgue integration of functions of a real variable (see the proofs of Lemma 1 and Proposition 2 on page 72). The additivity over domains formula follows from (2) and the observation that, since A and B are disjoint,

$$\psi \cdot \chi_{A \cup B} = \psi \cdot \chi_A + \psi \cdot \chi_B \text{ on } X.$$

To verify (5), first observe that since the integral of a simple function over a set of measure zero is zero, by (3), we may assume $\psi \le \varphi$ on X. Observe that since φ and ψ take only a finite number of real values, we may express X as $\bigcup_{k=1}^{n} X_k$, a disjoint union of measurable sets for which both φ and ψ are constant on each X_k. Therefore

$$\psi = \sum_{k=1}^{n} a_k \cdot \chi_{X_k} \text{ and } \varphi = \sum_{k=1}^{n} b_k \cdot \chi_{X_k} \text{ where } a_k \le b_k \text{ for } 1 \le k \le n. \tag{6}$$

But (2) extends to finite linear combinations of nonnegative simple functions and therefore (5) follows from (6).   □

Definition *Let $(X, \mathcal{M}, \mu)$ be a measure space and f a nonnegative extended real-valued measurable function on X. The **integral** of f over X with respect to μ, which is denoted by $\int_X f \, d\mu$, is defined to be the supremum of the integrals $\int_X \varphi \, d\mu$ as φ ranges over all simple functions φ for which $0 \le \varphi \le f$ on X. For a measurable subset E of X, the integral of f over E with respect to μ is defined to be $\int_X f \cdot \chi_E \, d\mu$ and denoted by $\int_E f \, d\mu$.*

We leave it as an exercise to verify the following three properties of the integral of nonnegative measurable functions. Let $(X, \mathcal{M}, \mu)$ be a measure space, g and h nonnegative measurable functions on X, X_0 a measurable subset of X, and α a positive real number. Then

$$\int_X \alpha \cdot g \, d\mu = \alpha \cdot \int_X g \, d\mu; \tag{7}$$

$$\text{if } g \le h \text{ a.e. on } X, \text{ then } \int_X g \, d\mu \le \int_X h \, d\mu; \tag{8}$$

$$\int_X g \, d\mu = \int_{X_0} g \, d\mu \text{ if } \mu(X \sim X_0) = 0. \tag{9}$$

Chebychev's Inequality *Let $(X, \mathcal{M}, \mu)$ be a measure space, f a nonnegative measurable function on X, and λ a positive real number. Then*

$$\mu\{x \in X \mid f(x) \ge \lambda\} \le \frac{1}{\lambda} \int_X f \, d\mu. \tag{10}$$

Proof Define $X_\lambda = \{x \in X \mid f(x) \ge \lambda\}$ and $\varphi = \lambda \cdot \chi_{X_\lambda}$. Observe that $0 \le \varphi \le f$ on X and φ is a simple function. Therefore, by definition,

$$\lambda \cdot \mu(X_\lambda) = \int_X \varphi \, d\mu \le \int_X f \, d\mu.$$

Divide this inequality by λ to obtain Chebychev's Inequality.   □

Proposition 9 *Let $(X, \mathcal{M}, \mu)$ be a measure space and f a nonnegative measurable function on X for which $\int_X f \, d\mu < \infty$. Then f is finite a.e. on X and $\{x \in X \mid f(x) > 0\}$ is σ-finite.*

Proof Define $X_\infty = \{x \in X \mid f(x) = \infty\}$ and consider the simple function $\psi = \chi_{X_\infty}$. By definition, $\int_X \psi \, d\mu = \mu(X_\infty)$ and since $0 \le \psi \le f$ on X, $\mu(X_\infty) \le \int_X f \, d\mu < \infty$. Therefore f is finite a.e. on X. Let n be a natural number. Define $X_n = \{x \in X \mid f(x) \ge 1/n\}$. By Chebychev's Inequality,

$$\mu(X_n) \le n \cdot \int_X f \, d\mu < \infty.$$

Moreover,

$$\{x \in X \mid f(x) > 0\} = \bigcup_{n=1}^{\infty} E_n$$

Therefore the set $\{x \in X \mid f(x) > 0\}$ is σ-finite. $\qquad\square$

Fatou's Lemma *Let $(X, \mathcal{M}, \mu)$ be a measure space and $\{f_n\}$ a sequence of nonnegative measurable functions on X for which $\{f_n\} \to f$ pointwise a.e. on X. Assume f is measurable. Then*

$$\int_X f \, d\mu \le \liminf \int_X f_n \, d\mu. \tag{11}$$

Proof Let X_0 be a measurable subset of X for which $\mu(X \sim X_0) = 0$ and $\{f_n\} \to f$ pointwise on X_0. According to (9), each side of (11) remains unchanged if X is replaced by X_0. We therefore assume $X = X_0$. By the definition of $\int_X f \, d\mu$ as a supremum, to verify (11) it is necessary and sufficient to show that if φ is any simple function for which $0 \le \varphi \le f$ on X, then

$$\int_X \varphi \, d\mu \le \liminf \int_X f_n \, d\mu. \tag{12}$$

Let φ be such a function. This inequality clearly holds if $\int_X \varphi \, d\mu = 0$. Assume $\int_X \varphi \, d\mu > 0$.

Case 1: $\int_X \varphi \, d\mu = \infty$. Then there is a measurable set $X_\infty \subseteq X$ and $a > 0$ for which $\mu(X_\infty) = \infty$ and $\varphi = a$ on X_∞. For each natural number n, define

$$A_n = \left\{ x \in X \mid f_k(x) \ge a/2 \text{ for all } k \ge n \right\}.$$

Then $\{A_n\}_{n=1}^{\infty}$ is an ascending sequence of measurable subsets of X. Since $X_\infty \subseteq \bigcup_{n=1}^{\infty} A_n$, by the continuity and monotonicity of measure,

$$\lim_{n \to \infty} \mu(A_n) = \mu\left(\bigcup_{n=1}^{\infty} A_n\right) \ge \mu(X_\infty) = \infty.$$

However, by Chebychev's Inequality, for each natural number n,

$$\mu(A_n) \le \frac{2}{a} \int_{A_n} f_n \, d\mu \le \frac{2}{a} \int_X f_n \, d\mu.$$

Therefore $\lim_{n \to \infty} \int_X f_n \, d\mu = \infty = \int_X \varphi \, d\mu$.

Case 2: $0 < \int_X \varphi \, d\mu < \infty$. By excising from X the set where φ takes the value 0, the left-hand side of (12) remains unchanged and the right-hand side does not increase. Thus we may suppose that $\varphi > 0$ on X and therefore, since φ is simple and $\int_X \varphi \, d\mu < \infty$, $\mu(X) < \infty$. To verify (12), choose $\epsilon > 0$. For each natural number n, define

$$X_n = \{x \in X \mid f_k(x) > (1 - \epsilon)\varphi(x) \text{ for all } k \geq n\}.$$

Then $\{X_n\}$ is an ascending sequence of measurable subsets of X whose union equals X. Therefore $\{X \sim X_n\}$ is a descending sequence of measurable subsets of X whose intersection is empty. Since $\mu(X) < \infty$, by the continuity of measure, $\lim_{n \to \infty} \mu(X \sim X_n) = 0$. Choose an index N such that $\mu(X \sim X_n) < \epsilon$ for all $n \geq N$. Define $M > 0$ to be the maximum of the finite number of values taken by φ on X. We infer from the monotonicity and positive homogeneity properties, (8) and (7), of integration for nonnegative measurable functions, the additivity over domains and monotonicity properties, (3) and (5), of integration for nonnegative simple function and the finiteness of $\int_X \varphi \, d\mu$ that, for $n \geq N$,

$$\int_X f_n \, d\mu \geq \int_{X_n} f_n \, d\mu \geq (1 - \epsilon) \int_{X_n} \varphi \, d\mu$$

$$= (1 - \epsilon) \int_X \varphi \, d\mu - (1 - \epsilon) \int_{X \sim X_n} \varphi \, d\mu$$

$$\geq (1 - \epsilon) \int_X \varphi \, d\mu - \int_{X \sim X_n} \varphi \, d\mu$$

$$\geq (1 - \epsilon) \int_X \varphi \, d\mu - \epsilon \cdot M$$

$$= \int_X \varphi \, d\mu - \epsilon \left[\int_X \varphi \, d\mu + M \right].$$

Hence

$$\liminf \int_X f_n \, d\mu \geq \int_X \varphi \, d\mu - \epsilon \left[\int_X \varphi \, d\mu + M \right].$$

This inequality holds for all $\epsilon > 0$ and hence, since $\int_X \varphi \, d\mu + M$ is finite, it also holds for $\epsilon = 0$.   □

In Fatou's Lemma, the limit function f is assumed to be measurable. In case $\{f_n\}$ converges pointwise to f on all of X or the measure space is complete, Theorem 6 tells us that f is measurable.

We have already seen in the case of Lebesgue integration on the real line that the inequality (11) may be strict. For instance, it is strict for Lebesgue measure on $X = [0, 1]$ and $f_n = n \cdot \chi_{[0, 1/n]}$ for all n. It is also strict for Lebesgue measure on $X = \mathbf{R}$ and $f_n = \chi_{[n, n+1]}$ for all n. However, for a sequence of measurable functions $\{f_n\}$ that converges pointwise on

X to f, in the case of Lebesgue integration for functions of a real variable, we established a number of criteria for justifying **passage of the limit under the integral sign**, that is,

$$\lim_{n \to \infty} \left[\int_X f_n \, d\mu \right] = \int_X \left[\lim_{n \to \infty} f_n \right] d\mu.$$

Each of these criteria has a correspondent in the general theory of integration. We first establish a general version of the Monotone Convergence Theorem.

The Monotone Convergence Theorem   *Let* $(X, \mathcal{M}, \mu)$ *be a measure space and* $\{f_n\}$ *an increasing sequence of nonnegative measurable functions on* X. *Define* $f(x) = \lim_{n \to \infty} f_n(x)$ *for each* $x \in X$. *Then*

$$\lim_{n \to \infty} \int_X f_n \, d\mu = \int_X f \, d\mu.$$

Proof Theorem 6 tells us that f is measurable. According to Fatou's Lemma,

$$\int_X f \, d\mu \le \liminf \int_X f_n \, d\mu.$$

However, for each n, $f_n \le f$ on X, and so, by (8), $\int_X f_n \, d\mu \le \int_X f \, d\mu$. Thus

$$\limsup \int_X f_n \, d\mu \le \int_X f \, d\mu.$$

Hence

$$\int_X f \, d\mu = \lim_{n \to \infty} \int_X f_n \, d\mu. \qquad \square$$

Beppo Levi's Lemma   *Let* $(X, \mathcal{M}, \mu)$ *be a measure space and* $\{f_n\}$ *an increasing sequence of nonnegative measurable functions on* X. *If the sequence of integrals* $\{\int_X f_n \, d\mu\}$ *is bounded, then* $\{f_n\}$ *converges pointwise on* X *to a measurable function* f *that is finite a.e. on* X *and*

$$\lim_{n \to \infty} \int_X f_n \, d\mu = \int_X f \, d\mu < \infty.$$

Proof Define $f(x) = \lim_{n \to \infty} f_n(x)$ for each $x \in X$. The Monotone Convergence Theorem tells us that $\left\{ \int_X f_n \, d\mu \right\} \to \int_X f \, d\mu$. Therefore, since the sequence of real numbers $\left\{ \int_X f_n \, d\mu \right\}$ is bounded, its limit is finite and so $\int_X f \, d\mu < \infty$. It follows from Proposition 9 that f is finite a.e. on X. $\qquad \square$

Proposition 10   *Let* $(X, \mathcal{M}, \mu)$ *be a measure space and* f *a nonnegative measurable function on* X. *Then there is an increasing sequence* $\{\psi_n\}$ *of simple functions on* X *that converges pointwise on* X *to* f *and*

$$\lim_{n \to \infty} \int_X \psi_n \, d\mu = \int_X f \, d\mu. \tag{13}$$

Proof Apply the Simple Approximation Theorem and the Monotone Convergence Theorem. $\qquad \square$

Proposition 11 *Let* $(X, \mathcal{M}, \mu)$ *be a measure space and* f *and* g *nonnegative measurable functions on* X. *If* α *and* β *are positive real numbers, then*[1]

$$\int_X [\alpha \cdot f + \beta \cdot g] \, d\mu = \alpha \cdot \int_X f \, d\mu + \beta \cdot \int_X g \, d\mu. \tag{14}$$

Proof In view of (7), it suffices to establish (14) for $\alpha = \beta = 1$. According to the preceding theorem, there are increasing sequences $\{\psi_n\}$ and $\{\varphi_n\}$ of nonnegative simple functions on X that converge pointwise on X to g and f, respectively,

$$\lim_{n \to \infty} \int_X \psi_n \, d\mu = \int_X g \, d\mu \text{ and } \lim_{n \to \infty} \int_X \varphi_n \, d\mu = \int_X f \, d\mu.$$

Then $\{\varphi_n + \psi_n\}$ is an increasing sequence of simple functions that converges pointwise on X to $f + g$. By the linearity of integration for nonnegative simple functions, the linearity of convergence for sequences of real numbers and the Monotone Convergence Theorem,

$$\int_X [f + g] \, d\mu = \lim_{n \to \infty} \int_X [\varphi_n + \psi_n] \, d\mu$$

$$= \lim_{n \to \infty} \left[\int_X \varphi_n \, d\mu + \int_X \psi_n \, d\mu \right]$$

$$= \lim_{n \to \infty} \int_X \varphi_n \, d\mu + \lim_{n \to \infty} \int_X \psi_n \, d\mu$$

$$= \int_X f \, d\mu + \int_X g \, d\mu. \qquad \square$$

We have defined the integral of a nonnegative measurable function but so far not defined what it means for such a function to be integrable.

Definition *Let* $(X, \mathcal{M}, \mu)$ *be a measure space and* f *a nonnegative measurable function on* X. *Then* f *is said be* **integrable** *over* X *with respect to* μ *provided* $\int_X f \, d\mu < \infty$.

The preceding proposition tells us that the sum of nonnegative integrable functions is integrable while Proposition 9 tells us that a nonnegative integrable function is finite a.e. and vanishes outside a σ-finite set.

PROBLEMS

In the following problems, $(X, \mathcal{M}, \mu)$ is a measure space, measurable means with respect to $\mathcal{M}$, and integrable means with respect to μ.

17. Prove (7) and (8). Use (8) to prove (9).

---

[1] Since α and β are positive and f and g are nonnegative extended real-valued functions, $\alpha f + \beta g$ is an extended real-valued function that is properly defined pointwise on all of X.

18. Let $\{u_n\}$ be a sequence of nonnegative measurable functions on X. For $x \in X$, define $f(x) = \sum_{n=1}^{\infty} u_n(x)$. Show that

$$\int_X f \, d\mu = \sum_{n=1}^{\infty} \left[\int_X u_n \, d\mu \right].$$

19. Show that if f is a nonnegative measurable function on X, then

$$\int_X f \, d\mu = 0 \text{ if and only if } f = 0 \text{ a.e. on } X.$$

20. Verify (2) in the case ψ and φ vanishes outside a set of finite measure.

21. Let f and g be nonnegative measurable functions on X for which $g \le f$ a.e. on X. Show that $f = g$ a.e. on X if and only if $\int_X g \, d\mu = \int_X f \, d\mu$.

22. Suppose f and g are nonnegative measurable functions on X for which f^2 and g^2 are integrable over X with respect to μ. Show that $f \cdot g$ also is integrable over X with respect to μ.

23. Let X be the union of a countable ascending sequence of measurable sets $\{X_n\}$ and f a nonnegative measurable function on X. Show that f is integrable over X if and only if there is an $M \ge 0$ for which $\int_{X_n} f \, d\mu \le M$ for all n.

24. Show that the definition of the integral of a nonnegative measurable function on a general measure space is consistent with the definition given in the particular case of the Lebesgue integral of a function of a real variable.

25. Let η be the counting measure on the natural numbers $\mathbf{N}$. Characterize the nonnegative real-valued functions (that is, sequences) that are integrable over $\mathbf{N}$ with respect to η and the value of $\int_{\mathbf{N}} f \, d\eta$.

26. Let x_0 be a point in a set X and δ_{x_0} the Dirac measure concentrated at x_0. Characterize the nonnegative real-valued functions on X that are integrable over X with respect to δ_{x_0} and the value of $\int_X f \, d\delta_{x_0}$.

18.3   INTEGRATION OF GENERAL MEASURABLE FUNCTIONS

Let $(X, \mathcal{M})$ be a measurable space and f a measurable function on X. The **positive part** and the **negative part** of f, f^+ and f^-, are defined by

$$f^+ = \max\{f, 0\} \text{ and } f^- = \max\{-f, 0\} \text{ on } X.$$

Both f^+ and f^- are nonnegative measurable functions on X for which

$$f = f^+ - f^- \text{ and } |f| = f^+ + f^- \text{ on } X.$$

Since $0 \le f^+ \le |f|$ and $0 \le f^- \le |f|$ on X, we infer from (8) that if $|f|$ is integrable over X, so are f^+ and f^- Conversely, by linearity of integration for nonnegative functions, if f^+ and f^- are integrable over X, so is $|f|$.

Definition   *Let* $(X, \mathcal{M}, \mu)$ *be a measure space. A measurable function f on X is said to be* **integrable** *over X with respect to μ provided $|f|$ is integrable over X with respect to μ. For such a function, we define the integral of f over X with respect to μ by*

$$\int_X f \, d\mu = \int_X f^+ \, d\mu - \int_X f^- \, d\mu.$$

For a measurable subset E of X, f is said to be integrable over E provided $f \cdot \chi_E$ is integrable over X with respect to μ. The integral of f over E with respect to μ is defined to be $\int_X f \cdot \chi_E \, d\mu$ and denoted by $\int_E f \, d\mu$.

The Integral Comparison Test   *Let* $(X, \mathcal{M}, \mu)$ *be a measure space and f a measurable function on X. If g is integrable over X and dominates f on X in the sense that $|f| \le g$ a.e. on X, then f is integrable over X and*

$$\left| \int_X f \, d\mu \right| \le \int_X |f| \, d\mu \le \int_X g \, d\mu. \tag{15}$$

Proof   The inequality (8) tells us that $|f|$ is integrable over X. We invoke Proposition 11 and the inequality (8) once more to conclude that

$$\left| \int_X f \, d\mu \right| = \left| \int_X f^+ \, d\mu - \int_X f^- \, d\mu \right| \le \int_X f^+ \, d\mu + \int_X f^- \, d\mu = \int_X |f| \, d\mu \le \int_X g \, d\mu.$$

$\square$

Remark   *Let* $(X, \mathcal{M}, \mu)$ *be a measure space and f be integrable over X. We infer from Proposition 9, when applied to the positive and negative parts of f, that f is finite a.e. on X. Therefore, if g and h are integrable over X, the sum $g + h$ is defined on X by the convention established in the remark on page 361. Furthermore, by (9), applied to the positive and negative parts of $g + h$, if X_0 is the set of points in X at which both g and h are finite, then*

$$\int_X [g + h] \, d\mu = \int_{X_0} [g + h] \, d\mu.$$

Therefore the integral of $h + g$ over X is properly defined, that is, it does not depend on the choice of functional value assigned to $h + g$ at those points in X at which h and g take infinite values of opposite sign.

Theorem 12   *Let* $(X, \mathcal{M}, \mu)$ *be a measure space and f and g be integrable over X.*

(Linearity) For real numbers α and β, $\alpha f + \beta g$ is integrable over X and

$$\int_X [\alpha f + \beta g] \, d\mu = \alpha \int_X f \, d\mu + \beta \int_X g \, d\mu.$$

(Monotonicity) If $f \le g$ a.e. on X, then

$$\int_X f \, d\mu \le \int_X g \, d\mu.$$

(*Additivity Over Domains*) *If A and B are disjoint measurable subsets of X, then*

$$\int_{A \cup B} f \, d\mu = \int_A f \, d\mu + \int_B f \, d\mu.$$

Proof We prove linearity for coefficients $\alpha = \beta = 1$ and leave the extension to the case of general coefficients as an exercise. Both $|f|$ and $|g|$ are integrable over X. According to Proposition 11, the sum $|f| + |g|$ also is integrable over X. Since $|f + g| \le |f| + |g|$ on X, we infer from (8) that $|f + g|$ is integrable over X. Therefore the positive and negative parts of f, g and $f + g$ are integrable over X. According to Proposition 9, by excising from X a set of measure zero and using (9), we may assume that f and g are finite on X. To verify linearity is to show that

$$\int_X [f + g]^+ \, d\mu - \int_X [f + g]^- \, d\mu = \left[\int_X f^+ \, d\mu - \int_X f^- \, d\mu \right] + \left[\int_X g^+ \, d\mu - \int_X g^- \, d\mu \right]. \quad (16)$$

But

$$(f + g)^+ - (f + g)^- = f + g = (f^+ - f^-) + (g^+ - g^-) \text{ on } X,$$

and therefore, since each of these six functions takes real values on X,

$$(f + g)^+ + f^- + g^- = (f + g)^- + f^+ + g^+ \text{ on } X.$$

We infer from Proposition 11 that

$$\int_X (f + g)^+ \, d\mu + \int_X f^- \, d\mu + \int_X g^- \, d\mu = \int_X (f + g)^- \, d\mu + \int_X f^+ \, d\mu + \int_X g^+ \, d\mu.$$

Since f, g and $f + g$ are integrable over X, each of these six integrals is finite. Rearrange these integrals to obtain (16). We have established the linearity of integration. The monotonicity property follows from linearity since if $f \le g$ a.e. on X, then $g - f \ge 0$ a.e. on X and therefore

$$0 \le \int_X (g - f) \, d\mu = \int_X g \, d\mu - \int_X f \, d\mu.$$

Additivity over domains follows from linearity and the observation that, since A and B are disjoint,

$$f \cdot \chi_{A \cup B} = f \cdot \chi_A + f \cdot \chi_B \text{ on } X. \qquad \square$$

As we have seen in the case of Lebesgue integration for functions of a real variable, the product of integrable functions is not, in general, integrable. In the following chapter we establish a general Hölder's Inequality and thereby describe integrability properties of products of functions.

Theorem 13 (**the Countable Additivity Over Domains of Integration**) *Let* $(X, \mathcal{M}, \mu)$ *be a measure space, the function f be integrable over X, and $\{X_n\}_{n=1}^{\infty}$ a disjoint countable collection of measurable sets whose union is X. Then*

$$\int_X f \, d\mu = \sum_{n=1}^{\infty} \int_{X_n} f \, d\mu. \qquad (17)$$

Proof We assume $f \geq 0$. The general case follows by considering the positive and negative parts of f. For each natural number n, define

$$f_n = \sum_{k=1}^{n} f \cdot \chi_{X_n} \text{ on } X.$$

The summation formula (17) now follows from the Monotone Convergence Theorem and the linearity of integration. $\square$

For a nonnegative integrable function g on X, this theorem tells us that the set function $E \mapsto \int_E g \, d\mu$ defines a finite measure on $\mathcal{M}^2$ and hence has the continuity properties possessed by measures. This observation, applied to the positive and negative parts of an integrable function, provides the proof of the following theorem.

Theorem 14 (the Continuity of Integration) *Let $(X, \mathcal{M}, \mu)$ be a measure space and the function f be integrable over X.*

(i) *If $\{X_n\}_{n=1}^{\infty}$ is an ascending countable collection of measurable subsets of X whose union is X, then*

$$\int_X f \, d\mu = \lim_{n \to \infty} \int_{X_n} f \, d\mu. \tag{18}$$

(ii) *If $\{X_n\}_{n=1}^{\infty}$ is a descending countable collection of measurable subsets of X, then*

$$\int_{\bigcap_{n=1}^{\infty} X_n} f \, d\mu = \lim_{n \to \infty} \int_{X_n} f \, d\mu. \tag{19}$$

So far the only class of integrable functions we have are simple functions that vanish outside a set of finite measure. The following theorem presents a much larger linear space of integrable functions.

Theorem 15 *Let $(X, \mathcal{M}, \mu)$ be a measure space and f a measurable function on X. If f is bounded on X and vanishes outside a set of finite measure, then f is integrable over X.*

Proof We assume $f \geq 0$ on X. The general case follows by considering the positive and negative parts of f. Let X_0 be a set of finite measure for which f vanishes on $X \sim X_0$. Choose $M \geq 0$ such that $0 \leq f \leq M$ on X. Define $\varphi = M \cdot \chi_{X_0}$. Then $0 \leq f \leq \varphi$ on X. We infer from (8) that

$$\int_X f \, d\mu \leq \int_X \varphi \, d\mu = M \cdot \mu(X_0) < \infty.$$ $\square$

Corollary 16 *Let X be a compact topological space and $\mathcal{M}$ a σ-algebra of subsets of X that contains the topology on X. If f is a continuous real-valued function on X and $(X, \mathcal{M}, \mu)$ is a finite measure space, then f is integrable over X with respect to μ.*

Proof Since f is continuous, for each open set $\mathcal{O}$ of real numbers, $f^{-1}(\mathcal{O})$ is open in X and therefore belongs to $\mathcal{M}$. Thus f is measurable. On the other hand, since X is compact, f is

---

[2]The integral over the empty-set is defined to be zero.

bounded. By assumption, $\mu(X) < \infty$. The preceding theorem tells us that f is integrable over X with respect to μ.   □

We now return to the task of establishing criteria that justify, for a sequence of integrable functions that converges pointwise to a limit function, passage of the limit under the integral sign.

The Lebesgue Dominated Convergence Theorem *Let $(X, \mathcal{M}, \mu)$ be a measure space and $\{f_n\}$ a sequence of measurable functions on X for which $\{f_n\} \to f$ pointwise a.e. on X and the function f is measurable. Assume there is a nonnegative function g that is integrable over X and dominates the sequence $\{f_n\}$ on X in the sense that*

$$|f_n| \le g \text{ a.e. on } X \text{ for all } n.$$

Then f is integrable over X and

$$\lim_{n \to \infty} \int_X f_n \, d\mu = \int_X f \, d\mu.$$

Proof For each natural number n, the nonnegative functions $g - f_n$ and $g + f_n$ are measurable. By the integral comparison test, for each n, f and f_n are integrable over X. Apply Fatou's Lemma and the linearity of integration to the two sequences of nonnegative measurable functions $\{g - f_n\}$ and $\{g + f_n\}$ in order to conclude that

$$\int_X g \, d\mu - \int_X f \, d\mu = \int_X [g - f] \, d\mu \le \liminf \int_X [g - f_n] \, d\mu = \int_X g \, d\mu - \limsup \int_X f_n \, d\mu;$$

$$\int_X g \, d\mu + \int_X f \, d\mu = \int_X [g + f] \, d\mu \le \liminf \int_X [g + f_n] \, d\mu = \int_X g \, d\mu + \liminf \int_X f_n \, d\mu;$$

Therefore

$$\limsup \int_X f_n \, d\mu \le \int_X f \, d\mu \le \liminf \int_X f_n \, d\mu.$$ □

We established the Vitali Convergence Theorem for the Lebesgue integral of a function of a single real variable, first for integrals over sets of finite Lebesgue measure (see page 94) and then for integrals over sets of infinite Lebesgue measure (see page 98). We now establish a slight variation of this theorem for general integrals.

Definition *Let $(X, \mathcal{M}, \mu)$ be a measure space and $\{f_n\}$ a sequence of functions on X, each of which is integrable over X. The sequence $\{f_n\}$ is said to be **uniformly integrable** over X provided for each $\epsilon > 0$, there is a $\delta > 0$ such that for any natural number n and measurable subset E of X,*

$$\text{if } \mu(E) < \delta, \text{ then } \int_E |f_n| \, d\mu < \epsilon. \tag{20}$$

*The sequence $\{f_n\}$ is said to be **tight** over X provided for each $\epsilon > 0$, there is a subset X_0 of X that has finite measure and, for any natural number n,*

$$\int_{X \sim X_0} |f_n| \, d\mu < \epsilon.$$

Proposition 17 *Let $(X, \mathcal{M}, \mu)$ be a measure space and the function f be integrable over X. Then for each $\epsilon > 0$, there is a $\delta > 0$ such that for any measurable subset E of X,*

$$\text{if } \mu(E) < \delta, \text{ then } \int_E |f| \, d\mu < \epsilon. \tag{21}$$

Furthermore, for each $\epsilon > 0$, there is a subset X_0 of X that has finite measure and

$$\int_{X \sim X_0} |f| \, d\mu < \epsilon. \tag{22}$$

Proof We assume $f \geq 0$ on X. The general case follows by considering the positive and negative parts of f. Let $\epsilon > 0$. Since $\int_X f \, d\mu$ is finite, by the definition of the integral of a nonnegative function, there is a simple function ψ on X for which

$$0 \leq \psi \leq f \text{ on } X \text{ and } 0 \leq \int_X f \, d\mu - \int_X \psi \, d\mu < \epsilon/2.$$

Choose $M > 0$ such that $0 \leq \psi \leq M$ on X. Therefore, by the linearity and monotonicity of integration, if $E \subseteq X$ is measurable, then

$$\int_E f \, d\mu = \int_E \psi \, d\mu + \int_E [f - \psi] \, d\mu \leq \int_E \psi \, d\mu + \epsilon/2 \leq M \cdot m(E) + \epsilon/2.$$

Thus (21) holds for $\delta = \epsilon/2M$. Since the simple function ψ is integrable over X, the measurable set $X_0 = \{x \in X \mid \psi(x) > 0\}$ has finite measure. Moreover,

$$\int_{X \sim X_0} f \, d\mu = \int_{X \sim X_0} [f - \psi] \, d\mu \leq \int_X [f - \psi] \, d\mu < \epsilon.$$

The proof is complete. $\qquad\square$

The Vitali Convergence Theorem *Let $(X, \mathcal{M}, \mu)$ be a measure space and $\{f_n\}$ a sequence of functions on X that is both uniformly integrable and tight over X. Assume $\{f_n\} \to f$ pointwise a.e. on X and the function f is integrable over X. Then*

$$\lim_{n \to \infty} \int_E f_n \, d\mu = \int_E f \, d\mu.$$

Proof Observe that for all n, $|f - f_n| \leq |f| + |f_n|$ on X. Therefore, by the integral comparison test and additivity over domains and monotonicity properties of integration, if X_0 and X_1 are measurable subsets of X for which $X_1 \subseteq X_0$, then for all n, since X is the disjoint union $X = X_1 \cup [X_0 \sim X_1] \cup [X \sim X_0]$,

$$\left| \int_X [f_n - f] \, d\mu \right| \leq \int_{X_1} |f_n - f| \, d\mu + \int_{X_0 \sim X_1} [|f_n| + |f|] \, d\mu + \int_{X \sim X_0} [|f_n| + |f|] \, d\mu. \tag{23}$$

Let $\epsilon > 0$. By the preceding proposition, the tightness of $\{f_n\}$, and the linearity of integration, there is a measurable subset X_0 of X of finite measure for which

$$\int_{X \sim X_0} [|f_n| + |f|] \, d\mu = \int_{X \sim X_0} |f_n| \, d\mu + \int_{X \sim X_0} |f| \, d\mu < \epsilon/3 \text{ for all } n. \tag{24}$$

By the preceding proposition, the uniform integrability of $\{f_n\}$, and the linearity of integration, there is a $\delta > 0$ such that for any measurable subset E of X,

$$\text{if } \mu(E) < \delta, \text{ then } \int_E [|f_n| + |f|]\,d\mu = \int_E |f_n|\,d\mu + \int_E |f|\,d\mu < \epsilon/3 \text{ for all } n. \tag{25}$$

By assumption, f is integrable over X. Therefore f is finite a.e. on X. Moreover, $\mu(X_0) < \infty$. We may therefore apply Egoroff's Theorem to infer that there is a measurable subset X_1 of X_0 for which $\mu(X_0 \sim X_1) < \delta$ and $\{f_n\}$ converge uniformly on X_1 to f. It follows from (25) that

$$\int_{X_0 \sim X_1} [|f_n| + |f|]\,d\mu < \epsilon/3 \text{ for all } n. \tag{26}$$

On the other hand, by the uniform convergence of $\{f_n\}$ to f on X_1, a set of finite measure, there is an N for which

$$\int_{X_1} |f_n - f|\,d\mu \le \sup_{x \in X_1} |f_n(x) - f(x)| \cdot \mu(X_1) < \epsilon/3 \text{ for all } n \ge N. \tag{27}$$

From the inequality (23), together with the three estimates (24), (26), and (27), we conclude that

$$\left| \int_X [f_n - f] \right| d\mu < \epsilon \text{ for all } n \ge N.$$

The proof is complete.   ☐

The Vitali Convergence Theorem for general measure spaces differs from the special case of Lebesgue measure on the real line. In the general case, we need to *assume* that the limit function f is integrable over E. The integrability of f does not follow from the uniform integrability and tightness of $\{f_n\}$ as it does in the case of Lebesgue integration on the real line (see, however, Problems 36 and 37). Indeed, let X be a set that contains a proper nonempty set E. Consider the σ-algebra $\mathcal{M} = \{\emptyset, E, X \sim E, X\}$ and define $\mu(\emptyset) = 0, \mu(E) = \mu(X \sim E) = 1/2$ and $\mu(X) = 1$. For each natural number n, define $f_n = n \cdot \chi_E - n \cdot \chi_{[X \sim E]}$. The sequence $\{f_n\}$ is uniformly integrable and tight and converges pointwise on X to the function f that takes the constant value ∞ on E and $-\infty$ on $X \sim E$. The limit function is not integrable over X with respect to μ.

We leave the proof of the following corollary as an exercise.

Corollary 18 *Let $(X, \mathcal{M}, \mu)$ be a measure space and $\{h_n\}$ a sequence of nonnegative integrable functions on X. Suppose that $\{h_n(x)\} \to 0$ for almost all x in X. Then*

$$\lim_{n \to \infty} \int_X h_n\,d\mu = 0 \text{ if and only if } \{h_n\} \text{ is uniformly integrable and tight.}$$

PROBLEMS

In the following problems, $(X, \mathcal{M}, \mu)$ is a reference measure space, measurable means with respect to $\mathcal{M}$, and integrable means with respect to μ.

27. For a set X, let $\mathcal{M}$ be the σ-algebra of all subsets of X.

   (i) Let η be the counting measure of $\mathcal{M}$. Characterize the real-valued functions f on X, which are integrable over X with respect to η and the value of $\int_X f\,d\eta$ for such functions.

(ii) Let x_0 be a member of X and δ_{x_0} the Dirac delta measure concentrated at x_0. Characterize the real-valued functions f on X, which are integrable over X with respect to δ_{x_0} and the value of $\int_X f \, d\delta_{x_0}$ for such functions.

28. Show that if f is integrable over X, then f is integrable over every measurable subset of X.

29. Let f be a measurable function on X and A and B measurable subsets of X for which $X = A \cup B$ and $A \cap B = \emptyset$. Show that f is integrable over X if and only if it is integrable over both A and B.

30. Let X be the disjoint union of the measurable sets $\{X_n\}_{n=1}^{\infty}$. For a measurable function f on X, characterize the integrability of f on X in terms of the integrability and the integral of f over the X_n's.

31. Let $(X, \mathcal{M}, \mu)$ be a measure space for which $\mu(X) = 0$ and the function f on X take the constant value ∞. Show that $\int_X f \, d\mu = 0$.

32. Let f be integrable over X with respect to μ. Show that $\int_E f \, d\mu = 0$ for every measurable subset E of X if and only if $f = 0$ a.e. on X.

33. Let $(X, \mathcal{M}, \mu)$ be a measure space and f a bounded measurable function on X that vanishes outside a set of finite measure. Show that

$$\int_X f \, d\mu = \sup \int_X \psi \, d\mu = \inf \int_X \varphi \, d\mu,$$

where ψ ranges over all simple functions on X for which $\psi \leq f$ on X and φ ranges over all simple functions on X for which $f \leq \varphi$ on X.

34. Let $(X, \mathcal{M}, \mu)$ be a measure space and f a bounded function on X that vanishes outside a set of finite measure. Assume

$$\sup \int_X \psi \, d\mu = \inf \int_X \varphi \, d\mu,$$

where ψ ranges over all simple functions on X for which $\psi \leq f$ on X and φ ranges over all simple functions on X for which $f \leq \varphi$ on X. Prove that f is measurable with respect to the completion of $(X, \mathcal{M}, \mu)$.

35. Prove the linearity property of integration for general coefficients α and β.

36. Let $\{f_n\}$ be a sequence of integrable functions on X that is uniformly integrable and tight. Suppose that $\{f_n\} \to f$ pointwise a.e. on X and f is measurable and finite a.e. on X. Prove that f is integrable over X.

37. Let $\{f_n\}$ be a sequence of integrable functions on X that is uniformly integrable. Suppose that $\{f_n\} \to f$ pointwise a.e. on X and f is measurable. Assume the measure space has the property that for each $\epsilon > 0$, X is the union of a finite collection of measurable sets, each of measure at most ϵ. Prove that f is integrable over X.

38. Prove Corollary 18.

39. Deduce the Lebesgue Dominated Convergence Theorem from the Vitali Convergence Theorem.

40. Show that almost everywhere convergence can be replaced by convergence in measure in the Lebesgue Dominated Convergence Theorem and the Vitali Convergence Theorem (see Problem 15 for the definition of convergence in measure).

41. Let $\{f_n\}$ be a sequence of functions on X, each of which is integrable over X. Show that $\{f_n\}$ is uniformly integrable if and only if for each $\epsilon > 0$, there is a $\delta > 0$ such that for any natural number n and measurable subset E of X,

$$\text{if } \mu(E) < \delta, \text{ then } \left| \int_E f_n \, d\mu \right| < \epsilon.$$

42. Let η be another measure on $\mathcal{M}$. For an extended real-valued function f on X that is measurable with respect to the measurable space $(X, \mathcal{M})$, under what conditions is it true that

$$\int_X f \, d[\mu + \eta] = \int_X f \, d\mu + \int_X f \, d\eta.$$

43. Let $\mathcal{M}_0$ be a σ-algebra that is contained in $\mathcal{M}$, μ_0 the restriction of μ to $\mathcal{M}_0$, and f a nonnegative function that is measurable with respect to $\mathcal{M}_0$. Show that f is measurable with respect to $\mathcal{M}$ and

$$\int_X f \, d\mu_0 \le \int_X f \, d\mu.$$

Can this inequality be strict?

44. Let ν be a signed measure on $(X, \mathcal{M})$. We define integration over X with respect to a signed measure ν by defining

$$\int_X f \, d\nu = \int_X f \, d\nu^+ - \int_X f \, d\nu^-,$$

provided f is integrable over X with respect to both ν^+ and ν^-. Show that if $|f| \le M$ on X, then

$$\left| \int_X f \, d\nu \right| \le M |\nu|(X).$$

Moreover, if $|\nu|(X) < \infty$, show that there is a measurable function f with $|f| \le 1$ on X for which

$$\int_X f \, d\nu = |\nu|(X).$$

45. Let g be a nonnegative function that is integrable over X. Define

$$\nu(E) = \int_E g \, d\mu \text{ for all } E \in \mathcal{M}.$$

(i) Show that ν is a measure on the measurable space $(X, \mathcal{M})$.

(ii) Let f be a nonnegative function on X that is measurable with respect to $\mathcal{M}$. Show that

$$\int_X f \, d\nu = \int_X fg \, d\mu.$$

(Hint: First establish this for the case when f is simple and then use the Simple Approximation Lemma and the Monotone Convergence Theorem.)

46. Let $\nu\colon \mathcal{M} \to [0, \infty)$ be a finitely additive set function. Show that if f is a bounded measurable function on X, then the integral of f over X with respect to ν, $\int_X f \, d\nu$, can be defined so that $\int_X \chi_E \, d\nu = \nu(E)$, if E is measurable and integration is linear, monotone, and additive over domains for bounded measurable functions.

47. Let μ be a finite premeasure on an algebra S and $\bar{\mu}$ its Carathéodory extension. Let E be μ^*-measurable. Show that for each $\epsilon > 0$, given there is an $A \in S$ with

$$\bar{\mu}([A \sim E] \cup [E \sim A]) < \epsilon.$$

48. Let S be an algebra of subsets of a set X. We say that a function $\varphi\colon X \to \mathbf{R}$ is S-simple provided $\varphi = \sum_{k=1}^{n} a_k \chi_{A_k}$, where each $A_k \in S$. Let μ be a premeasure on S and $\bar{\mu}$ its Carathéodory extension. Given $\epsilon > 0$ and a function f that is integrable over X with respect to $\bar{\mu}$, show that there is an S-simple function φ such that

$$\int_X |f - \varphi| \, d\bar{\mu} < \epsilon.$$

18.4   THE RADON-NIKODYM THEOREM

Let $(X, \mathcal{M})$ be a measurable space. For μ a measure on $(X, \mathcal{M})$ and f a nonnegative function on X that is measurable with respect to $\mathcal{M}$, define the set function ν on $\mathcal{M}$ by

$$\nu(E) = \int_E f \, d\mu \text{ for all } E \in \mathcal{M}. \tag{28}$$

We infer from the linearity of integration and the Monotone Convergence Theorem that ν is a measure on the measurable space $(X, \mathcal{M})$, and it has the property that

$$\text{if } E \in \mathcal{M} \text{ and } \mu(E) = 0, \text{ then } \nu(E) = 0. \tag{29}$$

The theorem named in the title of this section asserts that if μ is σ-finite, then every σ-finite measure ν on $(X, \mathcal{M})$ that possesses property (29) is given by (28) for some nonnegative function f on X that is measurable with respect to $\mathcal{M}$. A measure ν is said to be **absolutely continuous** with respect to the measure μ provided (29) holds. We use the symbolism $\nu \ll \mu$ for ν absolutely continuous with respect to μ. The following proposition recasts absolute continuity in the form of a familiar continuity criterion.

Proposition 19 *Let $(X, \mathcal{M}, \mu)$ be a measure space and ν a finite measure on the measurable space $(X, \mathcal{M})$. Then ν is absolutely continuous with respect to μ if and only if for each $\epsilon > 0$, there is a $\delta > 0$ such that for any set $E \in \mathcal{M}$,*

$$\text{if } \mu(E) < \delta, \text{ then } \nu(E) < \epsilon. \tag{30}$$

Proof It is clear that the ϵ–δ criterion (30) implies that ν is absolutely continuous with respect to μ, independently of the finiteness of ν. To prove the converse, we argue by contradiction. Suppose ν is absolutely continuous with respect to μ but the ϵ–δ criterion (30) fails. Then there is an $\epsilon_0 > 0$ and a sequence of sets in $\mathcal{M}$, $\{E_n\}$, such that for each n, $\mu(E_n) < 1/2^n$ while $\nu(E_n) \geq \epsilon_0$. For each n, define $A_n = \bigcup_{k=n}^{\infty} E_k$. Then $\{A_n\}$ is a descending sequence of sets in $\mathcal{M}$. By the monotonicity of ν and the countable subadditivity of μ,

$$\nu(A_n) \geq \epsilon_0 \text{ and } \mu(A_n) \leq 1/2^{n-1} \text{ for all } n.$$

Define $A_\infty = \bigcap_{k=1}^\infty A_n$. By the monotonicity of the measure μ, $\mu(A_\infty) = 0$. We infer from the continuity of the measure ν that, since $\nu(A_1) \le \nu(X) < \infty$ and $\nu(A_n) \ge \epsilon_0$ for all n, $\nu(A_\infty) \ge \epsilon_0$. This contradicts the absolute continuity of ν with respect to μ. $\qquad\square$

The Radon-Nikodym Theorem *Let $(X, \mathcal{M}, \mu)$ be a σ-finite measure space and ν a σ-finite measure defined on the measurable space $(X, \mathcal{M})$ that is absolutely continuous with respect to μ. Then there is a nonnegative function f on X that is measurable with respect to $\mathcal{M}$ for which*

$$\nu(E) = \int_E f \, d\mu \text{ for all } E \in \mathcal{M}. \tag{31}$$

The function f is unique in the sense that if g is any nonnegative measurable function on X that also has this property, then $g = f$ a.e. $[\mu]$.

Proof We assume that both μ and ν are finite measures and leave the extension to the σ-finite case as an exercise. If $\nu(E) = 0$, for all $E \in \mathcal{M}$, then (31) holds for $f \equiv 0$ on X. So assume ν does not vanish on all of $\mathcal{M}$. We first prove that there is a nonnegative measurable function f on X for which

$$\int_X f \, d\mu > 0 \text{ and } \int_E f \, d\mu \le \nu(E) \text{ for all } E \in \mathcal{M}. \tag{32}$$

For $\lambda > 0$, consider the finite signed measure $\nu - \lambda\mu$. According to the Hahn Decomposition Theorem, there is a Hahn decomposition $\{P_\lambda, N_\lambda\}$ for $\nu - \lambda\mu$, that is, $X = P_\lambda \cup N_\lambda$ and $P_\lambda \cap N_\lambda = \emptyset$, where P_λ is a positive set and N_λ is a negative set for $\nu - \lambda\mu$. We claim that there is some $\lambda > 0$ for which $\mu(P_\lambda) > 0$. Assume otherwise. Let $\lambda > 0$. Then $\mu(P_\lambda) = 0$. Therefore $\mu(E) = 0$ and hence, by absolute continuity, $\nu(E) = 0$, for all measurable subsets of P_λ. Since N_λ is a negative set for $\nu - \lambda\mu$,

$$\nu(E) \le \lambda\mu(E) \text{ for all } E \in \mathcal{M} \text{ and all } \lambda > 0. \tag{33}$$

We infer from these inequalities that $\nu(E) = 0$ if $\mu(E) > 0$ and of course, by absolute continuity, $\nu(E) = 0$ if $\mu(E) = 0$. Since $\mu(X) < \infty$, $\nu(E) = 0$ for all $E \in \mathcal{M}$. This is a contradiction. Therefore we may select $\lambda_0 > 0$ for which $\mu(P_{\lambda_0}) > 0$. Define f to be λ_0 times the characteristic function of P_{λ_0}. Observe that $\int_X f \, d\mu > 0$ and, since $\nu - \lambda_0\mu$ is positive on P_{λ_0},

$$\int_E f \, d\mu = \lambda_0\mu(P_{\lambda_0} \cap E) \le \nu(P_{\lambda_0} \cap E) \le \nu(E) \text{ for all } E \in \mathcal{M}.$$

Therefore (32) holds for this choice of f. Define $\mathcal{F}$ to be the collection of nonnegative measurable functions on X for which

$$\int_E f \, d\mu \le \nu(E) \text{ for all } E \in \mathcal{M},$$

and then define

$$M = \sup_{f \in \mathcal{F}} \int_X f \, d\mu. \tag{34}$$

We show that there is an $f \in \mathcal{F}$ for which $\int_X f \, d\mu = M$ and (31) holds for any such f. If g and h belong to $\mathcal{F}$, then so does $\max\{g, h\}$. Indeed, for any measurable set E, decompose

E into the disjoint union of $E_1 = \{x \in E \mid g(x) < h(x)\}$ and $E_2 = \{x \in E \mid g(x) \geq h(x)\}$ and observe that

$$\int_E \max\{g, h\} \, d\mu = \int_{E_1} h \, d\mu + \int_{E_2} g \, d\mu \leq \nu(E_1) + \nu(E_2) = \nu(E).$$

Select a sequence $\{f_n\}$ in $\mathcal{F}$ for which $\lim_{n \to \infty} \int_X f_n \, d\mu = M$. We assume $\{f_n\}$ is pointwise increasing on X, for otherwise, replace each f_n by $\max\{f_1, \ldots, f_n\}$. Define $f(x) = \lim_{n \to \infty} f_n(x)$ for each $x \in X$. We infer from the Monotone Convergence Theorem that $\int_X f \, d\mu = M$ and also that f belongs to $\mathcal{F}$. Define

$$\eta(E) = \nu(E) - \int_E f \, d\mu \text{ for all } E \in \mathcal{M}. \tag{35}$$

By assumption, $\nu(X) < \infty$. Therefore $\int_X f \, d\mu \leq \nu(X) < \infty$, and hence, by the countable additivity of integration, η is a signed measure. It is a measure since f belongs to $\mathcal{F}$, and it is absolutely continuous with respect to μ. We claim that $\eta = 0$ on $\mathcal{M}$ and hence (31) holds for this choice of f. Indeed, otherwise, we argue as we just did, with ν now replaced by η, to conclude that there is a nonnegative measurable function $\hat{f}$ for which

$$\int_X \hat{f} \, d\mu > 0 \text{ and } \int_E \hat{f} \, d\mu \leq \eta(E) = \nu(E) - \int_E f \, d\mu \text{ for all } E \in \mathcal{M}. \tag{36}$$

Therefore $f + \hat{f}$ belongs to $\mathcal{F}$ and $\int_X [f + \hat{f}] \, d\mu > \int_X f \, d\mu = M$, a contradiction of the choice of f. It remains to establish uniqueness. But if there were two, necessarily integrable, functions f_1 and f_2 for which (31) holds, then, by the linearity of integration,

$$\int_E [f_1 - f_2] \, d\mu = 0 \text{ for all } E \in \mathcal{M}.$$

Therefore $f_1 = f_2$ a.e. $[\mu]$ on X.   □

In Problem 59 we outline another proof of the Radon-Nikodym Theorem due to John von Neumann: it relies on the Riesz-Fréchet Representation Theorem for the dual of a Hilbert space.

Example The assumption of σ-finiteness is necessary in the Radon-Nikodym Theorem. Indeed, consider the measurable space $(X, \mathcal{M})$, where $X = [0, 1]$ and $\mathcal{M}$ is the collection of Lebesgue measurable subsets of $[0, 1]$. Define μ to be the counting measure on $\mathcal{M}$, so $\mu(E)$ is the number of points in E if E is finite, and otherwise $\mu(E) = \infty$. The only set of μ measure zero is the empty-set. Thus every measure on $\mathcal{M}$ is absolutely continuous with respect to μ. Define m to be Lebesgue measure on $\mathcal{M}$. We leave it as an exercise to show that there is no nonnegative Lebesgue measurable function f on X for which

$$m(E) = \int_E f \, d\mu \text{ for all } E \in \mathcal{M}.$$

Recall that for a measurable space $(X, \mathcal{M})$ and signed measure ν on $\mathcal{M}$, there is the Jordan decomposition $\nu = \nu_1 - \nu_2$, where ν_1 and ν_2 are measures on $\mathcal{M}$, one of which is finite:

We define the measure $|\nu|$ to be $\nu_1 + \nu_2$. If μ is a measure on $\mathcal{M}$, the signed measure ν is said to be absolutely continuous with respect to μ provided $|\nu|$ is absolutely continuous with respect to μ, which is equivalent to the absolute continuity of both ν_1 and ν_2 with respect to μ. From this decomposition of signed measures and the Radon-Nikodym Theorem, we have the following version of this same theorem for finite signed measures.

Corollary 20 *Let $(X, \mathcal{M}, \mu)$ be a σ-finite measure space and ν a finite signed measure on the measurable space $(X, \mathcal{M})$ that is absolutely continuous with respect to μ. Then there is a function f that is integrable over X with respect to μ and*

$$\nu(E) = \int_E f \, d\mu \text{ for all } E \in \mathcal{M}.$$

   Recall that given two measures μ and ν on a measurable space $(X, \mathcal{M})$, we say that μ and ν are **mutually singular** (and write $\mu \perp \nu$) provided there are disjoint sets A and B in $\mathcal{M}$ for which $X = A \cup B$ and $\nu(A) = \mu(B) = 0$.

The Lebesgue Decomposition Theorem *Let $(X, \mathcal{M}, \mu)$ be a σ-finite measure space and ν a σ-finite measure on the measurable space $(X, \mathcal{M})$. Then there is a measure ν_0 on $\mathcal{M}$, singular with respect to μ, and a measure ν_1 on $\mathcal{M}$, absolutely continuous with respect to μ, for which $\nu = \nu_0 + \nu_1$. The measures ν_0 and ν_1 are unique.*

Proof Define $\lambda = \mu + \nu$. We leave it as an exercise to show that if g is nonnegative and measurable with respect to $\mathcal{M}$, then

$$\int_E g \, d\lambda = \int_E g \, d\mu + \int_E g \, d\nu \text{ for all } E \in \mathcal{M}.$$

Since μ and ν are σ-finite measures, so is the measure λ. Moreover, μ is absolutely continuous with respect to λ. The Radon-Nikodym Theorem tells us that there is a nonnegative measurable function f for which

$$\mu(E) = \int_E f \, d\lambda = \int_E f \, d\mu + \int_E f \, d\nu \text{ for all } E \in \mathcal{M}. \tag{37}$$

Define $X_+ = \{x \in X \mid f(x) > 0\}$ and $X_0 = \{x \in X \mid f(x) = 0\}$. Since f is a measurable function, $X = X_0 \cup X_+$ is a disjoint decomposition of X into measurable sets and thus $\nu = \nu_0 + \nu_1$ is the expression of ν as the sum of mutually singular measures, where

$$\nu_0(E) = \nu(E \cap X_0) \text{ and } \nu_1(E) = \nu(E \cap X_+) \text{ for all } E \in \mathcal{M}.$$

Now $\mu(X_0) = \int_{X_0} f \, d\lambda = 0$, since $f = 0$ on X_0, and $\nu_0(X_+) = \nu(X_+ \cap X_0) = \nu(\emptyset) = 0$. Thus μ and ν_0 are mutually singular. It remains only to show that ν_1 is absolutely continuous with respect to μ. Indeed, let $\mu(E) = 0$. We must show $\nu_1(E) = 0$. However, since $\mu(E) = 0$, $\int_E f \, d\mu = 0$. Therefore, by (37) and the additivity of integration over domains,

$$\int_E f \, d\nu = \int_{E \cap X_0} f \, d\nu + \int_{E \cap X_+} f \, d\nu = 0.$$

But $f = 0$ on $E \cap X_0$ and $f > 0$ on $E \cap X_0$ and thus $\nu(E \cap X_+) = 0$, that is, $\nu_1(E) = 0$. $\square$

A few words are in order regarding the relationship between the concept of absolute continuity of one measure with respect to another and their integral representation and the representation of an absolutely continuous function as the indefinite integral of its derivative, which we established in Chapter 6. Let $[a, b]$ be a closed, bounded interval and the real-valued function h on $[a, b]$ be absolutely continuous. According to Theorem 10 of Chapter 6,

$$h(d) - h(c) = \int_c^d h' \, d\mu \text{ for all } [c, d] \subseteq [a, b]. \tag{38}$$

We claim that this is sufficient to establish the Radon-Nikodym Theorem in the case $X = [a, b]$, $\mathcal{M}$ is the σ-algebra of Borel subsets on $[a, b]$ and μ is Lebesgue measure on $\mathcal{M}$. Indeed, let ν be a finite measure on the measurable space $([a, b], \mathcal{M})$ that is absolutely continuous with respect to Lebesgue measure. Define the function h on $[a, b]$ by

$$h(x) = \nu([a, x]) \text{ for all } x \in [a, b]. \tag{39}$$

The function h is called the cumulative distribution function associated with ν. The function h inherits absolute continuity from the absolute continuity of the measure ν. Therefore, by (38),

$$\nu(E) = \int_E h' \, d\mu \text{ for all } E = [c, d] \subseteq [a, b].$$

However, we infer from Corollary 14 of the preceding chapter that two σ-finite measures that agree on closed, bounded subintervals of $[a, b]$ agree on the smallest σ-algebra containing these intervals, namely, the Borel sets contained in $[a, b]$. Therefore

$$\nu(E) = \int_E h' \, d\mu \text{ for all } E \in \mathcal{M}.$$

The Radon-Nikodym Theorem is a far-reaching generalization of the representation of absolutely continuous functions as indefinite integrals of their derivatives. The function f for which (31) holds is called the **Radon-Nikodym derivative** of ν with respect to μ. It is often denoted by $\frac{d\nu}{d\mu}$.

PROBLEMS

49. Show that the Radon-Nikodym Theorem for finite measures μ and ν implies the theorem for σ-finite measures μ and ν.

50. Establish the uniqueness of the function f in the Radon-Nikodym Theorem.

51. Let $[a, b]$ be a closed, bounded interval and the function f be of bounded variation on $[a, b]$. Show that there is an absolutely continuous function g on $[a, b]$, and a function h on $[a, b]$ that is of bounded variation and has $h' = 0$ a.e. on $[a, b]$, for which $f = g + h$ on $[a, b]$. Then show that this decomposition is unique except for addition of constants.

52. Let $(X, \mathcal{M}, \mu)$ be a finite measure space, $\{E_k\}_{k=1}^n$ a collection of measurable sets, and $\{c_k\}_{k=1}^n$ a collection of real numbers. For $E \in \mathcal{M}$, define

$$\nu(E) = \sum_{k=1}^n c_k \cdot \mu(E \cap E_k).$$

Show that ν is absolutely continuous with respect to μ and find its Radon-Nikodym derivative $\frac{d\mu}{d\nu}$.

53. Let $(X, \mathcal{M}, \mu)$ be a measure space and f a nonnegative function that is integrable over X with respect to μ. Find the Lebesgue decomposition with respect to μ of the measure ν defined by $\nu(E) = \int_E f \, d\mu$ for $E \in \mathcal{M}$.

54. Let μ, ν, and λ be σ-finite measures on the measurable space $(X, \mathcal{M})$.

   (i) If $\nu \ll \mu$ and f is a nonnegative function on X that is measurable with respect to $\mathcal{M}$, show that

   $$\int_X f \, d\nu = \int_X f \left[\frac{d\nu}{d\mu} \right] d\mu.$$

   (ii) If $\nu \ll \mu$ and $\lambda \ll \mu$, show that

   $$\frac{d(\nu + \lambda)}{d\mu} = \frac{d\nu}{d\mu} + \frac{d\lambda}{d\mu} \text{ a.e. } [\mu].$$

   (iii) If $\nu \ll \mu \ll \lambda$, show that

   $$\frac{d\nu}{d\lambda} = \frac{d\nu}{d\mu} \cdot \frac{d\mu}{d\lambda} \text{ a.e. } [\lambda].$$

   (iv) If $\nu \ll \mu$ and $\mu \ll \nu$, show that

   $$\frac{d\nu}{d\mu} \cdot \frac{d\mu}{d\nu} = 1 \text{ a.e. } [\mu].$$

55. Let μ, ν, ν_1, and ν_2 be measures on the measurable space $(X, \mathcal{M})$.

   (i) Show that if $\nu \perp \mu$ and $\nu \ll \mu$, then $\nu = 0$.

   (ii) Show that if ν_1 and ν_2 are singular with respect to μ, then, for any $\alpha \geq 0, \beta \geq 0$, so is the measure $\alpha\nu_1 + \beta\nu_2$.

   (iii) Show that if ν_1 and ν_2 are absolutely continuous with respect to μ, then, for any $\alpha \geq 0, \beta \geq 0$, so is the measure $\alpha\nu_1 + \beta\nu_2$.

   (iv) Prove the uniqueness assertion in the Lebesgue decomposition.

56. Characterize the measure spaces $(X, \mathcal{M}, \mu)$ for which the counting measure on $\mathcal{M}$ is absolutely continuous with respect to μ and those for which, given $x_0 \in X$, the Dirac measure δ_{x_0} on $\mathcal{M}$ is absolutely continuous with respect to μ.

57. Let $\{\mu_n\}$ be a sequence of measures on a measurable space $(X, \mathcal{M})$ for which there is a constant $c > 0$ such that $\mu_n(X) \leq c$ for all n. Define $\mu: \mathcal{M} \to [0, \infty]$ by

   $$\mu = \sum_{n=1}^{\infty} \frac{\mu_n}{2^n}.$$

   Show that μ is a measure on $\mathcal{M}$ and that each μ_n is absolutely continuous with respect to μ.

58. Let μ and ν be measures on the measurable space $(X, \mathcal{M})$ and define $\lambda = \mu + \nu$. Let the nonnegative function f on X be measurable with respect to $(X, \mathcal{M})$. Show that f is integrable over X with respect to λ if and only if it is integrable over X with respect to both μ and ν. Also show that if f is integrable over X with respect to λ, then

   $$\int_E g \, d\lambda = \int_E g \, d\mu + \int_E g \, d\nu \text{ for all } E \in \mathcal{M}.$$

59. (von Neumann's proof of the Radon-Nikodym Theorem) The basis of this proof is the following assertion, which is a corollary of the Riesz-Fréchet Representation Theorem for the dual of a Hilbert space: For a measure space $(X, \mathcal{M}, \lambda)$, let $L^2(X, \lambda)$ be the collection of measurable functions f on X such that f^2 is integrable over X with respect to λ. Suppose that the functional $\psi: L^2(X, \lambda) \rightarrow \mathbf{R}$ is linear, and bounded in the sense that there is some $c > 0$ such that

$$|\psi(f)|^2 \le c \cdot \int_X f^2 \, d\lambda \text{ for all } f \in L^2(X, \lambda).$$

Then there is a function $g \in L^2(X, \lambda)$ such that

$$\psi(f) = \int_X f \cdot g \, d\lambda \text{ for all } f \in L^2(X, \lambda).$$

Assuming this representation result, verify the following steps in another proof of the Radon-Nikodym Theorem, where μ and ν are finite measures on a measurable space $(X, \mathcal{M})$ and ν is absolutely continuous with respect to μ.

(i) Define the measure $\lambda = \mu + \nu$ on the measurable space $(X, \mathcal{M})$ and the functional ψ on $L^2(X, \lambda)$ by

$$\psi(f) = \int_X f \, d\mu \text{ for all } f \in L^2(X, \lambda).$$

Show that ψ is a bounded linear functional on $L^2(X, \lambda)$.

(ii) By the above representation result, choose a function $g \in L^2(X, \lambda)$ such that

$$\int_X f \, d\mu = \int_X f \cdot g \, d\lambda \text{ for all } f \in L^2(X, \lambda).$$

Conclude that

$$\int_X f \, d\mu = \int_X f \cdot g \, d\mu + \int_X f \cdot g \, d\nu \text{ for all } f \in L^2(X, \lambda),$$

and therefore

$$\mu(E) = \int_E g \, d\mu + \int_E g \, d\nu \text{ for all } E \in \mathcal{M}.$$

From this last identity conclude that $g > 0$ a.e. $[\lambda]$ on X and then use the absolute continuity of ν with respect to μ to conclude that $\lambda\{x \in X \mid g(x) = 0\} = 0$.

(iii) Use part (ii) to assume, without loss of generality, that $g > 0$ on X. Fix a natural number n and $E \in \mathcal{M}$ and define $f = \chi_E / [g + 1/n]$ on X. Show that f belongs to $L^2(X, \lambda)$. Conclude that

$$\int_E \frac{1}{g + 1/n} \, d\mu = \int_E \frac{1}{g + 1/n} \cdot g \, d\mu + \int_E \frac{1}{g + 1/n} \cdot g \, d\nu \text{ for all } n.$$

Justify taking limits as $n \to \infty$ on each side of this equality and conclude that

$$\nu(E) = \int_E [1/g - 1] \, d\mu \text{ for all } E \in \mathcal{M}.$$

60. Let $X = [0, 1]$, $\mathcal{M}$ the collection of Lebesgue measurable subsets of $[0, 1]$, and take ν to be Lebesgue measure and μ the counting measure of $\mathcal{M}$. Show that ν is finite and absolutely continuous with respect to μ, but there is no function f for which $\nu(E) = \int_E d\mu$ for all $E \in \mathcal{M}$.

18.5   THE NIKODYM METRIC SPACE: THE VITALI–HAHN–SAKS THEOREM

Let $(X, \mathcal{M}, \mu)$ be a finite measure space. Recall that the symmetric difference of two measurable sets A and B is the measurable set $A \Delta B$ defined by

$$A \Delta B = [A \sim B] \cup [B \sim A].$$

We leave the proof of the following set identity as an exercise:

$$(A \Delta B) \Delta (B \Delta C) = A \Delta C. \tag{40}$$

We introduce a relation $\simeq$ on $\mathcal{M}$ by defining $A \simeq B$ provided $\mu(A \Delta B) = 0$. The above identity implies that this relation is transitive, and it clearly is reflexive and symmetric. Therefore the equivalence relation $\simeq$ induces a decomposition of $\mathcal{M}$ into equivalence classes; denote this collection by $\mathcal{M}/_{\simeq}$. For $A \in \mathcal{M}$, denote the equivalence class of A by $[A]$. On $\mathcal{M}/_{\simeq}$, define the Nikodym metric ρ_μ by

$$\rho_\mu([A], [B]) = \mu(A \Delta B) \text{ for all } A, B \in \mathcal{M}.$$

We infer from the identity (40) that ρ_μ is properly defined and the triangle inequality holds; the remaining two properties of a metric are evident. We call $(\mathcal{M}/_{\simeq}, \rho_\mu)$ the **Nikodym metric space** associated with the measure space $(X, \mathcal{M}, \mu)$. Now let ν be a finite measure on $\mathcal{M}$ that is absolutely continuous with respect to μ. For $A, B \in \mathcal{M}$ with $A \simeq B$, since $\mu(A \Delta B) = 0$, $\nu(A \Delta B) = 0$, and hence

$$\nu(A) - \nu(B) = [\nu(A \cap B) + \nu(A \sim B)] - [\nu(A \cap B) + \nu(B \sim A)] = \nu(A \sim B) - \nu(B \sim A) = 0.$$

We may therefore properly define ν on $\mathcal{M}/_{\simeq}$ by setting

$$\nu([A]) = \nu(A) \text{ for all } A \in \mathcal{M}.$$

As we did with the L^p spaces, for convenience and simplicity, we denote members $[A]$ of $\mathcal{M}/_{\simeq}$ by A, and functions $\nu \colon \mathcal{M}/_{\simeq} \to [0, \infty)$ by $\nu \colon \mathcal{M} \to [0, \infty)$. A consequence of the Baire Category Theorem (Theorem 7 of Chapter 10) tells us that if a sequence of real-valued functions on a complete metric space converges pointwise to a real-valued function, then there is a point in the space at which the sequence is equicontinuous. To employ this result in the study of sequences of absolutely continuous measures, we now show that $\mathcal{M}/_{\simeq}$ is complete and that a measure on $\mathcal{M}$ that is absolutely continuous with respect to μ induces a uniformly continuous function on the Nikodym metric space $(\mathcal{M}/_{\simeq}, \rho_\mu)$.

In Chapter 7, we normed the linear space of Lebesgue measurable functions on a Lebesgue measurable set of real numbers, denoted it by L^1, and established the Riesz-Fischer Theorem which told us that L^1 is complete and every convergent sequence in L^1 had a subsequence that converges pointwise a.e. In the first section of the next chapter, for a general measure space $(X, \mathcal{M}, \mu)$, we define $L^1(X, \mu)$ in the obvious manner and prove the Riesz-Fischer Theorem in general.

Theorem 21 *Let $(X, \mathcal{M}, \mu)$ be a finite measure space. Then the Nikodym metric space $(\mathcal{M}, \rho_\mu)$ is complete, that is, every Cauchy sequence converges.*

Proof Observe that for $A, B \in \mathcal{M}$,

$$\mu(A \Delta B) = \int_X |\chi_A - \chi_B| \, d\mu. \tag{41}$$

Define the operator $T: \mathcal{M} \to L^1(X, \mu)$ by $T(E) = \chi_E$. Then (41) is the assertion that the operator T is an isometry, that is,

$$\rho_\mu(A, B) = \|T(A) - T(B)\|_1 \text{ for all } A, B \in \mathcal{M}. \tag{42}$$

Let $\{A_n\}$ be a Cauchy sequence in $(\mathcal{M}, \rho_\mu)$. Then $\{T(A_n)\}$ is a Cauchy sequence in $L^1(X, \mu)$. The Riesz-Fischer Theorem tells us that there is a function $f \in L^1(X, \mu)$ such that $\{T(A_n)\} \to f$ in $L^1(X, \mu)$ and a subsequence of $\{T(A_n)\}$ that converges pointwise to f almost everywhere on X. Since each $T(A_n)$ takes the values 0 and 1, if we define A_0 to be the points in X at which the pointwise convergent subsequence converges to 1, then $f = \chi_{A_0}$ almost everywhere on X. Therefore, by (41), $\{A_n\} \to A_0$ in $(\mathcal{M}, \rho_\mu)$. The proof is complete. $\qquad \square$

Lemma 22 *Let $(X, \mathcal{M}, \mu)$ be a finite measure space and ν a finite measure on $\mathcal{M}$. Let E_0 be a measurable set and $\epsilon > 0$ and $\delta > 0$ be such that for any measurable set E,*

$$\text{if } \rho_\mu(E, E_0) < \delta, \text{ then } |\nu(E) - \nu(E_0)| < \epsilon/4. \tag{43}$$

Then for any measurable sets A and B,

$$\text{if } \rho_\mu(A, B) < \delta, \text{ then } |\nu(A) - \nu(B)| < \epsilon. \tag{44}$$

Proof We first verify that

$$\text{if } \rho_\mu(A, \emptyset) < \delta, \text{ then } \nu(A) < \epsilon/2. \tag{45}$$

Observe that if $D \subseteq C$, then $C \Delta D = C \sim D$. Let A belong to $\mathcal{M}$ and $\rho(A, \emptyset) = \mu(A) < \delta$. Observe that

$$[E_0 \sim A] \Delta E_0 = E_0 \sim [E_0 \sim A] = E_0 \cap A \subseteq A.$$

Hence $\rho_\mu(E_0 \sim A, E_0) = \mu([E_0 \sim A] \Delta E_0) \leq \mu(A) < \delta$, and therefore, by assumption (43),

$$\nu(E_0) - \nu(E_0 \sim A) < \epsilon/4.$$

We infer from the excision property of ν that

$$\nu(A \cap E_0) = \nu(E_0) - \nu(E_0 \sim A) < \epsilon/4.$$

Now observe that

$$E_0 \Delta [E_0 \cup [A \sim E_0]] = [E_0 \cup [A \sim E_0]] \sim E_0 = A \sim E_0 \subseteq A.$$

Thus, arguing as above,

$$\nu(A \sim E_0) = \nu(E_0 \cup [A \sim E_0]) - \nu(E_0) < \epsilon/4.$$

Therefore

$$\nu(A) = \nu(A \cap E_0) + \nu(A \sim E_0) < \epsilon/2,$$

and so (45) is verified.

But for any two measurable sets, since ν is real-valued and finitely additive,

$$\nu(A) - \nu(B) = [\nu(A \sim B) + \nu(A \cap B)] - [\nu(B \sim A) + \nu(A \cap B)] = \nu(A \sim B) - \nu(B \sim A).$$

Therefore (45) implies (44).   □

Proposition 19 tells us that a finite measure ν on $\mathcal{M}$ is absolutely continuous with respect to μ if and only if each $\epsilon > 0$, there is a $\delta > 0$ such that if $\mu(E) < \delta$, then $\nu(E) < \epsilon$. This means that if ν is finite, then ν is absolutely continuous with respect to μ if and only if the set function ν is continuous with respect to the Nikodym metric at $\emptyset$. However, we infer from the preceding lemma that if a finite measure ν on $\mathcal{M}$ is continuous, with respect to the Nikodym metric at one set E_0 in $\mathcal{M}$, then it is uniformly continuous on $\mathcal{M}$. We therefore have established the following proposition.

Proposition 23 *Let $(X, \mathcal{M}, \mu)$ be a finite measure space and ν a finite measure on $\mathcal{M}$ that is absolutely continuous with respect to μ. Then ν induces a properly defined, uniformly continuous function on the Nikodym metric space associated with $(X, \mathcal{M}, \mu)$.*

Definition *Let $(X, \mathcal{M})$ be a measurable space. A sequence $\{\nu_n\}$ of measures on $\mathcal{M}$ is said to* **converge setwise** *on $\mathcal{M}$ to the set function ν provided*

$$\nu(E) = \lim_{n \to \infty} \nu_n(E) \text{ for all } E \in \mathcal{M}.$$

Definition *Let $(X, \mathcal{M}, \mu)$ be a finite measure space. A sequence $\{\nu_n\}$ of finite measures on $\mathcal{M}$, each of which is absolutely continuous with respect to μ, is said to be* **uniformly absolutely continuous**[3] *with respect to μ provided for each $\epsilon > 0$, there is a $\delta > 0$ such that for any measurable set E and any natural number n,*

$$\text{if } \mu(E) < \delta, \text{ then } \nu_n(E) < \epsilon.$$

It is not difficult to see, using Lemma 22, that a sequence of finite measures $\{\nu_n\}$ of $\mathcal{M}$ is uniformly absolutely continuous with respect to μ if and only if the sequence of functions $\{\nu_n : \mathcal{M} \to \mathbf{R}\}$ is equicontinuous[4] with respect to the Nikodym metric ρ_μ. Moreover, for each natural number n, the Radon-Nikodym Theorem tells us that there is a nonnegative integrable function f_n, the Radon-Nikodym derivative of μ with respect to ν_n, for which

$$\nu_n(E) = \int_E f_n \, d\mu \text{ for all } E \in \mathcal{M}$$

---

[3] What we here call "uniformly absolutely continuous" might also be called equi absolutely continuous. There is no standard terminology.

[4] Recall that a sequence of functions $\{h_n : S \to \mathbf{R}\}$ on the metric space (S, ρ) is said to be equicontinuous at a point $u \in S$ provided that for each $\epsilon > 0$, there is a $\delta > 0$ such that for $v \in S$ and natural number n, if $\rho(u, v) < \delta$, then $|h_n(u) - h_n(v)| < \epsilon$. The sequence $\{h_n : S \to \mathbf{R}\}$ is said to be equicontinuous provided it is equicontinuous at each point in S.

It is clear that the sequence of functions $\{f_n\}$ is uniformly integrable over X with respect to μ if and only if the sequence of measures $\{\nu_n\}$ is uniformly absolutely continuous with respect to μ. We therefore have the following proposition.

Proposition 24 *Let* $(X, \mathcal{M}, \mu)$ *be a finite measure space and* $\{\nu_n\}$ *a sequence of finite measures of* $\mathcal{M}$ *each of which is absolutely continuous with respect to* μ. *Then the following are equivalent:*

(i) *The sequence of measures* $\{\nu_n\}$ *is uniformly absolutely continuous with respect to the measure* μ.

(ii) *The sequence of functions* $\{\nu_n : \mathcal{M} \to \mathbf{R}\}$ *is equicontinuous with respect to the Nikodym metric* ρ_μ.

(iii) *The sequence of Radon-Nikodym derivatives* $\{\frac{d\mu}{d\nu_n}\}$ *is uniformly integrable over* X *with respect to the measure* μ.

Theorem 25 *Let* $(X, \mathcal{M}, \mu)$ *be a finite measure space and* $\{\nu_n\}$ *a sequence of finite measures on* $\mathcal{M}$ *that is uniformly absolutely continuous with respect to* μ. *If* $\{\nu_n\}$ *converges setwise on* $\mathcal{M}$ *to* ν, *then* ν *is a measure of* $\mathcal{M}$ *that is absolutely continuous with respect to* μ.

Proof Clearly, ν is a nonnegative set function. The setwise limit of finitely additive set functions is finitely additive. Therefore ν is finitely additive. We must verify that it is countably additive. Let $\{E_k\}_{k=1}^\infty$ be a disjoint collection of measurable sets. We must show that

$$\nu\left(\bigcup_{k=1}^\infty E_k\right) = \sum_{k=1}^\infty \nu(E_k). \tag{46}$$

If there is a k such that $\nu(E_k) = \infty$, then, by the monotonicity of ν, (46) holds since both sides are infinite. We therefore assume that $\nu(E_k) < \infty$ for all k. By the finite additivity of ν, for each natural number n,

$$\nu\left(\bigcup_{k=1}^\infty E_k\right) = \sum_{k=1}^n \nu(E_k) + \nu\left(\bigcup_{k=n+1}^\infty E_k\right). \tag{47}$$

Let $\epsilon > 0$. By the uniform absolute continuity with respect to μ of the sequence $\{\nu_n\}$, there is a $\delta > 0$ such that for E measurable and any natural number n,

$$\text{if } \mu(E) < \delta, \text{ then } \nu_n(E) < \epsilon/2, \tag{48}$$

and therefore

$$\text{if } \mu(E) < \delta, \text{ then } \nu(E) < \epsilon.$$

Since $\mu(X) < \infty$ and μ is countably additive, there is a natural number N for which

$$\mu\left(\bigcup_{k=N+1}^\infty E_k\right) < \delta.$$

By the choice of δ, (47), and the finiteness of each $\nu(E_k)$ we conclude that

$$\nu\left(\bigcup_{k=1}^\infty E_k\right) - \sum_{k=1}^N \nu(E_k) < \epsilon.$$

Thus (46) is verified. Therefore ν is a measure and we infer from (48) that if $\mu(E) = 0$, then $\nu(E) = 0$ and thus ν is absolutely continuous with respect to μ.   □

The following remarkable theorem tells us that, in the statement of the preceding theorem, if the sequence $\{\nu_n(X)\}$ is bounded, we can dispense with the assumption that the sequence is uniformly absolutely continuous: The uniform absolute continuity is a consequence of setwise convergence. The proof of this theorem rests beside the Uniform Boundedness Principle and the Open Mapping Theorem as one of the exceptional fruits of the Baire Category Theorem.

The Vitali–Hahn–Saks Theorem   *Let $(X, \mathcal{M}, \mu)$ be a finite measure space and $\{\nu_n\}$ a sequence of finite measures on $\mathcal{M}$, each of which is absolutely continuous with respect to μ. Suppose that $\{\nu_n(X)\}$ is bounded and $\{\nu_n\}$ converges setwise on $\mathcal{M}$ to ν. Then the sequence $\{\nu_n\}$ is uniformly absolutely continuous with respect to μ. Moreover, ν is a finite measure on $\mathcal{M}$ that is absolutely continuous with respect to μ.*

Proof   According to Theorem 21, the Nikodym metric space is complete, and $\{\nu_n\}$ induces a sequence of continuous functions on this metric space that converges pointwise (that is, setwise) to the function ν, which is real-valued since $\{\nu_n(X)\}$ is bounded. We infer from Theorem 7 of Chapter 10, a consequence of the Baire Category Theorem, that there is a set $E_0 \in \mathcal{M}$ for which the sequence of functions $\{\nu_n : \mathcal{M} \to \mathbf{R}\}$ is equicontinuous at E_0, that is, for each $\epsilon > 0$, there is a $\delta > 0$ such that for each measurable set E and natural number n,

$$\text{if } \rho_\mu(E, E_0) < \delta, \text{ then } |\mu_n(E) - \mu_n(E_0)| < \epsilon.$$

Since this holds for every $\epsilon > 0$ and each ν_n is finite, we infer from Lemma 22 that for each $\epsilon > 0$, there is a $\delta > 0$ such that for each measurable set E and natural number n,

$$\text{if } \rho_\mu(E) < \delta, \text{ then } \mu_n(E) < \epsilon.$$

Hence $\{\nu_n\}$ is uniformly absolutely continuous. According to the preceding theorem, ν is a finite measure that is absolutely continuous with respect to μ.   □

Remark   *Of course, sigma algebras are not linear spaces and measures are not linear operators. Nevertheless, there is a striking similarity between the Vitali-Hahn-Saks Theorem and the continuity of the pointwise limit of a sequence of continuous linear operators, and the Baire Category Theorem is the basis of the proofs of both these results. Also observe the similarity between Lemma 22 and the uniform continuity of a linear operator if it is continuous at a point.*

Theorem 26 (Nikodym)   *Let $(X, \mathcal{M})$ be a measurable space and $\{\nu_n\}$ a sequence of finite measures on $\mathcal{M}$ that converges setwise on $\mathcal{M}$ to the set function ν. Assume $\{\nu_n(X)\}$ is bounded. Then ν is a measure on $\mathcal{M}$.*

Proof   For a measurable set E, define

$$\mu(E) = \sum_{n=1}^{\infty} \frac{1}{2^n} \cdot \nu_n(E). \tag{49}$$

We leave the verification that μ is a finite measure on $\mathcal{M}$ as an exercise. It is clear that each ν_n is absolutely continuous with respect to μ. The conclusion now follows from the Vitali–Hahn–Saks Theorem.   □

PROBLEMS

61. For two measurable sets A and B, show that $A \Delta B = [A \cup B] \sim [A \cap B]$ and that

$$\rho_\mu(A, B) = \mu(A) + \mu(B) - 2 \cdot \mu(A \cap B).$$

62. Let $\{A_n\}$ be a sequence of measurable sets that converges to the measurable set A_0 with respect to the Nikodym metric. Show that $A_0 = \bigcup_{n=1}^\infty \left[\bigcap_{k=n}^\infty A_k \right]$.

63. Show that (49) defines a measure.

64. Prove Proposition 24.

65. Let $(X, \mathcal{M}, \mu)$ be a finite measure space and $\nu \colon \mathcal{M} \to [0, \infty)$ a finitely additive set function with the property that for each $\epsilon > 0$, there is a $\delta > 0$ such that for a measurable set E, if $\mu(E) < \delta$, then $\nu(E) < \epsilon$. Show that ν is a measure on $\mathcal{M}$.

66. Let $(X, \mathcal{M})$ be a measurable space and $\{\nu_n\}$ a sequence of finite measures on $\mathcal{M}$ that converges setwise on $\mathcal{M}$ to ν. Let $\{E_k\}$ be a descending sequence of measurable sets with empty intersection. Show that for each $\epsilon > 0$, there is a natural number K for which $\nu_n(E_k) < \epsilon$ for all n.

67. Give an example of a decreasing sequence $\{\mu_n\}$ of measures on a measurable space such that the set function μ defined by $\mu(E) = \lim \mu_n(E)$ is not a measure.

68. Let $(X, \mathcal{M})$ be a measurable space and $\{\mu_n\}$ a sequence of measures on $\mathcal{M}$ such that for each $E \in \mathcal{M}, \mu_{n+1}(E) \geq \mu_n(E)$. For each $E \in \mathcal{M}$, define $\mu(E) = \lim \mu_n(E)$. Show that μ is a measure on $\mathcal{M}$ if $\mu(x) < \infty$.

69. Formulate and prove a version of the Vitali–Hahn–Saks Theorem for signed measures.

70. Show that the Nikodym metric space associated with the finite measure space $(X, \mathcal{M}, \mu)$ is separable if and only if $L^p(X, \mu)$ is separable for all $1 \leq p < \infty$.

CHAPTER 19

General L^p Spaces: Completeness, Duality, and Weak Convergence

Contents

For a measure space $(X, \mathcal{M}, \mu)$ and $1 \le p \le \infty$, we define the linear spaces $L^p(X, \mu)$ just as we did in Part I for the case of Lebesgue measure on the real line. Arguments very similar to those used in the case of Lebesgue measure on the real line show that the Hölder and Minkowski Inequalities hold and that $L^p(X, \mu)$ is a Banach space. We devote the first section to these and related topics. The remainder of this chapter is devoted to establishing results whose proofs lie outside the scope of ideas presented in Part I. In the second section, we use the Radon-Nikodym Theorem to prove the Riesz Representation Theorem for the dual space of $L^p(X, \mu)$, for $1 \le p < \infty$ and μ a σ-finite measure. In the third section, we show that, for $1 < p < \infty$, the Banach space $L^p(X, \mu)$ is reflexive and therefore has the weak sequential compactness properties possessed by such spaces. In the following section, we prove the Kantorovitch Representation Theorem for the dual of $L^\infty(X, \mu)$. The final section is devoted to consideration of weak sequential compactness in the nonreflexive Banach space $L^1(X, \mu)$. We use the Vitali–Hahn–Saks Theorem to prove the Dunford-Pettis Theorem, which tells us that, if $\mu(X) < \infty$, then every bounded sequence in $L^1(X, \mu)$ that is uniformly integrable has a weakly convergent subsequence.

19.1 THE COMPLETENESS OF $L^p(X, \mu), 1 \le p \le \infty$

Let $(X, \mathcal{M}, \mu)$ be a measure space. Define $\mathcal{F}$ to be the collection of all measurable extended real-valued functions on X that are finite almost everywhere on X. Since a function that is integrable over X is finite a.e. on X, if f is a measurable function on X and there is a p in $(0, \infty)$ for which $\int_X |f|^p \, d\mu < \infty$, then f belongs to $\mathcal{F}$. Define two functions f and g in $\mathcal{F}$ to be equivalent, and write

$$f \cong g \text{ provided } f = g \text{ a.e. on } X.$$

This is an equivalence relation, that is, it is reflexive, symmetric, and transitive. Therefore it induces a partition of $\mathcal{F}$ into a disjoint collection of equivalence classes. We denote this collection of equivalence classes by $\mathcal{F}/_\cong$. There is a natural linear structure on $\mathcal{F}/_\cong$.

Given two equivalence classes $[f]$ and $[g]$ and real numbers α and β, we define the linear combination $\alpha \cdot [f] + \beta \cdot [g]$ to be the equivalence class of the functions belonging to $\mathcal{F}$ that take the value $\alpha f(x) + \beta g(x)$ on X_0, where X_0 is the set of points in X at which both f and g are finite. Observe that linear combinations of equivalence classes are properly defined in that they are independent of the choice of representatives of the equivalence classes. The zero element of this linear space is the equivalence class of functions that vanish almost everywhere on X.

Let $L^p(X, \mu)$ be the collection of equivalence classes $[f]$ for which

$$\int_E |f|^p < \infty.$$

This is properly defined since if $f \cong f_1$, then $|f|^p$ is integrable over X if and only if $|f_1|^p$ is. We infer from the inequality

$$|a + b|^p \leq 2^p[|a|^p + |b|^p] \text{ for all } a, b \in \mathbf{R}$$

and the integral comparison test that $L^p(X, \mu)$ is a linear space. For an equivalence class $[f]$ in $L^p(X, \mu)$ we define $\|[f]\|_p$ by

$$\|[f]\|_p = \left[\int_X |f|^p \, d\mu \right]^{1/p}$$

This is properly defined. It is clear that $\|[f]\|_p = 0$ if and only if $[f] = 0$ and $\|[\alpha \cdot f]\|_p = \alpha \cdot \|[f]\|_p$ for each real number α.

We call an equivalence class $[f]$ **essentially bounded** provided there is some $M \geq 0$, called an **essential upper bound** for $[f]$, for which

$$|f| \leq M \text{ a.e. on } X.$$

This also is properly defined, that is, independent of the choice of representative of the equivalence class. We define $L^\infty(X, \mu)$ to be the collection of equivalence classes $[f]$ for which f is essentially bounded. Then $L^\infty(X, \mu)$ also is a linear subspace of $\mathcal{F}/_\cong$. For $[f] \in L^\infty(X, \mu)$, define $\|[f]\|_\infty$ to be the infimum of the essential upper bounds for f. This is properly defined. It is easy to see that $\|[f]\|_\infty$ is the smallest essential upper bound for f. Moreover, $\|[f]\|_\infty = 0$ if and only if $[f] = 0$ and $\|[\alpha \cdot f]\|_\infty = \alpha \cdot \|[f]\|_\infty$ for each real number α. We infer from the triangle inequality for real numbers that the triangle inequality holds for $\| \cdot \|_\infty$ and hence it is a norm.

For simplicity and convenience, we refer to the equivalence classes in $\mathcal{F}/_\cong$ as functions and denote them by f rather than $[f]$. Thus to write $f = g$ means that $f(x) = g(\dot{x})$ for almost all $x \in X$.

Recall that the conjugate q of a number p in $(1, \infty)$ is defined by the relation $1/p + 1/q = 1$; we also call 1 the conjugate of ∞ and ∞ the conjugate of 1.

The proofs of the results in this section are very similar to those of the corresponding results in the case of Lebesgue integration of functions of a real variable.

Theorem 1 *Let $(X, \mathcal{M}, \mu)$ be a measure space, $1 \leq p < \infty$, and q the conjugate of p. If f belongs to $L^p(X, \mu)$ and g belongs to $L^q(X, \mu)$, then their product $f \cdot g$ belongs to $L^1(X, \mu)$ and*

Hölder's Inequality

$$\int_X |f \cdot g|\, d\mu = \|f \cdot g\|_1 \le \|f\|_p \cdot \|g\|_q.$$

Moreover, if $f \ne 0$, the function $f^* = \|f\|_p^{1-p} \cdot \operatorname{sgn}(f) \cdot |f|^{p-1}$ belongs to $L^q(X, \mu)$,

$$\int_X f f^*\, d\mu = \|f\|_p \text{ and } \|f^*\|_q = 1. \tag{1}$$

Minkowski's Inequality For $1 \le p \le \infty$ and $f, g \in L^p(X, \mu)$,

$$\|f + g\|_p \le \|f\|_p + \|g\|_p.$$

Therefore $L^p(X, \mu)$ is a normed linear space.

The Cauchy-Schwarz Inequality *Let f and g be measurable functions on X for which f^2 and g^2 are integrable over X. Then their product $f \cdot g$ also is integrable over X and, moreover,*

$$\int_X |fg|\, d\mu \le \sqrt{\int_X f^2\, d\mu} \cdot \sqrt{\int_X g^2\, d\mu}.$$

Proof If $p = 1$, then Hölder's Inequality follows from the monotonicity and homogeneity of integration, together with the observation that $\|g\|_\infty$ is an essential upper bound for g. Equality (1) is clear. Assume $p > 1$. Young's Inequality asserts that for nonnegative real numbers a and b,

$$ab \le \frac{1}{p} \cdot a^p + \frac{1}{q} \cdot b^q.$$

Define $\alpha = \int_X |f|^p\, d\mu$ and $\beta = \int_X |g|^q\, d\mu$. Assume α and β are positive. The functions f and g are finite a.e. on X. If $f(x)$ and $g(x)$ are finite, substitute $|f(x)|/\alpha^{1/p}$ for a and $|g(x)|/\beta^{1/b}$ for b in Young's Inequality to conclude that

$$\frac{1}{\alpha^{1/p} \cdot \beta^{1/q}} |f(x)g(x)| \le \frac{1}{p} \cdot \frac{1}{\alpha} \cdot |f(x)|^p + \frac{1}{q} \cdot \frac{1}{\beta} \cdot |g(x)|^q \text{ for almost all } x \in X.$$

Integrate across this inequality, using the monotonicity and linearity of integration, and multiply the resulting inequality by $\alpha^{1/p} \cdot \beta^{1/q}$ to obtain Hölder's Inequality. Verification of equality (1) is an exercise in the arithmetic of p's and q's. To verify Minkowski's Inequality, since we already established that $f + g$ belongs to $L^p(X, \mu)$, we may consider the associated function $(f+g)^*$ in $L^q(X, \mu)$ for which (1) holds with $f + g$ substituted for f. According to Hölder's Inequality, the functions $f \cdot (f+g)^* + g \cdot (f+g)^*$ are integrable over X. Therefore, by the linearity of integration and another employment of Hölder's Inequality,

$$
\begin{aligned}
\|f + g\|_p &= \int_X (f+g) \cdot (f+g)^*\, d\mu \\
&= \int_X f \cdot (f+g)^*\, d\mu + \int_X g \cdot (f+g)^*\, d\mu \\
&\le \|f\|_p \cdot \|(f+g)^*\|_q + \|g\|_p \cdot \|(f+g)^*\|_q \\
&= \|f\|_p + \|g\|_p.
\end{aligned}
$$

Of course, the Cauchy-Schwarz Inequality is Minkowski's Inequality for the case $p = q = 2$. $\square$

Corollary 2 *Let* (X, M, μ) *be a finite measure space and* $1 \leq p_1 < p_2 \leq \infty$. *Then* $L^{p_2}(X, \mu) \subseteq L^{p_1}(X, \mu)$. *Moreover, for*

$$c = [\mu(X)]^{\frac{p_2-p_1}{p_1 p_2}} \text{ if } p_2 < \infty \text{ and } c = [\mu(X)]^{\frac{1}{p_1}} \text{ if } p_2 = \infty, \tag{2}$$

$$\|f\|_{p_1} \leq c\|f\|_{p_2} \text{ for all } f \text{ in } L^{p_2}(X). \tag{3}$$

Proof For $f \in L^{p_2}(X, \mu)$, apply Hölder's Inequality, with $p = p_2$ and $g = 1$ on X, to confirm that (3) holds for c defined by (2). $\square$

Corollary 3 *Let* (X, M, μ) *be a measure space and* $1 < p \leq \infty$. *If* $\{f_n\}$ *is a bounded sequence of functions in* $L^p(X, \mu)$, *then* $\{f_n\}$ *is uniformly integrable over* X.

Proof Let $M > 0$ be such that $\|f\|_p \leq M$ for all n. Define $\gamma = 1$ if $p = \infty$ and $\gamma = (p-1)/p$ if $p < \infty$. Apply the preceding corollary, with $p_1 = 1$, $p_2 = p$, and $X = E$, a measurable subset of X of finite measure, to conclude that for any measurable subset E of X of finite measure and any natural number n,

$$\int_E |f_n| \, d\mu \leq M \cdot [\mu(E)]^\gamma.$$

Therefore $\{f_n\}$ is uniformly integrable over X. $\square$

For a linear space V normed by $\| \cdot \|$, we call a sequence $\{v_k\}$ in V **rapidly Cauchy** provided there is a convergent series of positive numbers $\sum_{k=1}^\infty \epsilon_k$ for which

$$\|v_{k+1} - v_k\| \leq \epsilon_k^2 \text{ for all natural numbers } k.$$

We observed earlier that a rapidly Cauchy sequence is Cauchy and that every Cauchy sequence has a rapidly Cauchy subsequence.[1]

Lemma 4 *Let* (X, M, μ) *be a measure space and* $1 \leq p \leq \infty$. *Then every rapidly Cauchy sequence in* $L^p(X, \mu)$ *converges to a function in* $L^p(X, \mu)$, *both with respect to the* $L^p(X, \mu)$ *norm and pointwise almost everywhere on* X.

Proof We leave the case $p = \infty$ as an exercise. Assume $1 \leq p < \infty$. Let $\sum_{k=1}^\infty \epsilon_k$ be a convergent series of positive numbers for which

$$\|f_{k+1} - f_k\|_p \leq \epsilon_k^2 \text{ for all natural numbers } k. \tag{4}$$

Then

$$\int_X |f_{n+k} - f_n|^p \, d\mu \leq \left[\sum_{j=n}^\infty \epsilon_j^2 \right]^p \text{ for all natural numbers } n \text{ and } k. \tag{5}$$

---

[1] See the footnote on page 146 regarding rapidly converging Cauchy sequences.

Fix a natural number k. According to Chebychev's Inequality,

$$\mu\left\{x \in X \mid |f_{k+1}(x) - f_k(x)|^p \geq \epsilon_k^p\right\} \leq \frac{1}{\epsilon_k^p} \cdot \int_X |f_{k+1} - f_k|^p \, d\mu = \frac{1}{\epsilon_k^p} \cdot \|f_{k+1} - f_k\|_p^p, \quad (6)$$

and therefore

$$\mu\left\{x \in X \mid |f_{k+1}(x) - f_k(x)| \geq \epsilon_k\right\} \leq \epsilon_k^p \text{ for all natural numbers } k.$$

Since $p \geq 1$, the series $\sum_{k=1}^{\infty} \epsilon_k^p$ converges. The Borel-Cantelli Lemma tells us that there is a subset X_0 of X for which $\mu(X \sim X_0) = 0$ and for each $x \in X_0$, there is an index $K(x)$ such that

$$|f_{k+1}(x) - f_k(x)| < \epsilon_k \text{ for all } k \geq K(x).$$

Hence, for $x \in X_0$,

$$|f_{n+k}(x) - f_n(x)| \leq \sum_{j=n}^{\infty} \epsilon_j \text{ for all } n \geq K(x) \text{ and all } k. \quad (7)$$

The series $\sum_{j=1}^{\infty} \epsilon_j$ converges, and therefore the sequence of real numbers $\{f_k(x)\}$ is Cauchy. The real numbers are complete. Denote the limit of $\{f_k(x)\}$ by $f(x)$. Define $f(x) = 0$ for $x \in X \sim X_0$. Taking the limit as $k \to \infty$ in (5) we infer from Fatou's Lemma that

$$\int_X |f - f_n|^p \, d\mu \leq \left[\sum_{j=n}^{\infty} \epsilon_j^2\right]^p \text{ for all } n.$$

Since the series $\sum_{k=1}^{\infty} \epsilon_k^2$ converges, f belongs to $L^p(X)$ and $\{f_n\} \to f$ in $L^p(X)$. We constructed f as the pointwise limit almost everywhere on X of $\{f_n\}$. □

The Riesz-Fischer Theorem *Let $(X, \mathcal{M}, \mu)$ be a measure space and $1 \leq p \leq \infty$. Then $L^p(X, \mu)$ is a Banach space. Moreover, if a sequence in $L^p(X, \mu)$ converges in $L^p(X, \mu)$ to a function f in L^p, then a subsequence converges pointwise a.e. on X to f.*

Proof Let $\{f_n\}$ be a Cauchy sequence in $L^p(X, \mu)$. To show that this sequence converges to a function in $L^p(X, \mu)$, it suffices to show it has a subsequence that converges to a function in $L^p(X, \mu)$. Choose $\{f_{n_k}\}$ to be a rapidly Cauchy subsequence of $\{f_n\}$. The preceding lemma tells us that $\{f_{n_k}\}$ converges to a function in $L^p(X, \mu)$ both with respect to the $L^p(X, \mu)$ norm and pointwise almost everywhere on X. □

Theorem 5 *Let $(X, \mathcal{M}, \mu)$ be a measure space and $1 \leq p < \infty$. Then the subspace of simple functions on X that vanish outside a set of finite measure is dense in $L^p(X, \mu)$.*

Proof Let f belong to $L^p(X, \mu)$. According to Proposition 9 of the preceding chapter, $\{x \in X \mid f(x) \neq 0\}$ is σ-finite. We therefore assume that X is σ-finite. The Simple Approximation Theorem tells us that there is a sequence $\{\psi_n\}$ of simple functions on X, each of which vanishes outside a set of finite measure, which converges pointwise on X to f and for which $|\psi_n| \leq |f|$ on X for all n. Then

$$|\psi_n - f|^p \leq 2^p \cdot |f|^p \text{ on } X \text{ for all } n.$$

Since $|f|^p$ is integrable over X, we infer from the Lebesgue Dominated Convergence Theorem that the sequence $\{\psi_n\}$ converges to f in $L^p(X, \mu)$.   □

We leave the proof of the following consequence of the Vitali Convergence Theorem as an exercise (see Corollary 18 of the preceding chapter).

The Vitali L^p Convergence Criterion   Let $(X, \mathcal{M}, \mu)$ be a measure space and $1 \leq p < \infty$. Suppose $\{f_n\}$ is a sequence in $L^p(X, \mu)$ that converges pointwise a.e. to f and f also belong to $L^p(X, \mu)$. Then $\{f_n\} \to f$ in $L^p(X, \mu)$ if and only if $\{|f|^p\}$ is uniformly integrable and tight.

PROBLEMS

1. For $1 \leq p < \infty$ and n a natural number, define $f_n(x) = n^{1/p}$ if $0 \leq x \leq 1/n$ and $f_n(x) = 0$ if $1/n < x \leq 1$. Let f be identically zero on $[0, 1]$. Show that $\{f_n\}$ converges pointwise to f but does not converge in L^p. Where does the Vitali Convergence Criterion in L^p fail?

2. For $1 \leq p < \infty$ and n a natural number, let f_n be the characteristic function of $[n, n+1]$. Let f be identically zero on $\mathbf{R}$. Show that $\{f_n\}$ converges pointwise to f but does not converge in L^p. Where does the Vitali L^p Convergence Criterion fail?

3. Let $(X, \mathcal{M}, \mu)$ be a measure space and $1 \leq p < \infty$. Let $\{f_n\}$ be a sequence in $L^p(X, \mu)$ and f a function $L^p(X, \mu)$ for which $\{f_n\} \to f$ pointwise a.e. on X. Show that

$$\{f_n\} \to f \text{ in } L^p(X, \mu) \text{ if and only if the sequence } \{|f|^p\} \text{ is uniformly integrable and tight.}$$

4. For a measure space $(X, \mathcal{M}, \mu)$ and $0 < p < 1$, define $L^p(X, \mu)$ to be the collection of measurable functions on X for which $|f|^p$ is integrable. Show that $L^p(X, \mu)$ is a linear space. For $f \in L^p(X, \mu)$, define $\|f\|_p^p = \int_X |f|^p \, d\mu$.

   (i)   Show that, in general, $\|\cdot\|_p$ is not a norm since Minkowski's Inequality may fail.

   (ii) Define

   $$\rho(f, g) = \int_X |f - g|^p \, d\mu \text{ for all } f, g \in L^p(X, \mu).$$

   Show that ρ is a metric with respect to which $L^p(X, \mu)$ is complete.

5. Let $(X, \mathcal{M}, \mu)$ be a measure space and $\{f_n\}$ a Cauchy sequence in $L^\infty(X, \mu)$. Show that there is a measurable subset X_0 of X for which $\mu(X \sim X_0) = 0$ and for each $\epsilon > 0$, there is an index N for which

   $$|f_n - f_m| \leq \epsilon \text{ on } X_0 \text{ for all } n, m \geq N.$$

   Use this to show that $L^\infty(X, \mu)$ is complete.

19.2   THE RIESZ REPRESENTATION THEOREM FOR THE DUAL OF $L^p(X, \mu)$, $1 \leq p \leq \infty$

For $1 \leq p < \infty$, let f belong to $L^q(X, \mu)$, where q is conjugate of p. Define the linear functional $T_f \colon L^p(X, \mu) \to \mathbf{R}$ by[2]

$$T_f(g) = \int_X fg \, d\mu \text{ for all } g \in L^p(X, \mu). \tag{8}$$

---

[2]Bear in mind that the "functions" are, in fact, equivalence classes of functions. This functional is properly defined on the equivalence classes since if $f = \tilde{f}$ and $g = \tilde{g}$ a.e. on X, then

$$\int_X f \cdot g \, d\mu = \int_X \tilde{f} \cdot \tilde{g} \, d\mu.$$

Hölder's Inequality tells us that T_f is a bounded linear functional on L^p and its norm is at most $\|f\|_q$, while (1) tells us that its norm is actually equal to $\|f\|_q$. Therefore $T: L^q(X, \mu) \to (L^p(X, \mu))^*$ is an isometry. In the case that X is a Lebesgue measurable set of real numbers and μ is Lebesgue measure, we proved that T maps $L^q(X, \mu)$ onto $(L^p(X, \mu))^*$, that is, every bounded linear functional on $L^p(X, \mu)$ is given by integration against a function in $L^q(X, \mu)$. This fundamental result holds for general σ-finite measure spaces.

The Riesz Representation Theorem for the Dual of $L^p(X, \mu)$ Let $(X, \mathcal{M}, \mu)$ be a σ-finite measure space, $1 \le p < \infty$, and q the conjugate to p. For $f \in L^q(X, \mu)$, define $T_f \in (L^p(X, \mu))^*$ by (8). Then T is an isometric isomorphism of $L^q(X, \mu)$ onto $(L^p(X, \mu))^*$.

Before we prove this theorem, a few words are in order contrasting the proof in the case of a closed, bounded interval with the general proof. In the case of Lebesgue measure m on $X = [a, b]$, a closed, bounded interval of real numbers, the heart of the proof of the Riesz Representation Theorem lay in showing if S is a bounded linear functional on $L^p([a, b], m)$, then the real-valued function $x \mapsto h(x) = S(\chi_{[a, x]})$ is absolutely continuous on $[a, b]$. Once this was established, we inferred from the characterization of absolutely continuous functions as indefinite integrals that

$$S(\chi_{[a, x]}) = h(x) = \int_{[a, x]} h' dm \text{ for all } x \in [a, b].$$

From this we argued that h' belonged to L^q and

$$S(g) = \int_{[a, b]} h' \cdot g \, dm \text{ for all } g \in L^p([a, b], m).$$

In the case of a general finite measure space, if S is a bounded linear functional on $L^p(X, \mu)$, we will show that the set function $E \mapsto \nu(E) = S(\chi_E)$ is a measure that is absolutely continuous with respect to μ. We then define f to be the Radon-Nikodym derivative of ν with respect to μ, that is,

$$S(\chi_E) = \int_E f \, d\mu \text{ for all } E \in \mathcal{M}.$$

We will argue that f belongs to L^q and

$$S(g) = \int_X f \cdot g \, d\mu \text{ for all } g \in L^p(X, \mu).$$

Lemma 6   Let $(X, \mathcal{M}, \mu)$ be a σ-finite measure space and $1 \le p < \infty$. For f an integrable function over X, suppose there is an $M \ge 0$ such that for every simple function g on X that vanishes outside of a set of finite measure,

$$\left| \int_X fg \, d\mu \right| \le M \cdot \|g\|_p. \tag{9}$$

Then f belongs to $L^q(X, \mu)$, where q is conjugate of p. Moreover, $\|f\|_q \le M$.

Proof First consider the case $p > 1$. Since $|f|$ is a nonnegative measurable function and the measure space is σ-finite, according to the Simple Approximation Theorem, there is a sequence of simple functions $\{\varphi_n\}$, each of which vanishes outside of a set of finite measure, that converges pointwise on X to $|f|$ and $0 \leq \varphi_n \leq |f|$ on E for all n. Since $\{\varphi_n^q\}$ converges pointwise on X to $|f|^q$, Fatou's Lemma tells us that to show that $|f|^q$ is integrable and $\|f\|_q \leq M$ it suffices to show that

$$\int_X \varphi_n^q \, d\mu \leq M^q \text{ for all } n. \tag{10}$$

Fix a natural number n. To verify (10), we estimate the functional values of φ_n^q as follows :

$$\varphi_n^q = \varphi_n \cdot \varphi_n^{q-1} \leq |f| \cdot \varphi_n^{q-1} = f \cdot \text{sgn}(f) \cdot \varphi_n^{q-1} \text{ on } X. \tag{11}$$

Define the simple function g_n by

$$g_n = \text{sgn}(f) \cdot \varphi_n^{q-1} \text{ on } X.$$

We infer from (11) and (9) that

$$\int_X \varphi_n^q \, d\mu \leq \int_X f \cdot g_n \, d\mu \leq M \|g_n\|_p. \tag{12}$$

Since p and q are conjugate, $p(q-1) = q$ and therefore

$$\int_X |g_n|^p \, d\mu = \int_X \varphi_n^{p(q-1)} \, d\mu = \int_X \varphi_n^q \, d\mu$$

Thus we may rewrite (12) as

$$\int_X \varphi_n^q \, d\mu \leq M \cdot \left[\int_X \varphi_n^q \, d\mu \right]^{1/p}$$

For each n, φ_n^q is a simple function that vanishes outside of a set of finite measure and therefore it is integrable. Thus the preceding integral inequality may be rewritten as

$$\left[\int_X \varphi_n^q \, d\mu \right]^{1-1/p} \leq M.$$

Since $1 - 1/p = 1/q$, we have verified (10).

It remains to consider the case $p = 1$. We must show that M is an essential upper bound for f. We argue by contradiction. If M is not an essential upper bound, then there is some $\epsilon > 0$ for which the set $X_\epsilon = \{x \in X \mid |f(x)| > M + \epsilon\}$ has nonzero measure. Since X is σ-finite, we may choose a subset of X_ϵ with finite positive measure. If we let g be the characteristic function of such a set we contradict (9). $\qquad \square$

Proof of the Riesz Representation Theorem We leave the case $p = 1$ as an exercise (see Problem 6). Assume $p > 1$. We first consider the case $\mu(X) < \infty$. Let $S: L^p(X, \mu) \to \mathbf{R}$ be a bounded linear functional. Define a set function ν on the collection of measurable sets $\mathcal{M}$ by setting

$$\nu(E) = S(\chi_E) \text{ for } E \in \mathcal{M}.$$

This is properly defined since $\mu(X) < \infty$ and thus the characteristic function of each measurable set belongs to $L^p(X, \mu)$. We claim that ν is a signed measure. Indeed, let $\{E_k\}_{k=1}^\infty$ be a countable disjoint collection of measurable sets and $E = \bigcup_{k=1}^\infty E_k$. By the countable additivity of the measure μ,

$$\mu(E) = \sum_{k=1}^\infty \mu(E_k) < \infty.$$

Therefore

$$\lim_{n \to \infty} \sum_{k=n+1}^\infty \mu(E_k) = 0.$$

Consequently,

$$\lim_{n \to \infty} \left\| \chi_E - \sum_{k=1}^n \chi_{E_k} \right\|_p = \lim_{n \to \infty} \left[\sum_{k=n+1}^\infty \mu(E_k) \right]^{1/p} = 0. \tag{13}$$

But S is both linear and continuous on $L^p(X, \mu)$ and hence

$$S(\chi_E) = \sum_{k=1}^\infty S(\chi_{E_k}),$$

that is,

$$\nu(E) = \sum_{k=1}^\infty \nu(E_k).$$

To show that ν is a signed measure it must be shown that the series on the right converges absolutely. However, if, for each k, we set $c_k = \operatorname{sgn}(S(\chi_{E_k}))$, then arguing as above we conclude that the series

$$\sum_{k=1}^\infty S(c_k \cdot \chi_{E_k}) \text{ is Cauchy and thus convergent, so } \sum_{k=1}^\infty |\nu(E_k)| = \sum_{k=1}^\infty S(c_k \cdot \chi_{E_k}) \text{ converges.}$$

Thus ν is a signed measure. We claim that ν is absolutely continuous with respect to μ. Indeed, if $E \in \mathcal{M}$ has $\mu(E) = 0$, then χ_E is a representative of the zero element of $L^p(X, \mu)$ and therefore, since S is linear, $\nu_k(E) = S(\chi_E) = 0$. According to Corollary 20 in Chapter 18, a consequence of the Radon-Nikodym Theorem, there is a function f that is integrable over X and

$$S(\chi_E) = \nu(E) = \int_E f \, d\mu \text{ for all } E \in \mathcal{M}.$$

For each simple function φ, by the linearity of S and of integration, since each simple function belongs to $L^p(X, \mu)$,

$$S(\varphi) = \int_X f\varphi \, d\mu.$$

Since the functional S is bounded on $L^p(X, \mu)$, $|S(g)| \leq \|S\| \|g\|_p$, for each $g \in L^p(X, \mu)$. Therefore,

$$\left| \int_X f\varphi \, d\mu \right| = |S(\varphi)| \leq \|S\| \|\varphi\|_p \text{ for each simple function } \varphi,$$

and consequently, by Lemma 6, f belongs to L^q. From Hölder's Inequality and the continuity of S on $L^p(X, \mu)$, we infer that the functional

$$g \mapsto S(g) - \int_X f \cdot g \, d\mu \text{ for all } g \in L^p(X, \mu)$$

is continuous. However, it vanishes on the linear space of simple functions that, according to Theorem 5, is a dense subspace of $L^p(X, \mu)$. Therefore $S - T_f$ vanishes on all of $L^p(X, \mu)$, that is, $S = T_f$.

Now consider the case that X is σ-finite. Let $\{X_n\}$ be an ascending sequence of measurable sets of finite measure whose union is X. Fix n. We have just shown that there is a function f_n in $L^q(X \, \mu)$ for which

$$f_n = 0 \text{ on } X{\sim}X_n, \quad \int_X |f_n|^q \, d\mu \leq \|S\|^q$$

and

$$S(g) = \int_{X_n} f_n g \, d\mu = \int_X f_n g \, d\mu \text{ if } g \in L^p(X, \mu) \text{ and } g = 0 \text{ on } X{\sim}X_n.$$

Since any function f_n with this property is uniquely determined on X_n except for changes on sets of measure zero and since the restriction of f_{n+1} to X_n also has this property, we may assume $f_{n+1} = f_n$ on X_n. For $x \in X = \bigcup_{n=1}^{\infty} X_n$, set $f(x) = f_n(x)$ if x belongs to X_n. Then f is a properly defined measurable function on X and the sequence $\{|f_n|^q\}$ converges pointwise a.e. to $|f|^q$. By Fatou's Lemma,

$$\int_X |f|^q \, d\mu \leq \liminf \int_X |f_n|^q \, d\mu \leq \|S\|^q.$$

Thus f belongs to L^q. Let g belong to $L^p(X, \mu)$. For each n, define $g_n = g$ on X_n and $g_n = 0$ on $X{\sim}X_n$. Since, by Hölder's Inequality, $|fg|$ is integrable over X and $|fg_n| \leq |fg|$ a.e. on X, by the Lebesgue Dominated Convergence Theorem,

$$\lim_{n \to \infty} \int_X f g_n \, d\mu = \int_X fg \, d\mu. \tag{14}$$

On the other hand, $\{|g_n - g|^p\} \to 0$ pointwise a.e. on X and $|g_n - g|^p \leq |g|^p$ a.e. on X, for all n. Once more invoking the Lebesgue Dominated Convergence Theorem, we conclude that $\{g_n\} \to g$ in $L^p(X, d\mu)$. Since the functional S is continuous on $L^p(X, \mu)$,

$$\lim_{n \to \infty} S(g_n) = S(g). \tag{15}$$

However, for each n,

$$S(g_n) = \int_{X_n} f_n g_n \, d\mu = \int_X f g_n \, d\mu,$$

so that, by (14) and (15), $S(g) = \int_X fg \, d\mu$. □

PROBLEMS

6. Prove the Riesz Representation Theorem for the case $p = 1$ by adapting the proof for the case $p > 1$.

7. Show that for the case of Lebesgue measure on a nontrivial closed, bounded interval $[a, b]$, the Riesz Representation Theorem does not extend to the case $p = \infty$.

8. Find a measure space $(X, \mathcal{M}, \mu)$ for which the Riesz Representation Theorem does extend to the case $p = \infty$.

19.3 THE KANTOROVITCH REPRESENTATION THEOREM FOR THE DUAL OF $L^\infty(X, \mu)$

In the preceding section, we characterized the dual of $L^p(X, \mu)$ for $1 \leq p < \infty$ and $(X, \mathcal{M}, \mu)$ a σ-finite measure space. We now characterize the dual of $L^\infty(X, \mu)$.

Definition *Let $(X, \mathcal{M})$ be a measurable space and the set function $\nu: \mathcal{M} \to \mathbf{R}$ be finitely additive. For $E \in \mathcal{M}$, the total variation of ν over E, $|\nu|(E)$, is defined by*

$$|\nu|(E) = \sup \sum_{k=1}^{n} |\nu(E_k)|, \tag{16}$$

*where the supremum is taken over finite disjoint collections $\{E_k\}_{k=1}^n$ of sets in $\mathcal{M}$ that are contained in E. We call ν a **bounded finitely additive signed measure** provided $|\nu|(X) < \infty$. The total variation of ν over X, which is denoted by $\|\nu\|_{var}$, is defined to be $|\nu|(X)$.*

Remark *If $\nu: \mathcal{M} \to \mathbf{R}$ is a measure, then $\|\nu\|_{var} = \nu(X)$. If $\nu: \mathcal{M} \to \mathbf{R}$ is a signed measure, we already observed that the total variation $\|\nu\|_{var}$ is given by*

$$\|\nu\|_{var} = |\nu|(X) = \nu^+(X) + \nu^-(X),$$

where $\nu = \nu^+ - \nu^-$ is the Jordan Decomposition of ν as the difference of measures (see page 345). For a real-valued signed measure ν, an analysis (which we will not present here) of the total variation set function $|\nu|$ defined by (16) shows that $|\nu|$ is a measure. Observe that $|\nu| - \nu$ also is a measure and $\nu = |\nu| - [|\nu| - \nu]$. This provides a different proof of the Jordan Decomposition Theorem for a finite signed measure.

If $\nu: \mathcal{M} \to \mathbf{R}$ is a bounded finitely additive signed measure on $\mathcal{M}$, and the simple function $\varphi = \sum_{k=1}^{n} c_k \cdot \chi_{E_k}$ is measurable with respect to $\mathcal{M}$, we define the integral of φ over X with respect to ν by

$$\int_X \varphi \, d\nu = \sum_{k=1}^{n} c_k \cdot \nu(E_k).$$

The integral is properly defined, linear with respect to the integrand and

$$\left| \int_X \varphi \, d\nu \right| \leq \|\nu\|_{var} \cdot \|\varphi\|_\infty. \tag{17}$$

Indeed, in our development of the integral with respect to a measure μ, only the finite additivity of μ was needed in order to show that integration is a properly defined, linear, monotone functional on the linear space of simple functions. Let $f: X \to \mathbf{R}$ be a measurable function that is bounded on X. According to the Simple Approximation Lemma, there are sequence $\{\psi_n\}$ and $\{\varphi_n\}$ of simple functions on X for which

$$\varphi_n \leq \varphi_{n+1} \leq f \leq \psi_{n+1} \leq \psi_n \text{ and } 0 \leq \psi_n - \varphi_n \leq 1/n \text{ on } X \text{ for all } n.$$

Therefore the sequence $\{\varphi_n\}$ converges uniformly to f on X. We infer from (17) that

$$\left| \int_X \varphi_{n+k} \, d\nu - \int_X \varphi_n \, d\nu \right| \leq \|\nu\|\text{var} \cdot \|\varphi_{n+k} - \varphi_n\|_\infty \text{ for all natural numbers } n \text{ and } k.$$

We define the integral of f over X with respect to ν by

$$\int_X f \, d\nu = \lim_{n \to \infty} \int_X \varphi_n \, d\nu$$

This does not depend on the choice of sequence of simple functions that converges uniformly on X to f. Now let $(X, \mathcal{M}, \mu)$ be a measure space. We wish to define $\int_X f \, d\nu$ for $f \in L^\infty(X, \mu)$, now formally viewed as a linear space of equivalence classes of essentially bounded measurable functions with respect to the relation of equality a.e. $[\mu]$. This requires that $\int_X f \, d\nu = \int_X f_1 \, d\nu$ if $f = f_1$ a.e. $[\mu]$ on X. If there is a set $E \in \mathcal{M}$ for which $\mu(E) = 0$, but $\nu(E) \neq 0$, then clearly this does not hold. We therefore single out the following class of bounded finitely additive signed measures.

Definition   *Let $(X, \mathcal{M}, \mu)$ be a measure space. By $\mathcal{BFA}(X, \mathcal{M}, \mu)$ we denote the normed linear space of bounded finitely additive signed measures ν on $\mathcal{M}$ that are absolutely continuous with respect to μ in the sense that if $E \in \mathcal{M}$ and $\mu(E) = 0$, then $\nu(E) = 0$. The norm of $\nu \in \mathcal{BFA}(X, \mathcal{M}, \mu)$ is the total variation norm $\|\nu\|_{\text{var}}$.*

It is clear that if ν belongs to $\mathcal{BFA}(X, \mathcal{M}, \mu)$ and φ and ψ are simple functions that are equal a.e. $[\mu]$ on X, then $\int_X \varphi \, d\nu = \int_X \psi \, d\nu$ and hence the same is true for essentially bounded measurable functions that are equal a.e. $[\mu]$ on X. Therefore the integral of an $L^\infty(X, \mu)$ function (that is, class of functions) over X with respect to ν is properly defined and

$$\left| \int_X f \, d\nu \right| \leq \|\nu\|\text{var} \cdot \|f\|_\infty \text{ for all } f \in L^\infty(X, \mu) \text{ and } \nu \in \mathcal{BFA}(X, \mathcal{M}, \mu). \tag{18}$$

Theorem 7 (the Kantorovitch Representation Theorem)   *Let $(X, \mathcal{M}, \mu)$ be a measure space. For $\nu \in \mathcal{BFA}(X, \mathcal{M}, \mu)$, define $T_\nu: L^\infty(X, \mu) \to \mathbf{R}$ by*

$$T_\nu(f) = \int_X f \, d\nu \text{ for all } f \in L^\infty(X, \mu). \tag{19}$$

Then T is an isometric isomorphism of the normed linear space $\mathcal{BFA}(X, \mathcal{M}, \mu)$ onto the dual of $L^\infty(X, \mu)$.

Proof   We first show that T is an isometry. In view of inequality (18), it suffices to show that $\|\nu\|\text{var} \leq \|T_\nu\|$. Indeed, let $\{E_k\}_{k=1}^n$ be a disjoint collection of sets in $\mathcal{M}$. For $1 \leq k \leq n$, define

$c_k = \text{sgn}(\nu(E_k))$ and then define $\varphi = \sum\limits_{k=1}^{n} c_k \cdot \chi_{E_k}$. Then $\|\varphi\|_\infty = 1$. Thus

$$\sum_{k=1}^{n} |\nu(E_k)| = \int_X \varphi \, d\nu = T_\nu(\varphi) \leq \|T_\nu\|.$$

Therefore $\|\nu\|_{\text{var}} \leq \|T_\nu\|$ and hence T is an isometry. It remains to show that T is onto. Let S belong to the dual of $L^\infty(X, \nu)$. Define $\nu: \mathcal{M} \to \mathbf{R}$ by

$$\nu(E) = S(\chi_E) \text{ for all } E \in \mathcal{M}. \tag{20}$$

The functon χ_E belongs to $L^\infty(X, \nu)$ and therefore ν is properly defined. Moreover, ν is finitely additive since S is linear. Furthermore, we claim that ν is absolutely continuous with respect to μ. Indeed, let $E \in \mathcal{M}$ have $\mu(E) = 0$. Thus $\nu(E) = S(\chi_E) = 0$.[3] We infer from the linearity of S and of integration with respect to ν that

$$\int_X f \, d\nu = S(f) \text{ for all simple functions in } L^\infty(X, \mu).$$

The Simple Approximation Lemma tells us that the simple functions are dense in $L^\infty(X, \mu)$. Therefore, since both S and integration with respect to ν are continuous on $L^\infty(X, \mu)$, $S = T_\nu$. □

Remark *Let $[a, b]$ be a closed, bounded interval of real numbers and consider the Lebesgue measure space $([a, b], \mathcal{L}, m)$. The operator $T: L^1([a, b], m) \to [L^\infty([a, b], m)]^*$ given by*

$$T_g(f) = \int_{[a, b]} g \cdot f \, dm \text{ for all } g \in L^1([a, b], m) \text{ and } f \in L^\infty([a, b], m)$$

is a linear isomorphism. Moreover, $L^1([a, b], m)$ is separable and therefore so is $T(L^1([a, b], m))$. On the other hand, $L^\infty([a, b], m)$ is not separable. According to Theorem 13 of Chapter 14, if the dual of a Banach space V is separable, then V also is separable. Therefore $T(L^1([a, b], m))$ is a proper subspace of $[L^\infty([a, b], m)]^*$. We therefore infer from the Kantorovitch Representation Theorem that there is a bounded finitely additive signed measure ν on $\mathcal{M}$ that is absolutely continuous with respect to m but for which there is no function $g \in L^1([a, b], m)$ for which

$$\int_{[a, b]} f \, d\nu = \int_{[a, b]} g \cdot f \, dm \text{ for all } f \in L^\infty([a, b], m). \tag{21}$$

The set function ν cannot be countably additive since if it were, according to Corollary 20, there would be an $L^1([a, b], m)$ function g for which (21) holds. Thus ν is a bounded set function on the Lebesgue measurable subsets of $[a, b]$, is absolutely continuous with respect to Lebesgue measure, is finitely additive but not countably additive. No such set function has been explicitly exhibited.

---

[3] Here we need to return to the formal definition of $L^\infty(X, \mu)$ as equivalence classes of functions with respect to the equivalence of equality almost everywhere $[\mu]$ and recognize that S is defined on these equivalence classes. Since χ_E is the representative of the zero equivalence class and S is linear, $S(\chi_E) = 0$.

PROBLEMS

In the following problems $(X, \mathcal{M}, \mu)$ is a complete measure space.

9. Show that $\mathcal{BFA}(X, \mathcal{M}, \mu)$ is a linear space on which $\| \cdot \|_{\text{var}}$ is a norm. Then show that this normed linear space is a Banach space.

10. Let $\nu: \mathcal{M} \to \mathbf{R}$ be a signed measure and $(X, \mathcal{M}, \mu)$ be σ-finite. Show that there is a function $f \in L^1(X, \mu)$ for which

$$\int_X g \, d\nu = \int_X g \cdot f \, d\mu \text{ for all } g \in L^\infty(X, \mu).$$

11. Let $\{\nu_n\}$ be a bounded sequence in $\mathcal{BFA}([a, b], \mathcal{L}, m)$. Show that there is a subsequence $\{\nu_{n_k}\}$ and $\nu \in \mathcal{BFA}([a, b], \mathcal{L}, m)$ such that

$$\lim_{k \to \infty} \int_X f \, d\nu_{n_k} = \int_X f \, d\nu \text{ for all } f \in L^1([a, b], m).$$

12. Let $\{\mu_n\}$ be a sequence of measures on the Lebesgue measurable space $([a, b], \mathcal{L})$ for which $\{\mu_n([a, b])\}$ is bounded and each ν_n is absolutely continuous with respect to Lebesgue measure m. Show that a subsequence of $\{\mu_n\}$ converges setwise on $\mathcal{M}$ to a measure on $([a, b], \mathcal{L})$ that is absolutely continuous with respect to m.

19.4   WEAK SEQUENTIAL COMPACTNESS IN $L^p(X, \mu), 1 < p < 1$

Recall that for X a normed linear space, the dual space of bounded linear functionals on X is denoted by X^* and the dual of X^* is denoted by X^{**}. The natural embedding $J: X \to X^{**}$ is defined by

$$J(x)[\psi] = \psi(x) \text{ for all } x \in X, \psi \in X^*.$$

We inferred from the Hahn-Banach Theorem that the natural embedding is an isometry and called X reflexive provided the natural embedding maps X onto X^{**}. Theorem 17 of Chapter 14 tells us that every bounded sequence in a reflexive Banach space has a weakly convergent subsequence.

Theorem 8 *Let $(X, \mathcal{M}, \mu)$ be a σ-finite measure space and $1 < p < \infty$. Then $L^p(X, \mu)$ is a reflexive Banach space.*

Proof The Riesz Representation Theorem tells us that for conjugate numbers $r, s \in (1, \infty)$, the operator $T_r: L^r \to (L^s)^*$, defined by

$$[T_r(h)](g) = \int_a^b g \cdot h \text{ for all } h \in L^r \text{ and } g \in L^s,$$

is an isometric isomorphism from L^r onto $(L^s)^*$. To verify the reflexivity of L^p we let $S: (L^p)^* \to \mathbf{R}$ be a continuous linear functional and seek a function $f \in L^p$ for which $S = J(f)$.[4] But observe that $S \circ T_q: L^q \to \mathbf{R}$, being the composition of continuous linear

---

[4] We repeat an earlier caveat pertaining to reflexivity. For a normed linear space X to be reflexive it is not sufficient that X be isomorphic to its bidual X^{**}; it is necessary that the natural embedding be an isomorphism of X onto X^{**}. See the article by R.C. James, "A non-reflexive Banach space isometric to its second dual," *Proc. Nat. Acad. Sci. U.S.A.* 37 (1951).

operators, also is a continuous linear functional. By the Riesz Representation Theorem, T_p maps L^p onto $(L^q)^*$, and hence there is a function $f \in L^p$ for which $S \circ T_q = T_p(f)$, that is

$$(S \circ T_q)[g] = T_p(f)[g] \text{ for all } g \in L^q.$$

Thus

$$S(T_q(g)) = T_p(f)[g] = T_q(g)[f] = J(f)(T_q(g)) \text{ for all } g \in L^q.$$

Since T_q maps L^q onto $(L^p)^*$, $S = J(f)$. □

The Riesz Weak Compactness Theorem *Let $(X, \mathcal{M}, \mu)$ be a σ-finite measure space and $1 < p < \infty$. Then every bounded sequence in $L^p(X, \mu)$ has a weakly convergent subsequence; that is, if $\{f_n\}$ is a bounded sequence $L^p(X, \mu)$, then there is a subsequence $\{f_{n_k}\}$ of $\{f_n\}$ and a function f in $L^p(X, \mu)$ for which*

$$\lim_{k \to \infty} \int_X f_{n_k} \cdot g \, d\mu = \int_X f \cdot g \, d\mu \text{ for all } g \in L^q(X, \mu), \text{ where } 1/p + 1/q = 1.$$

Proof The preceding theorem asserts that $L^p(X, \mu)$ is reflexive. However, according to Theorem 17 of Chapter 14, every bounded sequence in a reflexive Banach space has a weakly convergent subsequence. The conclusion now follows from the Riesz Representation Theorem for the dual of $L^p(X, \mu)$. □

In Chapter 8, we studied weak convergence in $L^p(E, m)$, where E is a Lebesgue measurable set of real numbers and m is Lebesgue measure. In Chapter 14, we studied properties of weakly convergent sequences in a general Banach spaces and these, of course, hold for weak convergence in $L^p(X, \mu)$. We record here, without proof, three general results about weak convergence in $L^p(X, \mu)$, for $1 < p < \infty$ and $(X, \mathcal{M}, \mu)$ a general σ-finite measure space. The proofs are the same as in the case of Lebesgue measure on the real line.

The Radon-Riesz Theorem *Let $(X, \mathcal{M}, \mu)$ be a σ-finite measure space, $1 < p < \infty$, and $\{f_n\}$ a sequence in $L^p(X, \mu)$ that converges weakly in $L^p(X, \mu)$ to f. Then*

$\{f_n\}$ converges strongly in $L^p(X, \mu)$ to f

if and only if

$$\lim_{n \to \infty} \|f_n\|_p = \|f\|_p.$$

Corollary 9 *Let $(X, \mathcal{M}, \mu)$ be a σ-finite measure space, $1 < p < \infty$ and $\{f_n\}$ a sequence in $L^p(X, \mu)$ that converges weakly in $L^p(X, \mu)$ to f. Then a subsequence of $\{f_n\}$ converges strongly in $L^p(X, \mu)$ to f if and only if*

$$\|f\|_p = \liminf \|f_n\|_p.$$

The Banach-Saks Theorem *Let $(X, \mathcal{M}, \mu)$ be a σ-finite measure space, $1 < p < \infty$, and $\{f_n\}$ a sequence in $L^p(X, \mu)$ that converges weakly in $L^p(X, \mu)$ to f. Then there is a subsequence $\{f_{n_k}\}$ for which the sequence of Cesàro means converges strongly in $L^p(X, \mu)$ to f, that is,*

$$\lim_{k \to \infty} \frac{f_{n_1} + f_{n_2} + \cdots + f_{n_k}}{k} = f \text{ strongly in } L^p(X, \mu). \tag{22}$$

PROBLEMS

13. A linear functional $S: L^p(X, \mu) \rightarrow \mathbf{R}$ is said to be positive provided $S(g) \geq 0$ for each nonnegative function g in $L^p(X, \mu)$. For $1 \leq p < \infty$ and μ σ-finite, show that each bounded linear functional on $L^p(X, \mu)$ is the difference of bounded positive linear functionals.

14. Prove the Radon-Riesz Theorem, and the Banach-Saks Theorem in the case $p = 2$.

15. Let X be the subspace of $L^\infty(\mathbf{R}, m)$, where m is Lebesgue measure, consisting of the continuous functions f that have a finite limit as $x \rightarrow \infty$. For $f \in X$, define $S(f) = \lim_{x \to \infty} f(x)$. Use the Hahn-Banach Theorem to extend S to a bounded linear functional on $L^\infty(\mathbf{R}, m)$. Show that there is not a function f in $L^1([a, b], m)$ such that

$$S(g) = \int_{\mathbf{R}} f \cdot g \, dm \text{ for all } g \in L^\infty(\mathbf{R}, m).$$

Does this contradict the Riesz Representation Theorem?

16. Let μ be the counting measure on the set of natural numbers $\mathbf{N}$.

(i) For $1 \leq p \leq \infty$, show that $L^p(\mathbf{N}, \mu) = l^p$ and thereby characterize the dual space of ℓ^p for $1 \leq p < \infty$.

(ii) Discuss the dual of $L^p(X, \mu)$ for $1 \leq p < \infty$, where μ is the counting measure on a not necessarily countable set X.

17. Find a measure space $(X, \mathcal{M}, \mu)$ with the property that all the theorems of this section hold in the case $p = 1$.

18. Show that for Lebesgue measure on a closed, bounded interval $[a, b]$ of real numbers and $p = 1$, neither the Riesz Weak Compactness Theorem, nor the Radon-Riesz Theorem, nor the Banach-Saks Theorem are true.

19.5 WEAK SEQUENTIAL COMPACTNESS IN $L^1(X, \mu)$: THE DUNFORD-PETTIS THEOREM

For a measure space $(X, \mathcal{M}, \mu)$, in general, the Banach space $L^1(X, \mu)$ is not reflexive, in which case, according to the Eberlein-Šmulian Theorem, there are bounded sequences in $L^1(X, \mu)$ that fail to have weakly convergent subsequences. It therefore is important to identify sufficient conditions for a bounded sequence in $L^1(X, \mu)$ to possess a weakly convergent subsequence. In this section we prove the Dunford-Pettis Theorem, which tells us that, for $\mu(X) < \infty$, if a bounded sequence in $L^1(X, \mu)$ is uniformly integrable, then it has a weakly convergent subsequence. Recall that a sequence $\{f_n\}$ in $L^1(X, \mu)$ is said to be uniformly integrable provided for each $\epsilon > 0$, there is a $\delta > 0$ such that for any measurable set E,

$$\text{if } \mu(E) < \delta, \text{ then } \int_E |f_n| \, d\mu < \epsilon \text{ for all } n.$$

For finite measure spaces, we have the following characterization of uniform integrability.

Proposition 10 *For a finite measure space $(X, \mathcal{M}, \mu)$ and bounded sequence $\{f_n\}$ in $L^1(X, \mu)$, the following two properties are equivalent:*

(i) $\{f_n\}$ is uniformly integrable over X.

(ii) For each $\epsilon > 0$, there is an $M > 0$ such that

$$\int_{\{x \in X \,||\, f_n(x)| \geq M\}} |f_n| < \epsilon \text{ for all } n. \tag{23}$$

Proof Since $\{f_n\}$ is bounded, we may choose $C > 0$ such that $\|f_n\|_1 \leq C$ for all n. First assume (i). Let $\epsilon > 0$. Choose $\delta > 0$ such that if E is measurable and $\mu(E) < \delta$, then, $\int_E |f_n| d\mu < \epsilon$ for all n. By Chebychev's Inequality,

$$\mu\{x \in X \mid |f_n(x)| \geq M\} \leq \frac{1}{M} \int_X |f_n| d\mu \leq \frac{C}{M} \text{ for all } n.$$

Hence if $M > C/\delta$, then $\mu\{x \in X \,||\, f_n(x)| \geq M\} < \delta$ and therefore (23) holds. Now assume that (ii) holds. Let $\epsilon > 0$. Choose $M > 0$ such that

$$\int_{\{x \in X \,||\, f_n(x)| \geq M\}} |f_n| < \epsilon/2 \text{ for all } n.$$

Define $\delta = \epsilon/2M$. Then by the choice of M and δ, for any measurable set E, if $\mu(E) < \delta$ and n is any natural number, then

$$\int_E |f_n| d\mu = \int_{\{x \in E \,||\, f_n(x)| \geq M\}} |f_n| d\mu + \int_{\{x \in E \,||\, f_n(x)| < M\}} |f_n| d\mu < \epsilon/2 + M \cdot \mu(E) < \epsilon.$$

Therefore $\{f_n\}$ is uniformly integrable over X. $\qquad\square$

For an extended real-valued measurable function f on X and $\alpha > 0$, define the **truncation at level** α of f, $f^{[\alpha]}$, on X by

$$f^{[\alpha]}(x) = \begin{cases} 0 & \text{if } f(x) > \alpha \\ f(x) & \text{if } -\alpha \leq f(x) \leq \alpha \\ 0 & \text{if } f(x) < -\alpha. \end{cases}$$

Observe that if $\mu(X) < \infty$, then for $f \in L^1(X, \mu)$ and $\alpha > 0$, $f^{[\alpha]}$ belongs to $L^1(X, \mu)$ and has the following approximation property:

$$\left| \int_X [f - f^{[\alpha]}] d\mu \right| \leq \int_{\{x \in X \,||\, f(x)| > \alpha\}} |f| d\mu. \tag{24}$$

Lemma 11 For a finite measure space $(X, \mathcal{M}, \mu)$ and bounded uniformly integrable sequence $\{f_n\}$ in $L^1(X, \mu)$, there is a subsequence $\{f_{n_k}\}$ such that for each measurable subset E of X,

$$\left\{ \int_E f_{n_k} d\mu \right\} \text{ is Cauchy.} \tag{25}$$

Proof We first describe the centerpiece of the proof. If $\{g_n\}$ is any bounded sequence in $L^1(X, \mu)$ and $\alpha > 0$, then, since $\mu(X) < \infty$, the truncated sequence $\{g_n^{[\alpha]}\}$ is bounded in

$L^2(X, \mu)$. The Riesz Weak Compactness Theorem tells us that there is a subsequence $\left\{g_{n_k}^{[\alpha]}\right\}$ that converges weakly in $L^2(X, \mu)$. Since $\mu(X) < \infty$, integration over a fixed measurable set is a bounded linear functional on $L^2(X, \mu)$ and therefore for each measurable subset E of X, $\left\{\int_E g_{n_k}^{[\alpha]} d\mu\right\}$ is Cauchy. The full proof uses this observation together with a diagonalization argument.

Indeed, let $\alpha = 1$. There is a subsequence of $\{f_n\}$ for which the truncation at level 1 converges weakly in $L^2(X, \mu)$. We can then take a subsequence of the first subsequence for which the truncation at level 2 converges weakly in $L^2(X, \mu)$. We continue inductively to find a sequence of sequences, each of which is a subsequence of its predecessor and the truncation at level k of the kth subsequence converges weakly in $L^2(X, \mu)$. Denote the diagonal sequence by $\{h_n\}$. Then $\{h_n\}$ is a subsequence of $\{f_n\}$ and for each natural number k and measurable subset E of X,

$$\left\{\int_E h_n^{[k]} d\mu\right\} \text{ is Cauchy.} \tag{26}$$

Let E be a measurable set. We claim that

$$\left\{\int_E h_n d\mu\right\} \text{ is Cauchy.} \tag{27}$$

Let $\epsilon > 0$. Observe that for natural numbers $k, n,$ and m,

$$h_n - h_m = \left[h_n^{[k]} - h_m^{[k]}\right] + \left[h_m^{[k]} - h_m\right] + \left[h_n - h_n^{[k]}\right].$$

Therefore, by (24),

$$\left|\int_E [h_n - h_m] d\mu\right| \leq \left|\int_E [h_n^{[k]} - h_m^{[k]}] d\mu\right| + \int_{\{x \in E \,|\, |h_m|(x) > k\}} |h_m| d\mu + \int_{\{x \in E \,|\, |h_n|(x) > k\}} |h_n| d\mu. \tag{28}$$

We infer from the uniform integrability of $\{f_n\}$ and Proposition 10 that we can choose a natural number k_0 such that

$$\int_{\{x \in E \,|\, |h_n|(x) > k_0\}} |h_n| d\mu < \epsilon/3 \text{ for all } n. \tag{29}$$

On the other hand, by (26) at $k = k_0$, there is an index N such that

$$\left|\int_E [h_n^{[k_0]} - h_m^{[k_0]}] d\mu\right| < \epsilon/3 \text{ for all } n, m \geq N. \tag{30}$$

We infer from (28), (29), and (30) that

$$\left|\int_E [h_n - h_m] d\mu\right| < \epsilon \text{ for all } n, m \geq N.$$

Therefore (27) holds and the proof is complete. $\square$

Theorem 12 (the Dunford-Pettis Theorem)   *For a finite measure space $(X, \mathcal{M}, \mu)$ and bounded sequence $\{f_n\}$ in $L^1(X, \mu)$, the following two properties are equivalent:*

(i) *$\{f_n\}$ is uniformly integrable over X.*

(ii) *Every subsequence of $\{f_n\}$ has a further subsequence that converges weakly in $L^1(X, \mu)$.*

Proof First assume (i). It suffices to show that $\{f_n\}$ has a subsequence that converges weakly in $L^1(X, \mu)$. Without loss of generality, by considering positive and negative parts, we assume that each f_n is nonnegative. According to the preceding lemma, there is a subsequence of $\{f_n\}$, which we denote by $\{h_n\}$, such that for each measurable subset E of X,

$$\left\{ \int_E h_n \, d\mu \right\} \text{ is Cauchy.} \tag{31}$$

For each n, define the set function ν_n on $\mathcal{M}$ by

$$\nu_n(E) = \int_E h_n \, d\mu \text{ for all } E \in \mathcal{M}.$$

Then, by the countable additivity over domains of integration, ν_n is a measure and it is absolutely continuous with respect to μ. Moreover, for each $E \in \mathcal{M}$, $\{\nu_n(E)\}$ is Cauchy. The real numbers are complete and hence we may define a real-valued set function ν on $\mathcal{M}$ by

$$\lim_{n \to \infty} \nu_n(E) = \nu(E) \text{ for all } E \in \mathcal{M}.$$

Since $\{h_n\}$ is bounded in $L^1(X, \mu)$, the sequence $\{\nu_n(X)\}$ is bounded. Therefore, the Vitali-Hahn-Saks Theorem tells us that ν is a measure on $(X, \mathcal{M})$ that is absolutely continuous with respect to μ. According to the Radon-Nikodym Theorem, there is a function $f \in L^1(X, \mu)$ for which

$$\nu(E) = \int_E f \, d\mu \text{ for all } E \in \mathcal{M}.$$

Since

$$\lim_{n \to \infty} \int_E f_n \, d\mu = \int_E f \, d\mu \text{ for all } E \in \mathcal{M},$$

$$\lim_{n \to \infty} \int_X f_n \cdot \varphi \, d\mu = \int_X f \cdot \varphi \, d\mu \text{ for every simple function } \varphi. \tag{32}$$

By assumption, $\{f_n\}$ is bounded in $L^1(X, \mu)$. Furthermore, by the Simple Approximation Lemma, the simple functions are dense in $L^\infty(X, \mu)$. Hence

$$\lim_{n \to \infty} \int_X f_n \cdot g \, d\mu = \int_X f \cdot g \, d\mu \text{ for all } g \in L^\infty(X, \mu), \tag{33}$$

that is, $\{f_n\}$ converges weakly in $L^1(X, \mu)$ to f.

It remains to show that (ii) implies (i). We argue by contradiction. Suppose $\{f_n\}$ satisfies (ii) but fails to be uniformly integrable. Then there is an $\epsilon > 0$, a subsequence $\{h_n\}$ of $\{f_n\}$, and a sequence $\{E_n\}$ of measurable sets for which

$$\lim_{n \to \infty} \mu_n(E_n) = 0 \text{ but } \int_{E_n} h_n \, d\mu \geq \epsilon_0 \text{ for all } n. \tag{34}$$

By assumption (ii) we may assume that $\{h_n\}$ converges weakly in $L^1(X, \mu)$ to h. For each n, define the measure ν_n on $\mathcal{M}$ by

$$\nu_n(E) = \int_E h_n \, d\mu \text{ for all } E \in \mathcal{M}.$$

Then each ν_n is absolutely continuous with respect to μ and the weak convergence in $L^1(X, \mu)$ of $\{h_n\}$ to h implies that

$$\{\nu_n(E)\} \text{ is Cauchy for all } E \in \mathcal{M}.$$

But the Vitali–Hahn–Saks Theorem tells us that $\{\nu_n(E)\}$ is uniformly absolutely continuous with respect to μ and this contradicts (34). Therefore (ii) implies (i) and the proof is complete. $\qquad \square$

Corollary 13 *Let* $(X, \mathcal{M}, \mu)$ *be a finite measure space and* $\{f_n\}$ *a sequence in* $L^1(X, \mu)$ *that is dominated by the function* $g \in L^1(X, \mu)$ *in the sense that*

$$|f_n| \leq g \text{ a.e. on } E \text{ for all } n.$$

Then $\{f_n\}$ *has a subsequence that converges weakly in* $L^1(X, \mu)$.

Proof The sequence $\{f_n\}$ is bounded in $L^1(X, \mu)$ and uniformly integrable. Apply the Dunford-Pettis Theorem. $\qquad \square$

Corollary 14 *Let* $(X, \mathcal{M}, \mu)$ *be a finite measure space,* $1 < p < \infty$, *and* $\{f_n\}$ *a bounded sequence in* $L^p(X, \mu)$. *Then* $\{f_n\}$ *has a subsequence that converges weakly in* $L^1(X, \mu)$.

Proof Since $\mu(X) < \infty$, we infer from Hölder's Inequality that $\{f_n\}$ is a bounded sequence in $L^1(X, \mu)$ and is uniformly integrable. Apply the Dunford-Pettis Theorem. $\qquad \square$

PROBLEMS

19. For a natural number n, let e_n be the sequence whose nth term is 1 and other terms are zero. For what values of p, $1 \leq p < \infty$, does $\{e_n\}$ converge weakly in ℓ^p?

20. Find a bounded sequence in $L^1([a, b], m)$, where m is Lebesgue measure, which fails to have a weakly convergent subsequence.

21. Find a measure space $(X, \mathcal{M}, \mu)$ for which every bounded sequence in $L^1(X, \mu)$ has a weakly convergent subsequence.

22. Fill in the details of the proof of Corollary 14.

23. Why is the Dunford-Pettis Theorem false if the assumption that the sequence is bounded in L^1 is dropped?

CHAPTER 20

The Construction of Particular Measures

Contents

In Chapter 17 we considered the Carathéodory construction of measure. In this chapter we first use the Carathéodory-Hahn Theorem to construct product measures and prove the classic theorems of Fubini and Tonelli. We then use this theorem to construct Lebesgue measure on Euclidean space $\mathbf{R}^n$ and show that this is a product measure and therefore iterated integration is justified. We conclude by briefly considering a few other selected measures.

20.1 PRODUCT MEASURES: THE THEOREMS OF FUBINI AND TONELLI

Throughout this section $(X, \mathcal{A}, \mu)$ and $(Y, \mathcal{B}, \nu)$ are two reference measure spaces. Consider the Cartesian product $X \times Y$ of X and Y. If $A \subseteq X$ and $B \subseteq Y$, we call $A \times B$ a rectangle. If $A \in \mathcal{A}$ and $B \in \mathcal{B}$, we call $A \times B$ a **measurable rectangle**.

Lemma 1 *Let $\{A_k \times B_k\}_{k=1}^{\infty}$ be a countable disjoint collection of measurable rectangles whose union also is a measurable rectangle $A \times B$. Then*

$$\mu(A) \times \nu(B) = \sum_{k=1}^{\infty} \mu(A_k) \times \nu(B_k).$$

Proof Fix a point $x \in A$. For each $y \in B$, the point (x, y) belongs to exactly one $A_k \times B_k$. Therefore we have the following disjoint union:

$$B = \bigcup_{\{k \,|\, x \in A_k\}} B_k.$$

By the countable additivity of the measure ν,

$$\nu(B) = \sum_{\{k \,|\, x \in A_k\}} \nu(B_k).$$

Rewrite this equality in terms of characteristic functions as follows:

$$\nu(B) \cdot \chi_A(x) = \sum_{k=1}^{\infty} \nu(B_k) \cdot \chi_{A_k}(x) \text{ for all } x \in A.$$

Since each A_k is contained in A, this equality also clearly holds for $x \in X \setminus A$. Therefore

$$\nu(B) \cdot \chi_A = \sum_{k=1}^{\infty} \nu(B_k) \cdot \chi_{A_k} \text{ on } X.$$

By the Monotone Convergence Theorem,

$$\mu(A) \times \nu(B) = \int_X \nu(B) \cdot \chi_A d\mu = \sum_{k=1}^{\infty} \int_X \nu(B_k) \cdot \chi_{A_k} d\mu = \sum_{k=1}^{\infty} \mu(A_k) \times \nu(B_k). \qquad \square$$

Proposition 2 *Let $\mathcal{R}$ be the collection of measurable rectangles in $X \times Y$ and for a measurable rectangle $A \times B$, define*

$$\lambda(A \times B) = \mu(A) \cdot \nu(B).$$

Then $\mathcal{R}$ is a semiring and $\lambda: \mathcal{R} \to [0, \infty]$ is a premeasure.

Proof It is clear that the intersection of two measurable rectangles is a measurable rectangle. The relative complement of two measurable rectangles is the disjoint union of two measurable rectangles. Indeed, let A and B be measurable subsets of X and C and D be measurable subsets of Y. Observe that

$$(A \times C) \sim (B \times D) = [(A \sim B) \times C] \cup [(A \cap B) \times (C \sim D)],$$

and the right-hand union is the disjoint union of two measurable rectangles.

It remains to show that λ is a premeasure. The finite additivity of λ follows from the preceding lemma. It is also clear that λ is monotone. To establish the countable monotonicity of λ, let the measurable rectangle E be covered by the collection $\{E_k\}_{k=1}^{\infty}$ of measurable rectangles. Since $\mathcal{R}$ is a semiring, without loss of generality, we may assume that $\{E_k\}_{k=1}^{\infty}$ is a disjoint collection of measurable rectangles. Therefore

$$E = \bigcup_{k=1}^{\infty} E \cap E_k,$$

this union is disjoint and each $E \cap E_k$ is a measurable rectangle. We infer from the preceding lemma and the monotonicity of λ that

$$\lambda(E) = \sum_{k=1}^{\infty} \lambda(E \cap E_k) \leq \sum_{k=1}^{\infty} \lambda(E_k).$$

Therefore λ is countably monotone. The proof is complete. $\qquad \square$

This proposition allows us to invoke the Carathéodory-Hahn Theorem in order to make the following definition of product measure, which assigns the natural measure, $\mu(A) \cdot \nu(B)$, to the Cartesian product $A \times B$ of measurable sets.

Definition   *Let $(X, \mathcal{A}, \mu)$ and $(Y, \mathcal{B}, \nu)$ be measure spaces, $\mathcal{R}$ the collection of measurable rectangles contained in $X \times Y$, and λ the premeasure defined on $\mathcal{R}$ by*

$$\lambda(A \times B) = \mu(A) \cdot \nu(B) \text{ for } A \times B \in \mathcal{R}.$$

By the **product measure** *$\lambda = \mu \times \nu$ we mean the Carathéodory extension of $\lambda: \mathcal{R} \to [0, \infty]$ defined on the σ-algebra of $(\mu \times \nu)^*$-measurable subsets of $X \times Y$.*

Let E be a subset of $X \times Y$ and f a function on E. For a point $x \in X$, we call the set

$$E_x = \{y \in Y \mid (x, y) \in E\} \subseteq Y$$

the **x-section** of E and the function $f(x, \cdot)$ defined on E_x by $f(x, \cdot)(y) = f(x, y)$ the **x-section** of f. Our goal now is to determine what is necessary in order that the integral of f over $X \times Y$ with respect to $\mu \times \nu$ be equal to the integral over X with respect to μ of the function on X that assigns to $x \in X$ the integral of $f(x, \cdot)$ over Y with respect to ν. This is called **iterated integration**. The following is the first of two fundamental results regarding iterated integration. [1]

Fubini's Theorem   *Let $(X, \mathcal{A}, \mu)$ and $(Y, \mathcal{B}, \nu)$ be two measure spaces and ν be complete. Let f be integrable over $X \times Y$ with respect to the product measure $\mu \times \nu$. Then for almost all $x \in X$, the x-section of f, $f(x, \cdot)$, is integrable over Y with respect to ν and*

$$\int_{X \times Y} f \, d(\mu \times \nu) = \int_X \left[\int_Y f(x, y) \, d\nu(y) \right] d\mu(x). \tag{1}$$

An integrable function vanishes outside a σ-finite set. Therefore, by the Simple Approximation Theorem and the Monotone Convergence Theorem, the integral of a general nonnegative integrable function may be arbitrarily closely approximated by the integral of a nonnegative simple function that vanishes outside a set of finite measure, that is, by a linear combination of characteristic functions of sets of finite measure. Thus the natural initial step in the proof of Fubini's Theorem is to prove it for the characteristic function of a measurable subset E of $X \times Y$ that has finite measure. Observe that for such a set, if we let f be the characteristic function of E, then

$$\int_{X \times Y} f \, d(\mu \times \nu) = (\mu \times \nu)(E).$$

On the other hand, for each $x \in X$, $f(x, \cdot) = \chi_{E_x}$ and therefore if the x-section of E, E_x, is ν-measurable, then

$$\int_Y f(x, y) \, d\nu(y) = \nu(E_x).$$

Therefore, for $f = \chi_E$, (1) reduces to the following:

$$(\mu \times \nu)(E) = \int_X \nu(E_x) \, d\mu(x).$$

---

[1] Let X_0 be a measurable subset of X for which $\mu(X \sim X_0) = 0$. For a measurable function h on X_0, we write $\int_X h \, d\mu$ to denote $\int_{X_0} h \, d\mu$, if the latter integral is defined. This convention is justified by the equality of $\int_X h \, d\mu$ and $\int_{X_0} h \, d\mu$ for every measurable extension of h to X.

Proposition 10 of Chapter 17 tells us that a measurable set $E \subseteq X \times Y$ is contained in an $\mathcal{R}_{\sigma\delta}$ set A for which $(\mu \times \nu)(A \sim E) = 0$. We therefore establish the above equality first for $\mathcal{R}_{\sigma\delta}$ sets and then for sets with product measure zero.

Lemma 3 *Let $E \subseteq X \times Y$ be an $\mathcal{R}_{\sigma\delta}$ set for which $(\mu \times \nu)(E) < \infty$. Then for all x in X, the x-section of E, E_x, is a ν-measurable subset of Y, the function $x \mapsto \nu(E_x)$ for $x \in X$ is a μ-measurable function and*

$$(\mu \times \nu)(E) = \int_X \nu(E_x) \, d\mu(x). \tag{2}$$

Proof First consider the case that $E = A \times B$, a measurable rectangle. Then, for $x \in X$,

$$E_x = \begin{cases} B & \text{for } x \in A \\ \emptyset & \text{for } x \notin A, \end{cases}$$

and therefore $\nu(E_x) = \nu(B) \cdot \chi_A(x)$. Thus

$$(\mu \times \nu)(E) = \mu(A) \cdot \nu(B) = \nu(B) \cdot \int_X \chi_A \, d\mu = \int_X \nu(E_x) \, d\mu(x).$$

We next show (2) holds if E is an $\mathcal{R}_\sigma$ set. Since $\mathcal{R}$ is a semiring, there is a disjoint collection of measurable rectangles $\{A_k \times B_k\}_{k=1}^\infty$ whose union is E. Fix $x \in X$. Observe that

$$E_x = \bigcup_{k=1}^\infty (A_k \times B_k)_x.$$

Thus E_x is ν-measurable since it is the countable union of B_k's, and since this union is disjoint, by the countable additivity of ν,

$$\nu(E_x) = \sum_{k=1}^\infty \nu((A_k \times B_k)_x).$$

Therefore, by the Monotone Convergence Theorem, the validity of (5) for each measurable rectangle $A_k \times B_k$ and the countable additivity of the measure $\mu \times \nu$,

$$\int_X \nu(E_x) \, d\mu(x) = \sum_{k=1}^\infty \int_X \nu((A_k \times B_k)_x) \, d\mu$$

$$= \sum_{k=1}^\infty \mu(A_k) \times \nu(B_k)$$

$$= (\mu \times \nu)(E).$$

Thus (2) holds if E is an $\mathcal{R}_\sigma$ set. Finally, we consider the case that E is in $\mathcal{R}_{\sigma\delta}$ and use the assumption that E has finite measure. Since $\mathcal{R}$ is a semiring, there is a descending sequence $\{E_k\}_{k=1}^\infty$ of sets in $\mathcal{R}_\sigma$ whose intersection is E. By the definition of the measure $\mu \times \nu$ in terms of the outer measure induced by the premeasure $\mu \times \nu$ on $\mathcal{R}$, since $(\mu \times \nu)(E) < \infty$, we may suppose that $(\mu \times \nu)(E_1) < \infty$. By the continuity of the measure $\mu \times \nu$,

$$\lim_{k \to \infty} (\mu \times \nu)(E_k) = (\mu \times \nu)(E). \tag{3}$$

Since E_1 is an $\mathcal{R}_\sigma$ set,

$$(\mu \times \nu)(E_1) = \int_X \nu((E_1)_x) \, d\mu(x),$$

and hence, since $(\mu \times \nu)(E_1) < \infty$,

$$\nu((E_1)_x) < \infty \text{ for almost all } x \in X. \tag{4}$$

Now for each $x \in X$, E_x is ν-measurable since it is the intersection of the descending sequence of ν-measurable sets $\{(E_k)_x\}_{k=1}^\infty$ and furthermore, by the continuity of the measure ν and (4), for almost all $x \in X$,

$$\lim_{k \to \infty} \nu((E_k)_x) = \nu(E_x).$$

Furthermore, the function $x \mapsto \nu((E_1)_x)$ is a nonnegative integrable function that, for each k, dominates almost everywhere the function $x \mapsto \nu((E_k)_x)$. Therefore by the Lebesgue Dominated Convergence Theorem, the validity of (5) for each $\mathcal{R}_\sigma$ set E_k and the continuity property (3),

$$\int_X \nu(E_x) \, d\mu(x) = \lim_{k \to \infty} \int_X \nu((E_k)_x) \, d\mu$$

$$= \lim_{k \to \infty} (\mu \times \nu)(E_k)$$

$$= (\mu \times \nu)(E).$$

The proof is complete. $\qquad\qquad\qquad\qquad\qquad\qquad\qquad\qquad\qquad\qquad\qquad\qquad\qquad\qquad\square$

Lemma 4 *Assume the measure ν is complete. Let $E \subseteq X \times Y$ be measurable with respect to $\mu \times \nu$. If $(\mu \times \nu)(E) = 0$, then for almost all $x \in X$, the x-section of E, E_x, is ν-measurable and $\nu(E_x) = 0$. Therefore*

$$(\mu \times \nu)(E) = \int_X \nu(E_x) \, d\mu(x).$$

Proof Since $(\mu \times \nu)(E) < \infty$, it follows from Proposition 10 of Chapter 17 that there is a set A in $\mathcal{R}_{\sigma\delta}$ for which $E \subseteq A$ and $(\mu \times \nu)(A) = 0$. According to the preceding lemma, for all $x \in X$, the x-section of A, A_x, is ν-measurable and

$$(\mu \times \nu)(A) = \int_X \nu(A_x) \, d\mu(x).$$

Thus $\nu(A_x) = 0$ for almost all $x \in X$. However, for all $x \in X$, $E_x \subseteq A_x$. Therefore we may infer from the completeness of ν that for almost all $x \in X$, E_x is ν-measurable and $\nu(E_x) = 0$. $\qquad\square$

Proposition 5 *Assume the measure ν is complete. Let $E \subseteq X \times Y$ be measurable with respect to $\mu \times \nu$ and $(\mu \times \nu)(E) < \infty$. Then for almost all x in X, the x-section of E, E_x, is a ν-measurable subset of Y, the function $x \mapsto \nu(E_x)$ for $x \in X$ is a μ-measurable function, and*

$$(\mu \times \nu)(E) = \int_X \nu(E_x) \, d\mu(x). \tag{5}$$

Proof Since $(\mu \times \nu)(E) < \infty$, it follows from Proposition 10 of Chapter 17 that there is a set A in $\mathcal{R}_{\sigma\delta}$ for which $E \subseteq A$ and $(\mu \times \nu)(E \sim A) = 0$. By the excision property of the measure $\mu \times \nu$, $(\mu \times \nu)(E) = (\mu \times \nu)(A)$. By the preceding lemma,

$$\nu(A_x) = \nu(E_x) + \nu((A \sim E)_x) = \nu(E_x) \text{ for almost all } x \in X.$$

Once more using the preceding lemma, we conclude that

$$(\mu \times \nu)(E) = (\mu \times \nu)(A)$$

$$= \int_X \nu(A_x) \, d\mu(x)$$

$$= \int_X \nu(E_x) \, d\mu(x).$$

The proof is complete. □

Theorem 6 *Assume the measure ν is complete. Let $\varphi \colon X \times Y \to \mathbf{R}$ be a simple function that is integrable over $X \times Y$ with respect to $\mu \times \nu$. Then for almost all $x \in X$, the x-section of φ, $\varphi(x, \cdot)$, is integrable over Y with respect to ν and*

$$\int_{X \times Y} \varphi \, d(\mu \times \nu) = \int_X \left[\int_Y \varphi(x, y) \, d\nu(y) \right] d\mu(x). \tag{6}$$

Proof The preceding proposition tells us that (6) holds if φ is the characteristic function of a measurable subset of $X \times Y$ of finite measure. Since φ is simple and integrable, it is a linear combination of characteristic functions of such sets. Therefore (6) follows from the preceding proposition and the linearity of integration. □

Proof of Fubini's Theorem Since integration is linear, we assume that f is nonnegative. The Simple Approximation Theorem tells us that there is an increasing sequence $\{\varphi_k\}$ of simple functions that converges pointwise on $X \times Y$ to f and, for each k, $0 \leq \varphi_k \leq f$ on $X \times Y$. Since f is integrable over $X \times Y$, each φ_k is integrable over $X \times Y$. According to the preceding proposition, for each k,

$$\int_{X \times Y} \varphi_k \, d(\mu \times \nu) = \int_X \left[\int_Y \varphi_k(x, y) \, d\nu(y) \right] d\mu(x).$$

Moreover, by the Monotone Convergence Theorem,

$$\int_{X \times Y} f \, d(\mu \times \nu) = \lim_{k \to \infty} \int_{X \times Y} \varphi_k \, d(\mu \times \nu).$$

It remains to prove that

$$\lim_{k\to\infty} \int_X \left[\int_Y \varphi_k(x, y)\, d\nu(y) \right] d\mu(x) = \int_X \left[\int_Y f(x, y)\, d\nu(y) \right] d\mu(x). \tag{7}$$

If we excise from $X \times Y$ a set of $\mu \times \nu$-measure zero, then the right-hand side of (7) remains unchanged and, by Lemma 4, so does the left-hand side. Therefore, by possibly excising from $X \times Y$ a set of $\mu \times \nu$-measure zero, we may suppose that for all $x \in X$ and all k, $\varphi_k(x, \cdot)$ is integrable over Y with respect to ν.

Fix $x \in X$. Then $\{\varphi_k(x, \cdot)\}$ is an increasing sequence of simple ν-measurable functions that converges pointwise on Y to $f(x, \cdot)$. Thus $f(x, \cdot)$ is ν-measurable and, by the Monotone Convergence Theorem,

$$\int_Y f(x, y)\, d\nu(y) = \lim_{k\to\infty} \int_Y \varphi_k(x, y)\, d\nu(y). \tag{8}$$

For each $x \in X$, define $h(x) = \int_Y f(x, y)\, d\nu(y)$ and $h_k(x) = \int_Y \varphi_k(x, y)\, d\nu(y)$. According to the preceding theorem, each $h_k \colon X \to \mathbf{R}$ is integrable over X with respect to μ. Since $\{h_k\}$ is an increasing sequence of nonnegative measurable functions that converges pointwise on X to h, by the Monotone Convergence Theorem,

$$\lim_{k\to\infty} \int_X \left[\int_Y \varphi_k(x, y)\, d\nu(y) \right] d\mu(x) = \lim_{k\to\infty} \int_X h_k\, d\mu = \int_X h\, d\mu = \int_X \left[\int_Y f(x, y)\, d\nu(y) \right] d\mu(x).$$

Therefore (7) is verified. The proof is complete.   □

In order to apply Fubini's Theorem, one must first verify that f is integrable with respect to $\mu \times \nu$; that is, one must show that f is a measurable function on $X \times Y$ and that $\int |f|\, d(\mu \times \nu) < \infty$. The measurability of f on $X \times Y$ is sometimes difficult to establish, but in many cases we can establish it by topological considerations (see Problem 9). In general, from the existence and finiteness of the iterated integral on the right-hand side of (1), we cannot infer that f in integrable over $X \times Y$ (see Problem 6). However, we may infer from the following theorem that if ν is complete, the measures μ and ν are σ-finite and f is *nonnegative* and measurable with respect to $\mu \times \nu$, then the finiteness of the iterated integral on the right-hand side of (1) implies that f is integrable over $X \times Y$ and the equality (1) does hold.

Tonelli's Theorem *Let $(X, \mathcal{A}, \mu)$ and $(Y, \mathcal{B}, \nu)$ be two σ-finite measure spaces and ν be complete. Let f be a nonnegative $(\mu \times \nu)$-measurable function $X \times Y$. Then for almost all $x \in X$, the x-section of f, $f(x, \cdot)$, is ν-measurable and the function defined almost everywhere on X by $x \mapsto$ the integral of $f(x, \cdot)$ over Y with respect to ν is μ-measurable. Moreover,*

$$\int_{X \times Y} f\, d(\mu \times \nu) = \int_X \left[\int_Y f(x, y)\, d\nu(y) \right] d\mu(x). \tag{9}$$

Proof The Simple Approximation Theorem tells us that there is an increasing sequence $\{\varphi_k\}$ of simple functions that converges pointwise on $X \times Y$ to f and, for each k, $0 \le \varphi_k \le f$ on $X \times Y$. At this point in the proof of Fubini's Theorem, we invoked the integrability of the nonnegative function $|f|$ to conclude that since each $0 \le \varphi_k \le |f|$ on X, each φ_k is integrable and hence we were able to apply Theorem 6 for each φ_k. Here we observe that the product measure $\mu \times \nu$ is σ-finite since both μ and ν are σ-finite. Therefore we may invoke assertion (i) of the Simple Approximation Theorem in order to choose the sequence to $\{\varphi_k\}$ to have the additional property that each φ_k vanishes outside of a set of finite measure and therefore is integrable. The proof from this point on is exactly the same as that of Fubini's Theorem. $\square$

Two comments regarding Tonelli's Theorem are in order. First, each of the integrals in (9) may be infinite. If one of them is finite, so is the other. Second, if μ is complete, then the right-hand integral in (9) may be replaced by an iterated integral in the reverse order. Indeed, we have considered iterated integration by integrating first with respect to y and then with respect to x. Of course, all the results hold if one integrates in the reverse order, provided in each place we required the completeness of ν we now require completeness of μ.

Corollary 7 (Tonelli) *Let $(X, \mathcal{A}, \mu)$ and $(Y, \mathcal{B}, \nu)$ be two σ-finite, complete measure spaces and f a nonnegative $(\mu \times \nu)$-measurable function on $X \times Y$. Then (i) for almost all $x \in X$, the x-section of f, $f(x, \cdot)$, is ν-measurable and the function defined almost everywhere on X by $x \mapsto$ the integral of $f(x, \cdot)$ over Y with respect to ν is μ-measurable and (ii) for almost all $y \in Y$, the y-section of f, $f(\cdot, y)$, is μ-measurable and the function defined almost everywhere on Y by $y \mapsto$ the integral of $f(\cdot, y)$ over X with respect to μ is ν-measurable. If*

$$\int_X \left[\int_Y f(x, y) \, d\nu(y) \right] d\mu(x) < \infty, \tag{10}$$

then f is integrable over $X \times Y$ with respect to $\mu \times \nu$ and

$$\int_Y \left[\int_X f(x, y) \, d\mu(x) \right] d\nu(y) = \int_{X \times Y} f \, d(\mu \times \nu) = \int_X \left[\int_Y f(x, y) \, d\nu(y) \right] d\mu(x). \tag{11}$$

Proof Tonelli's Theorem tells us that f is integrable over $X \times Y$ with respect to $\mu \times \nu$ and we have the right-hand equality in (11). Therefore f is integrable over $X \times Y$ with respect to $\mu \times \nu$. We now apply Fubini's Theorem to verify the left-hand equality in (11). $\square$

The examples in the problems show that we cannot omit the hypothesis of the integrability of f from Fubini's Theorem and cannot omit either σ-finiteness or nonnegativity from Tonelli's Theorem (see Problems 5 and 6). In Problem 5 we exhibit a bounded function f on the product $X \times Y$ of finite measure spaces for which

$$\int_X \left[\int_Y f(x, y) \, d\nu(y) \right] d\mu(x) \neq \int_Y \left[\int_X f(x, y) \, d\mu(x) \right] d\nu(y)$$

even though each of these iterated integrals is properly defined.

We conclude this section with some comments regarding a different approach to the development of a product measure. Given two measure spaces $(X, \mathcal{A}, \mu)$ and $(Y, \mathcal{B}, \nu)$, the smallest σ-algebra of subsets of $X \times Y$ containing the measurable rectangles is denoted by $\mathcal{A} \times \mathcal{B}$. Thus the product measure is defined on a σ-algebra containing $\mathcal{A} \times \mathcal{B}$. These two measures are related by Proposition 10, of Chapter 17, which tells us that the $\mu \times \nu$-measurable sets that have finite $\mu \times \nu$-measure are those that differ from sets in $\mathcal{A} \times \mathcal{B}$ by sets of $\mu \times \nu$-measure zero. Many authors prefer to define the product measure to be the restriction of $\mu \times \nu$ to $\mathcal{A} \times \mathcal{B}$. The advantage of our definition of the product measure is that this does what we want for Lebesgue measure: As we will see in the next section, the product of m-dimensional Lebesgue measure with k-dimensional Lebesgue measure is $(m + k)$-dimensional Lebesgue measure. Since our hypotheses for the Fubini and Tonelli Theorems require only measurability with respect to the product measure, they are weaker than requiring measurability with respect to $\mathcal{A} \times \mathcal{B}$. Moreover, a function that is integrable with respect to $\mathcal{A} \times \mathcal{B}$ is also integrable with respect to the product measure that we have defined.

The product measure is induced by an outer measure and therefore is complete. But we needed to assume that ν is complete in order to show that if $E \subseteq X \times Y$ is measurable with respect to our product measure, then almost all the x-sections of E are ν-measurable. If, however, E is measurable with respect to $\mathcal{A} \times \mathcal{B}$, then all of the x-sections on E belong to $\mathcal{A}$ even if ν is not complete. This follows from the observation that the collection of subsets of $X \times Y$ that have all of their x-sections belonging to $\mathcal{B}$ is a σ-algebra containing the measurable rectangles.

PROBLEMS

1. Let $A \subseteq X$ and let B be a ν-measurable subset of Y. If $A \times B$ is measurable with respect to the product measure $\mu \times \nu$, is A necessarily measurable with respect to μ?

2. Let $\mathbf{N}$ be the set of natural numbers, $\mathcal{M} = 2^{\mathbf{N}}$, and c the counting measure defined by setting $c(E)$ equal to the number of points in E if E is finite and ∞ if E is an infinite set. Prove that every function $f : \mathbf{N} \to \mathbf{R}$ is measurable with respect to c and that f is integrable over $\mathbf{N}$ with respect to c if and only if the series $\sum_{k=1}^{\infty} f(k)$ is absolutely convergent in which case

$$\int_{\mathbf{N}} f \, dc = \sum_{k=1}^{\infty} f(k).$$

3. Let $(X, \mathcal{A}, \mu) = (Y, \mathcal{B}, \nu) = (\mathbf{N}, \mathcal{M}, c)$, the measure space defined in the preceding problem. State the Fubini and Tonelli Theorems explicitly for this case.

4. Let $(\mathbf{N}, \mathcal{M}, c)$ be the measure space defined in Problem 2 and $(X, \mathcal{A}, \mu)$ a general measure space. Consider $\mathbf{N} \times X$ with the product measure $c \times \mu$.

   (i) Show that a subset E of $\mathbf{N} \times X$ is measurable with respect to $c \times \mu$ if and only if for each natural number k, $E_k = \{x \in X \mid (k, x) \in E\}$ is measurable with respect to μ.

   (ii) Show that a function $f : \mathbf{N} \times X \to \mathbf{R}$ is measurable with respect to $c \times \mu$ if and only if for each natural number k, $f(k, \cdot) : X \to \mathbf{R}$ is measurable with respect to μ.

   (iii) Show that a function $f : \mathbf{N} \times X \to \mathbf{R}$ is integrable over $\mathbf{N} \times X$ with respect to $c \times \mu$ if and only if for each natural number k, $f(k, \cdot) : X \to \mathbf{R}$ is integrable over X with respect to μ and

$$\sum_{k=1}^{\infty} \int_X |f(k, x)| \, d\mu(x) < \infty.$$

   (iv) Show that if the function $f : \mathbf{N} \times X \to \mathbf{R}$ is integrable over $\mathbf{N} \times X$ with respect to $c \times \mu$, then

$$\int_{\mathbf{N} \times X} f \, d(c \times \mu) = \sum_{k=1}^{\infty} \int_X f(k, x) \, d\mu(x) < \infty.$$

5. Let $(X, \mathcal{A}, \mu) = (Y, \mathcal{B}, \nu) = (\mathbf{N}, \mathcal{M}, c)$, the measure space defined in Problem 2. Define $f : \mathbf{N} \times \mathbf{N} \to \mathbf{R}$ by setting

$$f(x, y) = \begin{cases} 2 - 2^{-x} & \text{if } x = y \\ -2 + 2^{-x} & \text{if } x = y + 1 \\ 0 & \text{otherwise.} \end{cases}$$

Show that f is measurable with respect to the product measure $c \times c$. Also show that

$$\int_{\mathbf{N}} \left[\int_{\mathbf{N}} f(m, n) \, dc(m) \right] dc(n) \neq \int_{\mathbf{N}} \left[\int_{\mathbf{N}} f(m, n) \, dc(n) \right] dc(m).$$

Is this a contradiction either of Fubini's Theorem or Tonelli's Theorem?

6. Let $X = Y$ be the interval $[0, 1]$, with $\mathcal{A} = \mathcal{B}$ the class of Borel sets. Let μ be Lebesgue measure and $\nu = c$ the counting measure. Show that the diagonal $\Delta = \{(x, y) \mid x = y\}$ is measurable with respect to the product measure $\mu \times c$ (is an $\mathcal{R}_{\sigma\delta}$, in fact). Show that if f is the characteristic function of D,

$$\int_{[0, 1] \times [0, 1]} f \, d(\mu \times c) \neq \int_{[0, 1]} \left[\int_{[0, 1]} f(x, y) \, dc(y) \right] d\mu(x).$$

Is this a contradiction either of Fubini's Theorem or Tonelli's Theorem?

7. Prove that the conclusion of Tonelli's Theorem is true if one of the spaces is the space $(\mathbf{N}, \mathcal{M}, c)$ defined in Problem 2 and the other space is a general measure space that need not be σ-finite.

8. In the proof of Fubini's Theorem justify the excision from $X \times Y$ of a set of $\mu \times \nu$ measure zero.

9. Let $X = Y = [0, 1]$, and let $\mu = \nu$ be Lebesgue measure. Show that each open set in $X \times Y$ is measurable, and hence each Borel set in $X \times Y$ is measurable. Is every continuous real-valued function on $[0, 1] \times [0, 1]$ measurable with respect to the product measure?

10. Let h and g be integrable functions on X and Y, and define $f(x, y) = h(x)g(y)$. Show that f is integrable on $X \times Y$ with respect to the product measure, then

$$\int_{X \times Y} f \, d(\mu \times \nu) = \int_X h \, d\mu \int_Y g \, d\nu.$$

(Note: We do not need to assume that μ and ν are σ-finite.)

11. Show that Tonelli's Theorem is still true if, instead of assuming μ and ν to be σ-finite, we merely assume that $\{(x, y) \mid f(x, y) \neq 0\}$ is a set of σ-finite measure.

12. For two measure spaces $(X, \mathcal{A}, \mu)$ and $(Y, \mathcal{B}, \nu)$ we have defined $\mathcal{A} \times \mathcal{B}$ to be the smallest σ-algebra that contains the measurable rectangles.

   (i)   Show that if both measures are σ-finite, then $\mu \times \nu$ is the only measure on $\mathcal{A} \times \mathcal{B}$ that assigns the value $\mu(A) \cdot \nu(B)$ to each measurable rectangle $A \times B$. Also that this uniqueness property may fail if we do not have σ-finiteness.

   (ii) Show that if $E \in \mathcal{A} \times \mathcal{B}$, then $E_x \in \mathcal{B}$ for each x.

   (iii) Show that if f is measurable with respect to $\mathcal{A} \times \mathcal{B}$, then $f(x, \cdot)$ is measurable with respect to $\mathcal{B}$ for each x.

13. If $\{(X_k, \mathcal{A}_k, \mu_k)\}_{k=1}^n$ is a finite collection of measure spaces, we can form the product measure $\mu_1 \times \cdots \times \mu_n$ on the space $X_1 \times \cdots \times X_n$ by starting with the semiring of rectangles of the form $R = A_1 \times \cdots \times A_n$, define $\mu(R) = \prod \mu_k(A_k)$, show that μ is a premeasure and define the product measure to be the Carathéodory extension of μ. Show that if we identify $(X_1 \times \cdots \times X_p) \times (X_{p+1} \times \cdots \times X_n)$ with $(X_1 \times \cdots \times X_n)$, then $(\mu_1 \times \cdots \times \mu_p) \times (\mu_{p+1} \times \cdots \times \mu_n) = \mu_1 \times \cdots \times \mu_n$.

14. A measure space $(X, \mathcal{M}, \mu)$ such that $\mu(X) = 1$ is called a probability measure space. Let $\{(X_\lambda, \mathcal{A}_\lambda, \mu_\lambda)\}_{\lambda \in \Lambda}$ be a collection of probability measure spaces parametrized by the set Λ. Show that we can define a probability measure

$$\mu = \prod_{\lambda \in \Lambda} \mu_\lambda$$

on a suitable σ-algebra on the Cartesian product $\prod_{\lambda \in \Lambda} X_\lambda$ so that

$$\mu(A) = \prod_{\lambda \in \Lambda} \mu_\lambda(A_\lambda)$$

when $A = \prod_{\lambda \in \Lambda} A_\lambda$. (Note that $\mu(A)$ can only be nonzero if all but a countable number of the A_λ have $\mu(A_\lambda) = 1$.)

20.2   LEBESGUE MEASURE ON EUCLIDEAN SPACE $\mathbf{R}^n$

For a natural number n, by $\mathbf{R}^n$ we denote the collection of ordered n-tuples of real numbers $x = (x_1, \ldots, x_n)$. Then $\mathbf{R}^n$ is a linear space and there is a bilinear form $\langle \cdot, \cdot \rangle \colon \mathbf{R}^n \times \mathbf{R}^n \to \mathbf{R}$ defined by

$$\langle x, y \rangle = \sum_{k=1}^n x_k \cdot y_k \text{ for all } x, y \in \mathbf{R}^n.$$

This bilinear form is called the inner product or the scalar product. It induces a norm $\| \cdot \|$ defined by

$$\|x\| = \sqrt{\langle x, x \rangle} = \sqrt{\sum_{k=1}^n x_k^2} \text{ for all } x \in \mathbf{R}^n.$$

This norm is called the Euclidean norm. It induces a metric and thereby a topology on $\mathbf{R}^n$. The linear space $\mathbf{R}^n$, considered with this inner product and induced metric and topology, is called n-dimensional Euclidean space.

By a bounded interval in $\mathbf{R}$ we mean a set of the form $[a, b], [a, b), (a, b]$ or (a, b) for real numbers $a \leq b$. So here we are considering the empty-set and the set consisting of a single point to be a bounded interval. For a bounded interval I with end-points a and b, we define its length $\ell(I)$ to be $b - a$.

Definition   *By a* **bounded interval** *in* $\mathbf{R}^n$ *we mean a set* I *that is the Cartesian product of n bounded intervals on real numbers,*

$$I = I_1 \times I_2 \times \cdots \times I_n.$$

We define the **volume** *of* I, $\mathrm{vol}(I)$, *by*

$$\mathrm{vol}(I) = \ell(I_1) \cdot \ell(I_2) \cdots \cdot \ell(I_n).$$

Definition *We call a point in $\mathbf{R}^n$ an* **integral point** *provided each of its coordinates is an integer and for a bounded interval I in $\mathbf{R}^n$, we define its* **integral count**, $\mu^{integral}(I)$, *to be the number of integral points in I.*

Lemma 8 *For each $\epsilon > 0$, define the ϵ-dilation $T_\epsilon: \mathbf{R}^n \to \mathbf{R}^n$ by $T_\epsilon(x) = \epsilon \cdot x$. Then for each bounded interval I in $\mathbf{R}^n$,*

$$\lim_{\epsilon \to \infty} \frac{\mu^{integral}(T_\epsilon(I))}{\epsilon^n} = \text{vol}(I). \tag{12}$$

Proof For a bounded interval I in $\mathbf{R}$ with end-points a and b, we have the following estimate for the integral count of I (see Problem 18):

$$(b - a) - 1 \le \mu^{integral}(I) \le (b - a) + 1. \tag{13}$$

Therefore for the interval $I = I_1 \times I_2 \times \cdots \times I_n$, since

$$\mu^{integral}(I) = \mu^{integral}(I_1) \cdots \mu^{integral}(I_n),$$

if each I_k has end-points a_k and b_k, we have the estimate:

$$[(b_1 - a_1) - 1] \cdots [(b_n - a_n) - 1] \le \mu^{integral}(I) \le [(b_1 - a_1) + 1] \cdots [(b_n - a_n) + 1]. \tag{14}$$

For $\epsilon > 0$ we replace the interval I by the dilated interval $T_\epsilon(I)$ and obtain the estimate

$$[\epsilon \cdot (b_1 - a_1) - 1] \cdots [\epsilon \cdot (b_n - a_n) - 1] \le \mu^{integral}(T_\epsilon(I)) \le [\epsilon \cdot (b_1 - a_1) + 1] \cdots [\epsilon \cdot (b_n - a_n) + 1]. \tag{15}$$

Divide this inequality by ϵ^n and take the limit as $\epsilon \to \infty$ to obtain (12). $\qquad \square$

We leave the proof of the following proposition as an exercise in induction, using the property that the Cartesian product of two semirings is a semiring (see Problem 25).

Proposition 9 *The collection $\mathcal{I}$ of bounded intervals in $\mathbf{R}^n$ is a semiring.*

Proposition 10 *The set function volume, $\text{vol}: \mathcal{I} \to [0, \infty)$, is a premeasure on the semiring $\mathcal{I}$ of bounded intervals in $\mathbf{R}^n$.*

Proof We first show that volume is finitely additive over finite disjoint unions of bounded intervals. Let I be a bounded interval in $\mathbf{R}^n$ that is the union of the finite disjoint finite collection on bounded intervals $\{I^k\}_{k=1}^m$. Then for each $\epsilon > 0$, the bounded interval $T_\epsilon(I)$ is the union of the finite disjoint collection of bounded intervals $\{T_\epsilon(I^k)\}_{k=1}^m$. It is clear that the integral count $\mu^{integral}$ is finitely additive. Thus

$$\mu^{integral}(T_\epsilon(I)) = \sum_{k=1}^m \text{vol}(T_\epsilon(I^k)) \text{ for all } \epsilon > 0.$$

Divide each side by ϵ^n and take the limit as $\epsilon \to \infty$ to obtain, by (12),

$$\text{vol}(I) = \sum_{k=1}^m \text{vol}(I^k).$$

Therefore the set function volume is finitely additive.

It remains to establish the countable monotonicity of volume. Let I be a bounded interval in $\mathbf{R}^n$ that is covered by the countable collection on bounded intervals $\{I^k\}_{k=1}^{\infty}$. We first consider the case that I is a closed interval and each I^k is open. By the Heine-Borel Theorem, we may choose a natural number m for which I is covered by the finite subcollection $\{I^k\}_{k=1}^{m}$. It is clear that the integral count $\mu^{integral}$ is monotone and finitely additive and therefore, since the collection of intervals is a semiring, finitely monotone. Thus

$$\mu^{integral}(I) \leq \sum_{k=1}^{m} \mu^{integral}(I^k).$$

Dilate these intervals. Therefore

$$\mu^{integral}(T_\epsilon(I)) \leq \sum_{k=1}^{m} \mu^{integral}(T_\epsilon(I^k)) \text{ for all } \epsilon > 0.$$

Divide each side by ϵ^n and take the limit as $\epsilon \to \infty$ to obtain, by (12),

$$\text{vol}(I) \leq \sum_{k=1}^{m} \text{vol}(I^k) \leq \sum_{k=1}^{\infty} \text{vol}(I^k).$$

It remains to consider the case of a collection $\{I^k\}_{k=1}^{\infty}$ of general bounded intervals that cover the interval I. Let $\epsilon > 0$. Choose a closed interval $\hat{I}$ that is contained in I and a collection $\{\hat{I}^k\}_{k=1}^{\infty}$ of open intervals such that each $I^m \subseteq \hat{I}^m$ and, moreover,

$$\text{vol}(I) - \text{vol}(\hat{I}) < \epsilon \text{ and } \text{vol}(\hat{I}^m) - \text{vol}(I^m) < \epsilon/2^m \text{ for all } m.$$

By the case just considered,

$$\text{vol}(\hat{I}) \leq \sum_{k=1}^{\infty} \text{vol}(\hat{I}^k).$$

Therefore

$$\text{vol}(I) \leq \sum_{k=1}^{\infty} \text{vol}(I^k) + 2\epsilon.$$

Since this holds for all $\epsilon > 0$ it also holds for $\epsilon = 0$. Therefore the set function volume is a premeasure. $\square$

Definition *The outer measure μ_n^* induced by the premeasure volume on the semiring of bounded intervals in $\mathbf{R}^n$ is called* **Lebesgue outer measure** *on $\mathbf{R}^n$. The collection of μ_n^*-measurable sets is denoted by $\mathcal{L}^n$ and called the Lebesgue measurable sets. The restriction of μ_n^* to $\mathcal{L}^n$ is called* **Lebesgue measure** *on $\mathbf{R}^n$ or n-dimensional Lebesgue measure and denoted by μ_n.*

Theorem 11 *The σ-algebra $\mathcal{L}^n$ of Lebesgue measurable subsets of $\mathbf{R}^n$ contains the bounded intervals in $\mathbf{R}^n$ and, indeed, the Borel subsets of $\mathbf{R}^n$. Moreover, the measure space $(\mathbf{R}^n, \mathcal{L}^n, \mu_n)$ is both σ-finite and complete and for a bounded interval I in $\mathbf{R}^n$,*

$$\mu_n(I) = \text{vol}(I).$$

Proof According to the preceding proposition, volume is a premeasure on the semiring of bounded intervals in $\mathbf{R}^n$. It clearly is σ-finite. Therefore the Carathéodory-Hahn Theorem tells us that Lebesgue measure is an extension of volume and the measure space $(\mathbf{R}^n, \mathcal{L}^n, \mu_n)$ is both σ-finite and complete. It remains to show that each Borel set is Lebesgue measurable. Since the collection of Borel sets is the smallest σ-algebra containing the open sets, it suffices to show that each open subset $\mathcal{O}$ of $\mathbf{R}^n$ is Lebesgue measurable. Let $\mathcal{O}$ be open in $\mathbf{R}^n$. The collection of points in $\mathcal{O}$ that have rational coordinates is a countable dense subset of $\mathcal{O}$. Let $\{z_k\}_{k=1}^\infty$ be an enumeration of this collection. For each k, consider the open cube [2] $I_{k,n}$ centered at z_k of edge-length $1/n$. We leave it as an exercise to show that

$$\mathcal{O} = \bigcup_{I_{k,n} \subseteq \mathcal{O}} I_{k,n} \tag{16}$$

and therefore since each $I_{k,n}$ is measurable so is $\mathcal{O}$, the countable union of these sets. $\square$

Corollary 12 *Let E be a Lebesgue measurable subset of $\mathbf{R}^n$ and $f: E \to \mathbf{R}$ be continuous. Then f is measurable with respect to n-dimensional Lebesgue measure.*

Proof Let $\mathcal{O}$ be an open set of real numbers. Then, by the continuity of f on E, $f^{-1}(\mathcal{O}) = E \cap \mathcal{U}$, where $\mathcal{U}$ is open in $\mathbf{R}^n$. According to the preceding theorem, $\mathcal{U}$ is measurable and hence so is $f^{-1}(\mathcal{O})$. $\square$

The Regularity of Lebesgue Measure   The following theorem and its corollary strongly relate Lebesgue measure on $\mathbf{R}^n$ to the topology on $\mathbf{R}^n$ induced by the Euclidean norm.

Theorem 13 *Let E of a Lebesgue measurable subset of $\mathbf{R}^n$. Then*

$$\mu_n(E) = \inf \left\{ \mu_n(\mathcal{O}) \mid E \subseteq \mathcal{O}, \mathcal{O} \text{ open} \right\} \tag{17}$$

and

$$\mu_n(E) = \sup \left\{ \mu_n(K) \mid K \subseteq E, K \text{ compact} \right\}. \tag{18}$$

Proof We consider the case in which E is bounded, and hence of finite Lebesgue measure, and leave the extension to unbounded E as an exercise. We first establish (17). Let $\epsilon > 0$. Since $\mu_n(E) = \mu_n^*(E) < \infty$, by the definition of Lebesgue outer measure, we may choose a countable collection of bounded intervals in $\mathbf{R}^n$, $\{I^m\}_{m=1}^\infty$, which covers E and

$$\sum_{m=1}^\infty \mu_n(I^m) < \mu_n(E) + \epsilon/2.$$

For each m, choose an open interval that contains I^m and has measure less than $\mu_n(I^m) + \epsilon/[2^{m+1}]$. The union of this collection of open intervals is an open set that we denote by $\mathcal{O}$. Then $E \subseteq \mathcal{O}$ and, by the countable monotonicity of measure, $\mu_n(\mathcal{O}) < \mu_n(E) + \epsilon$. Thus (17) is established.

---

[2] By a cube in $\mathbf{R}^n$ we mean an interval that is the Cartesian product of n intervals of equal length.

We now establish (18). Since E is bounded, we may choose a closed and bounded set K' that contains E. Since $K' \sim E$ is bounded, we infer from the first part of the proof that there is an open set $\mathcal{O}$ for which $K' \sim E \subseteq \mathcal{O}$ and, by the excision property of μ_n,

$$\mu_n(\mathcal{O} \sim [K' \sim E]) < \epsilon. \tag{19}$$

Define

$$K = K' \sim \mathcal{O}.$$

Then K is closed and bounded and therefore compact. From the inclusions $K' \sim E \subseteq \mathcal{O}$ and $E \subseteq K'$ we infer that

$$K = K' \sim \mathcal{O} \subseteq K' \sim [K' \sim E] = K' \cap E \subseteq E$$

and therefore $K \subseteq E$. On the other hand, from the inclusion $E \subseteq K'$ we infer that

$$E \sim K = E \sim [K' \sim \mathcal{O}] = E \cap \mathcal{O}$$

and

$$E \cap \mathcal{O} \subseteq \mathcal{O} \sim [K' \sim E].$$

Therefore, by the excision and monotonicity properties of measure and (19),

$$\mu_n(E) - \mu_n(K) = \mu_n(E \sim K) \le \mu_n(\mathcal{O} \sim [K' \sim E]) < \epsilon.$$

Thus (18) is established and the proof is complete. $\qquad\square$

Each Borel subset of $\mathbf{R}^n$ is Lebesgue measurable and hence so is any G_δ or F_σ set. Moreover, each set that has outer Lebesgue measure zero is Lebesgue measurable. Therefore the preceding theorem, together with the continuity and excision properties of measure, provides the following relatively simple characterization of Lebesgue measurable sets. It should be compared with Proposition 10 of Chapter 17.

Corollary 14   *For a subset E of $\mathbf{R}^n$, the following assertions are equivalent:*

(i) *E is measurable with respect to n-dimensional Lebesgue measure.*

(ii) *There is a G_δ subset G of $\mathbf{R}^n$ such that*

$$E \subseteq G \text{ and } \mu_n^*(G \sim E) = 0.$$

(iii) *There is a F_σ subset F of $\mathbf{R}^n$ such that*

$$F \subseteq E \text{ and } \mu_n^*(E \sim F) = 0.$$

We leave it as an exercise (see Problem 20) to infer from the above characterization of Lebesgue measurable sets that Lebesgue measure is **translation invariant** in the following sense: For $E \subseteq \mathbf{R}^n$ and $z \in \mathbf{R}^n$, define the translation of E by z by

$$E + z = \{x + z \mid x \in E\}.$$

If E is μ_n-measurable, then so is $E + z$ and

$$\mu_n(E) = \mu_n(E + z).$$

Lebesgue Measure as a Product Measure   For natural numbers n, m, and k such that $n = m + k$, consider the sets $\mathbf{R}^n$, $\mathbf{R}^m$, $\mathbf{R}^k$, and $\mathbf{R}^m \times \mathbf{R}^k$ and the mapping

$$\varphi \colon \mathbf{R}^n \to \mathbf{R}^m \times \mathbf{R}^k$$

defined by

$$\varphi(x_1, \ldots, x_n) = ((x_1, \ldots, x_m), (x_{m+1}, \ldots, x_{m+k})) \text{ for all } x \in \mathbf{R}^n. \tag{20}$$

This mapping is one-to-one and onto. Each of the sets $\mathbf{R}^n$, $\mathbf{R}^m$, and $\mathbf{R}^k$ has a linear structure, a topological structure, and a measure structure, and the product space $\mathbf{R}^m \times \mathbf{R}^k$ inherits a linear structure, a topological structure, and a measure structure from its component spaces $\mathbf{R}^m$ and $\mathbf{R}^k$. The mapping φ is an isomorphism with respect to the linear and topological structures. The following proposition tells us that the mapping φ is also an isomorphism from the viewpoint of measure.

Proposition 15   *For the mapping $\varphi \colon \mathbf{R}^n \to \mathbf{R}^m \times \mathbf{R}^k$ defined by (20), a subset E of $\mathbf{R}^n$ is measurable with respect to n-dimensional Lebesgue measure if and only if its image $\varphi(E)$ is measurable with respect to the product measure $\mu_m \times \mu_k$ on $\mathbf{R}^m \times \mathbf{R}^k$, and*

$$\mu_n(E) = (\mu_m \times \mu_k)(\varphi(E)).$$

Proof   Define $\mathcal{I}_n$ to be the collection of intervals in $\mathbf{R}^n$ and vol_n the set function volume defined on $\mathcal{I}_n$. Since vol_n is a σ-finite premeasure, it follows from the uniqueness part of the Carathéodory-Hahn Theorem that Lebesgue measure μ_n is the unique measure on $\mathcal{L}^n$ which extends $\text{vol}_n \colon \mathcal{I}_n \to [0, \infty]$. It is clear that

$$\mu_n(I) = (\mu_m \times \mu_k)(\varphi(I)) \text{ for all } I \in \mathcal{I}_n. \tag{21}$$

We leave it as an exercise for the reader to show that this implies that outer measures are preserved by φ and therefore E belongs to $\mathcal{L}^n$ if and only if $\varphi(E)$ is $(\mu_m \times \mu_k)$-measurable. Since φ is one-to-one and onto it follows that if we define

$$\mu'(E) = (\mu_m \times \mu_k)(\varphi(E)) \text{ for all } E \in \mathcal{L}^n,$$

then μ' is a measure on $\mathcal{L}^n$ that extends $\text{vol}_n \colon \mathcal{I}_n \to [0, \infty]$. Therefore, by the above uniqueness assertion regarding μ_n,

$$\mu_n(E) = \mu'(E) = (\mu_m \times \mu_k)(\varphi(E)) \text{ for all } E \in \mathcal{L}^n.$$

This completes the proof. $\square$

From this proposition, the completeness and σ-finiteness of Lebesgue measure and the Theorems of Fubini and Tonelli, we have the following theorem regarding integration with respect to Lebesgue measure on $\mathbf{R}^n$.

Theorem 16   *For natural numbers n, m, and k such that $n = m + k$, consider the mapping $\varphi \colon \mathbf{R}^n \to \mathbf{R}^m \times \mathbf{R}^k$ defined by (20). A function $f \colon \mathbf{R}^m \times \mathbf{R}^k \to \mathbf{R}$ is measurable with respect to* the product measure $\mu_m \times \mu_k$ if and only if the composition $f \circ \varphi \colon \mathbf{R}^n \to \mathbf{R}$ is measurable with respect to Lebesgue measure μ_n. If f is integrable over $\mathbf{R}^n$ with respect to Lebesgue measure μ_n, then

$$\int_{\mathbf{R}^n} f \, d\mu_n = \int_{\mathbf{R}^k} \left[\int_{\mathbf{R}^m} f(x, y) d\mu_m(x) \right] d\mu_k(y). \tag{22}$$

Moreover, if f is nonnegative and measurable with respect to Lebesgue measure μ_n, the above equality also holds.

Lebesgue Integration and Linear Changes of Variables   We denote by $\mathcal{L}(\mathbf{R}^n)$ the linear space of linear operators $T \colon \mathbf{R}^n \to \mathbf{R}^n$. We denote by $GL(n, \mathbf{R})$ the subset of $\mathcal{L}(\mathbf{R}^n)$ consisting of invertible linear operators $T \colon \mathbf{R}^n \to \mathbf{R}^n$, that is, linear operators that are one-to-one and onto. The inverse of an invertible operator is linear. Under the operation of composition, $GL(n, \mathbf{R})$ is a group called the **general linear group** of $\mathbf{R}^n$. For $1 \leq k \leq n$, we denote by e_k the point in $\mathbf{R}^n$ whose kth coordinate is 1 and other coordinates are zero. Then $\{e_1, \ldots, e_n\}$ is the canonical basis for $\mathcal{L}(\mathbf{R}^n)$. Observe that a linear operator $T \colon \mathbf{R}^n \to \mathbf{R}^n$ is uniquely determined once $T(e_k)$ is prescribed for $1 \leq k \leq n$, since if $x = (x_1, \ldots, x_n)$, then

$$T(x) = T(x_1 e_1 + \cdots + x_n e_n) = x_1 T(e_1) + \cdots + x_n T(e_n) \text{ for all } x \in \mathbf{R}^n.$$

The only analytical property of linear operator that we need is that they are Lipschitz.

Proposition 17   *A linear operator $T \colon \mathbf{R}^n \to \mathbf{R}^n$ is Lipschitz.*

Proof   Let x belong to $\mathbf{R}^n$. As we have just observed, by the linearity of T,

$$T(x) = x_1 T(e_1) + \cdots + x_n T(e_n) \text{ for all } x \in \mathbf{R}^n.$$

Therefore, by the subadditivity and positivity homogeneity of the norm,

$$\|T(x)\| = \|x_1 T(e_1) + \cdots + x_n T(e_n)\| \leq \sum_{k=1}^{n} |x_k| \cdot \|T(e_k)\|.$$

Hence, if we define $c = \sqrt{\sum_{k=1}^{n} \|T(e_k)\|^2}$, by the Cauchy-Schwarz Inequality,

$$\|T(x)\| \leq c \cdot \|x\|.$$

For any $u, v \in \mathbf{R}^n$, set $x = u - v$. Then, by the linearity of T, $T(x) = T(u-v) = T(u) - T(v)$, and therefore

$$\|T(u) - T(v)\| \leq c \cdot \|u - v\|. \qquad \square$$

We have already observed in our study of Lebesgue measure on the real line that a continuous function will not, in general, map Lebesgue measurable sets to Lebesgue measurable sets. However, a continuous mapping that is Lipschitz does map Lebesgue measurable sets to Lebesgue measurable sets.

Proposition 18 *Let the mapping* $\Psi: \mathbf{R}^n \to \mathbf{R}^n$ *be Lipschitz. If E is a Lebesgue measurable subset of $\mathbf{R}^n$, so is $\Psi(E)$. In particular, a linear operator $T: \mathbf{R}^n \to \mathbf{R}^n$ maps Lebesgue measurable sets to Lebesgue measurable sets.*

Proof A subset of $\mathbf{R}^n$ is compact if and only if it is closed and bounded and a continuous mapping maps compact sets to compact sets. Since Ψ is Lipschitz, it is continuous. Therefore Ψ maps bounded F_σ sets to F_σ sets.

Let E be a Lebesgue measurable subset of $\mathbf{R}^n$. Since $\mathbf{R}^n$ is the union of a countable collection of bounded measurable sets, we may assume that E is bounded. According to Corollary 14, $E = A \cup D$, where A is an F_σ subset of $\mathbf{R}^n$ and D has Lebesgue outer measure zero. We just observed that $\Psi(A)$ is an F_σ set. Therefore to show that $\Psi(E)$ is Lebesgue measurable it suffices to show that the set $\Psi(D)$ has Lebesgue outer measure zero.

Let $c > 0$ be such that

$$\|\Psi(u) - \Psi(v)\| \le c \cdot \|u - v\| \text{ for all } u, v \in \mathbf{R}^n.$$

There is a constant c' (see Problem 24) that depends solely on c and n such that for any interval I in $\mathbf{R}^n$,

$$\mu_n^*(\Psi(I)) \le c' \cdot \text{vol}(I). \tag{23}$$

Let $\epsilon > 0$. Since $\mu_n^*(D) = 0$, there is a countable collection $\{I^k\}_{k=1}^\infty$ of intervals in $\mathbf{R}^n$ that cover D and for which $\sum_{k=1}^\infty \text{vol}(I^k) < \epsilon$. Then $\{\Psi(I^k)\}_{k=1}^\infty$ is a countable cover of $\Psi(D)$. Therefore by the estimate (23) and the countable monotonicity of outer measure,

$$\mu_n^*(\Psi(I)) \le \sum_{k=1}^\infty \mu_n^*(\Psi(I_k)) \le \sum_{k=1}^\infty c' \cdot \text{vol}(I_k) < c' \cdot \epsilon.$$

Since this holds for all $\epsilon > 0$ it also holds for $\epsilon = 0$. $\qquad\square$

Corollary 19 *Let the function $f: \mathbf{R}^n \to \mathbf{R}$ be measurable with respect to Lebesgue measure and the operator $T: \mathbf{R}^n \to \mathbf{R}^n$ be linear and invertible. Then the composition $f \circ T: \mathbf{R}^n \to \mathbf{R}$ also is measurable with respect to Lebesgue measure.*

Proof Let $\mathcal{O}$ be an open subset of $\mathbf{R}$. We must show that $(f \circ T)^{-1}(\mathcal{O})$ is Lebesgue measurable. However,

$$(f \circ T)^{-1}(\mathcal{O}) = T^{-1}(f^{-1}(\mathcal{O})).$$

But the function f is measurable and therefore the set $f^{-1}(\mathcal{O})$ is measurable. On the other hand, the mapping T^{-1} is linear and therefore, by the preceding proposition, maps Lebesgue measurable sets to Lebesgue measurable sets. Thus $(f \circ T)^{-1}(\mathcal{O})$ is Lebesgue measurable. $\qquad\square$

We will establish a general formula for the change in the value of a Lebesgue integral over $\mathbf{R}^n$ under a linear change of variables and begin with dimensions $n = 1$ and 2.

Proposition 20 *Let $f: \mathbf{R} \to \mathbf{R}$ be integrable over $\mathbf{R}$ with respect to one-dimensional Lebesgue measure. If $\alpha, \beta \in \mathbf{R}, \alpha \neq 0$, then*

$$\int_{\mathbf{R}} f\, d\mu_1 = \frac{1}{|\alpha|} \cdot \int_{\mathbf{R}} f(\alpha x)\, d\mu_1(x) \text{ and } \int_{\mathbf{R}} f\, d\mu_1 = \int_{\mathbf{R}} f(x+\beta)\, d\mu_1(x). \tag{24}$$

Proof By the linearity of integration we may assume f is nonnegative. Approximate the function f an increasing sequence of simple integrable functions and thereby use the Monotone Convergence Theorem to reduce the proof to the case that f is the characteristic function of a set of finite Lebesgue measure. For such a function the formulas are evident. $\square$

Proposition 21 *Let $f: \mathbf{R}^2 \to \mathbf{R}$ be integrable over $\mathbf{R}^2$ with respect to Lebesgue measure μ_2 and $c \neq 0$ be a real number. Define $\varphi: \mathbf{R}^2 \to \mathbf{R}, \psi: \mathbf{R}^2 \to \mathbf{R}$ and $\eta: \mathbf{R}^2 \to \mathbf{R}$ by*

$$\varphi(x, y) = f(y, x), \; \psi(x, y) = f(x, x+y) \text{ and } \eta(x, y) = f(cx, y) \text{ for all } (x, y) \in \mathbf{R}^2.$$

Then $\varphi, \psi,$ and η are integrable over $\mathbf{R}^2$ with respect to Lebesgue measure μ_2. Moreover,

$$\int_{\mathbf{R}^2} f\, d\mu_2 = \int_{\mathbf{R}^2} \varphi\, d\mu_2 = \int_{\mathbf{R}^2} \psi\, d\mu_2,$$

and

$$\int_{\mathbf{R}^2} f\, d\mu_2 = \frac{1}{|c|} \cdot \int_{\mathbf{R}^2} \eta\, d\mu_2.$$

Proof We infer from Corollary 19 that each of the functions $\varphi, \psi,$ and η is μ_2-measurable. Since integration is linear, we may assume that f is nonnegative. We compare the integral of f with that of φ and leave the other two as exercises. Since f is μ_2-measurable, we infer from Fubini's Theorem, as expressed in Theorem 16, that

$$\int_{\mathbf{R}^2} f\, d\mu_2 = \int_{\mathbf{R}} \left[\int_{\mathbf{R}} f(x, y)\, d\mu_1(x) \right] d\mu_1(y).$$

However, by the definition of the function φ, for almost all $y \in \mathbf{R}$,

$$\int_{\mathbf{R}} f(x, y)\, d\mu_1(x) = \int_{\mathbf{R}} \varphi(y, x)\, d\mu_1(x)$$

and therefore

$$\int_{\mathbf{R}} \left[\int_{\mathbf{R}} f(x, y)\, d\mu_1(x) \right] d\mu_1(y) = \int_{\mathbf{R}} \left[\int_{\mathbf{R}} \varphi(y, x)\, d\mu_1(x) \right] d\mu_1(y).$$

Since φ is nonnegative and μ_2-measurable we infer from Tonelli's Theorem, as expressed in Theorem 16, that

$$\int_{\mathbf{R}} \left[\int_{\mathbf{R}} \varphi(y, x)\, d\mu_1(x) \right] d\mu_1(y) = \int_{\mathbf{R}^2} \varphi\, d\mu_2.$$

Therefore

$$\int_{\mathbf{R}^2} f \, d\mu_2 = \int_{\mathbf{R}^2} \varphi \, d\mu_2.$$

□

So far the sole analytical property of linear mappings that we used is that such mappings are Lipschitz. We now need two results from linear algebra. The first is that every operator $T \in GL(n, \mathbf{R})$ may be expressed as the composition of linear operators of the following three elementary types:

Type 1: $T(e_j) = c \cdot e_j$ and $T(e_k) = e_k$ for $k \neq j$:
Type 2: $T(e_j) = e_{j+1}$, $T(e_{j+1}) = e_j$ and $T(e_k) = e_k$ for $k \neq j, j+1$:
Type 3: $T(e_j) = e_j + e_{j+1}$, and $T(e_k) = e_k$ for $k \neq j$:

That every invertible linear operator may be expressed as the composition of elementary operators is an assertion in terms of linear operator of a property of matrices: every invertible $n \times n$ matrix may be reduced by row operations to the identity matrix.

The second property of linear operators that we need is the following: To each linear operator $T: \mathbf{R}^n \to \mathbf{R}^n$ there is associated a real number called the **determinant** of T and denoted by $\det T$, which possesses the following three properties:

(i) For any two linear operators $T, S: \mathbf{R}^n \to \mathbf{R}^n$

$$\det(S \circ T) = \det S \cdot \det T, \tag{25}$$

(ii) $\det T = c$ if T is of Type 1, $\det T = -1$ if T is of Type 2, and $\det T = 1$ if T is of Type 3.
(iii) If $T(e_n) = 1$ and T maps the subspace $\{x \in \mathbf{R}^n \mid x = (x_1, x_2, \ldots, x_{n-1}, 0)\}$ into itself, then $\det T = \det T'$, where $T': \mathbf{R}^{n-1} \to \mathbf{R}^{n-1}$ is the restriction of T to $\mathbf{R}^{n-1}$.

Theorem 22 *Let the linear operator $T: \mathbf{R}^n \to \mathbf{R}^n$ be invertible and the function $f: \mathbf{R}^n \to \mathbf{R}$ be integrable over $\mathbf{R}^n$ with respect to Lebesgue measure. Then the composition $f \circ T: \mathbf{R}^n \to \mathbf{R}$ also is integrable over $\mathbf{R}^n$ with respect to Lebesgue measure and*

$$\int_{\mathbf{R}^n} f \circ T \, d\mu_n = \frac{1}{|\det T|} \cdot \int_{\mathbf{R}^n} f \, d\mu_n. \tag{26}$$

Proof Integration is linear. We therefore suppose f is nonnegative. In view of the multiplicative property of the determinant and the decomposability of an invertible linear operator into the composition of elementary operators, we may also suppose that T is elementary. The case $n = 1$ is covered by (24). By Proposition 21, (26) holds if $n = 2$. We now apply an induction argument. Assume we have proven (26) for $m \geq 2$ and consider the case $n = m + 1$. Since T is elementary and $n \geq 3$, , either (i) $T(e_n) = e_n$ and T maps the subspace $\{x \in \mathbf{R}^n \mid x = (x_1, \ldots, x_{n-1}, 0)\}$ into itself or (ii) $T(e_1) = e_1$ and T maps the subspace $\{x \in \mathbf{R}^n \mid x = (0, x_2, \ldots, x_n)\}$ into itself. We consider case (i) and leave the similar consideration of case (ii) as an exercise. Let T' be the operator induced on $\mathbf{R}^{n-1}$ by T. Observe that $|\det T'| = |\det T|$. We now again argue as we did in the proof of Proposition 21. The function $f \circ T$ is μ_n-measurable. Therefore we infer from Fubini's Theorem and Tonelli's Theorem, as formulated for Lebesgue measure in Theorem 16, together with the validity of (26) for $m = n - 1$, that

$$\int_{\mathbf{R}^n} f \circ T \, d\mu_n = \int_{\mathbf{R}} \left[\int_{\mathbf{R}^{n-1}} f \circ T(x_1, x_2, \dots, x_n) \, d\mu_{n-1}(x_1, \dots, x_{n-1}) \right] d\mu_1(x_n)$$

$$= \int_{\mathbf{R}} \left[\int_{\mathbf{R}^{n-1}} f(T'(x_1, \dots, x_{n-1}), x_n)) \, d\mu_{n-1}(x_1, \dots, x_{n-1}) \right] d\mu_1(x_n)$$

$$= \frac{1}{|\det T'|} \int_{\mathbf{R}} \left[\int_{\mathbf{R}^{n-1}} f(x_1, x_2, \dots, x_n) \, d\mu_{n-1}(x_1, \dots, x_{n-1}) \right] d\mu_1(x_n)$$

$$= \frac{1}{|\det T|} \int_{\mathbf{R}^n} f \, d\mu_n.$$

□

Corollary 23 *Let the linear operator* $T: \mathbf{R}^n \to \mathbf{R}^n$ *be invertible. Then for each Lebesgue measurable subset* E *of* $\mathbf{R}^n$, $T(E)$ *is Lebesgue measurable and*

$$\mu_n(T(E)) = |\det(T)| \cdot \mu_n(E). \tag{27}$$

Proof We assume that E is bounded and leave the unbounded case as an exercise. Since T is Lipschitz, $T(E)$ is bounded. We infer from Proposition 18 that the set $T(E)$ is Lebesgue measurable and it has finite Lebesgue measure since it is bounded. Therefore the function $f = \chi_{T(E)}$ is integrable over $\mathbf{R}^n$ with respect to Lebesgue measure. Observe that $f \circ T = \chi_E$. Therefore

$$\int_{\mathbf{R}^n} f \circ T \, d\mu_n = \mu_n(E) \text{ and } \int_{\mathbf{R}^n} f \, d\mu_n = \mu_n(T(E)).$$

Hence (27) follows from (26) for this particular choice of f.   □

By a **rigid motion** of $\mathbf{R}^n$ we mean a mapping Ψ of $\mathbf{R}^n$ onto $\mathbf{R}^n$ that preserves Euclidean distances between points, that is,

$$\|\Psi(u) - \Psi(v)\| = \|u - v\| \text{ for all } u, v \in \mathbf{R}^n.$$

A theorem of Mazur and Ulam[3] tells us that every rigid motion is a constant perturbation of a linear rigid motion, that is, there is a point x_0 in $\mathbf{R}^n$ and $T: \mathbf{R}^n \to \mathbf{R}^n$ linear such that $\Psi(x) = T(x) + x_0$ for all $x \in \mathbf{R}^n$, where T is a rigid motion. However, since a linear rigid motion maps the origin to the origin, T preserves the norm, that is,

$$\|T(u)\| = \|u\| \text{ for all } u \in \mathbf{R}^n.$$

---

[3] See pages 49–51 of Peter Lax's *Functional Analysis* [Lax02].

Thus the following polarization identity (see Problem 28),

$$\langle u, v \rangle = \frac{1}{4}\{\|u + v\|^2 - \|u - v\|^2\} \text{ for all } u, v \in \mathbf{R}^n, \tag{28}$$

tells us that a linear rigid motion T preserves the inner product, that is,

$$\langle T(u), T(v) \rangle = \langle u, v \rangle \text{ for all } u, v \in \mathbf{R}^n.$$

This identity means that $T^*T = \text{Id}$. From the multiplicative property of the determinant and the fact that $\det T = \det T^*$, we conclude that $|\det T| = 1$. Therefore by the translation invariance of Lebesgue measure (see Problem 20) and (27) we have the following interesting geometric result: If a mapping on Euclidean space preserves distances between points, then it preserves Lebesgue measure.

Corollary 24 *Let* $\Psi\colon \mathbf{R}^n \to \mathbf{R}^n$ *be a rigid motion. Then for each Lebesgue measurable subset E of $\mathbf{R}^n$,*

$$\mu_n(\Psi(E)) = \mu_n(E).$$

It follows from the definition of Lebesgue outer measure μ_n^* that the subspace $V = \{x \in \mathbf{R}^n \,|\, x = (x_1, x_2, \ldots, x_{n-1}, 0)\}$ of $\mathbf{R}^n$ has n-dimensional Lebesgue measure zero (see Problem 30). We may therefore infer from (27) that any proper subspace W of $\mathbf{R}^n$ has n-dimensional Lebesgue measure zero since it may be mapped by an operator in $GL(n, \mathbf{R})$ onto a subspace of V. It follows that if a linear operator $T\colon \mathbf{R}^n \to \mathbf{R}^n$ fails to be invertible, then, since its range lies in a subspace of dimension less than n, it maps every subset of $\mathbf{R}^n$ to a set of n-dimensional Lebesgue measure zero. This may be restated by asserting that (27) continues to hold for linear operators T that fail be invertible.

PROBLEMS

15. Consider the triangle $\Delta = \{(x, y) \in \mathbf{R}^2 \,|\, 0 \le x \le a, 0 \le y \le [b/a]x\}$. By covering Δ with finite collections of rectangles and using the continuity of measure, determine the Lebesgue measure of Δ.

16. Let $[a, b]$ be a closed, bounded interval of real numbers. Suppose that $f\colon [a, b] \to \mathbf{R}$ is bounded and Lebesgue measurable. Show that the graph of f has measure zero with respect to Lebesgue measure on the plane. Generalize this to bounded real-valued functions of several real variables.

17. Every open set of real numbers is the union of a countable disjoint collection of open intervals. Is the open subset of the plane $\{(x, y) \in \mathbf{R}^2 \,|\, 0 < x, y < 1\}$ the union of a countable disjoint collection of open balls?

18. Verify inequality (13).

19. Verify the set equality (16).

20. Let $E \subseteq \mathbf{R}^n$ and $z \in \mathbf{R}^n$.
    (i) Show that $E + z$ is open if E is open.
    (ii) Show that $E + z$ is G_δ if E is G_δ.
    (iii) Show that $\mu_n^*(E + z) = \mu_n^*(E)$.
    (iv) Show that E is μ_n-measurable if and only if $E + z$ is μ_n-measurable.

21. For each natural number n, show that every subset of $\mathbf{R}^n$ of positive outer Lebesgue measure contains a subset that is not Lebesgue measurable.

22. For each natural number n, show that there is a subset of $\mathbf{R}^n$ that is not a Borel set but is μ_n-measurable.

23. If (27) holds for each interval in $\mathbf{R}^n$, use the uniqueness assertion of the Carathéodory-Hahn Theorem to show directly that it also holds for every measurable subset of $\mathbf{R}^n$.

24. Let $\Psi: \mathbf{R}^n \to \mathbf{R}^n$ be Lipschitz with Lipschitz constant c. Show that there is a constant c' that depends only on the dimension n and c for which the estimate (23) holds.

25. Prove that the Cartesian product of two semirings is a semiring. Based on this use an induction argument to prove that the collection of intervals in $\mathbf{R}^n$ is a semiring.

26. Show that if the function $f: [0, 1] \times [0, 1] \to \mathbf{R}$ is continuous with respect to each variable separately, then it is measurable with respect to Lebesgue measure μ_2.

27. Let $g: \mathbf{R} \to \mathbf{R}$ be a mapping of $\mathbf{R}$ onto $\mathbf{R}$ for which there is a constant $c > 0$ for which

$$|g(u) - g(v)| \geq c \cdot |u - v| \text{ for all } u, v \in \mathbf{R}.$$

Show that if $f: \mathbf{R} \to \mathbf{R}$ is Lebesgue measurable, then so is the composition $f \circ g: \mathbf{R} \to \mathbf{R}$.

28. By using the bilinearity of the inner product, prove (28).

29. Let the mapping $T: \mathbf{R}^n \to \mathbf{R}^n$ be linear. Define $c = \sup \{\|T(x)\| \mid \|x\| \leq 1\}$. Show that c is the smallest Lipschitz constant for T.

30. Show that a subspace of W of $\mathbf{R}^n$ of dimension less than n has n-dimensional Lebesgue measure zero by first showing this is so for the subspace $\{x \in \mathbf{R}^n \mid x_n = 0\}$.

31. Prove the two change of variables formulas (24) first for characteristic functions of sets of finite measure, then for simple functions that vanish outside a set of finite measure and finally for nonnegative integrable functions of a single real variable.

32. For a subset E of $\mathbf{R}$, define

$$\sigma(E) = \left\{(x, y) \in \mathbf{R}^2 \mid x - y \in E\right\}.$$

(i) If E is a Lebesgue measurable subset of $\mathbf{R}$, show that $\sigma(E)$ is a measurable subset of $\mathbf{R}^2$. (Hint: Consider first the cases when E open, E a G_δ, E of measure zero, and E measurable.)

(ii) If f is a Lebesgue measurable function on $\mathbf{R}$, show that the function F defined by $F(x, y) = f(x - y)$ is a Lebesgue measurable function on $\mathbf{R}^2$.

(iii) If f and g belong to $L^1(\mathbf{R}, \mu_1)$, show that for almost all x in $\mathbf{R}$, the function φ given by $\varphi(y) = f(x - y)g(y)$ belongs to $L^1(\mathbf{R}, \mu_1)$. If we denote its integral by $h(x)$, show that h is integrable and

$$\int_{\mathbf{R}} |h| \, d\mu_1 \leq \int_{\mathbf{R}} |f| \, d\mu_1 \cdot \int_{\mathbf{R}} |g| \, d\mu_1.$$

33. Let f and g be functions in $L^1(\mathbf{R}, \mu_1)$, and define $f * g$ on $\mathbf{R}$ by

$$(f * g)(y) = \int_{\mathbf{R}} f(y - x)g(x) \, d\mu_1(x).$$

(i) Show that $f * g = g * f$.

(ii) Show that $(f * g) * h = f * (g * h)$ for each $h \in L^1(\mathbf{R}, \mu_1)$.

34. Let f be a nonnegative function that is integrable over **R** with respect to μ_1. Show that

$$\mu_2\left\{(x, y) \in \mathbf{R}^2 \mid 0 \le y \le f(x)\right\} = \mu_2\left\{(x, y) \in \mathbf{R}^2 \mid 0 < y < f(x)\right\} = \int_\mathbf{R} f(x)\, dx.$$

For each $t \ge 0$, define $\varphi(t) = \mu_1\{x \in \mathbf{R} \mid f(x) \ge t\}$. Show that φ is a decreasing function and

$$\int_0^\infty \varphi(t)\, d\mu_1(t) = \int_\mathbf{R} f(x)\, d\mu_1(x).$$

20.3 CUMULATIVE DISTRIBUTION FUNCTIONS AND BOREL MEASURES ON R

Let $I = [a, b]$ be a closed, bounded interval of real numbers and $\mathcal{B}(I)$ the collection of Borel subsets of I. We call a finite measure μ on $\mathcal{B}(I)$ a **Borel measure**. For such a measure, define the function $g_\mu\colon I \to \mathbf{R}$ by

$$g_\mu(x) = \mu[a, x] \text{ for all } x \text{ in } I.$$

The function g_μ is called the **cumulative distribution function** of μ.

Proposition 25 *Let μ be a Borel measure on $\mathcal{B}(I)$. Then its cumulative distribution function g_μ is increasing and continuous on the right. Conversely, each function $g\colon I \to \mathbf{R}$ that is increasing and continuous on the right is the cumulative distribution function of a unique Borel measure μ_g on $\mathcal{B}(I)$.*

Proof First let μ be a Borel measure on $\mathcal{B}(I)$. Its cumulative distribution function is certainly increasing and bounded. Let x_0 belong to $[a, b)$ and $\{x_k\}$ be a decreasing sequence in $(x_0, b]$ that converges to x_0. Then $\bigcap_{k=1}^\infty (x_0, x_k] = \emptyset$ so that, since μ is finite, by the continuity of measure,

$$0 = \mu(\emptyset) = \lim_{k\to\infty} \mu(x_0, x_k] = \lim_{k\to\infty} [g_\mu(x_k) - g_\mu(x_0)].$$

Thus g_μ is continuous on the right at x_0.

To prove the converse, let $g\colon I \to \mathbf{R}$ be an increasing function that is continuous on the right. Consider the collection $\mathcal{S}$ of subsets of I consisting of the empty set, the singleton set $\{a\}$, and all subintervals of I of the form $(c, d]$. Then $\mathcal{S}$ is a semiring. Consider the set function $\mu\colon \mathcal{S} \to \mathbf{R}$ defined by setting $\mu(\emptyset) = 0$, $\mu\{a\} = g(a)$ and

$$\mu(c, d] = g(d) - g(c) \text{ for } (c, d] \subseteq I.$$

We leave it as an exercise (see Problem 39) to verify that if $(c, d] \subseteq I$ is the union of finite disjoint collection $\bigcup_{k=1}^n (c_k, d_k]$, then

$$g(d) - g(c) = \sum_{k=1}^n [g(d_k) - g(c_k)]$$

and that if $(c, d] \subseteq I$ is covered by the countable collection $\bigcup_{k=1}^\infty (c_k, d_k]$, then

$$g(d) - g(c) \le \sum_{k=1}^\infty [g(d_k) - g(c_k)]. \tag{29}$$

This means that μ is a premeasure on the semiring S. By the Carathéodory-Hahn Theorem, the Carathéodory measure $\overline{\mu}$ induced by μ is an extension of μ. In particular, each open subset of $[a, b]$ is μ^*-measurable. By the minimality of the Borel σ-algebra, the σ-algebra of μ^* measurable sets contains $\mathcal{B}(I)$. The function g is the cumulative distribution function for the restriction of $\overline{\mu}$ to $\mathcal{B}(I)$ since for each $x \in [a, b]$,

$$\mu[a, x] = \mu\{a\} + \mu(a, x] = g(a) + [g(x) - g(a)] = g(x). \qquad \square$$

It is natural to relate the continuity properties of a Borel measure to those of its cumulative distribution function. We have the following very satisfactory relation whose proof we leave as an exercise.

Proposition 26 *Let μ be a Borel measure on $\mathcal{B}(I)$ and g_μ its cumulative distribution function. Then the measure μ is absolutely continuous with respect to Lebesgue measure if and only if the function g_μ is absolutely continuous.*

For a bounded Lebesgue measurable function f on $[a, b]$, the Lebesgue integral $\int_{[a, b]} f \, dm$ is defined, where m denotes Lebesgue measure. For a bounded function f on $[a, b]$ whose set of discontinuities has Lebesgue measure zero, we proved that the Riemann integral $\int_a^b f(x) \, dx$ is defined and

$$\int_{[a, b]} f \, dm = \int_a^b f(x) \, dx.$$

There are two generalizations of these integrals, the Lebesgue-Stieltjes and Riemann-Stieltjes integrals, which we now briefly consider.

Let the function $g: I \to \mathbf{R}$ be increasing and continuous on the right. For a bounded Borel measurable function $f: I \to \mathbf{R}$, we define the **Lebesgue-Stieltjes integral** of f with respect to g over $[a, b]$, which we denote by $\int_a^b f \, dg$, by

$$\int_{[a, b]} f \, dg = \int_{[a, b]} f \, d\mu_g. \tag{30}$$

Now suppose that f is a bounded Borel measurable function and g is increasing and absolutely continuous. Then g' Lebesgue integrable function over $[a, b]$ and hence so is $f \cdot g'$. We have

$$\int_{[a, b]} f \, dg = \int_{[a, b]} fg' \, dm, \tag{31}$$

where the right-hand integral is the integral of $f \cdot g'$ with respect to Lebesgue measure m. To verify this formula, observe that it holds for f a Borel simple function and then, by the Simple Approximation Theorem and the Lebesgue Dominated Convergence Theorem, it also holds for a bounded Borel measurable function f. In this case, by Proposition 26, μ_g is absolutely continuous with respect to m. We leave it to the reader to verify that function g' is the Radon-Nikodym derivative of μ_g with respect to m (see Problem 44).

There is a **Riemann-Stieltjes** integral that generalizes the Riemann integral in the same manner that the Lebesgue-Stieltjes integral generalizes the Lebesgue integral. We briefly describe this extension.[4] If $P = \{x_0, x_1, \ldots, x_n\}$ is a partition of $[a, b]$, we let $\|P\|$ denote the maximum of the lengths on the intervals determined by P and let $C = \{c_1, \ldots, c_n\}$, where each c_i belongs to $[x_{i-1}, x_i]$. For two bounded functions $f: [a, b] \to \mathbf{R}$ and $g: [a, b] \to \mathbf{R}$, consider sums of the form

$$S(f, g, P, C) = \sum_{k=1}^{n} f(c_i) \cdot [g(x_i) - g(x_{i-1})].$$

If there is a real number A such that for each $\epsilon > 0$, there is a $\delta > 0$ such that

$$\text{if } \|P\| < \delta, \text{ then } |S(f, g, P, C) - A| < \epsilon,$$

then f is said to be Riemann-Stieltjes integrable over I with respect to g and we set

$$A = \int_a^b f(x)\, dg(x).$$

It is clear that if $g(x) = x$ for all $x \in [a, b]$, then the Riemann-Stieltjes integral of f with respect to g is just the Riemann integral of f. Moreover, if f is continuous and g is monotone, then f is Riemann-Stieltjes integrable over I with respect to g.[5] However, a theorem of Camille Jordan tells us a function of bounded variation is the difference of increasing functions. Therefore a continuous function on I is Riemann-Stieltjes integrable over I with respect to a function of bounded variation. The Lebesgue-Stieltjes integral and the Riemann-Stieltjes integrals are defined for different classes of functions. However, they are both defined if f is continuous and g is increasing and absolutely continuous. In this case, they are equal, that is,

$$\int_a^b f(x)\, dg(x) = \int_{[a, b]} f\, dg,$$

since (see Problems 36 and 37) each of these integrals is equal to $\int_{[a, b]} fg'\, dm$, the Lebesgue integral of $f \cdot g'$ over $[a, b]$ with respect to Lebesgue measure m.

PROBLEMS

35. Prove Proposition 26.

36. Suppose f is a bounded Borel measurable function on $[a, b]$ and g is increasing and absolutely continuous on $[a, b]$. Prove that if m denotes Lebesgue measure, then

$$\int_{[a, b]} f\, dg = \int_{[a, b]} fg'\, dm.$$

37. Suppose f is a continuous function on $[a, b]$ and g is increasing and absolutely continuous on $[a, b]$. Prove that if m denotes Lebesgue measure, then

$$\int_a^b f(x)\, dg(x) = \int_{[a, b]} fg'\, dm.$$

---

[4]On pages 23–31 of Richard Wheedon and Antoni Zygmund's *Measure and Integral* [WZ77] there is a precise exposition of the Riemann-Stieltjes integral.

[5]The proof of this is a slight variation of the proof of the Riemann integrability of a continuous function.

38. Let f and g be functions on $[-1, 1]$ such that $f = 0$ on $[-1, 0]$, $f = 1$ and $(0, 1]$, and $g = 0$ on $[-1, 0)$, $g = 1$ and $[0, 1]$. Show that f is not Riemann-Stieltjes integrable with respect to g over $[-1, 1]$ but is Riemann-Stieltjes integrable with respect to g on $[-1, 0]$ and on $[0, 1]$.

39. Prove the inequality (29). (Hint: Choose $\epsilon > 0$. By the continuity on the right of g, choose $\eta_i > 0$ so that $g(b_i + \eta_i) < g(b_i) + \epsilon 2^{-i}$, and choose $\delta > 0$ so that $g(a + \delta) < g(a) + \epsilon$. Then the open intervals $(a_i, b_i + \eta_i)$ cover the closed interval $[a + \delta, b]$.)

40. For an increasing function $g \colon [a, b] \to \mathbf{R}$, define

$$g^*(x) = \lim_{y \to x+} g(y).$$

Show that g^* is an increasing function that is continuous on the right and agrees with g wherever g is continuous on the right. Conclude that $g = g^*$, except possibly at a countable number of points. Show that $(g^*)^* = g^*$, and if g and G are increasing functions that agree wherever they are both continuous, then $g^* = G^*$. If f is a bounded Borel measurable function on $[a, b]$, show that

$$\int_{[a, b]} f \, dg = \int_{[a, b]} f \, dg^*.$$

41. (i) Show that each bounded function g of bounded variation gives rise to a finite signed Borel measure ν such that

$$\nu(c, d] = g(d^+) - g(c^+) \text{ for all } (c, d] \subseteq [a, b].$$

(ii) Extend the definition of the Lebesgue-Stieltjes integral $\int_{[a, b]} f \, dg$ to functions g of bounded variation and bounded Borel measurable functions f.

(iii) Show that if $|f| \le M$ on $[a, b]$ and if the total variation of g is T, then $|\int_{[a, b]} f \, dg| \le MT$.

42. Let g be a continuous increasing function on $[a, b]$ with $g(a) = c$, $g(b) = d$, and let f be a nonnegative Borel measurable function on $[c, d]$. Show that

$$\int_{[a, b]} f \circ g \, dg = \int_{[c, d]} f \, dm.$$

43. Let g be increasing on $[a, b]$. Find a Borel measure μ on $\mathcal{B}([a, b])$ such that

$$\int_a^b f(x) \, dg(x) = \int_{[a, b]} f \, d\mu \text{ for all } f \in C[a, b].$$

44. If the Borel measure μ is absolutely continuous with respect to Lebesgue measure, show that its Radon-Nikodym derivative is the derivative of its cumulative distribution function.

45. For a finite measure μ on the collection $\mathcal{B}(\mathbf{R})$ of all Borel subsets of $\mathbf{R}$, define $g \colon \mathbf{R} \to \mathbf{R}$ by setting $g(x) = \mu(-\infty, x]$. Show that each bounded, increasing function $g \colon \mathbf{R} \to \mathbf{R}$ that is continuous on the right and $\lim_{x \to -\infty} g(x) = 0$ is the cumulative distribution function of a unique finite Borel measure on $\mathcal{B}(\mathbf{R})$.

20.4 CARATHÉODORY OUTER MEASURES AND HAUSDORFF MEASURES ON A METRIC SPACE

Lebesgue outer measure on Euclidean space $\mathbf{R}^n$ has the property that if A and B are subsets of $\mathbf{R}^n$ and there is a $\delta > 0$ for which $\|u - v\| \geq \delta$ for all $u \in A$ and $v \in B$, then

$$\mu_n^*(A \cup B) = \mu_n^*(A) + \mu_n^*(B).$$

We devote this short section to the study of measures induced by outer measures on a metric space that possess this property and a particular class of such measures called Hausdorff measures.

Let X be a set and Γ a collection of real-valued functions on X. It is often of interest to know conditions under which an outer measure μ^* has the property that every function in Γ is measurable with respect to the measure induced by μ^* through the Carathéodory construction. We present a sufficient criterion for this. Two subsets A and B of X are said to be separated by the real-valued function f on X provided there are real numbers a and b with $a < b$ for which $f \leq a$ on A and $f \geq b$ on B.

Proposition 27 *Let φ be a real-valued function on a set X and $\mu^*: 2^X \to [0, \infty]$ an outer measure with the property that whenever two subsets A and B of X are separated by φ, then*

$$\mu^*(A \cup B) = \mu^*(A) + \mu^*(B)$$

Then φ is measurable with respect to the measure induced by μ^*.

Proof Let a be a real number. We must show that the set

$$E = \{x \in X \mid \varphi(x) > a\}$$

is μ^*-measurable, that is, that for any $\epsilon > 0$ and any subset A of X of finite outer measure,

$$\mu^*(A) + \epsilon \geq \mu^*(A \cap E) + \mu^*(A \cap E^C). \tag{32}$$

Define $B = A \cap E$ and $C = A \cap E^C$. For each natural number n, define

$$B_n = \{x \in B \mid \varphi(x) > a + 1/n\} \text{ and } R_n = B_n \sim B_{n-1}.$$

We have

$$B = B_n \cup \left[\bigcup_{k=n+1}^{\infty} R_k \right].$$

Now on B_{n-2} we have $\varphi > a + 1/(n-2)$, while on R_n we have $\varphi \leq a + 1/(n-1)$. Thus φ separates R_n and B_{n-2} and hence separates R_{2k} and $\bigcup_{j=1}^{k-1} R_{2j}$, since the latter set is contained in B_{2k-2}. Consequently, we argue by induction to show that for each k,

$$\mu^* \left[\bigcup_{j=1}^{k} R_{2j} \right] = \mu^*(R_{2k}) + \mu^* \left[\bigcup_{j=1}^{k-1} R_{2j} \right] = \sum_{j=1}^{k} \mu^*(R_{2j}).$$

Since $\sum_{j=1}^{k} R_{2j} \subseteq B \subseteq A$, we have $\sum_{j=1}^{k} \mu^*(R_{2j}) \leq \mu^*(A)$, and so the series $\sum_{j=1}^{\infty} \mu^*(R_{2j})$ converges. Similarly, the series $\sum_{j=1}^{\infty} \mu^*(R_{2j+1})$ converges, and therefore so does the series $\sum_{k=1}^{\infty} \mu^*(R_k)$. Choose n so large that $\sum_{k=n+1}^{\infty} \mu^*(R_k) < \epsilon$. Then by the countable monotonicity of μ^*,

$$\mu^*(B) \leq \mu^*(B_n) + \sum_{k=n+1}^{\infty} \mu^*(R_k) < \mu^*(B_n) + \epsilon$$

or

$$\mu^*(B_n) > \mu^*(B) - \epsilon.$$

Now

$$\mu^*(A) \geq \mu^*(B_n \cup C) = \mu^*(B_n) + \mu^*(C)$$

since φ separates B_n and C. Consequently,

$$\mu^*(A) \geq \mu^*(B) + \mu^*(C) - \epsilon.$$

We have established the desired inequality (32). $\square$

Let (X, ρ) be a metric space. Recall that for two subsets A and B of X, we define the distance between A and B, which we denote by $\rho(A, B)$, by

$$\rho(A, B) = \inf_{u \in A, v \in B} \rho(u, v).$$

By the Borel σ-algebra associated with this metric space, which we denote by $\mathcal{B}(X)$, we mean the smallest σ-algebra containing the topology induced by the metric.

Definition *Let (X, ρ) be a metric space. An outer measure $\mu^*: 2^X \to [0, \infty]$ is called a **Carathéodory outer measure** provided whenever A and B are subsets of X for which $\rho(A, B) > 0$, then*

$$\mu^*(A \cup B) = \mu^*(A) + \mu^*(B).$$

Theorem 28 *Let μ^* be a Carathéodory outer measure on a metric space (X, ρ). Then every Borel subset of X is measurable with respect to μ^*.*

Proof The collection of Borel sets is the smallest σ-algebra containing the closed sets, and the measurable sets are a σ-algebra. Therefore it suffices to show that each closed set is measurable. However, each closed subset F of X can be expressed as $F = f^{-1}(0)$ where f is the continuous function on X defined by $f(x) = \rho(F, \{x\})$. It therefore suffices to show that every continuous function is measurable. To do so, we apply Proposition 27. Indeed, let A and B be subsets of X for which there is a continuous function on X and real numbers $a < b$ such that $f \leq a$ on A and $f \geq b$ on B. By the continuity of f, $\rho(A, B) > 0$. Hence, by assumption, $\mu^*(A \cup B) = \mu^*(A) + \mu^*(B)$. According to Proposition 27, each continuous function is measurable. The proof is complete. $\square$

We now turn our attention to a particular family of Carathéodory outer measures on the metric space (X, ρ). First recall that we define the diameter of a subset A of X, diam(A), by

$$\text{diam}(A) = \sup_{u, v \in A} \rho(u, v).$$

Fix $\alpha > 0$. For each positive real number α, we define a measure H_α on the Borel σ-algebra $\mathcal{B}(X)$ called the Hausdorff measure on X of dimension α. These measures are particularly important for the Euclidean spaces $\mathbf{R}^n$, in which case they provide a gradation of size among sets of n-dimensional Lebesgue measure zero.

Fix $\alpha > 0$. Take $\epsilon > 0$ and for a subset E of X, define

$$H_\alpha^{(\epsilon)}(E) = \inf \sum_{k=1}^\infty [\text{diam}(A_k)]^\alpha,$$

where $\{A_k\}_{k=1}^\infty$ is a countable collection of subsets of X that covers E and each A_k has a diameter less than ϵ. Observe that $H_\alpha^{(\epsilon)}$ increases as ϵ decreases. Define

$$H_\alpha^*(E) = \sup_{\epsilon > 0} H_\alpha^{(\epsilon)}(E) = \lim_{\epsilon \to 0} H_\alpha^{(\epsilon)}(E).$$

Proposition 29 *Let (X, ρ) be a metric space and α a positive real number. Then $H_\alpha^*: 2^X \to [0, \infty]$ is a Carathéodory outer measure.*

Proof It is readily verified that H_α^* is a countably monotone set function on 2^X and $H_\alpha^*(\emptyset) = 0$. Therefore H_α^* is an outer measure on 2^X. We claim it is a Carathéodory outer measure. Indeed, let E and F be two subsets of X for which $\rho(E, F) > \delta$. Then

$$H_\alpha^{(\epsilon)}(E \cup F) \geq H_\alpha^{(\epsilon)}(E) + H_\alpha^{(\epsilon)}(F)$$

as soon as $\epsilon < \delta$: For if $\{A_k\}$ is a countable collection of sets, each of diameter at most ϵ, that covers $E \cup F$, no A_k can have nonempty intersection with both E and F. Taking limits as $\epsilon \to 0$, we have

$$H_\alpha^*(E \cup F) \geq H_\alpha^*(E) + H_\alpha^*(F). \qquad \square$$

We infer from Theorem 28 that H_α^* induces a measure on a σ-algebra that contains the Borel subsets of X. We denote the restriction of this measure to $\mathcal{B}(X)$ by H_α and call it **Hausdorff α-dimensional measure** on the metric space X.

Proposition 30 *Let (X, ρ) be a metric space, A a Borel subset of X, and α, β positive real numbers for which $\alpha < \beta$. If $H_\alpha(A) < \infty$, then $H_\beta(A) = 0$.*

Proof Let $\epsilon > 0$. Choose $\{A_k\}_{k=1}^\infty$ to be a covering of A by sets of diameter less than ϵ for which

$$\sum_{k=1}^\infty [\text{diam}(A_k)]^\alpha \leq H_\alpha(A) + 1.$$

Then

$$H_\beta^{(\epsilon)}(A) \leq \sum_{k=1}^\infty [\text{diam}(A_k)^\beta] \leq \epsilon^{\beta-\alpha} \cdot \sum_{k=1}^\infty [\text{diam}(A_k)]^\alpha \leq \epsilon^{\beta-\alpha} \cdot [H_\alpha(A) + 1].$$

Take the limit as $\epsilon \to 0$ to conclude that $H_\beta(A) = 0$. $\qquad \square$

For a subset E of $\mathbf{R}^n$, we define the Hausdorff dimension of E, $\dim_H(E)$, by

$$\dim_H(E) = \inf \{\beta \geq 0 \mid H_\beta(E) = 0\}.$$

Hausdorff measures are particularly significant for Euclidean space $\mathbf{R}^n$. In the case $n = 1$, H_1 equals Lebesgue measure. To see this, let $I \subseteq \mathbf{R}$ be an interval. Given $\epsilon > 0$, the interval I may be expressed as the disjoint union of subintervals of length less that ϵ and the diameter of each subinterval is its length. Thus H_1 and Lebesgue measure agree on the semiring of intervals of real numbers. Therefore, by the construction of these measures from outer measures, these measures also agree on the Borel sets. Thus $H_1^{(\epsilon)}(E)$ is the Lebesgue outer measure of E. For $n > 1$, H_n is not equal to Lebesgue measure (see Problem 48) but it can be shown that it is a constant multiple of n-dimesional Lebesgue measure (see Problem 55). It follows from the above proposition that if A is a subset of $\mathbf{R}^n$ that has positive Lebesgue measure, then $\dim_H(A) = n$. There are many specific calculations of Hausdorff dimension of subsets of Euclidean space. For instance, it can be shown that the Hausdorff dimension of the Cantor set is $\log 2/\log 3$. Further results on Hausdorff measure, including specific calculations of Hausdorff dimensions, may be found in Yakov Pesin's book *Dimension Theory and Dynamical Systems* [Pes98].

PROBLEMS

46. Show that in the definition of Hausdorff measure one can take the coverings to be by open sets or by closed sets.

47. Show that the set function outer Hausdorff measure H_α^* is countably monotone.

48. In the plane $\mathbf{R}^2$ show that a bounded set may be enclosed in a ball of the same diameter. Use this to show that for a bounded subset A of $\mathbf{R}^2$, $H_2(A) \geq 4/\pi \cdot \mu_2(A)$, where μ_2 is Lebesgue measure on $\mathbf{R}^2$.

49. Let (X, ρ) be a metric space and $\alpha > 0$. For $E \subseteq X$, define

$$H_\alpha'(E) = \inf \sum_{k=1}^\infty [\operatorname{diam}(A_k)]^\alpha,$$

where $\{A_k\}_{k=1}^\infty$ is a countable collection of subsets of X that covers E: there is no restriction regarding the size of the diameters of the sets in the cover. Compare the set functions H_α' and H_α.

50. Show that each Hausdorff measure H_α on Euclidean space $\mathbf{R}^n$ is invariant with respect to rigid motions.

51. Give a direct proof to show that if I is a nontrivial interval in $\mathbf{R}^n$, then $H_n(I) > 0$.

52. Show that in any metric space, H_0 is counting measure.

53. Let $[a, b]$ be a closed, bounded interval of real numbers and $R = \{(x, y) \in \mathbf{R}^2 \mid a \leq x \leq b, y = 0.\}$ Show that $H_2(R) = 0$. Then show that $H_1(R) = b - a$. Conclude that the Hausdorff dimension of R is 1.

54. Let $f: [a, b] \to \mathbf{R}$ be a continuous bounded function on the closed, bounded interval $[a, b]$ that has a continuous bounded derivative on the open interval (a, b). Consider the graph G of f as a subset of the plane. Show that $H_1(G) = \int_a^b \sqrt{1 + |f'(x)|^2}\, dx$.

55. Let J be an interval in $\mathbf{R}^n$, each of whose sides has length 1. Define $\gamma_n = H_n(J)$. Show that if I is any bounded interval in $\mathbf{R}^n$, then $H_n(I) = \gamma_n \cdot \mu_n(I)$. From this infer, using the uniqueness assertion of the Carathéodory-Hahn Theorem, that $H_n = \gamma_n \cdot \mu_n$ on the Borel subsets of $\mathbf{R}^n$.

CHAPTER 21

Measure and Topology

Contents

In the study of Lebesgue measure, μ_n, and Lebesgue integration on the Euclidean spaces $\mathbf{R}^n$ and, in particular, on the real line, we explored connections between Lebesgue measure and the Euclidean topology and between the measurable functions and continuous ones. The Borel σ-algebra $\mathcal{B}(\mathbf{R}^n)$ is contained in the σ-algebra of Lebesgue measurable sets. Therefore, if we define $C_c(\mathbf{R}^n)$ to be the linear space of continuous real-valued functions on $\mathbf{R}^n$ that vanish outside a closed, bounded set, the operator

$$f \mapsto \int_{\mathbf{R}^n} f \, d\mu_n \text{ for all } f \in C_c(\mathbf{R}^n)$$

is properly defined, positive,[1] and linear. Moreover, for K a closed, bounded subset of $\mathbf{R}^n$, the operator

$$f \mapsto \int_K f \, d\mu_n \text{ for all } f \in C(K)$$

is properly defined, positive, and is a bounded linear operator if $C(K)$ has the maximum norm.

In this chapter we consider a general locally compact topological space $(X, \mathcal{T})$, the Borel σ-algebra $\mathcal{B}(X)$ comprising the smallest σ-algebra containing the topology $\mathcal{T}$, and integration with respect to a Borel measure $\mu: \mathcal{B}(X) \to [0, \infty)$. The chapter has two centerpieces. The first is the Riesz-Markov Theorem, which tells us that if $C_c(X)$ denotes the linear space of continuous real-valued functions on X that vanish outside a compact set, then every positive linear function on $C_c(X)$ is given by integration against a Borel measure on $\mathcal{B}(X)$. The Riesz-Markov Theorem enables us to prove the Riesz Representation Theorem, which tells us that, for X a compact Hausdorff topological space, every bounded linear functional on the linear space $C(X)$, normed with the maximum norm, is given by

---

[1] A linear functional L on a space of real-valued functions on a set X is called positive, provided $L(f) \geq 0$ if $f \geq 0$ on X. But, for a linear functional, positivity means $L(h) \geq L(g)$ if $h \geq g$ on X. So in our view our perpetual dependence on the monotonicity property of integration, the adjective "monotone" is certainly better than "positive." However, we will respect convention and use of the adjective "positive."

integration against a signed Borel measure. Furthermore, in each of these representations it is possible to choose the representing measure to belong to a class of Borel measures that we here name Radon, within which the representing measures are unique. The Riesz Representation Theorem provides the opportunity for the application of Alaoglu's Theorem and Helley's Theorem to collections of measures.

The proofs of these two representation theorems require an examination of the relationship between the topology on a set and the measures on the Borel sets associated with the topology. The technique by which we construct Borel measures that represent functionals is the same one we used to construct Lebesgue measure on Euclidean space: We study the Carathéodory extension of premeasures defined on particular collection S of subsets of X, now taking $S = \mathcal{T}$, the topology on X. We begin the chapter with a preliminary section on locally compact topological spaces. In the second section we gather all the properties of such spaces that we need into a single theorem and provide a separate very simple proof of this theorem for X a locally compact metric space.[2]

21.1 LOCALLY COMPACT TOPOLOGICAL SPACES

A topological space X is called **locally compact** provided each point in X has a neighborhood that has compact closure. Every compact space is locally compact, while the Euclidean spaces $\mathbf{R}^n$ are examples of spaces that are locally compact but not compact. Riesz's Theorem tells us that an infinite dimensional normed linear space, with the topology induced by the norm, is not locally compact. In this section we establish properties of locally compact spaces, which will be the basis of our subsequent study of measure and topology.

Variations on Urysohn's Lemma Recall that we extended the meaning of the word *neighborhood* and for a subset K of a topological space X call an open set that contains K a neighborhood of K.

Lemma 1 *Let x be a point in a locally compact Hausdorff space X and $\mathcal{O}$ a neighborhood of x. Then there is a neighborhood $\mathcal{V}$ of x that has compact closure contained in $\mathcal{O}$, that is,*

$$x \in \mathcal{V} \subseteq \overline{\mathcal{V}} \subseteq \mathcal{O} \text{ and } \overline{\mathcal{V}} \text{ is compact.}$$

Proof Let $\mathcal{U}$ be a neighborhood of x that has compact closure. Then the topological space $\overline{\mathcal{U}}$ is compact and Hausdorff and therefore is normal. The set $\mathcal{O} \cap \mathcal{U}$ is a neighborhood, with respect to the $\overline{\mathcal{U}}$ topology, of x. Therefore, by the normality of $\overline{\mathcal{U}}$, there is a neighborhood $\mathcal{V}$ of x that has compact closure contained in $\mathcal{O} \cap \mathcal{U}$: Here both neighborhood and closure mean with respect to the $\overline{\mathcal{U}}$ topology. Since $\mathcal{O}$ and $\mathcal{U}$ are open in X, it follows from the definition of the subspace topology that $\mathcal{V}$ is open in X and $\overline{\mathcal{V}} \subseteq \mathcal{O}$ where the closure now is with respect to the X topology. $\qquad \square$

Proposition 2 *Let K be a compact subset of a locally compact Hausdorff space X and $\mathcal{O}$ a neighborhood of K. Then there is a neighborhood $\mathcal{V}$ of K that has compact closure contained in $\mathcal{O}$, that is,*

$$K \subseteq \mathcal{V} \subseteq \overline{\mathcal{V}} \subseteq \mathcal{O} \text{ and } \overline{\mathcal{V}} \text{ is compact.}$$

---

[2]There is no loss in understanding the interplay between topologies and measure if the reader, at first reading, just considers the case of metric spaces and skips Section 1.

Proof By the preceding lemma, each point $x \in K$ has a neighborhood $\mathcal{N}_x$ that has compact closure contained in $\mathcal{O}$. Then $\{\mathcal{N}_x\}_{x \in K}$ is an open cover of the compact set K. Choose a finite subcover $\{\mathcal{N}_{x_i}\}_{i=1}^n$ of K. The set $\mathcal{V} = \bigcup_{i=1}^n \mathcal{N}_{x_i}$ is a neighborhood of K and

$$\mathcal{V} \subseteq \bigcup_{i=1}^n \overline{\mathcal{N}}_{x_i} \subseteq \mathcal{O}.$$

The set $\bigcup_{i=1}^n \overline{\mathcal{N}}_{x_i}$, being the union of a finite collection of compact sets, is compact and hence so is $\overline{\mathcal{V}}$ since it is a closed subset of a compact space. $\square$

For a real-valued function f on a topological space X, the **support** of f, which we denote by supp f, is defined [3] to be the closure of the set $\{x \in X \mid f(x) \neq 0\}$, that is,

$$\text{supp } f = \overline{\{x \in X \mid f(x) \neq 0\}}.$$

We denote the collection of continuous functions $f: X \to \mathbf{R}$ that have compact support by $C_c(X)$. Thus a function belongs to $C_c(X)$ if and only if it is continuous and vanishes outside of a compact set.

Proposition 3 *Let K be a compact subset of a locally compact Hausdorff space X and $\mathcal{O}$ a neighborhood of K. Then there is a function f belonging to $C_c(X)$ for which*

$$f = 1 \text{ on } K, \, f = 0 \text{ on } X \sim \mathcal{O} \text{ and } 0 \leq f \leq 1 \text{ on } X. \tag{1}$$

Proof By the preceding proposition, there is a neighborhood $\mathcal{V}$ of K that has compact closure contained in $\mathcal{O}$. Since $\overline{\mathcal{V}}$ is compact and Hausdorff, it is normal. Moreover, K and $\overline{\mathcal{V}} \sim \mathcal{V}$ are disjoint closed subsets of $\overline{\mathcal{V}}$. According to Urysohn's Lemma, there is a continuous real-valued function f on $\overline{\mathcal{V}}$ for which

$$f = 1 \text{ on } K, \, f = 0 \text{ on } \overline{\mathcal{V}} \sim \mathcal{V} \text{ and } 0 \leq f \leq 1 \text{ on } \overline{\mathcal{V}}.$$

Extend f to all of X by setting $f = 0$ on $X \sim \overline{\mathcal{V}}$. Then f belongs to $C_c(X)$ and has the properties described in (1). $\square$

Recall that a subset of a topological space is called a G_δ set provided it is the intersection of a countable number of open sets.

Corollary 4 *Let K be a compact G_δ subset of a locally compact Hausdorff space X. Then there a function $f \in C_c(X)$ for which*

$$K = \{x \in X \mid f(x) = 1\}.$$

Proof According to Proposition 2, there is a neighborhood $\mathcal{U}$ of K that has compact closure. Since K is a G_δ set, there is a countable collection $\{\mathcal{O}_k\}_{k=1}^\infty$ of open sets whose intersection

---

[3]This is different from the definition of support in the discussion of measurable sets in which the support of f was defined to be the set $\{x \in X \mid f(x) \neq 0\}$, not its closure.

is K. We may assume $\mathcal{O}_k \subseteq \mathcal{U}$ for all k. By the preceding proposition, for each k there is a continuous real-valued function f_k on X for which

$$f_k = 1 \text{ on } K, \ f_k = 0 \text{ on } X \sim \overline{\mathcal{O}}_k \text{ and } 0 \le f_k \le 1 \text{ on } X.$$

The function f defined by

$$f = \sum_{k=1}^{\infty} 2^{-k} f_k \text{ on } X$$

has the desired property. $\qquad\qquad\qquad\qquad\qquad\qquad\qquad\qquad\qquad\qquad\qquad\qquad\qquad\quad\square$

Partitions of Unity

Definition *Let K be a subset of a topological space X that is covered by the open sets $\{\mathcal{O}_k\}_{k=1}^{n}$. A collection of continuous real-valued functions on X, $\{\varphi_k\}_{k=1}^{n}$, is called a* **partition of unity** *for K subordinate to $\{\mathcal{O}_k\}_{k=1}^{n}$ provided*

$$\operatorname{supp}\varphi_i \subseteq \mathcal{O}_i, \ 0 \le \varphi_i \le 1 \text{ on } X \text{ for } 1 \le i \le n$$

and

$$\varphi_1 + \varphi_2 + \ldots + \varphi_n = 1 \text{ on } K.$$

Proposition 5 *Let K be a compact subset of a locally compact Hausdorff space X and $\{\mathcal{O}_k\}_{k=1}^{n}$ a finite cover of K by open sets. Then there is a partition of unity $\{\varphi_k\}_{k=1}^{n}$ for K subordinate to this finite cover and each φ_k has compact support.*

Proof We first claim that there is an open cover $\{\mathcal{U}_k\}_{k=1}^{n}$ of K such that for each k, $\overline{\mathcal{U}}_k$ is a compact subset of $\mathcal{O}_k$. Indeed, invoking Proposition 2 n times, for each $x \in K$, there is a neighborhood $\mathcal{N}_x$ of x that has compact closure and such that if $1 \le j \le n$ and x belongs to $\mathcal{O}_j$, then $\overline{\mathcal{N}}_x \subseteq \mathcal{O}_j$. The collection of open sets $\{\mathcal{N}_x\}_{x \in K}$ is a cover of K and K is compact. Therefore there is a finite set of points $\{x_k\}_{k=1}^{m}$ in K for which $\{\mathcal{N}_{x_k}\}_{1 \le k \le m}$ also covers K. For $1 \le k \le n$, let $\mathcal{U}_k$ be the unions of those $\mathcal{N}_{x_j}$'s that are contained in $\mathcal{O}_k$. Then $\{\mathcal{U}_1, \ldots, \mathcal{U}_n\}$ is an open cover of K and for each k, $\overline{\mathcal{U}}_k$ is a compact subset of $\mathcal{O}_k$ since it is the finite union of such sets. We infer from Proposition 3 that for each $k, 1 \le k \le n$, there is a function $f_k \in C_c(X)$ for which $f_k = 1$ on $\overline{\mathcal{U}}_k$ and $f = 0$ on $X \sim \mathcal{O}_k$. The same proposition tells us that there is a function $h \in C(X)$ for which $h = 1$ on K and $h = 0$ on $X \sim \bigcup_{k=1}^{n} \mathcal{U}_k$. Define

$$f = \sum_{k=1}^{n} f_k \text{ on } X.$$

Observe that $f + [1 - h] > 0$ on X and $h = 0$ on K. Therefore if we define

$$\varphi_k = \frac{f_k}{f + [1 - h]} \text{ on } X \text{ for } 1 \le k \le n,$$

$\{\varphi_k\}_{k=1}^{n}$ is a partition of unity for K subordinate to $\{\mathcal{O}_k\}_{k=1}^{n}$ and each φ_k has compact support. $\qquad\qquad\qquad\qquad\qquad\qquad\qquad\qquad\qquad\qquad\qquad\qquad\qquad\qquad\qquad\quad\square$

The Alexandroff One-Point Compactification   If X is a locally compact Hausdorff space, we can form a new space X^* by adjoining to X a single point ω not in X and defining a set in X^* to be open provided it is either an open subset of X or the complement of a compact subset in X. Then X^* is a compact Hausdorff space, and the identity mapping of X into X^* is a homeomorphism of X and $X^* \sim \{\omega\}$. The space X^* is called the **Alexandroff one-point compactification** of X, and ω is often referred to as **the point at infinity** in X^*.

The proof of the the following variant, for locally compact Hausdorff spaces, of the Tietze Extension Theorem nicely illustrates the usefulness of the Alexandroff compactification.

Theorem 6   *Let K be a compact subset of a locally compact Hausdorff space X and f a continuous real-valued function on K. Then f has an extension to a continuous real-valued function on all of X.*

Proof   The Alexandroff compactification of X, X^*, is a compact Hausdorff space. Moreover, K is a closed subset of X^*, since its complement in X^* is open. A compact Hausdorff space is normal. Therefore we infer from the Tietze Extension Theorem that f may be extended to a continuous real-valued function on all of X^*. The restriction to X of this extension is a continuous extension of f to all of X. $\square$

PROBLEMS

1. Let X be a locally compact Hausdorff space, and F a set that has closed intersection with each compact subset of X. Show that F is closed.

2. Regarding the proof of Proposition 3:
   (i) Show that F and $\overline{\mathcal{V}} \sim \mathcal{V}$ are closed subsets of $\overline{\mathcal{V}}$.
   (ii) Show that the function f is continuous.

3. Let X be a locally compact Hausdorff space and X^* the Alexandroff one-point compactification of X:
   (i)   Prove that the subsets of X^* that are either open subsets of X or the complements of compact subsets of X are a topology for X^*.
   (ii) Show that the identity mapping from X to the subspace $X^* \sim \{\omega\}$ is a homeomorphism.
   (iii) Show that X^* is compact and Hausdorff.

4. Show that the Alexandroff one-point compactification of $\mathbf{R}^n$ is homeomorphic to the n-sphere $S^n = \{x \in \mathbf{R}^{n+1} \mid \|x\| = 1\}$.

5. Show that an open subset of a locally compact Hausdorff space, with its subspace topology, is locally compact.

6. Show that a closed subset of a locally compact space, with its subspace topology, is locally compact.

7. Show that a locally compact Hausdorff space X is compact if and only if the set consisting of the point at infinity is an open subset of the Alexandroff one-point compactification X^* of X.

8. Let X be a locally compact Hausdorff space. Show that the Alexandroff one-point compactification X^* is separable if and only if X is separable.

9. Consider the topological space X consisting of the set of real numbers with the topology that has complements of countable sets as a base. Show that X is not locally compact.

10. Provide a proof of Proposition 3 by applying Urysohn's Lemma to the Alexandroff one-point compactification of X.

11. Let f continuously map the locally compact Hausdorff space X onto the topological space Y. Is Y necessarily locally compact?

12. Let X be a topological space and f a continuous function of X that has compact support. Define $K = \{x \in X \mid f(x) = 1\}$. Show that K is a compact G_δ set.

13. Let $\mathcal{O}$ be an open subset of a compact Hausdorff space X. Show that the mapping of X to the Alexandroff one-point compactification of $\mathcal{O}$ that is the identity on $\mathcal{O}$ and takes each point in $X \sim \mathcal{O}$ into ω is continuous.

14. Let X and Y be locally compact Hausdorff spaces, and f a continuous mapping of X into Y. Let X^* and Y^* be the Alexandroff one-point compactifications of X and Y, and f^* the mapping of X^* into Y^* whose restriction to X is f and that takes the point at infinity in X^* into the point at infinity in Y^*. Show that f^* is continuous if and only if $f^{-1}(K)$ is compact whenever $K \subseteq Y$ is compact. A mapping f with this property is said to be proper.

15. Let X be a locally compact Hausdorff space. Show that a subset F of X is closed if and only if $F \cap K$ is closed for each compact subset K of X. Moreover, show that the same equivalence holds if instead of being locally compact the space X is first countable.

16. Let $\mathcal{F}$ be a family of real-valued continuous functions on a locally compact Hausdorff space X which has the following properties:
    (i) If $f \in \mathcal{F}$ and $g \in \mathcal{F}$, then $f + g \in \mathcal{F}$.
    (ii) If $f \in \mathcal{F}$ and $g \in \mathcal{F}$, then $f/g \in \mathcal{F}$, provided that $\operatorname{supp} f \subseteq \{x \in X \mid g(x) \neq 0\}$.
    (iii) Given a neighborhood $\mathcal{O}$ of a point $x_0 \in X$, there is a $f \in \mathcal{F}$ with $f(x_0) = 1, 0 \leq f \leq 1$ and $\operatorname{supp} f \subseteq \mathcal{O}$.

    Show that Proposition 5 is still true if we require that the functions in the partition of unity belong to $\mathcal{F}$.

17. Let K be a compact G_δ subset of a locally compact Hausdorff space X. Show that there is a decreasing sequence of continuous nonnegative real-valued functions on X that converges pointwise on X to the characteristic function of K.

18. The Baire Category Theorem asserts that in a complete metric space the intersection of a countable collection of open dense sets is dense. At the heart of its proof lies the Cantor Intersection Theorem. Show that the Fréchet Intersection Theorem is a sufficiently strong substitute for the Cantor Intersection Theorem to provide a proof of the following assertion by first proving it in the case in which X is compact: Let X be a locally compact Hausdorff space.
    (i) If $\{F_n\}_{n=1}^{\infty}$ is a countable collection of closed subsets of X for which each F_n has empty interior, then the union $\bigcup_{n=1}^{\infty} F_n$ also has empty interior.
    (ii) If $\{\mathcal{O}_n\}_{n=1}^{\infty}$ is a countable collection of open dense subsets of X, then the intersection $\bigcap_{n=1}^{\infty} \mathcal{O}_n$ also is dense.

19. Use the preceding problem to prove the following: Let X be a locally compact Hausdorff space. If $\mathcal{O}$ is an open subset of X that is contained in a countable union $\bigcup_{n=1}^{\infty} F_n$ of closed subsets of X, then the union of their interiors, $\bigcup_{n=1}^{\infty} \operatorname{int} F_n$, is an open dense subset of $\mathcal{O}$.

20. For a map $f: X \to Y$ and a collection C of subsets of Y we define f^*C to be the collection of subsets of X given by

$$f^*C = \left\{ E \mid E = f^{-1}[C] \text{ for some } C \in C \right\}.$$

Show that if A is the σ-algebra generated by C, then f^*A is the σ-algebra generated by f^*C.

21. For a map $f: X \to Y$ and a collection C of subsets of X, let A be the σ-algebra generated by C. If $f^{-1}[f[C]] = C$ for each $C \in C$, show that $f^{-1}[f[A]] = A$ for each $A \in A$.

21.2 SEPARATING SETS AND EXTENDING FUNCTIONS

We gather in the statement of the following theorem the three properties of locally compact Hausdorff spaces which we will employ in the proofs of our forthcoming representation theorems.

Theorem 7 *Let (X, T) be a Hausdorff space. Then the following four properties are equivalent:*

(i) *(X, T) is locally compact.*

(ii) *If O is a neighborhood of a compact subset K of X, then there is a neighborhood U of K that has compact closure contained in O.*

(iii) *If O is a neighborhood of a compact subset K of X, then the constant function on K that takes the value 1 may be extended to a function f in $C_c(X)$ for which $0 \leq f \leq 1$ on X and f vanishes outside of O.*

(iv) *For K a compact subset of X and F a finite open cover of K, there is a partition of unity subordinate to F consisting of functions of compact support.*

Proof We first establish the equivalence of (i) and (ii). Assume (ii) holds. Let x be a point in X. Then X is a neighborhood of the compact set $\{x\}$. By property (ii) there is a neighborhood of $\{x\}$ that has compact closure. Thus X is locally compact. Now assume that X is locally compact. Proposition 2 tells us that (ii) holds.

Next we establish the equivalence of (i) and (iii). Assume (iii) holds. Let x be a point in X. Then X is a neighborhood of the compact set $\{x\}$. By property (iii) there is a function f in $C_c(X)$ to take the value 1 at x. Then $O = f^{-1}(1/2, 3/2)$ is a neighborhood of x and it has compact closure since f has compact support and $\overline{O} \subseteq f^{-1}[1/2, 3/2]$. Thus X is locally compact. Now assume that X is locally compact. Proposition 3 tells us that (iii) holds.

Finally, we establish the equivalence of (1) and (iv). Assume property (iv) holds. Let x be a point in X. Then X is a neighborhood of the compact set $\{x\}$. By property (iv) there is a single function f that is a partition of unity subordinate to the covering of the compact set $\{x\}$ by single open set X. Then $O = f^{-1}(1/2, 3/2)$ is a neighborhood of x and it has compact closure. Thus X is locally compact. Now assume that X is locally compact. Proposition 5 tells us that (iv) holds. $\square$

The substantial implications in the above theorem are that a locally compact Hausdorff space possesses properties (ii), (iii), and (iv). Their proofs, which we presented in the preceding section, depend on Urysohn's Lemma. It is interesting to note, however, that if X

is a locally compact metric space, then very direct proofs show that X possesses properties (ii), (iii), and (iv). Indeed, suppose there is a metric $\rho: X \times X \to \mathbf{R}$ that induces the topology $\mathcal{T}$ and X is locally compact.

Proof of Property (ii)   For each $x \in K$, since $\mathcal{O}$ is open and X is locally compact, there is an open ball $B(x, r_x)$ of compact closure that is contained in $\mathcal{O}$. Then $\{B(x, r_x/2)\}_{x \in K}$ is a cover of K by open sets. The set K is compact. Therefore there are a finite set of points $x_1, \ldots, x_n$ in K for which $\{B(x, r_{x_k}/2)\}_{1 \le k \le n}$ cover K. Then $\mathcal{U} = \bigcup_{1 \le k \le n} B(x, r_{x_k}/2)$ is a neighborhood of K that, since $\overline{\mathcal{U}} \subseteq \bigcup_{1 \le k \le n} \overline{B}(x, r_{x_k}/2)$, has closure contained in $\mathcal{O}$.

Proof of Property (iii)   For a subset A of X, define the function called the distance to A and denoted by $\mathrm{dist}_A : X \to [0, \infty)$ by

$$\mathrm{dist}_A(x) = \inf_{y \in A} \rho(x, y) \text{ for } x \in X.$$

The function dist_A is continuous; indeed, it is Lipschitz with Lipschitz constant 1 (see Problem 25). Moreover, if A is closed subset of X, then $\mathrm{dist}_A(x) = 0$ if and only if $x \in A$. For $\mathcal{O}$ a neighborhood of a compact set K, by part (i) choose $\mathcal{U}$ to be a neighborhood of K that has compact closure contained in $\mathcal{O}$. Define

$$f = \frac{\mathrm{dist}_{X \sim \mathcal{U}}}{\mathrm{dist}_{X \sim \mathcal{U}} + \mathrm{dist}_K} \text{ on } X.$$

Then f belongs to $C_c(X)$, takes values in $[0, 1]$, $f = 1$ on K and $f = 0$ on $X \sim \mathcal{O}$.

Proof of Property (iv)   This follows from properties (ii) and (i) as it did in the case in which X is Hausdorff but not necessarily metrizable; see the proof of Proposition 5.
We see that property (ii) is equivalent to the assertion that two disjoint closed subsets of X, one of which is compact, may be separated by disjoint neighborhoods. We therefore refer to property (ii) as **the locally compact separation property**. It is convenient to call (iii) **the locally compact extension property**.

PROBLEMS

22. Show that Euclidean space $\mathbf{R}^n$ is locally compact.

23. Show that ℓ^p, for $1 \le p \le \infty$, fails to be locally compact.

24. Show that $C([0, 1])$, with the topology induced by the maximum norm, is not locally compact.

25. Let $\rho: X \times X \to \mathbf{R}$ be a metric on a set X. For $A \subseteq X$, consider the distance function

$$\mathrm{dist}_A : X \to [0, \infty).$$

(i)   Show that the function dist_A is continuous.

(ii)   If $A \subseteq X$ is closed and x is a point in X, show that $\mathrm{dist}_A(x) = 0$ if and only if x belongs to A.

(iii)   If $A \subseteq X$ is closed and x belongs to X, show that there may not exist a point x_0 in A for which $\mathrm{dist}_A(x) = \rho(x, x_0)$, but there is such a point x_0 if K is compact.

26. Show that property (ii) in the statement of Theorem 7 is equivalent to the assertion that two disjoint closed subsets of X, one of which is compact, may be separated by disjoint neighborhoods.

21.3   THE CONSTRUCTION OF RADON MEASURES

Let $(X, \mathcal{T})$ be a topological space. The purpose of this section is to construct measures on the Borel σ-algebra, $\mathcal{B}(X)$, comprising the smallest σ-algebra that contains the topology $\mathcal{T}$. A natural place to begin is to consider premeasures $\mu \colon \mathcal{T} \to [0, \infty]$ defined on the topology $\mathcal{T}$ and consider the Carathéodory measure induced by μ. If we can establish that each open set is measurable with respect to μ^*, then, by the minimality with respect to inclusion of the Borel σ-algebra among all σ-algebras containing the open sets, each Borel set will be μ^*-measurable and the restriction of μ^* to $\mathcal{B}(X)$ will be an extension of μ. We ask the following question: What properties of $\mu \colon \mathcal{T} \to [0, \infty]$ are sufficient in order that every open set be measurable with respect to μ^*, the outer measure induced by μ. It is not useful to invoke the Carathéodory-Hahn Theorem here. A topology, in general, is not a semiring. Indeed, it is not difficult to see that a Hausdorff topology $\mathcal{T}$ is a semiring if and only if $\mathcal{T}$ is the discrete topology, that is, every subset of X is open (see Problem 27).

Lemma 8 *Let $(X, \mathcal{T})$ be a topological space, $\mu \colon \mathcal{T} \to [0, \infty]$ a premeasure, and μ^* the outer measure induced by μ. Then for any subset E of X,*

$$\mu^*(E) = \inf \left\{ \mu(\mathcal{U}) \mid \mathcal{U} \text{ a neighborhood of } E \right\}. \tag{2}$$

Furthermore, E is μ^*-measurable if and only if

$$\mu(\mathcal{O}) \geq \mu^*(\mathcal{O} \cap E) + \mu^*(\mathcal{O} \sim E) \text{ for each open set } \mathcal{O} \text{ for which } \mu(\mathcal{O}) < \infty. \tag{3}$$

Proof Since the union of any collection of open sets is open, (2) follows from the countable monotonicity of μ. Let E be a subset of X for which (3) holds. To show that E is μ^*-measurable, let A be a subset of X for which $\mu^*(A) < \infty$ and let $\epsilon > 0$. We must show that

$$\mu^*(A) + \epsilon \geq \mu^*(A \cap E) + \mu^*(A \sim E). \tag{4}$$

By the above characterization (2) of outer measure, there is an open set $\mathcal{O}$ for which

$$A \subseteq \mathcal{O} \text{ and } \mu^*(A) + \epsilon \geq \mu^*(\mathcal{O}). \tag{5}$$

On the other hand, by (3) and the monotonicity of μ^*,

$$\mu^*(\mathcal{O}) \geq \mu^*(\mathcal{O} \cap E) + \mu^*(\mathcal{O} \sim E) \geq \mu^*(A \cap E) + \mu^*(A \sim E). \tag{6}$$

Inequality (4) follows from the inequalities (5) and (6). $\square$

Proposition 9 *Let $(X, \mathcal{T})$ be a topological space and $\mu \colon \mathcal{T} \to [0, \infty]$ a premeasure. Assume that for each open set $\mathcal{O}$ for which $\mu(\mathcal{O}) < \infty$,*

$$\mu(\mathcal{O}) = \sup \left\{ \mu(\mathcal{U}) \mid \mathcal{U} \text{ open and } \overline{\mathcal{U}} \subseteq \mathcal{O} \right\}. \tag{7}$$

Then every open set is μ^*-measurable and the measure $\mu^* \colon \mathcal{B}(X) \to [0, \infty]$ is an extension of μ.

Proof A premeasure is countable monotone and hence, for each open set $\mathcal{V}$, $\mu^*(\mathcal{V}) = \mu(\mathcal{V})$. Therefore, by the minimality property of $\mathcal{B}(X)$, to complete the proof it suffices to show that each open set is μ^*-measurable.

Let $\mathcal{V}$ be open. To verify the μ^*-measurability of $\mathcal{V}$ it suffices, by the preceding lemma, to let $\mathcal{O}$ be open with $\mu(\mathcal{O}) < \infty$, let $\epsilon > 0$ and show that

$$\mu(\mathcal{O}) + \epsilon \geq \mu(\mathcal{O} \cap \mathcal{V}) + \mu^*(\mathcal{O} \sim \mathcal{V}). \tag{8}$$

However, $\mathcal{O} \cap \mathcal{V}$ is open and, by the monotonicity of μ, $\mu(\mathcal{O} \cap \mathcal{V}) < \infty$. By assumption (7) there is an open set $\mathcal{U}$ for which $\overline{\mathcal{U}} \subseteq \mathcal{O} \cap \mathcal{V}$ and

$$\mu(\mathcal{U}) > \mu(\mathcal{O} \cap \mathcal{V}) - \epsilon.$$

The pair of sets $\mathcal{U}$ and $\mathcal{O} \sim \overline{\mathcal{U}}$ are disjoint open subsets of $\mathcal{O}$. Therefore by the monotonicity and finite additivity of the premeasure μ,

$$\mu(\mathcal{O}) \geq \mu(\mathcal{U} \cup [\mathcal{O} \sim \overline{\mathcal{U}}]) = \mu(\mathcal{U}) + \mu(\mathcal{O} \sim \overline{\mathcal{U}}).$$

On the other hand, since $\overline{\mathcal{U}} \subseteq \mathcal{V} \cap \mathcal{O}$,

$$\mathcal{O} \sim \mathcal{V} = \mathcal{O} \sim [\mathcal{O} \cap \mathcal{V}] \subseteq \mathcal{O} \sim \overline{\mathcal{U}}.$$

Hence, by the monotonicity of outer measure,

$$\mu(\mathcal{O} \sim \overline{\mathcal{U}}) \geq \mu^*(\mathcal{O} \sim \mathcal{V}).$$

Therefore

$$\begin{aligned}
\mu(\mathcal{O}) &\geq \mu(\mathcal{U}) + \mu(\mathcal{O} \sim \overline{\mathcal{U}}) \\
&\geq \mu(\mathcal{O} \cap \mathcal{V}) - \epsilon + \mu(\mathcal{O} \sim \overline{\mathcal{U}}) \\
&\geq \mu(\mathcal{O} \cap \mathcal{V}) - \epsilon + \mu^*(\mathcal{O} \sim \mathcal{V}).
\end{aligned}$$

We have established (8). The proof is complete. $\qquad\square$

Definition Let $(X, \mathcal{T})$ be a topological space. We call a measure μ on the Borel σ-algebra $\mathcal{B}(X)$ a **Borel measure** provided every compact subset of X has finite measure. A Borel measure μ is called a **Radon measure** provided

(i) (Outer Regularity) for each Borel subset E of X,

$$\mu(E) = \inf \{\mu(\mathcal{U}) \mid \mathcal{U} \text{ a neighborhood of } E\};$$

(ii) (Inner Regularity) for each open subset $\mathcal{O}$ of X,

$$\mu(\mathcal{O}) = \sup \{\mu(K) \mid K \text{ a compact subset of } \mathcal{O}\}.$$

We proved that the restriction to the Borel sets of Lebesgue measure on a Euclidean space $\mathbf{R}^n$ is a Radon measure. A Dirac delta measure on a topological space is a Radon measure.

While property (7) is sufficient in order for a premeasure $\mu: \mathcal{T} \to [0, \infty]$ to be extended by the measure $\mu^*: \mathcal{B} \to [0, \infty]$, in order that this extension be a Radon measure it is necessary, if X is locally compact Hausdorff space, that μ be what we now name a Radon premeasure (see Problem 35).

Definition *Let $(X, \mathcal{T})$ be a topological space. A premeasure $\mu: \mathcal{T} \to [0, \infty]$ is called a* **Radon premeasure**[4] *provided*

(i) *for each open set $\mathcal{U}$ that has compact closure, $\mu(\mathcal{U}) < \infty$;*

(ii) *for each open set $\mathcal{O}$,*

$$\mu(\mathcal{O}) = \sup \left\{ \mu(\mathcal{U}) \;\middle|\; \mathcal{U} \text{ open and } \overline{\mathcal{U}} \text{ a compact subset of } \mathcal{O} \right\}.$$

Theorem 10 *Let $(X, \mathcal{T})$ be a locally compact Hausdorff space and $\mu: \mathcal{T} \to [0, \infty]$ a Radon premeasure. Then the restriction to the Borel σ-algebra $\mathcal{B}(X)$ of the Carathéodory outer measure μ^* induced by μ is a Radon measure that extends μ.*

Proof A compact subset of the Hausdorff space X is closed, and hence assumption (ii) implies property (7). According to Proposition 9, the set function $\mu^*: \mathcal{B}(X) \to [0, \infty]$ is a measure that extends μ. Assumption (i) and the locally compact separation property possessed by X imply that if K is compact, then $\mu^*(K) < \infty$. Therefore $\mu^*: \mathcal{B}(X) \to [0, \infty]$ is a Borel measure. Since μ is a premeasure, Lemma 8 tells us that every subset of X and, in particular, every Borel subset of X, is outer regular with respect to μ^*. It remains only to establish the inner regularity of every open set with respect to μ^*. However, this follows from assumption (ii) and the monotonicity of μ^*. $\qquad\square$

The natural functions on a topological space are the continuous ones. Of course every continuous function on a topological space X is measurable with respect to the Borel σ-algebra $\mathcal{B}(X)$. For Lebesgue measure on **R**, we proved Lusin's Theorem, which made precise J. E. Littlewood's second principle: a measurable function is "nearly continuous." We leave it as an exercise (see Problem 39) to prove the following general version of Lusin's Theorem.

Lusin's Theorem *Let X be a locally compact Hausdorff space, $\mu: \mathcal{B}(X) \to [0, \infty)$ a Radon measure, and $f: X \to \mathbf{R}$ a Borel measurable function that vanishes outside of a set of finite measure. Then for each $\epsilon > 0$, there is a Borel subset X_0 of X and a function $g \in C_c(X)$ for which*

$$f = g \text{ on } X_0 \text{ and } \mu(X \sim X_0) < \epsilon.$$

PROBLEMS

27. Let $(X, \mathcal{T})$ be a Hausdorff topological space. Show that $\mathcal{T}$ is a semiring if and only if $\mathcal{T}$ is the discrete topology.

28. (Tyagi) Let $(X, \mathcal{T})$ be a topological space and $\mu: \mathcal{T} \to [0, \infty]$ a premeasure. Assume that if $\mathcal{O}$ is open and $\mu(\mathcal{O}) < \infty$, then $\mu(\text{bd }\mathcal{O}) = 0$. Show that every open set is μ^*-measurable.

---

[4]What is here called a Radon measure is often called a regular Borel measure or a quasi-regular Borel measure. What is here called a *Radon premeasure* is sometimes called a *content* or *inner content* or *volume*.

29. Show that the restriction of Lebesgue measure on the real line to the Borel σ-algebra is a Radon measure.

30. Show that the restriction of Lebesgue measure on the Euclidean space $\mathbf{R}^n$ to the Borel σ-algebra is a Radon measure.

31. Show that a Dirac delta measure on a topological space is a Radon measure.

32. Let X be an uncountable set with the discrete topology and $\{x_k\}_{1 \leq k < \infty}$ a countable subset of X. For $E \subseteq X$, define

$$\mu(E) = \sum_{\{n \,|\, x_n \in E\}} 2^{-n}.$$

Show that $2^X = B(X)$ and $\mu: B(X) \to$ is a Radon measure.

33. Show that the sum of two Radon measures also is Radon.

34. Let μ and ν be Borel measures on $B(X)$, where X is a compact topological space, and suppose that μ is absolutely continuous with respect to ν. If ν is Radon show that μ also is Radon.

35. Let (X, T) be a locally compact Hausdorff space and $\mu: T \to [0, \infty]$ a premeasure for which the restriction to $B(X)$ of μ^* is a Radon measure. Show that μ is a Radon premeasure.

36. Let X be a locally compact Hausdorff space and $\mu: B(X) \to [0, \infty]$ a Radon measure. Show that any Borel set E of finite measure is inner regular in the sense that

$$\mu(E) = \sup \{\mu(K) \mid K \subseteq E, K \text{ compact}\}.$$

Conclude that if μ is σ-finite, then every Borel set is inner regular.

37. Let X be a topological space, $\mu: B(X) \to [0, \infty]$ a σ-finite Radon measure, and $E \subseteq X$ a Borel set. Show that there is a G_δ subset A of X and an F_σ subset B of X for which

$$A \subseteq E \subseteq B \text{ and } \mu(B \sim E) = \mu(E \sim A) = 0.$$

38. For a metric space X, show that $B(X)$ is the smallest σ-algebra with respect to which all of the continuous real-valued functions on X are measurable.

39. Prove Lusin's Theorem as follows:

   (i) First prove it for simple functions by using the inner regularity of open sets and the locally compact extension property.

   (ii) Use part (i) together with Egoroff's Theorem and the Simple Approximation Theorem to complete the proof.

21.4 THE REPRESENTATION OF POSITIVE LINEAR FUNCTIONALS ON $C_c(X)$: THE RIESZ-MARKOV THEOREM

Let X be a topological space. A real-valued functional ψ on $C(X)$ is said to be **monotone** provided $\psi(g) \geq \psi(h)$ if $g \geq h$ on X, and said to be **positive** provided $\psi(f) \geq 0$ if $f \geq 0$ on X. If ψ is linear, $\psi(g - h) = \psi(g) - \psi(h)$ and, of course, if $f = g - h$, then $f \geq 0$ on X if and only if $g \geq h$ on X. Therefore, for a linear functional, positivity is the same as monotonicity.

Proposition 11 *Let X be a locally compact Hausdorff space and μ_1, μ_2 be Radon measures on $B(X)$ for which*

$$\int_X f \, d\mu_1 = \int_X f \, d\mu_2 \text{ for all } f \in C_c(X).$$

Then $\mu_1 = \mu_2$.

Proof By the outer regularity of every Borel set, these measures are equal if and only if they agree on open sets and therefore, by the inner regularity of every open set, if and only if they agree on compact sets. Let K be a compact subset of X. We will show that

$$\mu_1(K) = \mu_2(K).$$

Let $\epsilon > 0$. By the outer regularity of both μ_1 and μ_1 and the excision and monotonicity properties of measure, there is a neighborhood $\mathcal{O}$ of K for which

$$\mu_1(\mathcal{O} \sim K) < \epsilon/2 \text{ and } \mu_2(\mathcal{O} \sim K) < \epsilon/2. \tag{9}$$

Since X is locally compact and Hausdorff, it has the locally compact extension property. Hence there is a function $f \in C_c(X)$ for which $0 \le f \le 1$ on X, $f = 0$ on $X \sim \mathcal{O}$, and $f = 1$ on K. For $i = 1, 2$,

$$\int_X f \, d\mu_i = \int_\mathcal{O} f \, d\mu_i = \int_{\mathcal{O} \sim K} f \, d\mu_i + \int_K f \, d\mu_i = \int_{X \sim \mathcal{O}} f \, d\mu_i + \mu_i(K).$$

By assumption,

$$\int_X f \, d\mu_1 = \int_X f \, d\mu_2.$$

Therefore

$$\mu_1(K) - \mu_2(K) = \int_{\mathcal{O} \sim K} f \, d\mu_2 - \int_{\mathcal{O} \sim K} f \, d\mu_2.$$

But $0 \le f \le 1$ on X and we have the measure estimates (9). Hence, by the monotonicity of integration,

$$|\mu_1(K) - \mu_2(K)| \le \int_{\mathcal{O} \sim K} f \, d\mu_2 + \int_{\mathcal{O} \sim K} f \, d\mu_2 < \epsilon.$$

Therefore $\mu_1(K) = \mu_2(K)$. The proof is complete. $\qquad \square$

The Riesz-Markov Theorem *Let X be a locally compact Hausdorff space and I a positive linear functional on $C_c(X)$. Then there is a unique Radon measure $\widehat{\mu}$ on $\mathcal{B}(X)$, the Borel σ-algebra associated with the topology on X, for which*

$$I(f) = \int_X f \, d\widehat{\mu} \text{ for all } f \in C_c(X). \tag{10}$$

Proof[5] Define $\mu(\emptyset) = 0$. For each nonempty open subset $\mathcal{O}$ of X, define

$$\mu(\mathcal{O}) = \sup \left\{ I(f) \mid f \in C_c(X), \ 0 \le f \le 1, \text{supp} \, f \subseteq \mathcal{O} \right\}.$$

---

[5]To prove the theorem we need to determine the measure of a set by knowing the values of the "integrals" of certain functions. It is an instructive exercise to show that if μ is Lebesgue measure of $\mathbf{R}$ and $I = (a, b)$, an open, bounded interval, then

$$\mu(I) = b - a = \sup \left\{ \int_{\mathbf{R}} f \, d\mu \ \Big| \ f \in C_c(\mathbf{R}), \ 0 \le f \le 1, \text{supp} \, f \subseteq I \right\}.$$

Our strategy is to first show that μ is a Radon premeasure. Hence, by Theorem 10, if we denote by $\widehat{\mu}$ the restriction to the Borel sets of the outer measure induced by μ, then $\widehat{\mu}$ is a Radon measure that extends μ. We then show that integration with respect to $\widehat{\mu}$ represents the functional I. The uniqueness assertion is a consequence of the preceding proposition.

Since I is positive, μ takes values in $[0, \infty]$. We begin by showing that μ is a premeasure. To establish countable monotonicity, let $\{\mathcal{O}_k\}_{k=1}^{\infty}$ be a collection of open subsets of X that covers the open set $\mathcal{O}$. Let f be a function in $C_c(X)$ with $0 \le f \le 1$ and supp $f \subseteq \mathcal{O}$. Define $K = \text{supp } f$. By the compactness of K there is a finite collection $\{\mathcal{O}_k\}_{k=1}^{n}$ that also covers K. According to Proposition 5, there is a partition of unity subordinate to this finite cover, that is, there are functions $\varphi_1, \ldots, \varphi_n$ in $C_c(X)$ such that

$$\sum_{i=1}^{n} \varphi_i = 1 \text{ on } K \text{ and, for } 1 \le k \le n, 0 \le \varphi_k \le 1 \text{ on } X \text{ and } \text{supp } \varphi_k \subseteq \mathcal{O}_k.$$

Then, since $f = 0$ on $X \sim K$,

$$f = \sum_{k=1}^{n} \varphi_k \cdot f \text{ on } X \text{ and, for } 1 \le k \le n, \; 0 \le f \cdot \varphi_k \le 1 \text{ and } \text{supp}(\varphi_k \cdot f) \subseteq \mathcal{O}_k.$$

By the linearity of the functional I and the definition of μ,

$$I(f) = I\left(\sum_{k=1}^{n} \varphi_k \cdot f\right) = \sum_{k=1}^{n} I(\varphi_k \cdot f) \le \sum_{k=1}^{n} \mu(\mathcal{O}_k) \le \sum_{k=1}^{\infty} \mu(\mathcal{O}_k).$$

Take the supremum over all such f to conclude that

$$\mu(\mathcal{O}) \le \sum_{k=1}^{\infty} \mu(\mathcal{O}_k).$$

Therefore μ is countably monotone.

Since μ is countably monotone and, by definition, $\mu(\emptyset) = 0$, μ is finitely monotone. Therefore to show that μ is finitely additive it suffices, using an induction argument, to let $\mathcal{O} = \mathcal{O}_1 \cup \mathcal{O}_2$ be the disjoint union of two open sets and show that

$$\mu(\mathcal{O}) \ge \mu(\mathcal{O}_1) + \mu(\mathcal{O}_2). \tag{11}$$

Let the functions f_1, f_2 belong to $C_c(X)$ and have the property that for $1 \le k \le 2$,

$$0 \le f_k \le 1 \text{ and } \text{supp } f_k \subseteq \mathcal{O}_k.$$

Then the function $f = f_1 + f_2$ has support contained in $\mathcal{O}$, and, since $\mathcal{O}_1$ and $\mathcal{O}_2$ are disjoint, $0 \le f \le 1$. Again using the linearity of I and the definition of μ, we have

$$I(f_1) + I(f_2) = I(f) \le \mu(\mathcal{O}).$$

If we first take the supremum over all such f_1 and then over all such f_2 we have

$$\mu(\mathcal{O}_1) + \mu(\mathcal{O}_2) \le \mu(\mathcal{O}).$$

Hence we have established (11) and thus the finite additivity of μ. Therefore μ is a premeasure.

We next establish the inner regularity property of a Radon premeasure. Let $\mathcal{O}$ be open. Suppose $\mu(\mathcal{O}) < \infty$. We leave the case $\mu(\mathcal{O}) = \infty$ as an exercise (see Problem 43). Let $\epsilon > 0$. We have to establish the existence of an open set $\mathcal{U}$ that has compact closure contained in $\mathcal{O}$ and $\mu(\mathcal{U}) > \mu(\mathcal{O}) - \epsilon$. Indeed, by the definition of μ, there is a function $f_\epsilon \in C_c(X)$ that has support contained in $\mathcal{O}$ and for which $I(f_\epsilon) > \mu(\mathcal{O}) - \epsilon$. Let $K = \operatorname{supp} f$. But X is locally compact and Hausdorff and therefore has the locally compact separation property. Choose $\mathcal{U}$ to be a neighborhood of K that has compact closure contained in $\mathcal{O}$. Then

$$\mu(\mathcal{U}) \geq I(f_\epsilon) > \mu(\mathcal{O}) - \epsilon.$$

It remains only to show that if $\mathcal{O}$ is an open set of compact closure, then $\mu(\overline{\mathcal{O}}) < \infty$. But X is locally compact and Hausdorff and therefore has the locally compact extension property. Choose a function in $C_c(X)$ that takes the constant value 1 on $\overline{\mathcal{O}}$. Thus, since I is positive, $\mu(\mathcal{O}) \leq I(f) < \infty$. This concludes the proof that μ is a Radon premeasure.

Theorem 10 tells us that the Carathéodory measure induced by μ restricts to a Radon measure $\widehat{\mu}$ on $\mathcal{B}(X)$ that extends μ. We claim that (10) holds for $\widehat{\mu}$. The first observation is that a continuous function is measurable with respect to any Borel measure and that a continuous function of compact support is integrable with respect to such a measure since compact sets have finite measure and continuous functions on compact sets are bounded. By the linearity of I and of integration with respect to a given measure and the representation of each $f \in C_c(X)$ as the difference of nonnegative functions in $C_c(X)$, to establish (10) it suffices to verify that

$$I(f) = \int_X f \, d\widehat{\mu} \text{ for all } f \in C_c(X) \text{ for which } 0 \leq f \leq 1. \tag{12}$$

Let f belong to $C_c(X)$. Fix a natural number n. For $1 \leq k \leq n$, define the function $\varphi_k \colon X \to [0, 1]$ as follows:

$$\varphi_k(x) = \begin{cases} 1 & \text{if } f(x) > \frac{k}{n} \\ nf(x) - (k-1) & \text{if } \frac{k-1}{n} < f(x) \leq \frac{k}{n} \\ 0 & \text{if } f(x) \leq \frac{k-1}{n}. \end{cases}$$

The function φ_k is continuous. We claim that

$$f = \frac{1}{n} \sum_{k=1}^{n} \varphi_k \text{ on } X. \tag{13}$$

To verify this claim, let x belong to X. If $f(x) = 0$, then $\varphi_k(x) = 0$ for $1 \leq k \leq n$, and therefore (13) holds. Otherwise, choose k_0 such that $1 \leq k_0 \leq n$ and $\frac{k_0-1}{n} < f(x) \leq \frac{k_0}{n}$. Then

$$\varphi_k(x) = \begin{cases} 1 & \text{if } 1 \leq k \leq k_0 - 1 \\ nf(x) - (k_0 - 1) & \text{if } k = k_0 \\ 0 & \text{if } k_0 < k \leq n. \end{cases}$$

Thus (13) holds.

Since X is locally compact and Hausdorff, it has the locally compact separation property. Therefore, since supp f is compact, we may choose an open set $\mathcal{O}$ of compact closure for which supp $f \subseteq \mathcal{O}$. Define $\mathcal{O}_0 = \mathcal{O}, \mathcal{O}_{n+1} = \emptyset$ and, for $1 \le k \le n$, define

$$\mathcal{O}_k = \left\{ x \in \mathcal{O} \;\middle|\; f(x) > \frac{k-1}{n} \right\}.$$

By construction,

$$\text{supp } \varphi_k \subseteq \overline{\mathcal{O}}_k \subseteq \mathcal{O}_{k-1} \text{ and } \varphi_k = 1 \text{ on } \mathcal{O}_{k+1}.$$

Therefore, by the monotonicity of I and of integration with respect to $\widehat{\mu}$, and the definition of μ,

$$\mu(\mathcal{O}_{k+1}) \le I(\varphi_k) \le \mu(\mathcal{O}_{k-1}) = \mu(\mathcal{O}_k) + [\mu(\mathcal{O}_{k-1}) - \mu(\mathcal{O}_k)]$$

and

$$\mu(\mathcal{O}_{k+1}) \le \int_X \varphi_k \, d\widehat{\mu} \le \mu(\mathcal{O}_{k-1}) = \mu(\mathcal{O}_k) + [\mu(\mathcal{O}_{k-1}) - \mu(\mathcal{O}_k)].$$

However,

$$\mu(\mathcal{O}) = \mu(\mathcal{O}_0) \ge \mu(\mathcal{O}_1) \ge \ldots \ge \mu(\mathcal{O}_{n-1}) \ge \ldots \ge \mu(\mathcal{O}_n) = 0.$$

Therefore, since the compactness of $\overline{\mathcal{O}}$ implies the finiteness of $\mu(\mathcal{O})$, we have

$$-\mu(\mathcal{O}) - \mu(\mathcal{O}) \le \sum_{k=1}^{n} \left[I(\varphi_k) - \int_X \varphi_k \, d\widehat{\mu} \right] \le \mu(\mathcal{O}) + \mu(\mathcal{O}).$$

Divide this inequality by n, use the linearity of I and of integration, together with (13) to obtain

$$\left| I(f) - \int_X f \, d\widehat{\mu} \right| \le \frac{4}{n}\mu(\mathcal{O}).$$

This holds for all natural numbers n and $\mu(\mathcal{O}) < \infty$. Hence (10) holds. $\square$

PROBLEMS

40. Let X be a locally compact Hausdorff space, and $C_0(X)$ the space of all uniform limits of functions in $C_c(X)$.
    (i)   Show that a continuous real-valued function f on X belongs to $C_0(X)$ if and only if for each $\alpha > 0$ the set $\{x \in X \mid |f(x)| \ge \alpha\}$ is compact.
    (ii) Let X^* be the one-point compactification of X. Show that $C_0(X)$ consists precisely of the restrictions to X of those functions in $C(X^*)$ that vanish at the point at infinity.

41. Let X be an uncountable set with the discrete topology.
    (i)   What is $C_c(X)$?
    (ii) What are the Borel subsets of X?
    (iii) Let X^* be the one-point compactification of X. What is $C(X^*)$?
    (iv) What are the Borel subsets of X^*?
    (v)   Show that there is a Borel measure μ on X^* such that $\mu(X^*) = 1$ and $\int_X f \, d\mu = 0$ for each f in $C_c(X)$.

42. Let X and Y be two locally compact Hausdorff spaces.

   (i) Show that each $f \in C_c(X \times Y)$ is the limit of sums of the form

$$\sum_{i=1}^{n} \varphi_i(x)\psi_i(y)$$

   where $\varphi_i \in C_c(X)$ and $\psi_i = C_c(Y)$. (The Stone-Weierstrass Theorem is useful.)

   (ii) Show that $\mathcal{B}(X \times Y) \subseteq \mathcal{B}(X) \times \mathcal{B}(Y)$.

   (iii) Show that $\mathcal{B}(X \times Y) = \mathcal{B}(X) \times \mathcal{B}(Y)$ if and only if X or Y is the union of a countable collection of compact subsets.

43. In the proof of the Riesz-Markov Theorem, establish inner regularity in the case in which $\mu(\mathcal{O}) = \infty$.

44. Let $k(x, y)$ be a bounded Borel measurable function on $X \times Y$, and let μ and ν be Radon measures on X and Y.

   (i) Show that

$$\iint_{X \times Y} \varphi(x)k(x, y)\psi(y)d(\mu \times \nu) = \int_Y \left[\int_X \varphi(x)k(x, y)d\mu \right] \psi(y)d\nu$$

$$= \int_X \varphi(x) \left[\int_Y k(x, y)\psi(y)d\nu \right] d\mu$$

   for all $\varphi \in C_c(X)$ and $\psi \in C_c(Y)$.

   (ii) If the integral in (i) is zero for all φ and ψ in $C_c(X)$ and $C_c(Y)$, show that then $k = 0$ a.e. $[\mu \times \nu]$.

45. Let X be a compact Hausdorff space and μ a Borel measure on $\mathcal{B}(X)$. Show that there is a constant $c > 0$ such that

$$\left| \int_X f d\mu \right| \leq c\|f\|_{\max} \text{ for all } f \in C(X).$$

21.5 THE RIESZ REPRESENTATION THEOREM FOR THE DUAL OF $C(X)$

Let X be a compact Hausdorff space and $C(X) = C_c(X)$ the space of real-valued continuous functions on X. In the preceding section, we described the positive linear functionals on $C(X)$. We now consider $C(X)$ as a normed linear space with the maximum norm and characterize the continuous linear functionals on $C(X)$. First observe that each positive linear functional is continuous, that is, is bounded. Indeed, if L is a positive linear functional on $C(X)$ and $f \in C(X)$ with $\|f\| \leq 1$, then $-1 \leq f \leq 1$ on X and hence, by the homogeneity and positivity of L, $-L(1) \leq L(f) \leq L(1)$, that is, $|L(f)| \leq L(1)$. Therefore L is bounded and the norm of the functional L equals the value of L at the constant function with value 1, that is,

$$\|L\| = L(1).$$

Jordan's Theorem tells us that a function of bounded variation may be expressed as the difference of increasing functions. Therefore, for $X = [a, b]$, Lebesgue-Stieltjes integration against a function of bounded variation may be expressed as the difference of positive linear functionals. According to the Jordan Decomposition Theorem, a signed measure may be expressed as the difference of two measures. Therefore integration with respect to a signed measure may be expressed as the difference of positive linear functionals. The following proposition is a variation, for general continuous linear functionals on $C(X)$, of these decomposition properties.

Proposition 12 *Let X be a compact Hausdorff space and $C(X)$ the linear space of continuous real-valued functions on X, normed by the maximum norm. Then for each continuous linear functional L on $C(X)$, there are two positive linear functionals L_+ and L_- on $C(X)$ for which*

$$L = L_+ - L_- \text{ and } \|L\| = L_+(1) + L_-(1).$$

Proof For $f \in C(X)$ such that $f \geq 0$, define

$$L_+(f) = \sup_{0 \leq \psi \leq f} L(\psi).$$

Since the functional L is bounded, $L_+(f)$ is a real number. We first show that for $f \geq 0, g \geq 0$ and $c \geq 0$,

$$L_+(cf) = cL_+(f) \text{ and } L_+(f+g) = L_+(f) + L_+(g).$$

Indeed, by the positive homogeneity of L, $L_+(cf) = cL_+(f)$ for $c \geq 0$. Let f and g be two nonnegative functions in $C(X)$. If $0 \leq \varphi \leq f$ and $0 \leq \psi \leq g$, then $0 \leq \varphi + \psi \leq f + g$ and so

$$L(\varphi) + L(\psi) = L(\varphi + \psi) \leq L_+(f+g).$$

Taking suprema, first over all such φ and then over all such ψ, we obtain

$$L_+(f) + L_+(g) \leq L_+(f+g).$$

On the other hand, if $0 \leq \psi \leq f+g$, then $0 \leq \min\{\psi, f\} \leq f$ and thus $0 \leq \psi - \min\{\psi, f\} \leq g$, and therefore

$$L(\psi) \quad = L(\min\{\psi, f\}) + L(\psi - [\min\{\psi, f\}])$$
$$\leq L_+(f) + L_+(g).$$

Taking the supremum over all such ψ, we get

$$L_+(f+g) \leq L_+(f) + L_+(g).$$

Therefore

$$L_+(f+g) = L_+(f) + L_+(g).$$

Let f be an arbitrary function in $C(X)$, and let M and N be two nonnegative constants for which $f + M$ and $f + N$ are nonnegative. Then

$$L_+(f + M + N) = L_+(f + M) + L_+(N) = L_+(f + N) + L_+(M).$$

Hence

$$L_+(f+M) - L_+(M) = L_+(f+N) - L_+(N).$$

Thus the value of $L_+(f+M) - L_+(M)$ is independent of the choice of M, and we define $L_+(f)$ to be this value.

Clearly, $L_+: C(X) \to \mathbf{R}$ is positive and we claim that it is linear. Indeed, it is clear that $L_+(f+g) = L_+(f) + L_+(g)$. We also have $L_+(cf) = cL_+(f)$ for $c \geq 0$. On the other hand, $L_+(-f) + L_+(f) = L_+(0) = 0$, so that we have $L_+(-f) = -L_+(f)$. Thus $L_+(cf) = cL_+(f)$ for all c. Therefore L_+ is linear.

Define $L_- = L_+ - L$. Then L_- is a linear functional on $C(X)$ and it is positive since, by the definition of L_+, $L(f) \leq L_+(f)$ for $f \geq 0$. We have expressed L as the difference, $L_+ - L_-$, of two positive linear functionals on $C(X)$.

We always have $\|L\| \leq \|L_+\| + \|L_-\| = L_+(1) + L_-(1)$. To establish the inequality in the opposite direction, let φ be any function in $C(X)$ for which $0 \leq \varphi \leq 1$. Then $\|2\varphi - 1\| \leq 1$ and hence

$$\|L\| \geq L(2\varphi - 1) = 2L(\varphi) - L(1).$$

Taking the supremum over all such φ, we have

$$\|L\| \geq 2L_+(1) - L(1) = L_+(1) + L_-(1).$$

Hence $\|L\| = L_+(1) + L_-(1)$.   □

For a compact topological space X, we call a signed measure on $\mathcal{B}(X)$ a **signed Radon measure** provided it is the difference of Radon measures. We denote by $\mathcal{R}adon(X)$ the normed linear space of signed Radon measures on X with the norm of $\nu \in \mathcal{R}adon(X)$ given by its total variation $\|\nu\|_{\text{var}}$, which, we recall, may be expressed as

$$\|\nu\|_{\text{var}} = \nu^+(X) + \nu^-(X),$$

where $\nu = \nu^+ - \nu^-$ is the Jordan decomposition of ν. We leave it as an exercise to show that $\| \cdot \|_{\text{var}}$ is a norm on the linear space of signed Radon measures.

The Riesz Representation Theorem for the Dual of $C(X)$ *Let X be a compact Hausdorff space and $C(X)$ the linear space of continuous real-valued functions on X, normed by the maximum norm. Define the operator $T: \mathcal{R}adon(X) \to [C(X)]^*$ by setting, for $\nu \in \mathcal{R}adon(X)$,*

$$T_\nu(f) = \int_X f \, d\nu \text{ for all } f \text{ in } C(X).$$

Then T is a linear isometric isomorphism of $\mathcal{R}adon(X)$ onto $[C(X)]^*$.

Proof Let L be a bounded linear functional on $C(X)$. By the preceding proposition, we may choose positive linear functionals L_1 and L_2 on $C(X)$ for which $L = L_1 - L_2$. According to the Riesz-Markov Theorem, there are Radon measures on X, μ_1 and μ_2, for which

$$L_1(f) = \int_X f \, d\mu_1 \text{ and } L_2(f) = \int_X f \, d\mu_2 \text{ for all } f \in C(X).$$

Define $\mu = \mu_1 - \mu_2$. Thus μ is a signed Radon measure for which $L = T_\mu$. Hence T is onto. We infer from this and Proposition 11 that the representation of L as the difference of positive linear functionals is unique. Therefore, again by the preceding proposition,

$$\|L\| = L_1(1) + L_2(1) = \mu_1(X) + \mu_2(X) = |\mu|(X).$$

Therefore T is an isomorphism. □

Corollary 13 *Let X be a compact Hausdorff space and K^* a bounded subset of $\mathcal{R}adon(X)$ that is weak-* closed. Then K^* is weak-* compact. If, furthermore, K^* is convex, then K^* is the weak-* closed convex hull of its extreme points.*

Proof Alaoglu's Theorem tells us that each closed ball in $[C(X)]^*$ is weak-* compact. A closed subset of a compact topological space is compact. Thus K^* is weak-* compact. We infer from the Krein-Milman Theorem, applied to the locally convex topological space comprising $[C(X)]^*$ with its weak-* topology, that if K^* is convex, then K^* is the weak-* closed convex hull of its extreme points. □

The original Riesz Representation Theorem was proven in 1909 by Frigyes Riesz for the dual of $C(X)$, where $X = [a, b]$, a closed, bounded interval of real numbers. The general case for X a compact Hausdorff space was proven by Shizuo Kakutani in 1941. There were two intermediate theorems: in 1913 Johann Radon proved the theorem for X a cube in Euclidean space and in 1937 Stefan Banach proved it for X a compact metric space.[6] In each of these two theorems the representing measure is a finite measure on the Borel sets and is unique among such measures: there is no mention of regularity. The following theorem explains why this is so.

Theorem 14 *Let X be a compact metric space and μ a finite measure on the Borel σ-algebra $\mathcal{B}(X)$. Then μ is a Radon measure.*

Proof Define the functional $I: C(X) \to \mathbf{R}$ by

$$I(f) = \int_X f \, d\mu \text{ for all } f \in C(X).$$

Then I is a positive linear functional on $C_c(X) = C(X)$. The Riesz-Markov Theorem tells us that there is Radon measure $\mu_0: \mathcal{B}(X) \to [0, \infty)$ for which

$$\int_X f \, d\mu = \int_X f \, d\mu_0 \text{ for all } f \in C(X). \tag{14}$$

We will show that $\mu = \mu_0$. First, consider an open set $\mathcal{O}$. For each natural number n, let $K_n = \{x \in X \mid \text{dist}_{X \sim \mathcal{O}}(x) \geq 1/n\}$. Then $\{K_n\}$ is an ascending sequence of compact subsets of $\mathcal{O}$ whose union is $\mathcal{O}$. Since X is compact it is locally compact and therefore possesses the

---

[6] Albrecht Pietsch's *History of Banach Spaces and Functional Analysis* [Pie07] contains an informative discussion of the antecedents of the general Riesz Representation Theorem. Further interesting historical information is contained in the chapter notes of Nelson Dunford and Jacob Schwartz's *Linear Operators, Part I* [DS71].

locally compact extension property. Select a sequence $\{f_n\}$ of functions in $C(X)$ for which each $f_n = 1$ on K_n and $f_n = 0$ on $X \sim \mathcal{O}$. Substitute f_n for f in (14). Then

$$\mu(K_n) + \int_{\mathcal{O} \sim K_n} f_n \, d\mu = \mu_0(K_n) + \int_{\mathcal{O} \sim K_n} f_n \, d\mu_0 \text{ for all } n.$$

We infer from the continuity of the measures μ and μ_0 and the uniform boundedness of the f_n's that for every open set $\mathcal{O}$,

$$\mu(\mathcal{O}) = \lim_{n \to \infty} \mu(K_n) = \lim_{n \to \infty} \mu_0(K_n) = \mu_0(\mathcal{O}).$$

Now let F be a closed set. For each natural number n, define

$$\mathcal{O}_n = \bigcup_{x \in F} B(x, 1/n).$$

Then $\mathcal{O}_n$, being the union of open balls, is open. On the other hand, since F is compact,

$$F = \bigcap_{n=1}^{\infty} \mathcal{O}_n.$$

By the continuity of the measures μ and μ_0 and their equality on open sets,

$$\mu(F) = \lim_{n \to \infty} \mu(\mathcal{O}_n) = \lim_{n \to \infty} \mu_0(\mathcal{O}_n) = \mu_0(F).$$

We conclude that for every closed set F, $\mu(F) = \mu_0(F)$.

Now let E be a Borel set. We leave it as an exercise (see Problem 51) to show that the Radon measure μ_0 on the compact metric space X has the following approximation property: for each $\epsilon > 0$, there is an open set $\mathcal{O}_\epsilon$ and a closed set F_ϵ for which

$$F_\epsilon \subseteq E \subseteq \mathcal{O}_\epsilon \text{ and } \mu_0(\mathcal{O}_\epsilon \sim F_\epsilon) < \epsilon. \tag{15}$$

Therefore, by the excision property of measure,

$$\mu(\mathcal{O}_\epsilon \sim F_\epsilon) = \mu(\mathcal{O}_\epsilon) - \mu(F_\epsilon) < \epsilon.$$

From these two estimates we infer that $|\mu_0(E) - \mu(E)| < 2 \cdot \epsilon$. Thus the two measures agree on the Borel sets and therefore are equal. ☐

Corollary 15 *Let X be a compact metric space and $\{\mu_n : B(X) \to [0, \infty)\}$ a sequence of Borel measures for which the sequence $\{\mu_n(X)\}$ is bounded. Then there is a subsequence $\{\mu_{n_k}\}$ and a Borel measure μ for which*

$$\lim_{k \to \infty} \int_X f \, d\mu_{n_k} = \int_X f \, d\mu \text{ for all } f \in C(X).$$

Proof Borsuk's Theorem tells us that $C(X)$ is separable. The Riesz Representation Theorem and the preceding regularity theorem tell us that all the bounded linear functionals on $C(X)$ are given by integration against finite signed Borel measures. The weak-$*$ sequential compactness conclusion now follows from Helley's Theorem.   □

In 1909 Frigyes Riesz proved the representation theorem which bears his name for the dual of $C[a, b]$, in the following form: For each bounded linear functional L on $C[a, b]$, there is a function $g \colon [a, b] \to \mathbf{R}$ of bounded variation for which

$$L(f) = \int_a^b f(x)\,dg(x) \text{ for all } f \in C[a, b]:$$

the integral is in the sense of Riemann-Stieltjes. According to Jordan's Theorem, any function of bounded variation is the difference of increasing functions. Therefore it is interesting, given an increasing function g on $[a, b]$, to identify, with respect to the properties of g, the unique Borel measure μ for which

$$\int_a^b f(x)\,dg(x) = \int_{[a, b]} f\,d\mu \text{ for all } f \in C[a, b]. \tag{16}$$

For a closed, bounded interval $[a, b]$, let S be the semiring of subsets of $[a, b]$ comprising the singleton set $\{a\}$ together with subintervals of the form $(c, d]$. Then $\mathcal{B}[a, b]$ is the smallest σ-algebra containing S. We infer from the uniqueness assertion in the Carathéodory-Hahn Theorem that a Borel measure on $\mathcal{B}[a, b]$ is uniquely determined by its values on S. Therefore the following proposition characterizes the Borel measure that represents Lebesgue-Stieltjes integration against a given increasing function. For an increasing real-valued function on the closed, bounded interval $[a, b]$ we define, for $a < c < b$,

$$f(c^+) = \inf_{c < x \le b} f(x) \text{ and } f(c^-) = \sup_{a \le x < c} f(x).$$

Define $f(a^+)$ and $f(b^-)$ in the obvious manner, and set $f(a^-) = f(a)$, $f(b^+) = f(b)$. The function f is said to be continuous on the right at $x \in [a, b)$ provided $f(x) = f(x^+)$.

Proposition 16 *Let g be an increasing function on the closed, bounded interval $[a, b]$ and μ the unique Borel measure for which (16) holds. Then $\mu\{a\} = g(a^+) - g(a)$ and*

$$\mu(c, d] = g(d^+) - g(c^+) \text{ for all } (c, d] \subseteq (a, b]. \tag{17}$$

Proof We first verify that

$$\mu[c, b] = g(b) - g(c^-) \text{ for all } c \in (a, b]. \tag{18}$$

Fix a natural number n. The increasing function g is continuous except at a countable number of points in $[a, b]$. Choose a point $c_n \in (a, c)$ at which g is continuous and $c - c_n < 1/n$. Now choose a point $c_n' \in (a, c_n)$ at which g is continuous and $g(c_n) - g(c_n') < 1/n$. Construct a continuous function f_n on $[a, b]$ for which $0 \le f_n \le 1$ on $[a, b]$, $f_n = 1$ on $[c_n, b]$ and $f_n = 0$ on $[a, c'_n]$. By the additivity over intervals property of the Riemann-Stieltjes integral,

$$\int_a^b f_n(x)\, dg(x) = \int_{c'_n}^{c_n} f_n(x)\, dg(x) + [g(b) - g(c_n)].$$

By the additivity of integration with respect to μ over finite disjoint unions of Borel sets,

$$\int_{[a, b]} f_n\, d\mu = \int_{(c'_n, c_n)} f_n\, d\mu + \mu[c_n, b].$$

Substitute $f = f_n$ in (16) to conclude that

$$\int_{c'_n}^{c_n} f_n(x)\, dg(x) + [g(b) - g(c_n)] = \int_{(c'_n, c_n)} f_n\, d\mu + \mu[c_n, b]. \tag{19}$$

However, since $0 \le f_n \le 1$ on $[a, b]$,

$$\left| \int_{c'_n}^{c_n} f_n(x)\, dg(x) \right| \le g(c_n) - g(c'_n) < 1/n$$

and

$$\left| \int_{(c'_n, c_n)} f_n\, d\mu \right| \le \mu(c'_n, c_n) \le \mu(c'_n, c).$$

Take the limit as $n \to \infty$ in (19) and use the continuity of measure to conclude that (18) holds. A similar argument shows that $\mu\{a\} = g(a^+) - g(a)$ and

$$\mu\{c\} = g(c^+) - g(c^-) \text{ for all } c \in (a, b). \tag{20}$$

Finally, we infer from (18), (20), and the finite additivity of μ that for $a < c < d \le b$,

$$\mu(c, d] = \mu[c, b] - \mu[d, b] - \mu\{c\} + \mu\{d\} = g(d^+) - g(c^+).$$

The proof is complete. $\qquad\qquad\qquad\qquad\qquad\qquad\qquad\qquad\qquad\qquad\qquad\qquad\quad$ $\square$

We have the following, slightly amended, version of Riesz's original representation theorem from 1909.

Theorem 17 (Riesz) *Let $[a, b]$ be a closed, bounded interval and $\mathcal{F}$ the collection of real-valued functions on $[a, b]$ that are of bounded variation on $[a, b]$, continuous on the right on (a, b), and vanish at a. Then for each bounded linear functional ψ on $C[a, b]$, there is a unique function g belonging to $\mathcal{F}$ for which*

$$\psi(f) = \int_a^b f(x)\, dg(x) \text{ for all } f \in C[a, b]. \tag{21}$$

Proof To establish existence, it suffices, by the Riesz-Markov Theorem, to do so for ψ a positive bounded linear functional on $C[a, b]$. For such a ψ, the Riesz Representation Theorem tells us there is a Borel measure μ for which

$$\psi(f) = \int_a^b f \, d\mu \text{ for all } f \in C[a, b].$$

Consider the increasing real-valued function g defined on $[a, b]$ by $g(a) = 0$ and $g(x) = \mu(a, x] + \mu\{a\}$ for $x \in (a, b]$. The functon g inherits continuity on the right at each point in (a, b) from the continuity of the measure μ. Thus g belongs to $\mathcal{F}$. We infer from Proposition 16 that

$$\int_a^b f \, d\widehat{\mu} = \int_a^b f(x) \, dg(x) \text{ for all } f \in C[a, b],$$

where $\widehat{\mu}$ is the unique Borel measure on $\mathcal{B}[a, b]$ for which

$$\widehat{\mu}(c, b] = g(b) - g(c^+) = g(b) - g(c) \text{ for all } c \in (a, b) \text{ and } \widehat{\mu}\{a\} = g(a^+) - g(a).$$

However, the measure μ has these properties. This completes the proof of existence.

To establish uniqueness, by Jordan's Theorem regarding the expression of a function of bounded variation as the difference of increasing functions, it suffices to let $g_1, g_2 \in \mathcal{F}$ be increasing functions which have the property that

$$\psi(f) = \int_a^b f(x) \, dg_1(x) = \int_a^b f(x) \, dg_2(x) \text{ for all } f \in C[a, b],$$

and show that $g_1 = g_2$. Take $f \equiv 1$ in this integral equality to conclude that

$$g_1(b) = g_1(b) - g_1(a) = g_2(b) - g_2(a) = g_2(b).$$

Let ψ be represented by integration against the Borel measure μ. We infer from Proposition 16 and the right continuity of g_1 and g_2 at each point in (a, b) that if x belongs to (a, b), then

$$g_1(b) - g_1(x) = \mu(x, b] = g_2(b) - g_2(x),$$

and hence $g_1(x) = g_2(x)$. Therefore $g_1 = g_2$ on $[a, b]$.   □

PROBLEMS

46. Let x_0 be a point in the compact Hausdorff space X. Define $L(f) = f(x_0)$ for each $f \in C(X)$. Show that L is a bounded linear functional on $C(X)$. Find the signed Radon measure that represents L.

47. Let X be a compact Hausdorff space and μ a Borel measure on $\mathcal{B}(X)$. Show that there is a Radon measure μ_0 for which

$$\int_X f \, d\mu = \int_X f \, d\mu_0 \text{ for all } f \text{ in } C(X).$$

48. Let g_1 and g_2 be two increasing functions on the closed, bounded interval $[a, b]$ that agree at the end-points. Show that

$$\int_a^b f(x)\,dg_1(x) = \int_a^b f(x)\,dg_2(x) \text{ for all } f \in C[a, b]$$

if and only if $g_1(x^+) = g_2(x^+)$ for all $a \leq x < b$.

49. Let X be a compact Hausdorff space. Show that the Jordan Decomposition Theorem for signed Borel measures on $\mathcal{B}(X)$ follows from the Riesz Representation Theorem for the dual of $C(X)$ and Proposition 12.

50. What are the extreme points of the unit ball of the linear space of signed Radon measures $Radon(X)$, where X is a compact Hausdorff space?

51. Verify (15) for E a Borel subset of a compact metric space X and μ a Radon measure on $\mathcal{B}(X)$.

52. Let X be a compact metric space. On the linear space of functions $\mathcal{F}$ defined in the statement of Theorem 17, define the norm of a function to be its total variation. Show that with this norm $\mathcal{F}$ is a Banach space.

53. (*Alternate proof of the Stone-Weierstrass Theorem (de Branges)*) Let $\mathcal{A}$ be an algebra of real-valued continuous functions on a compact space X that separates points and contains the constants. Let $\mathcal{A}^\perp$ be the set of signed Radon measures on X such that $|\mu|(X) \leq 1$ and $\int_X f\,d\mu = 0$ for all $f \in \mathcal{A}$.

   (i)   Use the Hahn-Banach Theorem and the Riesz Representation Theorem to show that if $\mathcal{A}^\perp$ contains only the zero measure, then $\overline{\mathcal{A}} = C(X)$.

   (ii) Use the Krein-Milman Theorem and the weak-* compactness of the unit ball in $Radon(X)$ to show that if the zero measure is the only extreme point of $\mathcal{A}^\perp$, then $\mathcal{A}^\perp$ contains only the zero measure.

   (iii) Let μ be an extreme point of $\mathcal{A}^\perp$. Let f belong to $\mathcal{A}$, with $0 \leq f \leq 1$. Define measures μ_1 and μ_2 by

   $$\mu_1(E) = \int_E f\,d\mu \text{ and } \mu_2(E) = \int_E (1 - f)\,d\mu \text{ for } E \in \mathcal{B}(X).$$

   Show that μ_1 and μ_2 belong to $\mathcal{A}^\perp$ and, moreover, $\|\mu_1\| + \|\mu_2\| = \|\mu\|$, and $\mu_1 + \mu_2 = \mu$. Since μ is an extreme point, conclude that $\mu_1 = c\mu$ for some constant c.

   (iv) Show that $f = c$ on the support of μ.

   (v)   Since $\mathcal{A}$ separates points, show that the support of μ can contain at most one point. Since $\int_X 1\,d\mu = 0$, conclude that the support of μ is empty and hence μ is the zero measure.

21.6 REGULARITY PROPERTIES OF BAIRE MEASURES

Definition *Let X be a topological space. The* **Baire** *σ-algebra, which is denoted by $Ba(X)$, is defined to be the smallest σ-algebra of subsets of X for which the functions in $C_c(X)$ are measurable.*

Evidently

$$Ba(X) \subseteq \mathcal{B}(X).$$

There are compact Hausdorff spaces for which this inclusion is strict (see Problem 58). The forthcoming Theorem 20 tells us that these two σ-algebras are equal if X is a compact metric space. A measure on $Ba(X)$ is called a **Baire measure** provided it is finite on compact sets. Given a Borel measure μ on the Borel σ-algebra $B(X)$, we define μ_0 to be the restriction of μ to the Baire σ-algebra $Ba(X)$. Then μ_0 is a Baire measure. Moreover, each function $f \in C_c(X)$ is integrable over X with respect to μ_0 since it is measurable with respect to $Ba(X)$, bounded, and vanishes outside a set of finite measure. Since $Ba(X) \subseteq B(X)$,

$$\int_X f \, d\mu = \int_X f \, d\mu_0 \text{ for all } f \in C_c(X). \tag{22}$$

We will establish regularity properties for Baire measures from which we obtain finer uniqueness properties for Baire representations than are possible for Borel representations in the Riesz-Markov and Riesz Representation Theorems.

Let X be a topological space, S a σ-algebra of subsets of X, and $\mu: S \to [0, \infty]$ a measure. A set $E \in S$ is said to be **outer regular** provided

$$\mu(E) = \inf \{\mu(\mathcal{O}) \mid \mathcal{O} \text{ open, } \mathcal{O} \in S, \, E \subseteq \mathcal{O}\}$$

and said to be **inner regular** provided

$$\mu(E) = \sup \{\mu(K) \mid K \text{ compact, } K \in S, \, K \subseteq E\}.$$

A set that is both inner and outer regular is called **regular** with respect to μ. The measure $\mu: S \to [0, \infty]$ is called **regular** provided each set in S is regular.

We showed that Lebesgue measure on the Euclidean space $\mathbf{R}^n$ is regular. We defined a Borel measure to be a Radon provided each Borel set is outer regular and each open set is inner regular.

Proposition 18 *Let X be a locally compact Hausdorff space and μ_1 and μ_2 be two regular Baire measures on $Ba(X)$. Suppose*

$$\int_X f \, d\mu_1 = \int_X f \, d\mu_2 \text{ for all } f \in C_c(X).$$

Then $\mu_1 = \mu_2$.

Proof The proof is exactly the same as the corresponding uniqueness result for integration with respect to Radon measures. $\qquad\Box$

Proposition 19 *Let X be a compact Hausdorff space, S a σ-algebra of subsets of X, and $\mu: S \to [0, \infty)$ a finite measure. Then the collection of sets in S that are regular with respect to μ is a σ-algebra.*

Proof Define $\mathcal{F}$ to be the collection of sets in S that are regular with respect to μ. Since X is compact and Hausdorff, a subset of X is open if and only if its complement in X is compact. Thus, since μ is finite, by the excision property of measure, a set belongs to $\mathcal{F}$ if and only if its complement in X belongs to $\mathcal{F}$. We leave it as an exercise to show that the union of two regular sets is regular. Therefore the regular sets are closed with respect to the formation of finite unions, finite intersections, and relative complements. It remains to show that $\mathcal{F}$ is closed with respect to the formation of countable unions. Let $E = \bigcup_{n=1}^{\infty} E_n$, where each E_n is a regular set. By replacing each E_n by $E_n \sim \bigcup_{i=1}^{n-1} E_i$, we may suppose that the E_n's are disjoint. Let $\epsilon > 0$. For each n, by the outer regularity of E_n, we may choose a neighborhood $\mathcal{O}_n$ of E_n, which belongs to S and $\mu(\mathcal{O}_n) < \mu(E_n) + \epsilon/2^n$. Define $\mathcal{O} = \bigcup_{n=1}^{\infty} \mathcal{O}_n$. Then $\mathcal{O}$ is a neighborhood of E, $\mathcal{O}$ belongs to S, and, since

$$\mathcal{O} \sim E \subseteq \bigcup_{n=1}^{\infty} [\mathcal{O}_n \sim K_n],$$

by the excision and countable monotonicity properties of the measure μ,

$$\mu(\mathcal{O}) - \mu(E) = \mu(\mathcal{O} \sim E) \le \sum_{n=1}^{\infty} \mu(\mathcal{O}_n \sim E_n) < \epsilon.$$

Thus E is outer regular. A similar argument established inner regularity of E. This completes the proof. $\qquad\square$

Theorem 20 *Let X be a compact Hausdorff space in which every closed set is a G_δ set. Then the Borel σ-algebra equals the Baire σ-algebra and every Borel measure is regular. In particular, if X is a compact metric space, then the Borel σ-algebra equals the Baire σ-algebra and every Borel measure is regular.*

Proof To show that the Baire σ-algebra equals the Borel σ-algebra, it is necessary and sufficient to show that every closed set is a Baire set. Let K be a closed subset of X. Then K is compact and, by assumption, is a G_δ set. According to Proposition 4, there is a function $f \in C_c(X)$ for which $K = \{x \in X \mid f(x) = 1\}$. Since f belongs to $C_c(X)$, the set $\{x \in X \mid f(x) = 1\}$ is a Baire set.

Let μ be a Borel measure on $\mathcal{B}(X)$. The preceding proposition tells us that the collection of regular Borel sets is a σ-algebra. Therefore, to establish the regularity of $\mathcal{B}(X)$ it is necessary and sufficient to show that every closed set is regular with respect to the Borel σ-algebra. Let K be a closed subset of X. Then K is compact since X is compact and thus K is inner regular. Since K is a G_δ set and $\mu(X) < \infty$, we infer from the continuity of measure that K is outer regular with respect to the Borel σ-algebra.

To conclude the proof, assume X is a compact metric space. Let K be a closed subset of X. We will show that K is a G_δ set. Let n be a natural number. Define $\mathcal{O}_n = \bigcup_{x \in K} B(x, 1/n)$. Then $\mathcal{O}$ is a neighborhood of the compact set K. According to the locally compact extension property, the function that takes the value 1 on K may be extended to a function $f_n \in C_c(X)$ that has support contained in $\mathcal{O}_n$. Define $\mathcal{U}_n = f_n^{-1}(-1/n, 1/n)$. Then $\mathcal{U}_n$ is an open Baire set. By the compactness of K, $K = \bigcup_{n=1}^{\infty} \mathcal{U}_n$. We infer from the continuity of measure that K is outer regular. $\qquad\square$

In the preceding section we used the Riesz-Markov Theorem to show that if X is a compact metric space, then every Borel measure on $\mathcal{B}(X)$ is a Radon measure.

Proposition 21 *Let X be locally compact Hausdorff space. The Baire σ-algebra $Ba(X)$ is the smallest σ-algebra that contains all the compact G_δ subsets of X.*

Proof Define $\mathcal{F}$ to be the smallest σ-algebra that contains all the compact G_δ sets. Let K be a compact G_δ set. According to Proposition 4 there is a function $f \in C_c(X)$ for which $K = \{x \in X \mid f(x) = 1\}$. Therefore K belongs to $\mathcal{F}$. Thus $\mathcal{F} \subseteq Ba(X)$. To establish the inclusion in the opposite direction we let f belong to $C_c(X)$ and show it is measurable with respect to the Baire σ-algebra. For a closed, bounded interval $[a, b]$ that does not contain 0, $f^{-1}[a, b]$ is compact and equal to $\cap_{n=1}^{\infty}(a - 1/n, b + 1/n)$ since f is continuous and has compact support. Since $\mathcal{F}$ is closed with respect to the formation of countable unions, $f^{-1}(I)$ also belongs to $\mathcal{F}$ if I is any interval that does not contain 0. Finally, since

$$f^{-1}\{0\} = X \sim [f^{-1}(-\infty, 0) \cup f^{-1}(0, \infty)]$$

we infer that the inverse image under f of any nonempty interval belongs to $\mathcal{F}$ and therefore f is measurable with respect to the Baire σ-algebra. $\qquad\square$

Proposition 22 *Let X be a compact Hausdorff space. Then every Baire measure on $Ba(X)$ is regular.*

Proof Let μ be a Baire measure on $Ba(X)$. Proposition 19 tells us that the collection of subsets of $Ba(X)$ that are regular with respect to μ is a σ-algebra. We infer from Proposition 21 that to prove the proposition it is sufficient to show that each compact G_δ subset K of X is regular. Let K be such a set. Clearly K is inner regular. Since $\mu(X) < \infty$ and K is a G_δ set, by the continuity of measure, K is outer regular. $\qquad\square$

We have the following small improvement regarding uniqueness of the Riesz Representation Theorem.

Theorem 23 *Let X be a compact Hausdorff space and $I: C(X) \to \mathbf{R}$ a bounded linear functional. Then there is a unique signed Baire measure μ for which*

$$I(f) = \int_X f \, d\mu \text{ for all } f \in C_c(X).$$

Proof The Riesz Representation Theorem tells us that I is given by integration against a signed Radon measure μ' on the Borel subsets of X. Let μ be the restriction of μ' to the Baire σ-algebra. Then, arguing as we did in establishing (22), integration against μ represents I. The uniqueness assertion follows from Proposition 18 and the preceding regularity result. $\square$

Definition *A topological space X is said to be σ-**compact** provided it is the countable union of compact subsets.*

Each Euclidean space $\mathbf{R}^n$ is σ-compact. The discrete topology on an uncountable space is not σ-compact. Our final goal of this chapter is to prove regularity for Baire measures on a locally compact, σ-compact Hausdorff space. To that end we need the following three lemmas whose proof we leave as exercises.

Lemma 24 *Let X be a locally compact Hausdorff space and $F \subseteq X$ a closed Baire set. Then for $A \subseteq F$,*

$$A \in Ba(X) \text{ if and only if } A \in Ba(F).$$

Lemma 25 *Let X be a locally compact Hausdorff space and $E \subseteq X$ a Baire set that has compact closure. Then E is regular with respect to any Baire measure μ on $Ba(X)$.*

Lemma 26 *Let X be a locally compact, σ-compact Hausdorff space and $A \subseteq X$ a Baire set. Then $A = \bigcup_{k=1}^{n} A_k$ where each A_k is a Baire set that has compact closure.*

Theorem 27 *Let X be a locally compact, σ-compact Hausdorff space. Then every Baire measure on $Ba(X)$ is regular.*

Proof Since X is locally compact, Lemma 25 tells us that any Baire set of compact closure is regular. Moreover, by the preceding lemma, since X is σ-compact, every Baire set is the union of a countable collection of Baire sets each of which has compact closure. Therefore to complete the proof it is sufficient to show that the countable union of Baire sets, each of which has compact closure, is regular.

Let $E = \bigcup_{k=1}^{\infty} E_k$, where each E_k is a Baire set of compact closure. Since the Baire sets are an algebra, we may suppose that the E_k's are disjoint. Let $\epsilon > 0$. For each k, by the regularity of E_k, we may choose Baire sets K_k and $\mathcal{O}_k$, with K_k compact and $\mathcal{O}_k$ open, for which

$$K_k \subseteq E_k \subseteq \mathcal{O}_k$$

and

$$\mu(E_k) - \epsilon/2^k < \mu(K_k) \le \mu(\mathcal{O}_k) < \mu(E_k) + \epsilon/2^k.$$

If $\mu(E) = \infty$ then, of course, E is outer regular. Moreover, since

$$\mu\left(\bigcup_{k=1}^{\infty} E_k\right) = \mu(E) = \infty \text{ and } \mu\left(\bigcup_{k=1}^{\infty} K_k\right) = \lim_{n \to \infty} \mu\left(\bigcup_{k=1}^{n} K_k\right)$$

E contains compact Baire sets of the form $\bigcup_{k=1}^{N} K_k$, which have arbitrarily large measure and therefore E is inner regular.

Now suppose that $\mu(E) < \infty$. Then $\mathcal{O} = \bigcup_{k=1}^{\infty} \mathcal{O}_k$ is again an open Baire set and since

$$\mathcal{O} \sim E \subseteq \bigcup_{k=1}^{\infty} [\mathcal{O}_k \sim E_k],$$

by the countable monotonicity and excision properties of measure,

$$\mu(\mathcal{O}) - \mu(E) = \mu(\mathcal{O} \sim E) \le \sum_{k=1}^{\infty} \mu(\mathcal{O}_k \sim E_k) < \epsilon.$$

Thus E is outer regular. To establish inner regularity observe that

$$\mu(E) = \lim_{N \to \infty} \sum_{k=1}^{N} \mu(E_k) \le \lim_{N \to \infty} \sum_{k=1}^{N} \mu(K_k) + \epsilon$$

Thus E contains compact Baire subsets of the form $\bigcup_{k=1}^{N} K_k$, which have measure arbitrarily close to the measure of E. Therefore E is inner regular. $\square$

We have the following small improvement regarding uniqueness of the Riesz-Markov Theorem for σ-compact spaces.

Theorem 28 *Let X be a locally compact, σ-compact Hausdorff space and $I: C_c(X) \to \mathbf{R}$ a positive linear functional. Then there is a unique Baire measure μ for which*

$$I(f) = \int_X f \, d\mu \text{ for all } f \in C_c(X).$$

The reader should be warned that standard terminology regarding sets and measures that are either Baire or Borel has not been established. Neither has the terminology regarding Radon measures. Some authors take the class of Baire sets to be the smallest σ-algebra for which all continuous real-valued functions on X are measurable. Others do not assume every Borel or Baire measure is finite on every compact set. Others restrict the class of Borel sets to be the smallest σ-algebra that contains the compact sets. Authors (such as Halmos [Hal50]) who do measure theory on σ-rings rather than σ-algebras often take the Baire sets to be the smallest σ-ring containing the compact G_δ's and the Borel sets to be the smallest σ-ring containing the compact sets. In reading works dealing with Baire and Borel sets or measures and Radon measures, it is imperative to check carefully the author's definitions. A given statement may be true for one usage and false for another.

PROBLEMS

54. Let X be a separable compact Hausdorff space. Show that every closed set is a G_δ set.

55. Let X be a Hausdorff space and $\mu: \mathcal{B}(X) \to [0, \infty]$ a σ-finite Borel measure. Show that μ is Radon if and only if it is regular.

56. Show that a Hausdorff space X is both locally compact and σ-compact if and only if there is an ascending countable collection $\{\mathcal{O}_k\}_{k=1}^{\infty}$ of open subsets of X that covers X and for each k,

$$\overline{\mathcal{O}}_k \text{ is a compact subet of } \mathcal{O}_{k+1}.$$

57. Let x_0 be a point in the locally compact Hausdorff space X. Is the Dirac delta measure concentrated at x_0, δ_{x_0}, a regular Baire measure?

58. Let X be an uncountable set with the discrete topology and X^* its Alexandroff compactification with x^* the point at infinity. Show that the singleton set $\{x^*\}$ is a Borel set that is not a Baire set.

59. Let X be a locally compact Hausdorff space. Show that a Borel measure $\mu: \mathcal{B}(X) \to [0, \infty]$ is Radon if and only if every Borel set is measurable with respect to the Carathéodory measure induced by the premeasure $\mu: \mathcal{B}(X) \to [0, \infty]$.

60. Prove Lemmas 24, 25, and 26.

61. Let X be a compact Hausdorff space and $f_1, \ldots, f_n$ continuous real-valued functions on X. Let ν be a signed Radon measure on X with $|\nu|(X) \le 1$ and let $c_i = \int_X f_i d\nu$, for $1 \le i \le n$.

   (i)   Show that there is a signed Radon measure μ on X with $|\mu|(X) \le 1$ for which

$$\int_X f_i \, d\mu = c_i$$

   and

$$\int_X g \, d\mu \le \int_X g \, d\lambda \text{ for all } g \in C(X)$$

   for any signed Radon measure λ with $|\lambda|(X) \le 1$ and such that $\int_X f_i \, d\lambda = c_i$ for $1 \le i \le n$.

   (ii)   Suppose that there is a Radon measure ν on X with $\nu(X) = 1$ and $\int_X f_i d\nu = c_i$, $1 \le i \le n$. Show that there is a Radon measure μ on X with $\mu(X) = 1$ and $\int_X f_i \, d\mu = c_i$, for $1 \le i \le n$, which minimizes $\int_X g d\mu$ among all Radon measures that satisfy these conditions.

CHAPTER 22

Invariant Measures

Contents

A topological group is a group G together with a Hausdorff topology on G for which the group operation and inversion are continuous. We prove a seminal theorem of John von Neumann which tells us that on any compact topological group G there is a unique measure μ on the Borel σ- algebra $\mathcal{B}(G)$, called Haar measure, that is invariant under the left action of the group, that is,

$$\mu(g \cdot E) = \mu(E) \text{ for all } g \in G, E \in \mathcal{B}(G).$$

Uniqueness follows from Fubini's Theorem; existence is a consequence of a fixed point theorem of Shizuo Kakutani which asserts that for a compact group G, there is a functional $\psi \in [C(G)]^*$ for which

$$\psi[f \equiv 1] = 1 \text{ and } \psi[x \mapsto f(x)] = \psi[x \mapsto f(g \cdot x)] \text{ for all } g \in G, f \in C(G).$$

Alaoglu's Theorem is crucial in the proof of this fixed point theorem. Details of the proof of the existence of Haar measure are framed in the context of a group homomorphism of G into the general linear group of $[C(G)]^*$. We also consider mappings f of a compact metric space X into itself and finite measures on $\mathcal{B}(X)$. Based on Helley's Theorem, we prove the Bogoliubov-Krilov Theorem which tells us that if f is a continuous mapping on a compact metric space X, then there is a measure μ on $\mathcal{B}(X)$ for which

$$\mu(X) = 1 \text{ and } \int_X \varphi \circ f \, d\mu = \int_X \varphi \, d\mu \text{ for all } \varphi \in L^1(X, \mu).$$

Based on the Krein-Milman Theorem, we prove that the above μ may be chosen so that f is ergodic with respect to μ, that is, if A belongs to $\mathcal{B}(X)$ and $\mu([A \sim f(A)] \cup [f(A) \sim A]) = 0$, then $\mu(A) = 0$ or $\mu(A) = 1$.

22.1 TOPOLOGICAL GROUPS: THE GENERAL LINEAR GROUP

Consider a group $\mathcal{G}$ together with a Hausdorff topology on $\mathcal{G}$. For two members g_1, g_2 of $\mathcal{G}$, denote the group operation by $g_1 \cdot g_2$, denote the inverse of a member g of the group by

g^{-1}, and let e be the identity of the group. We say that $\mathcal{G}$ is a **topological group** provided the mapping $(g_1, g_2) \mapsto g_1 \cdot g_2$ is continuous from $\mathcal{G} \times \mathcal{G}$ to $\mathcal{G}$, where $\mathcal{G} \times \mathcal{G}$ has the product topology, and the mapping $g \mapsto g^{-1}$ is continuous from $\mathcal{G}$ to $\mathcal{G}$. By a **compact group** we mean a topological group that is compact as a topological space. For subsets $\mathcal{G}_1$ and $\mathcal{G}_2$ of $\mathcal{G}$, we define $\mathcal{G}_1 \cdot \mathcal{G}_2 = \{g_1 \cdot g_2 \mid g_1 \in \mathcal{G}_1, g_2 \in \mathcal{G}_2\}$ and $\mathcal{G}_1^{-1} = \{g^{-1} \mid g \in \mathcal{G}_1\}$. If $\mathcal{G}_1$ has just one member g, we denote $\{g\} \cdot \mathcal{G}_2$ by $g \cdot \mathcal{G}_2$.

Let E be a Banach space and $\mathcal{L}(E)$ the Banach space of continuous linear operators on E.[1] The composition of two operators in $\mathcal{L}(E)$ also belongs to $\mathcal{L}(E)$ and clearly, for operators $T, S \in \mathcal{L}(E)$,

$$\|S \circ T\| \le \|S\| \cdot \|T\|. \tag{1}$$

Define $GL(E)$ to be the collection of invertible operators in $\mathcal{L}(E)$. An operator in $\mathcal{L}(E)$ is invertible if and only if it is one-to-one and onto; the inverse is continuous by the Open Mapping Theorem. Observe that for $T, S \in GL(E)$, $(S \circ T)^{-1} = T^{-1} \circ S^{-1}$. Therefore, under the operation of composition, $GL(E)$ is a group called the **general linear group** of E. We denote its identity element by Id. It also is a topological space with the topology induced by the operator norm.

Lemma 1 *Let E be a Banach space and the operator $C \in \mathcal{L}(E)$ have $\|C\| < 1$. Then $\mathrm{Id} - C$ is invertible and*

$$\|(\mathrm{Id} - C)^{-1}\| \le (1 - \|C\|)^{-1}. \tag{2}$$

Proof We infer from (1) that for each natural number k, $\|C^k\| \le \|C\|^k$. Hence, since $\|C\| < 1$, the series of real numbers $\sum_{k=0}^{\infty} \|C^k\|$ converges. The normed linear space $\mathcal{L}(E)$ is complete. Therefore the series[2] of operators $\sum_{k=0}^{\infty} C^k$ converges in $\mathcal{L}(E)$ to a continuous linear operator. But observe that

$$(\mathrm{Id} - C) \circ \left(\sum_{k=0}^{n} C^k \right) = \left(\sum_{k=0}^{n} C^k \right) \circ (\mathrm{Id} - C) = \mathrm{Id} - C^{n+1} \text{ for all } n.$$

Therefore the series $\sum_{k=0}^{\infty} C^k$ converges to the inverse of $\mathrm{Id} - C$. The estimate (2) follows from this series representation of the inverse of $\mathrm{Id} - C$. $\qquad \square$

Theorem 2 *Let E be a Banach space. Then the general linear group of E, $GL(E)$, is a topological group with respect to the group operation of composition and the topology induced by the operator norm on $\mathcal{L}(E)$.*

Proof For operators T, T', S, S' in $GL(E)$, observe that

$$T \circ S - T' \circ S' = T \circ (S - S') + (T - T') \circ S'.$$

Therefore, by the triangle inequality for the operator norm and inequality (1),

$$\|T \circ S - T' \circ S'\| \le \|T\| \cdot \|S - S'\| + \|T - T'\| \cdot \|S'\|.$$

---

[1] Recall that the operator norm, $\|T\|$, of $T \in \mathcal{L}(E)$ is defined by $\|T\| = \sup \{\|T(x)\| \mid x \in E, \|x\| \le 1\}$.

[2] The series $\sum_{k=0}^{\infty} C^k$ is called the Neumann series for the inverse of $I - C$.

The continuity of composition follows from this inequality.

If S belongs to $GL(E)$ and $\|S - \text{Id}\| < 1$, then from the identity

$$S^{-1} - \text{Id} = (\text{Id} - S)S^{-1} = (\text{Id} - S)[\text{Id} - (I - S)]^{-1},$$

together with the inequalites (1) and (2), we infer that

$$\|S^{-1} - \text{Id}\| \leq \frac{\|S - \text{Id}\|}{1 - \|S - \text{Id}\|}. \tag{3}$$

Therefore inversion is continuous at the identity. Now let T and S belong to $GL(E)$ and $\|S - T\| < \|T^{-1}\|^{-1}$. Then

$$\|T^{-1}S - \text{Id}\| = \|T^{-1}(S - T)\| \leq \|T^{-1}\| \cdot \|S - T\| < 1.$$

Thus, if we substitute $T^{-1}S$ for S in (3) we have

$$\|S^{-1}T - \text{Id}\| \leq \frac{\|T^{-1}S - \text{Id}\|}{1 - \|T^{-1}S - \text{Id}\|}.$$

From this inequality and the identities

$$S^{-1} - T^{-1} = (S^{-1}T - \text{Id})T^{-1} \text{ and } T^{-1}S - \text{Id} = T^{-1}(S - T)$$

we infer that

$$\|S^{-1} - T^{-1}\| \leq \frac{\|T^{-1}\|^2 \cdot \|T - S\|}{1 - \|T^{-1}\| \cdot \|T - S\|}.$$

The continuity of inversion at T follows from this inequality. $\square$

In the case E is the Euclidean space $\mathbf{R}^n$, $GL(E)$ is denoted by $GL(n, \mathbf{R})$. If a choice of basis is made for $\mathbf{R}^n$, then the topology on $GL(n, \mathbf{R})$ is the topology imposed by the requirement that each of the $n \times n$ entries of the matrix representing the operator with respect to this basis is a continuous function.

A subgroup of a topological group with the subspace topology is also a topological group. For example, if H is a Hilbert space, then the subset of $GL(H)$ consisting of those operators that leave invariant the inner product is a topological group that is called the orthogonal linear group of H and denoted by $\mathcal{O}(H)$.

PROBLEMS

In the following exercises, $\mathcal{G}$ is a topological group with unit element e and E is a Banach space.

1. If $\mathcal{T}_e$ is a base for the topology at e, show that $\{g \cdot \mathcal{O} \mid \mathcal{O} \in \mathcal{T}_e\}$ is a base for the topology at $g \in \mathcal{G}$.

2. Show that $K_1 \cdot K_2$ is compact if K_1 and K_2 are compact subsets of $\mathcal{G}$.

3. Let $\mathcal{O}$ be a neighborhood of e. Show that there is also a neighborhood $\mathcal{U}$ of e for which $\mathcal{U} = \mathcal{U}^{-1}$ and $\mathcal{U} \cdot \mathcal{U} \subseteq \mathcal{O}$.

4. Show that the closure $\overline{H}$ of a subgroup H is a subgroup of $\mathcal{G}$.

5. Let $\mathcal{G}_1$ and $\mathcal{G}_2$ be topological groups and $h: \mathcal{G}_1 \rightarrow \mathcal{G}_2$ a group homomorphism. Show that h is continuous if and only if it is continuous at the identity element of $\mathcal{G}_1$.

6. Use the Contraction Mapping Principle to prove Lemma 1.

7. Use the completeness of $\mathcal{L}(E)$ to show that if $C \in \mathcal{L}(E)$ and $\|C\| < 1$, then $\sum_{k=0}^{\infty} C^k$ converges in $\mathcal{L}(E)$.

8. Show that the set of $n \times n$ invertible real matrices with determinant 1 is a topological group if the group operation is matrix multiplication and the topology is entrywise continuity. This topological group is called the special linear group and denoted by $SL(n, \mathbf{R})$.

9. Let H be a Hilbert space. Show that an operator in $GL(H)$ preserves the norm if and only if it preserves the inner product.

10. Consider $\mathbf{R}^n$ with the Euclidean inner product and norm. Characterize those $n \times n$ matrices that represent orthogonal operators with respect to an orthonormal basis.

11. Show that $GL(E)$ is open in $\mathcal{L}(E)$.

12. Show that the set of operators in $GL(E)$ comprising operators that are linear compact perturbations of the identity is a subgroup of $GL(E)$. It is denoted by $GL_c(E)$.

22.2   KAKUTANI'S FIXED POINT THEOREM

For two groups $\mathcal{G}$ and $\mathcal{H}$, a mapping $\varphi: \mathcal{G} \rightarrow \mathcal{H}$ is called a **group homomorphism** provided for each pair of elements g_1, g_2 in $\mathcal{G}$, $\varphi(g_1 \cdot g_2) = \varphi(g_1) \cdot \varphi(g_2)$.

Definition   *Let $\mathcal{G}$ be a topological group and E a Banach space. A group homomorphism $\pi: \mathcal{G} \rightarrow GL(E)$ is called a* **representation**[3] *of $\mathcal{G}$ on E.*

As usual, for a Banach space E, its dual space, the Banach space of bounded linear functionals on E, is denoted by E^*. We recall that the weak-$*$ topology on E^* is the topology with the fewest number of sets among the topologies on E^* such that, for each $x \in E$, the functional on E^* defined by $\psi \mapsto \psi(x)$ is continuous. Alaoglu's Theorem tells us that the closed unit ball of E^* is compact with respect to the weak-$*$ topology.

Definition   *Let $\mathcal{G}$ be a topological group, E a Banach space, and $\pi: \mathcal{G} \rightarrow GL(E)$ a representation of $\mathcal{G}$ on E. The* **adjoint representation** *$\pi^*: \mathcal{G} \rightarrow GL(E^*)$ is a representation of $\mathcal{G}$ on E^* defined for $g \in \mathcal{G}$ by*

$$\pi^*(g)\psi = \psi \circ \pi(g^{-1}) \text{ for all } \psi \in E^*. \tag{4}$$

We leave it as an exercise to verify that π^* is a group homomorphism.

Recall that a gauge or Minkowski functional on a vector space V is a positively homogeneous, subadditive functional $p: V \rightarrow \mathbf{R}$. Such functionals determine a base at the origin for the topology of a locally convex topological vector space V. In the presence of a representation π of a compact group $\mathcal{G}$ on a Banach space E, the following lemma establishes the existence of a family, parametrized by $\mathcal{G}$, of positively homogeneous, subadditive functionals on E^*, each of which is invariant under π^* and, when restricted to bounded subsets of E^*, is continuous with respect to the weak-$*$ topology.

---

[3]Observe that no continuity assumption is made regarding a representation. It is convenient to view it as a purely algebraic object and impose continuity assumptions as they are required in a particular context.

Lemma 3 *Let G be a compact group, E a Banach space, and $\pi: G \to GL(E)$ a representation of G on E. Let x_0 belong to E and assume that the mapping $g \mapsto \pi(g)x_0$ is continuous from G to E, where E has the norm topology. Define $p: E^* \to \mathbf{R}$ by*

$$p(\psi) = \sup_{g \in G} |\psi(\pi(g)x_0)| \text{ for } \psi \in E^*.$$

Then p is a positively homogeneous, subadditive functional on E^*. It is invariant under π^*, that is,

$$p(\pi^*(g)\psi) = p(\psi) \text{ for all } \psi \in E^* \text{ and } g \in G.$$

Furthermore, the restriction of p to any bounded subset of E^* is continuous with respect to the weak-$*$ topology on E^*.

Proof Since G is compact and, for $\psi \in G$, the functional $g \mapsto \psi(\pi(g)x_0)$ is continuous on G, $p: E^* \to \mathbf{R}$ is properly defined. It is clear that p is positively homogeneous, subadditive, and invariant with respect to π^*. Let B^* be a bounded subset of E^*. To establish the weak-$*$ continuity at $p: B^* \to \mathbf{R}$, it suffices to show that for each $\psi_0 \in B^*$ and $\epsilon > 0$, there is a weak-$*$ neighborhood $\mathcal{N}(\psi_0)$ of ψ_0 for which

$$|\psi(\pi(g)x_0) - \psi_0(\pi(g)x_0)| < \epsilon \text{ for all } \psi \in \mathcal{N}(\psi_0) \cap B^* \text{ and } g \in G. \tag{5}$$

Let ψ_0 belong to B^* and $\epsilon > 0$. Choose $M > 0$ such that $\|\psi\| \le M$ for all $\psi \in B^*$. The mapping $g \mapsto \pi(g)x_0$ is continuous and G is compact. Therefore there are a finite number of points $\{g_1, \dots, g_n\}$ in G and for each $k, 1 \le k \le n$, a neighborhood $\mathcal{O}_k$ of g_k such that $\{\mathcal{O}_{g_k}\}_{k=1}^n$ covers G and, for $1 \le k \le n$,

$$\|\pi(g)x_0 - \pi(g_k)x_0\| < \epsilon/4M \text{ for all } g \in \mathcal{O}_{g_k}. \tag{6}$$

Define the weak-$*$ neighborhood $\mathcal{N}(\psi_0)$ of ψ_0 by

$$\mathcal{N}(\psi_0) = \{\psi \in E^* \mid |(\psi - \psi_0)(\pi(g_k)x_0)| < \epsilon/2 \text{ for } 1 \le k \le n\}.$$

Observe that for any $g \in G$, $\psi \in E^*$ and $1 \le k \le n$,

$$\psi(\pi(g)x_0) - \psi_0(\pi(g)x_0) = (\psi - \psi_0)[\pi(g_k)x_0] + (\psi - \psi_0)[\pi(g)x_0 - \pi(g_k)x_0]. \tag{7}$$

To verify (5), let g belong to G and ψ belong to $\mathcal{N}(\psi_0) \cap B^*$. Choose $k, 1 \le k \le n$, for which g belongs to $\mathcal{O}_k$. Then $|(\psi - \psi_0)[\pi(g_k)x_0]| < \epsilon/2$ since ψ belongs to $\mathcal{N}(\psi_0)$. On the other hand, since $\|\psi - \psi_0\| \le 2M$, we infer from (6) that $|(\psi - \psi_0)[\pi(g)x_0 - \pi(g_k)x_0]| < \epsilon/2$. Therefore, by (7), (5) holds for $\mathcal{N}(\psi_0)$. $\qquad \square$

Definition *Let G be a topological group, E a Banach space, and $\pi: G \to GL(E)$ a representation of G on E. A subset K of E is said to be **invariant** under π provided $\pi(g)(K) \subseteq K$ for all $g \in G$. A point $x \in E$ is said to be **fixed** under π provided $\pi(g)x = x$ for all $g \in G$.*

Theorem 4 *Let G be a compact group, E a Banach space, and $\pi: G \to GL(E)$ a representation of G on E. Assume that for each $x \in E$, the mapping $g \mapsto \pi(g)x$ is continuous from G to E, where E has the norm topology. Assume there is a nonempty, convex, weak-$*$ compact subset K^* of E^* that is invariant under π^*. Then there is a functional ψ in K^* that is fixed under π^*.*

Proof Let $\mathcal{F}$ be the collection of all nonempty, convex, weak-$*$ closed subsets of K^* that are invariant under π^*. The collection $\mathcal{F}$ is nonempty since K^* belongs to $\mathcal{F}$. Order $\mathcal{F}$ by set inclusion. This defines a partial ordering on $\mathcal{F}$. Every totally ordered subcollection of $\mathcal{F}$ has the finite intersection property. But for any compact topological space, a collection of nonempty closed subsets that has the finite intersection property has nonempty intersection. The intersection of any collection of convex sets is convex and the intersection of any collection of π^* invariant sets is π^* invariant. Therefore every totally ordered subcollection of $\mathcal{F}$ has its nonempty intersection as a lower bound. We infer from Zorn's Lemma that there is a set K_0^* in $\mathcal{F}$ that is minimal with respect to containment, that is, no proper subset of K_0^* belongs to $\mathcal{F}$. This minimal subset is weak-$*$ closed and therefore weak-$*$ compact. We relabel and assume K^* itself is this minimal subset.

We claim that K^* consists of a single functional. Otherwise, choose two distinct functionals ψ_1 and ψ_2 in K^*. Choose $x_0 \in E$ such that $\psi_1(x_0) \neq \psi_2(x_0)$. Define the functional $p \colon K^* \to \mathbf{R}$ by

$$p(\psi) = \sup_{g \in \mathcal{G}} |\psi(\pi(g)x_0)| \text{ for } \psi \in K^*.$$

Since K^* is weak-$*$ compact, the Uniform Boundedness Principle tells us that K^* is bounded. According to the preceding lemma, p is continuous with respect to the weak-$*$ topology. Therefore, if, for $r > 0$ and $\eta \in K^*$, we define

$$B_0(\eta, r) = \{\psi \in K^* \mid p(\psi - \eta) < r\} \text{ and } \overline{B}_0(\eta, r) = \{\psi \in K^* \mid p(\psi - \eta) \leq r\}, \qquad (8)$$

then $B_0(\eta, r)$ is open with respect to the weak-$*$ topology on K^* and $\overline{B}_0(\eta, r)$ is closed with respect to the same topology. Each of these sets is convex since, again by the preceding lemma, p is positively homogeneous and subadditive.

Define $d = \sup\{p(\psi - \varphi) \mid \psi, \varphi \in K^*\}$. Then d is finite since p is continuous on the weak-$*$ compact set K^*, and $d > 0$ since $p(\psi_1 - \psi_2) > 0$. Since K^* is weak-$*$ compact and each $B_0(\eta, r)$ is weak-$*$ open, we may choose a finite subset $\{\psi_k\}_{k=1}^n$ of K^* for which

$$K^* = \bigcup_{k=1}^{n} B_0(\psi_k, d/2).$$

Define

$$\psi^* = \frac{\psi_1 + \ldots + \psi_k + \ldots + \psi_n}{n}.$$

The functional ψ^* belongs to K^* since K^* is convex. Let ψ be any functional in K^*. By the definition of d, $p(\psi - \psi_k) \leq d$ for $1 \leq k \leq n$. Since $\{B_0(\psi_k, d/2)\}_{k=1}^n$ covers K^*, ψ belongs to some $B_0(\psi_{k_0}, d/2)$ for some k_0. Thus, by the positive homogeneity and subadditivity of p,

$$p(\psi - \psi^*) \leq d' \text{ where } d' = \frac{n-1}{n} \cdot d + \frac{d}{2} < d.$$

Define

$$K' = \bigcap_{\psi \in K^*} \overline{B}_0(\psi, d').$$

Then K' is a weak-$*$ closed, and hence weak-$*$ compact, convex subset of K^*. It is nonempty since it contains the functional ψ^*. We claim that K' is invariant under π^*. To verify this, for

$\eta \in K'$, $\psi \in K^*$ and $g \in \mathcal{G}$, we must show that $p(\pi^*(g)\eta - \psi) \le d'$. Since p is π^* invariant and $p(\eta - \pi^*(g^{-1})\psi) \le d'$,

$$p(\pi^*(g)\eta - \psi) = p(\eta - \pi^*(g^{-1})\psi) \le d'.$$

By the minimality of K^*, $K^* = K'$. This is a contradiction since, by the definition of d, there are functionals ψ' and ψ'' in K^* for which $p(\psi' - \psi'') > d'$ and hence ψ'' does not belong to $\overline{B}_0(\psi', d')$. We infer from this contradiction that K^* consists of a single functional. The proof is complete.   □

Definition *Let $\mathcal{G}$ be a compact group and $C(\mathcal{G})$ the Banach space of continuous real-valued functions on $\mathcal{G}$, normed by the maximum norm. By the* **regular representation** *of $\mathcal{G}$ on $C(\mathcal{G})$ we mean the representation $\pi \colon \mathcal{G} \to GL(C(\mathcal{G}))$ defined by*

$$[\pi(g)f](x) = f(g^{-1} \cdot x) \text{ for all } f \in C(\mathcal{G}), x \in \mathcal{G} \text{ and } g \in \mathcal{G}.$$

We leave it as an exercise to show that the regular representation is indeed a representation. The following lemma shows that the regular representation of a compact group $\mathcal{G}$ on $C(\mathcal{G})$ possesses the continuity property imposed in Theorem 4.

Lemma 5 *Let $\mathcal{G}$ be a compact group and $\pi \colon \mathcal{G} \to GL(C(\mathcal{G}))$ the regular representation of $\mathcal{G}$ on $C(\mathcal{G})$. Then for each $f \in C(\mathcal{G})$, the mapping $g \mapsto \pi(g)f$ is continuous from $\mathcal{G}$ to $C(\mathcal{G})$, where $C(\mathcal{G})$ has the topology induced by the maximum norm.*

Proof Let f belong to $C(\mathcal{G})$. It suffices to check that the mapping $g \mapsto \pi(g)f$ is continuous at the identity $e \in \mathcal{G}$. Let $\epsilon > 0$. We claim that there is a neighborhood of the identity, $\mathcal{U}$, for which

$$|f(g \cdot x) - f(x)| < \epsilon \text{ for all } g \in \mathcal{U}, x \in \mathcal{G}. \tag{9}$$

Let x belong to $\mathcal{G}$. Choose a neighborhood of x, $\mathcal{O}_x$, for which

$$|f(x') - f(x)| < \epsilon/2 \text{ for all } x' \in \mathcal{O}_x.$$

Thus

$$|f(x') - f(x'')| < \epsilon \text{ for all } x', x'' \in \mathcal{O}_x. \tag{10}$$

By the continuity of the group operation, we may choose a neighborhood of the identity, $\mathcal{U}_x$, and a neighborhood x, $\mathcal{V}_x$, for which $\mathcal{V}_x \subseteq \mathcal{O}_x$ and $\mathcal{U}_x \cdot \mathcal{V}_x \subseteq \mathcal{O}_x$. By the compactness of $\mathcal{G}$, there is a finite collection $\{\mathcal{V}_{x_k}\}_{k=1}^n$ that covers $\mathcal{G}$. Define $\mathcal{U} = \bigcap_{k=1}^n \mathcal{U}_{x_k}$. Then $\mathcal{U}$ is a neighborhood of the identity in $\mathcal{G}$. We claim that (9) holds for this choice of $\mathcal{U}$. Indeed, let g belong in $\mathcal{U}$ and x belong to $\mathcal{G}$. Then x belongs to some $\mathcal{V}_{x_k}$. Hence

$$x \in \mathcal{V}_{x_k} \subseteq \mathcal{O}_{x_k} \text{ and } g \cdot x \in \mathcal{U} \times \mathcal{V}_{x_k} \subseteq \mathcal{U}_{x_k} \times \mathcal{V}_{x_k} \subseteq \mathcal{O}_{x_k}.$$

Therefore both x and $g \cdot x$ belong to $\mathcal{O}_{x_k}$ so that, by (10), $|f(g \cdot x) - f(x)| < \epsilon$. Thus (9) is established. Replace $\mathcal{U}$ by $\mathcal{U} \cap \mathcal{U}^{-1}$. Therefore

$$|f(g^{-1} \cdot x) - f(x)| < \epsilon \text{ for all } g \in \mathcal{U}, x \in \mathcal{G},$$

that is,

$$\|\pi(g)f - \pi(e)f\|_{\max} < \epsilon \text{ for all } g \in \mathcal{U}.$$

This establishes the required continuity.   □

For $\mathcal{G}$ a compact group, we call a functional $\psi \in [C(\mathcal{G})]^*$ a **probability functional** provided it takes the value 1 at the constant function $f = 1$ and is **positive** in the sense that for $f \in C(\mathcal{G})$, if $f \geq 0$ on $\mathcal{G}$, then $\psi(f) \geq 0$.

Theorem 6 (Kakutani) *Let $\mathcal{G}$ be a compact group and $\pi: \mathcal{G} \to GL(C(\mathcal{G}))$ the regular representation of $\mathcal{G}$ on $C(\mathcal{G})$. Then there is a probability functional $\psi \in [C(\mathcal{G})]^*$ that is fixed under the adjoint action π^*, that is,*

$$\psi(f) = \psi(\pi(g)f) \text{ for all } f \in C(\mathcal{G}) \text{ and } g \in \mathcal{G}. \tag{11}$$

Proof According to Alaoglu's Theorem, the closed unit ball of $[C(\mathcal{G})]^*$ is weak-$*$ compact. Let K^* be the collection of positive probability functionals on $C(\mathcal{G})$. Observe that if ψ is a probability functional and f belongs to $C(\mathcal{G})$ with $\|f\|_{\max} \leq 1$, then, by the positivity and linearity of ψ, since $-1 \leq f \leq 1$,

$$-1 = \psi(-1) \leq \psi(f) \leq \psi(1) = 1.$$

Thus $|\psi(f)| \leq 1$ and hence $\|\psi\| \leq 1$. Therefore K^* is a convex subset of the closed unit ball of E^*. We claim that K^* is weak-$*$ closed. Indeed, for each nonnegative function $f \in C(\mathcal{G})$, the set $\{\psi \in [C(\mathcal{G})]^* \mid \psi(f) \geq 0\}$ is weak-$*$ closed, as is the set of functionals ψ that take the value 1 at the constant function $f \equiv 1$. The set K^* is therefore the intersection of weak-$*$ closed sets and so it is weak-$*$ closed. As a closed subset of a compact set, K^* is weak-$*$ compact. Finally, the set K^* is nonempty since if x_0 is any point in $\mathcal{G}$, the Dirac functional that takes the value $f(x_0)$ at each $f \in C(\mathcal{G})$ belongs to K^*.

It is clear that K^* is invariant under π^*. The preceding lemma tells us that the regular representation possesses the continuity required to apply Theorem 4. According to that theorem, there is a functional in $\psi \in K^*$ that is fixed under π^*, that is, (11) holds. $\qquad \square$

PROBLEMS

13. Show that the adjoint of a representation also is a representation.

14. Show that a probability functional has norm 1.

15. Let E be a reflexive Banach space and K^* a convex subset of E^* that is closed with respect to the metric induced by the norm. Show that K^* is weak-$*$ closed. On the other hand, show that if E is not reflexive, then the image of the closed unit ball of E under the natural embedding of E in $(E^*)^* = E^{**}$ is a subset of E^{**} that is convex, closed and bounded with respect to the metric induced by the norm but is not weak-$*$ closed.

16. Let $\mathcal{G}$ be a compact group, E a reflexive Banach space, and $\pi: \mathcal{G} \to GL(E)$ a representation. Suppose that for each $x \in E$, the mapping $g \mapsto \pi(g)x$ is continuous. Assume there is a nonempty strongly closed, bounded, convex subset K of E that is invariant with respect to π. Show that K contains a point that is fixed by π.

17. Let $\mathcal{G}$ be a topological group, E be a Banach space, and $\pi: \mathcal{G} \to GL(E)$ a representation. For $x \in E$, show that the mapping $g \mapsto \pi(g)x$ is continuous if and only if it is continuous at e.

18. Suppose $\mathcal{G}$ is a topological group, X a topological space, and $\varphi: \mathcal{G} \times X \to X$ a mapping. For $g \in \mathcal{G}$, define the mapping $\pi(g): X \to X$ by $\pi(g)x = \varphi(g, x)$ for all $x \in X$. What properties must φ possess in order for π to be a representation on $\mathcal{G}$ on $C(X)$? What further properties must φ possess in order that for each $x \in X$, the mapping $g \mapsto \pi(g)x$ is continuous?

22.3 INVARIANT BOREL MEASURES ON COMPACT GROUPS: VON NEUMANN'S THEOREM

A Borel measure on a compact topological space X is a finite measure on $\mathcal{B}(X)$, the smallest σ-algebra that contains the topology on X. We now consider Borel measures on compact groups and their relation to the group operation.

Lemma 7 *Let $\mathcal{G}$ be a compact group and μ a Borel measure on $\mathcal{B}(\mathcal{G})$. For $g \in \mathcal{G}$, define the set function $\mu_g \colon \mathcal{B}(\mathcal{G}) \to [0, \infty)$ by*

$$\mu_g(A) = \mu(g \cdot A) \text{ for all } A \in \mathcal{B}(\mathcal{G}).$$

Then μ_g is a Borel measure. If μ is Radon, so is μ_g. Furthermore, if π is the regular representation of $\mathcal{G}$ on $C(\mathcal{G})$,[4] then

$$\int_{\mathcal{G}} \pi(g) f \, d\mu = \int_{\mathcal{G}} f \, d\mu_g \text{ for all } f \in C(\mathcal{G}). \tag{12}$$

Proof Let g belong to $\mathcal{G}$. Observe that multiplication on the left by g defines a topological homeomorphism of G onto G. From this we infer that A is a Borel set if and only if $g \cdot A$ is a Borel set. Therefore the set function μ_g is properly defined on $\mathcal{B}(\mathcal{G})$. Clearly, μ_g inherits countable additivity from μ and hence, since $\mu_g(\mathcal{G}) = \mu(\mathcal{G}) < \infty$, μ_g is a Borel measure. Now suppose μ is a Radon measure. To establish the inner regularity of μ_g, let $\mathcal{O}$ be open in $\mathcal{G}$ and $\epsilon > 0$. Since μ is inner regular and $g \cdot \mathcal{O}$ is open, there is a compact set K contained in $g \cdot \mathcal{O}$ for which $\mu(g \cdot \mathcal{O} \sim K) < \epsilon$. Hence $K' = g^{-1} \cdot K$ is compact, contained in $\mathcal{O}$, and $\mu_g(\mathcal{O} \sim K') < \epsilon$. Thus μ_g is inner regular. A similar argument shows μ_g is outer regular. Therefore μ_g is a Radon measure.

We now verify (12). Integration is linear. Therefore, if (12) holds for characteristic functions of Borel sets it also holds for simple Borel functions. We infer from the Simple Approximation Theorem and the Bounded Convergence Theorem that (12) holds for all $f \in C(\mathcal{G})$ if it holds for simple Borel functions. It therefore suffices to verify (12) in the case $f = \chi_A$, the characteristic function of the Borel set A. However, for such a function,

$$\int_{\mathcal{G}} \pi(g) f \, d\mu = \mu(g \cdot A) = \int_{\mathcal{G}} f \, d\mu_g. \qquad \square$$

Definition *Let $\mathcal{G}$ be a compact group. A Borel measure $\mu \colon \mathcal{B}(\mathcal{G}) \to [0, \infty)$ is said to be* **left-invariant** *provided*

$$\mu(A) = \mu(g \cdot A) \text{ for all } g \in \mathcal{G} \text{ and } A \in \mathcal{B}(\mathcal{G}). \tag{13}$$

It is said to be a **probability measure** *provided $\mu(\mathcal{G}) = 1$.*

A right-invariant measure is defined similarly. If we consider $\mathbf{R}^n$ as a topological group under the operation of addition, we showed that the restriction of Lebesgue measure μ_n on

---

[4]A continuous function on a topological space is measurable with respect to the Borel σ-algebra on the space and, if the space is compact and the measure is Borel, it is integrable with respect to this measure. Therefore, each side of the following formula is properly defined because, for each $f \in C(\mathcal{G})$ and $g \in \mathcal{G}$, both f and $\pi(g)f$ are continuous functions on the compact topological space $\mathcal{G}$ and both μ and μ_g are Borel measures.

$\mathbf{R}^n$ to $\mathcal{B}(\mathbf{R}^n)$ is left-invariant with respect to addition, that is, $\mu_n(E + x) = \mu_n(E)$ for each Borel subset E of $\mathbf{R}^n$ and each point $x \in \mathbf{R}^n$. Of course, this also holds for any Lebesgue measurable subset E of $\mathbf{R}^n$.

Proposition 8 *On each compact group $\mathcal{G}$ there is a Radon probability measure on $\mathcal{B}(\mathcal{G})$ that is left-invariant and also one that is right-invariant.*

Proof Theorem 6 tells us that there is a probability functional $\psi \in [C(\mathcal{G})]^*$ that is fixed under the adjoint of the regular representation on $\mathcal{G}$ on $C(\mathcal{G})$. This means that $\psi(1) = 1$ and

$$\psi(f) = \psi(\pi(g^{-1})f) \text{ for all } f \in C(\mathcal{G}) \text{ and } g \in \mathcal{G}. \tag{14}$$

On the other hand, according to the Riesz-Markov Theorem, there is a unique Radon measure μ on $\mathcal{B}(\mathcal{G})$ that represents ψ in the sense that

$$\psi(f) = \int_{\mathcal{G}} f \, d\mu \text{ for all } f \in C(\mathcal{G}). \tag{15}$$

Therefore, by (14),

$$\psi(f) = \psi(\pi(g^{-1})f) = \int_{\mathcal{G}} \pi(g^{-1}) f \, d\mu \text{ for all } f \in C(\mathcal{G}) \text{ and } g \in \mathcal{G}. \tag{16}$$

Hence, by Lemma 7,

$$\psi(f) = \int_{\mathcal{G}} f \, d\mu_{g^{-1}} \text{ for all } f \in C(\mathcal{G}) \text{ and } g \in \mathcal{G}.$$

By the same lemma, $\mu_{g^{-1}}$ is a Radon measure. We infer from the uniqueness of the representation of the functional ψ that

$$\mu = \mu_{g^{-1}} \text{ for all } g \in \mathcal{G}.$$

Thus μ is a left-invariant Radon measure. It is a probability measure because ψ is a probability functional and thus

$$1 = \psi(1) = \int_{\mathcal{G}} d\mu = \mu(\mathcal{G}).$$

A dual argument (see Problem 25) establishes the existence of a right-invariant Radon probability measure. $\square$

Definition *Let $\mathcal{G}$ be a topological group. A Radon measure on $\mathcal{B}(\mathcal{G})$ is said to be a* **Haar** *measure provided it is a left-invariant probability measure.*

Theorem 9 (von Neumann) *Let $\mathcal{G}$ be a compact group. Then there is a unique Haar measure μ on $\mathcal{B}(\mathcal{G})$. The measure μ is also right-invariant.*

Proof According to the preceding proposition, there is a left-invariant Radon probability measure μ on $\mathcal{B}(\mathcal{G})$ and a right-invariant Radon probability measure ν on $\mathcal{B}(\mathcal{G})$. We claim that

$$\int_{\mathcal{G}} f \, d\mu = \int_{\mathcal{G}} f \, d\nu \text{ for all } f \in C(\mathcal{G}). \tag{17}$$

Once this is verified, we infer from the uniqueness of representations of bounded linear functionals on $C(G)$ by integration against Radon measures that $\mu = \nu$. Therefore every left-invariant Radon measure equals ν. Hence there is only one left-invariant Radon measure and it is right-invariant.

To verify (17), let f belong to $C(G)$. Define $h: G \times G \to \mathbb{R}$ by $h(x, y) = f(x \cdot y)$ for $(x, y) \in G \times G$. Then h is a continuous function on $G \times G$. Moreover the product measure $\nu \times \mu$ is defined on a σ-algebra of subsets of $G \times G$ containing $\mathcal{B}(G \times G)$. Therefore, since h is measurable and bounded on a set $G \times G$ of finite $\nu \times \mu$ measure, it is integrable with respect to the product measure $\nu \times \mu$ over $G \times G$. To verify (17) it suffices to show that

$$\int_{G \times G} h\, d[\nu \times \mu] = \int_G f\, d\mu \text{ and } \int_{G \times G} h\, d[\mu \times \nu] = \int_G f\, d\nu \qquad (18)$$

However, by Fubini's Theorem,[5]

$$\int_{G \times G} h\, d[\nu \times \mu] = \int_G \left[\int_G h(x, \cdot)\, d\mu(y) \right] d\nu(x).$$

By the left-invariance of μ and (12),

$$\int_G h(x, \cdot)\, d\mu(y) = \int_G f\, d\mu \text{ for all } x \in G.$$

Thus, since $\nu(G) = 1$,

$$\int_{G \times G} h\, d[\mu \times \nu] = \int_G f\, d\mu \cdot \nu(G) = \int_G f\, d\mu.$$

A similar argument establishes the right-hand equality in (18) and thereby completes the proof. $\qquad\qquad\qquad\qquad\qquad\qquad\qquad\qquad\qquad\qquad\qquad\qquad\qquad$ $\square$

The methods studied here may be extended to show that there is a left-invariant Haar measure on any locally compact group G, although it may not be right-invariant. Here we investigated one way in which the topology on a topological group determines its measure theoretic properties. Of course, it is also interesting to investigate the influence of measure on topology. For further study of this interesting circle of ideas it is still valuable to read John von Neumann's classic lecture notes *Invariant Measures* [vN91].

PROBLEMS

19. Let μ be a Borel probability measure on a compact group G. Show that μ is Haar measure if and only if

$$\int_G f \circ \varphi_g\, d\mu = \int_G f\, d\mu \text{ for all } g \in G, f \in C(G),$$

where $\varphi_g(g') = g \cdot g'$ for all $g' \in G$.

---

[5]See the last paragraph of Section 20.1 for an explanation of why, for this product of Borel measures and continuous function h, the conclusion of Fubini's Theorem holds without the assumption that the measure μ is complete.

20. Let μ be Haar measure on a compact group $\mathcal{G}$. Show that $\mu \times \mu$ is Haar measure on $\mathcal{G} \times \mathcal{G}$.

21. Let $\mathcal{G}$ be a compact group whose topology is given by a metric. Show that there is a $\mathcal{G}$-invariant metric. (Hint: Use the preceding two problems and average the metric over the group $\mathcal{G} \times \mathcal{G}$.)

22. Let μ be Haar measure on a compact group $\mathcal{G}$. If $\mathcal{G}$ has infinitely many members, show that $\mu(\{g\}) = 0$ for each $g \in \mathcal{G}$. If $\mathcal{G}$ is finite, explicitly describe μ.

23. Show that if μ is Haar measure on a compact group, then $\mu(\mathcal{O}) > 0$ for every open subset $\mathcal{O}$ of $\mathcal{G}$.

24. Let $S^1 = \{z = e^{i\theta} \mid \theta \in \mathbf{R}\}$ be the circle with the group operation of complex multiplication and the topology it inherits from the Euclidean plane.

   (i) Show that S^1 is a topological group.

   (ii) Define $\Lambda = \{(\alpha, \beta) \mid \alpha, \beta \in \mathbf{R}, 0 < \beta - \alpha < 2\pi\}$. For $\lambda = (\alpha, \beta) \in \Lambda$, define $I_\alpha = \{e^{i\theta} \mid \alpha < \theta < \beta\}$. Show that every proper open subset of S^1 is the countable disjoint union of sets of the form I_λ, $\lambda \in \Lambda$.

   (iii) For $\lambda = (\alpha, \beta) \in \Lambda$, define $\mu(I_\alpha) = (\beta - \alpha)/2\pi$. Define $\mu(S^1) = 1$. Use part (ii) to extend μ to set function defined on the topology $\mathcal{T}$ of S^1. Then verify that, by Proposition 9 from the preceding chapter, μ may be extended to a Borel measure μ on $\mathcal{B}(S^1)$.

   (iv) Show that the measure defined in part (ii) is Haar measure on S^1.

   (v) The torus T^n is the topological group consisting of the Cartesian product of n copies of S^1 with the product topology and group structure. What is Haar measure on T^n?

25. Let μ be a Borel measure on a topological group $\mathcal{G}$. For a Borel set E, define $\mu'(E) = \mu(E^{-1})$, where $E^{-1} = \{g^{-1} \mid g \in E\}$. Show that μ' also is a Borel measure. Moreover, show that μ is left-invariant if and only if μ' is right-invariant.

22.4 MEASURE PRESERVING TRANSFORMATIONS AND ERGODICITY: THE BOGOLIUBOV-KRILOV THEOREM

For a measurable space $(X, \mathcal{M})$, a mapping $T: X \to X$ is said to be a **measurable transformation** provided for each measurable set E, $T^{-1}(E)$ also is measurable. Observe that for a mapping $T: X \to X$,

T is measurable if and only if $g \circ T$ is measurable whenever the function g is measurable.

$$(19)$$

For a measure space $(X, \mathcal{M}, \mu)$, a measurable transformation $T: X \to X$ is said to be **measure preserving** provided

$$\mu(T^{-1}(A)) = \mu(A) \text{ for all } A \in \mathcal{M}.$$

Proposition 10 *Let $(X, \mathcal{M}, \mu)$ be a finite measure space and $T: X \to X$ a measurable transformation. Then T is measure preserving if and only if $g \circ T$ is integrable over X whenever g is, and*

$$\int_X g \circ T \, d\mu = \int_X g \, d\mu \text{ for all } g \in L^1(X, \mu). \qquad (20)$$

Proof First assume (20) holds. For $A \in \mathcal{M}$, since $\mu(X) < \infty$, the function $g = \chi_A$ belongs to $L^1(X, \mu)$ and $g \circ T = \chi_{T^{-1}(A)}$. We infer from (20) that $\mu(T^{-1}(A)) = \mu(A)$.

Conversely, assume T is measure preserving. Let g be integrable over X. If g^+ is the positive part of g, then $(g \circ T)^+ = g^+ \circ T$. Similarly for the negative part. We may therefore assume that g is nonnegative. For a simple function $g = \sum_{k=1}^n c_k \cdot \chi_{A_k}$, since T is measure preserving,

$$\int_X g \circ T \, d\mu = \int_X \left[\sum_{k=1}^n c_k \cdot \chi_{A_k} \circ T \right] d\mu = \int_X \left[\sum_{k=1}^n c_k \cdot \chi_{T^{-1}(A_k)} \right] d\mu = \sum_{k=1}^n c_k \cdot \mu(A_k) = \int_X g \, d\mu.$$

Therefore (20) holds for g simple. According to the Simple Approximation Theorem, there is an increasing sequence $\{g_n\}$ of simple functions on X that converge pointwise on X to g. Hence $\{g_n \circ T\}$ is an increasing of simple functions on X that converge pointwise on X to $g \circ T$. Using the Monotone Convergence Theorem twice and the validity of (20) for simple functions, we have

$$\int_X g \circ T \, d\mu = \lim_{n \to \infty} \left[\int_X g_n \circ T \, d\mu \right] = \lim_{n \to \infty} \left[\int_X g_n \, d\mu \right] = \int_X g \, d\mu. \qquad \square$$

For a measure space $(X, \mathcal{M}, \mu)$ and measurable transformation $T: X \to X$, a measurable set A is said to be **invariant** under T (with respect to μ) provided

$$\mu(A \sim T^{-1}(A)) = \mu(T^{-1}(A) \sim A) = 0,$$

that is, modulo sets of measure 0, $T^{-1}(A) = A$. It is clear that

$$A \text{ is invariant under } T \text{ if and only if } \chi_A \circ T = \chi_A \text{ a.e. on } X. \qquad (21)$$

If $(X, \mathcal{M}, \mu)$ also is a probability space, that is, $\mu(X) = 1$, a measure preserving transformation T is said to be **ergodic** provided any set A that is invariant under T with respect to μ has $\mu(A) = 0$ or $\mu(A) = 1$.

Proposition 11 *Let $(X, \mathcal{M}, \mu)$ be a probability space and $T: X \to X$ a measure preserving transformation. Then, among real-valued measurable functions g on X,*

T is ergodic if and only if whenever $g \circ T = g$ a.e. on X, then g is constant a.e. on X.   (22)

Proof First assume that whenever $g \circ T = g$ a.e. on X, the g is constant a.e. on X. Let $A \in \mathcal{M}$ be invariant under T. Then $g = \chi_A$, the characteristic function of A, is measurable and $\chi_A \circ T = \chi_A$ a.e. on X. Thus χ_A is constant a.e., that is, $\mu(A) = 0$ or $\mu(A) = 1$.

Conversely, assume T is ergodic. Let g be a real-valued measurable function on X for which $g \circ T = g$ a.e. on X. Let k be an integer. Define $X_k = \{x \in X \mid k \le g(x) < k + 1\}$. Then X_k is a measurable set that is invariant under T. By the ergodicity of T, either $\mu(X_k) = 0$ or $\mu(X_k) = 1$. The countable collection $\{X_k\}_{k \in \mathbb{Z}}$ is disjoint and its union is X. Since $\mu(X) = 1$ and μ is countably additive, $\mu(X_k) = 0$, except for exactly one integer k'. Define $I_1 = [k', k' + 1]$. Then $\mu\{x \in X \mid g(x) \in I_1\} = 1$ and the length of I_1, $\ell(I_1)$, is 1.

Let n be a natural number for which the descending finite collection $\{I_k\}_{k=1}^n$ of closed, bounded intervals have been defined for which

$$\ell(I_k) = 1/2^{k-1} \text{ and } \mu\{x \in X \mid g(x) \in I_k\} = 1 \text{ for } 1 \le k \le n.$$

Let $I_n = [a_n, b_n]$, define $c_n = (b_n - a_n)/2$,

$$A_n = \{x \in X \mid a_n \leq g(x) < c_n\} \text{ and } B_n = \{x \in X \mid c_n \leq g(x) \leq b_n\}.$$

Then A_n and B_n are disjoint measurable sets whose union is $\mu\{x \in X \mid g(x) \in I_n\}$, a set of measure 1. Since both A_n and B_n are invariant under T, we infer from the ergodicity of T that exactly one of these sets has measure 1. If $\mu(A_n) = 1$, define $I_{n+1} = [a_n, c_n]$. Otherwise, define $I_{n+1} = [c_n, b_n]$. Then $\ell(I_{n+1}) = 1/2^n$ and $\mu\{x \in X \mid g(x) \in I_{n+1}\} = 1$. We have inductively defined a descending countable collection $\{I_n\}_{n=1}^{\infty}$ of closed, bounded intervals such that

$$\ell(I_n) = 1/2^{n-1} \text{ and } \mu\{x \in X \mid g(x) \in I_n\} = 1 \text{ for all } n.$$

By the Nested Set Theorem for the real numbers, there is a number c that belongs to every I_n. We claim that $g = c$ a.e. on X. Indeed, observe that if $g(x)$ belongs to I_n, then $|g(x) - c| \leq 1/2^{n-1}$ and therefore

$$1 = \mu\{x \in X \mid g(x) \in I_n\} \leq \mu\{x \in X \mid |g(x) - c| \leq 1/2^{n-1}\} \leq 1.$$

Since

$$\{x \in X \mid g(x) = c\} = \bigcap_{n=1}^{\infty} \{x \in X \mid |g(x) - c| \leq 1/2^{n-1}\},$$

we infer from the continuity of measure that

$$\mu\{x \in X \mid g(x) = c\} = \lim_{n \to \infty} \mu\{x \in X \mid |g(x) - c| \leq 1/2^{n-1}\} = 1.$$

$\square$

Theorem 12 (Bogoliubov-Krilov) *Let X be a compact metric space and the mapping $f: X \to X$ be continuous. Then there is a probability measure μ on the Borel σ-algebra $\mathcal{B}(X)$ with respect to which f is measure preserving.*

Proof Consider the Banach space $C(X)$ of continuous real-valued functions on X with the maximum norm. Since X is a compact metric space, Borsuk's Theorem tells us that $C(X)$ is separable. Let η be any Borel probability measure on $\mathcal{B}(X)$. Define the sequence $\{\psi_n\}$ of linear functionals on $C(X)$ by

$$\psi_n(g) = \int_X \left[\frac{1}{n} \sum_{k=0}^{n-1} g \circ f^k \right] d\eta \text{ for all } n \in \mathbf{N} \text{ and } g \in C(X). \tag{23}$$

Observe that

$$|\psi_n(g)| \leq \|g\|_{\max} \text{ for all } n \in \mathbf{N} \text{ and } g \in C(X).$$

Thus $\{\psi_n\}$ is a bounded sequence in $[C(X)]^*$. Since the Banach space $C(X)$ is separable, we infer from Helley's Theorem that there is a subsequence $\{\psi_{n_k}\}$ of $\{\psi_n\}$ that converges, with respect to the weak-$*$ topology, to a bounded functional $\psi \in [C(X)]^*$, that is,

$$\lim_{k \to \infty} \psi_{n_k}(g) = \psi(g) \text{ for all } g \in C(X).$$

Therefore
$$\lim_{k \to \infty} \psi_{n_k}(g \circ f) = \psi(g \circ f) \text{ for all } g \in C(X).$$

However, for each k and $g \in C(X)$,

$$\psi_{n_k}(g \circ f) - \psi_{n_k}(g) = \frac{1}{n_k}\left[\int_X [g \circ f^{n_k+1} - g]\, d\eta\right].$$

Take the limit as $k \to \infty$ and conclude that

$$\psi(g \circ f) = \psi(g) \text{ for all } g \in C(X). \tag{24}$$

Since each ψ_n is a positive functional, the limit functional ψ also is positive. The Riesz-Markov Theorem tells us that there is a Borel measure μ for which

$$\psi(g) = \int_X g\, d\mu \text{ for all } g \in C(X).$$

We infer from (24) that

$$\int_X g \circ f\, d\mu = \int_X g\, d\mu \text{ for all } g \in C(X).$$

According to Proposition 10, f is measure preserving with respect to μ. Finally, for the constant function $g = 1$, $\psi_n(g) = 1$ for all n. Therefore $\psi(g) = 1$, that is, μ is a probability measure. □

Proposition 13 *Let $f: X \to X$ be a continuous mapping on a compact metric space X. Define $\mathcal{M}_f$ to be the set of probability measures on $\mathcal{B}(X)$ with respect to which f is measure preserving. Then a measure μ in $\mathcal{M}_f$ is an extreme point of $\mathcal{M}_f$ if and only if f is ergodic with respect to μ.*

Proof First suppose that μ is an extreme point of $\mathcal{M}_f$. To prove that f is ergodic, we assume otherwise. Then there is a Borel subset A of X that is invariant under f with respect to μ and yet $0 < \mu(A) < 1$. Define

$$\nu(E) = \mu(E \cap A)/\mu(A) \text{ and } \eta(E) = \mu(E \cap [X \sim A])/\mu(X \sim A) \text{ for all } E \in \mathcal{B}(X).$$

Then, since $\mu(X) = 1$,

$$\mu = \lambda \cdot \nu + (1 - \lambda) \cdot \eta \text{ where } \lambda = \mu(A).$$

Both ν and η are Borel probability measures on $\mathcal{B}(X)$. We claim that f is measure preserving with respect to each of these measures. Indeed, since f is measure preserving with respect to μ and A is invariant under f with respect to μ, for each $E \in \mathcal{B}(X)$,

$$\mu(E \cap A) = \mu(f^{-1}(E \cap A)) = \mu(f^{-1}(E) \cap f^{-1}(A)) = \mu(f^{-1}(E) \cap A).$$

Therefore f is invariant with respect to ν. By a similar argument, it is also invariant with respect to η. Therefore ν and η belong to $\mathcal{M}_f$ and hence μ is not an extreme point of $\mathcal{M}_f$. Therefore f is ergodic.

Now suppose f is ergodic with respect to $\mu \in \mathcal{M}_f$. To show that μ is an extreme point of $\mathcal{M}_f$, let $\lambda \in (0, 1)$ and $\nu, \eta \in \mathcal{M}_f$ be such that

$$\mu = \lambda \nu + (1 - \lambda)\eta. \tag{25}$$

The measure ν is absolutely continuous with respect to μ. Since $\mu(X) < \infty$, the Radon-Nikodym Theorem tells us that there is a function $h \in L^1(X, \mu)$ for which

$$\nu(A) = \int_A h \, d\mu \text{ for all } A \in \mathcal{B}(X).$$

It follows from the Simple Approximation Theorem and the Bounded Convergence Theorem that

$$\int_X g \, d\nu = \int_X g \cdot h \, d\mu \text{ for all } g \in L^\infty(X, \mu). \tag{26}$$

Fix $\epsilon > 0$, and define $X_\epsilon = \{x \in X \mid h(x) \geq 1/\lambda + \epsilon\}$. We infer from (25) that

$$\mu(X_\epsilon) \geq \lambda \cdot \int_{X_\epsilon} h \, d\mu \geq (1 + \lambda \cdot \epsilon) \cdot \mu(X_\epsilon).$$

Hence $\mu(X_\epsilon) = 0$. Therefore h and $h \circ f$ are essentially bounded on X with respect to μ. Hence, using (26), first with $g = h \circ f$ and then with $g = h$, and the invariance of f with respect to ν, we have

$$\int_X h \circ f \cdot h \, d\mu = \int_X h \circ f \, d\nu = \int_X h \, d\nu = \int_X h^2 \, d\mu.$$

We infer from this equality and the invariance of f with respect to μ that

$$\int_X [h \circ f - h]^2 \, d\mu = \int_X [h \circ f]^2 \, d\mu - 2 \cdot \int_X h \circ f \cdot h \, d\mu + \int_X h^2 \, d\mu$$

$$= 2 \cdot \int_X h^2 \, d\mu - 2 \cdot \int_X h \circ f \cdot h \, d\mu$$

$$= 2 \cdot \int_X h^2 \, d\mu - 2 \cdot \int_X h^2 \, d\mu = 0.$$

Therefore $h \circ f = h$ a.e. $[\mu]$ on X. By the ergodicity of f and Proposition 11, there is a constant c for which $h = c$ a.e. $[\mu]$ on X. But μ and ν are probability measures and hence

$$1 = \nu(X) = \int_X h \, d\mu = c \cdot \mu(X) = c.$$

Hence $\mu = \nu$ and thus $\mu = \eta$. Therefore μ is an extreme point of $\mathcal{M}_f$. $\qquad \square$

Theorem 14 *Let $f: X \to X$ be a continuous mapping on a compact metric space X. Then there is a probability measure μ on the Borel σ-algebra $\mathcal{B}(X)$ with respect to which f is ergodic.*

Proof Let $\mathcal{R}adon(X)$ be the Banach space of signed Radon measures on $\mathcal{B}(X)$ and the linear operator $\Phi: \mathcal{R}adon(X) \to [C(X)]^*$ be defined by

$$\Phi(\mu)(g) = \int_X g \, d\mu \text{ for all } \mu \in \mathcal{R}adon(X) \text{ and } g \in C(X).$$

The Riesz Representation Theorem for the dual of $C(X)$ tells us that Φ is a linear isomorphism of $\mathcal{R}adon(X)$ onto $[C(X)]^*$. Define $\mathcal{M}_f$ to be the set of probability measures on $\mathcal{B}(X)$ with respect to which f is measure preserving. Then the measure μ is an extreme point of $\mathcal{M}_f$ if and only if $\Phi(\mu)$ is an extreme point of $\Phi(\mathcal{M}_f)$. Therefore, by the preceding proposition, to prove the theorem we must show that the set $\Phi(\mathcal{M}_f)$ possesses an extreme point. According to the Bogoliubov-Krilov Theorem, $\mathcal{M}_f$ is nonempty. A consequence of the Krein-Milman Theorem, Corollary 13 of the preceding chapter, tells us that $\Phi(\mathcal{M}_f)$ possesses an extreme point provided it is bounded, convex, and closed with respect to the weak-$*$ topology. The Riesz-Markov Theorem tells us that Φ defines an isomorphism of Radon measures onto positive functionals. The positive functionals are certainly weak-$*$ closed, as are the functionals that take the value 1 at the constant function 1. According to Proposition 11, a functional $\psi \in [C(X)]^*$ is the image under Φ of a measure that is invariant with respect to f if and only if

$$\psi(g \circ f) - \psi(g) = 0 \text{ for all } g \in C(X).$$

Fix $g \in C(X)$. Evaluation at the function $g \circ f - g$ is a linear functional on $[C(X)]^*$ that is continuous with respect to the weak-$*$ topology and therefore its kernel is weak-$*$ closed. Hence the intersection

$$\bigcap_{g \in C(X)} \{\psi \in [C(X)]^* \mid \psi(g \circ f) = \psi(g)\}$$

also is a weak-$*$ closed set. This completes the proof of the weak-$*$ closedness of $\Phi(\mathcal{M}_f)$ and also the proof of the theorem. $\qquad\square$

Asymptotic averaging phenomena were originally introduced in the analysis of the dynamics of gases. One indication of the significance of ergodicity in the study of such phenomena is revealed in the statement of the following theorem. Observe that the right-hand side of (27) is independent of the point $x \in X$.

Theorem 15 *Let T be a measure preserving transformation on the probability space $(X, \mathcal{M}, \mu)$. Then T is ergodic if and only if for every $g \in L^1(X, \mu)$,*

$$\lim_{n \to \infty} \left[\frac{1}{n} \sum_{k=0}^{n-1} g(T^k(x)) \right] = \frac{1}{\mu(X)} \int_X g \, d\mu \text{ for almost all } x \in X. \tag{27}$$

A proof of this theorem may be found in the books *Introduction to Dynamical Systems* [BS02] by Michael Brin and Garrett Stuck and *Lectures on Ergodic Theory* [Hal06] by Paul Halmos. These books also contain varied examples of measure preserving and ergodic transformations.

PROBLEMS

26. Let X be a compact metric space. Use the Stone-Weierstrass Theorem to show that the Banach space $C(X)$ of continuous functions on X, normed with the maximum norm, is separable.

27. Does the proof of the the Bogoliubov-Krilov Theorem also provide a proof in the case X is compact Hausdorff but not necessarily metrizable?

28. Let $(X, \mathcal{M}, \mu)$ be a finite space and $T: X \to X$ a measurable transformation. For a measurable function g on X, define the measurable function $U_T(g)$ by $U_T(g)(x) = g(T(x))$. Show that T is measure preserving if and only if for every $1 \le p < \infty$, U_T maps $L^p(X, \mu)$ into itself and is an isometry.

29. Suppose that $T: \mathbf{R}^n \to \mathbf{R}^n$ is linear. Establish necessary and sufficient conditions for T to be measure preserving with respect to Lebesgue measure on $\mathbf{R}^n$.

30. Let $S^1 = \{z = e^{i\theta} \mid \theta \in \mathbf{R}\}$ be the circle with the group operation of complex multiplication and μ be Haar measure on this group (see Problem 24). Define $T: S^1 \to S^1$ by $T(z) = z^2$. Show that T preserves μ.

31. Define $f: \mathbf{R}^2 \to \mathbf{R}^2$ by $f(x, y) = (2x, y/2)$. Show that f is measure preserving with respect to Lebesgue measure.

32. (Poincaré Recurrence) Let T be a measure preserving transformation on a finite measure space $(X, \mathcal{M}, \mu)$ and the set A be measurable. Show that for almost all $x \in X$, there are infinitely many natural numbers n for which $T^n(x)$ belongs to A.

33. Let $(X, \mathcal{M}, \mu)$ be a probability space and $T: X \to X$ an ergodic transformation. Let the function $g \in L^1(X, \mu)$ have the property that $g \circ T = g$ a.e. on X. For a natural number n, show that there is a unique integer $k(n)$ for which $\mu\{x \in X \mid k(n)/n \le g(x) < (k(n)+1)/n\} = 1$. Then use this to show that if $c = \int_X g \, d\mu$, then

$$\left| \int_A [g - c] \, d\mu \right| \le \frac{1}{n} \cdot \mu(A) \le \frac{1}{n} \text{ for all } n \in \mathbf{N} \text{ and } A \in \mathcal{M}.$$

From this conclude that $g = c$ a.e. and thereby provide a different proof of one implication in Proposition 11.

Bibliography

[Ban55] Stefan Banach, *Théorie des Opérations Linéaires*, Chelsea Publishing Company, 1955.

[Bar95] Robert G. Bartle, *The Elements of Integration and Lebesgue Measure*, Wiley Classics Library, 1995.

[BBT96] Andrew M. Bruckner, Judith B. Bruckner, and Brian S. Thomson, *Real Analysis*, Prentice Hall, 1996.

[BC09] John Benedetto and Wojciech Czaja, *Integration and Modern Analysis*, Birkhaüser, 2009.

[Bir73] Garrett Birkhoff, *A Source Book in Classical Analysis*, Harvard University Press, 1973.

[BM97] Garrett Birkhoff and Saunders MacLane, *A Survey of Modern Algebra*, AK Peters, Ltd., 1997.

[BS02] Michael Brin and Garrett Stuck, *Introduction to Dynamical Systems*, Cambridge University Press, 2002.

[CC74] Micha Cotlar and Roberto Cignoli, *An Introduction to Functional Analysis*, Elsevier, 1974.

[DS71] Nelson Dunford and Jacob Schwartz, *Linear Operators Volumes I and II*, Interscience, 1958–71.

[Eva90] L.C. Evans, *Weak Convergence Methods for Nonlinear Partial Differential Equations*, Conference Board for Mathematical Sciences, no. 74, American Mathematical Society, 1990.

[Fit09] Patrick M. Fitzpatrick, *Advanced Calculus*, Pure and Applied Undergraduate Texts, American Mathematical Society, 2009.

[Fol99] Gerald B. Folland, *Real Analysis: Modern Techniques and Their Applications*, John Wiley and Sons, 1999.

[Hal50] Paul R. Halmos, *Measure Theory*, Van Nostrand, 1950.

[Hal98] ———, *Naive Set Theory*, Undergraduate Texts in Mathematics, Springer, 1998.

[Hal06] ———, *Lectures on Ergodic Theory*, American Mathematical Society, 2006.

[Haw01] Thomas Hawkins, *Lebesgue's Theory of Integration: Its Origins and Development*, American Mathematical Society, 2001.

[HS75] Edwin Hewitt and Karl Stromberg, *Real and Abstract Analysis*, Graduate Texts in Mathematics, Springer, 1975.

[Jec06] Thomas Jech, *Set Theory*, Springer, 2006.

[Kel75] John L. Kelley, *General Topology*, Springer, 1975.

[Lax97] Peter D. Lax, *Linear Algebra*, John Wiley and Sons, 1997.

[Lax02] ———, *Functional Analysis*, Wiley-Interscience, 2002.

[Lit41] J.E. Littlewood, *Lectures on the Theory of Functions*, Oxford University Press, 1941.

[Meg98] Robert E. Megginson, *An Introduction to Banach Space Theory*, Graduate Texts in Mathematics, Springer, 1998.

[Nat55] I. P. Natanson, *Theory of Functions of a Real Variable*, Fredrick Ungar, 1955.

[Pes98]   Yakov Pesin, *Dimension Theory in Dynamical Systems*, University of Chicago Press, 1998.

[Pie07]   Albrecht Pietsch, *History of Banach Spaces and Linear Operators*, Birkhaüser, 2007.

[RSN90]   Frigyes Riesz and Béla Sz.-Nagy, *Functional Analysis*, Dover, 1990.

[Rud87]   Walter Rudin, *Real and Complex Analysis*, McGraw-Hill, 1987.

[Sak64]   Stanislaw Saks, *Theory of the Integral*, Dover, 1964.

[Sim63]   George F. Simmons, *Introduction to Topology and Analysis*, International Series in Pure and Applied Mathematics, McGraw-Hill, 1963.

[vN50]   John von Neumann, *Functional Operators, Volume I: Measures and Integrals*, Annals of Mathematics Studies, Princeton University Press, 1950.

[vN91]   _____, *Invariant Measures*, American Mathematical Society, 1991.

[WZ77]   Richard L. Wheeden and Antoni Zygmund, *Measure and Integral*, Marcel Dekker, 1977.

[Zim90]   Robert Zimmer, *Essential Results of Functional Analysis*, University of Chicago Press, 1990.

Index